ABOUT T

Gary Acton studied medicine at Oxford and London Universities. He subsequently held a number of oncology appointments within London teaching hospitals.

For the last decade he has been involved in cancer medicine within the biotechnology industry. He has worked on some of the most innovative drugs of the era and has been associated with most areas of the biotechnology revolution. He has extensive experience of cancer drug development in Europe, the US and Japan.

He has served at board level in a number of biotechnology companies and was most recently Chief Medical Officer of Antisoma Research Ltd, which at the time was the UK's largest cancer biotechnology company.

He lives in Surrey, with Heathrow Airport as a second home.

Sympathy

for the

Devil

THE DEFINITIVE TRUE STORY OF CANCER BIOTECHNOLOGY
AND ITS BATTLE AGAINST DISEASE, DEATH AND DESTRUCTION

GARY ACTON

Matador
9 Priory Business Park,
Wistow Road, Kibworth Beauchamp,
Leicestershire. LE8 0RX
Tel: (+44) 116 279 2299
Fax: (+44) 116 279 2277
Email: books@troubador.co.uk
Web: www.troubador.co.uk/matador

ISBN 978 1780885 117

British Library Cataloguing in Publication Data.
A catalogue record for this book is available from the British Library.

Typeset by Troubador Publishing Ltd, Leicester, UK

Matador is an imprint of Troubador Publishing Ltd

Printed and bound in the UK by TJ International, Padstow, Cornwall

"It's just a matter of looking him in the face. He's there all the time. I've had very close contact with Lucifer – I've met him several times."

Keith Richards, on the Devil[1]

It was the best of times, it was the worst of times, it was the age of wisdom, it was the age of foolishness, it was the epoch of belief, it was the epoch of incredulity, it was the season of Light, it was the season of Darkness, it was the spring of hope, it was the winter of despair, we had everything before us, we had nothing before us, we were all going direct to heaven, we were all going direct the other way.

Charles Dickens, A Tale of Two Cities

This is just a true story of life and death, told as it happened to happen

CONTENTS

PREFACE

Rock and roll is all about exuberance and excess. It's the definition of defiance and disorder.

Cancer is just the same. It is characterised by equally egregious extremes of behaviour.

The biology of cancer is more aggressive and destructive than pretty much all other illnesses put together. It has an unparalleled ability to evade control and containment, even with the most modern medicines. It's a disease resulting in the grossest clinical pathologies, the bleakest prognoses and the greatest remaining therapeutic challenge to mankind.

If cancer were a musical genre, it could only be rock and roll. It's beyond the law and no one can stop it.

If it were a single song, it would be *Sympathy For The Devil.*

The 1968 Stones classic says it all. It's about Lucifer and the puzzling nature of his game. The song captures cancer in a couplet. They could just as well have been writing about the disease itself.

This work is an attempt to outline the nature of the game that is biotechnology. Coming up with new cancer drugs is a fiendish puzzle that sometimes doesn't seem to have a solution.

No one, from inside cancer biotechnology, has told a personal story about it before. There are innumerable technical textbooks and corporate tomes, detailing the biotechnology industrial revolution on a grand scale. And yet there are no works documenting the individual struggles of any of those involved.

Few people have attempted to capture the unique peculiarity of the world within which drug development takes place. It's not that different from a rock and roll tour. Both require a suspension of belief and a surrender of normal rational points of reference. They are each far removed from routine reality and everyday experiences. There aren't quite so many groupies and trashed hotel rooms in cancer medicine though.

This book is a series of observations collected by someone who has been a long-term traveller on the cancer concert tour. It follows the final fateful roadshow of one particular London based biotechnology company, Antisoma Research. They are struggling to stay alive, as all their experimental cancer agents seem to wither and die, as surely as the patients for whom they were intended. Now they are left with one remaining drug, one last shot at the Top Ten. It's their only chance of salvation. The odds aren't exactly in their favour though.

Battling for their existence turns into a race against time, ranging from New York to New Delhi and most places in between. This is a tragicomic true story which is never far from the surreal. It reveals, for the first time, what it's really like for the people involved at the sharp end of drug development. It's a place where money, medicine and magic all collide and coincide. You need the luck of the Devil to survive. A similar set of ethics often comes in handy too.

The particular difficulties Antisoma encounter are also a metaphor for the wider challenges currently confronting cancer medicine in general. The war against malignancy is mankind's last great stand. Mostly, this is hand to hand combat and it's often difficult to tell who's winning, from day to day.

Cancer is a formidable enemy. It has survived and flourished since the dawn of time, just like the satanic protagonist of the Stones song. The disease has continually evaded all attempts at capture, reeking untold misery and stealing innumerable souls along the way.

At last though, biotechnology is beginning to notch up some significant victories. Chemicals languishing in test tubes are being transformed into science fiction treatments in the clinic. A revolution in molecular biology is leading to the laws of nature being rewritten. As a result, we now face a future, the promise of which would have been unimaginable to those in even the most immediate past.

However, a new cancer drug costs at least one hundred million dollars and takes over ten years to develop. And yet, despite all that time and effort to get it right, less than one tenth of one per cent make it all the way. This book looks at some of the drugs not surviving that arduous journey and which fall by the wayside.

It's important not to overlook these casualties, many of which work extremely well. They are instead victims of a paradox bedevilling cancer drug development at the moment. Here nothing is black or white anymore. Except death itself.

We are increasingly struggling to cope with the explosion of potential new drugs being thrown up by the biotechnology bonanza. This is because we have only progressively more and more outdated methods, with which to evaluate them clinically. Drug development remains steadfastly analogue, whilst drug discovery went digital a long time ago. Perversely therefore, the further biotechnology advances, the greater is the challenge of not falling behind.

The more novel drugs we have at our disposal, the harder it becomes to assess the individual merits of each new arrival. They interact and interrelate too tightly, rather like listening to an orchestra play, instead of the solo performances we've been accustomed to hearing in the past. In turn, this is creating a conceptual vacuum which by default is being filled with an increasingly unpredictable drug approval system, itself often run with all the untrammelled eccentricity of the worst monsters of rock.

These regulatory reactionaries are capriciously assuming the right to decide which drugs are made available and which are denied, based on precepts and propositions which long ago ceased to have much relevance to the molecular maelstrom going on all around us. In doing so, they are also interposing themselves between the physician and the patient, thereby disrupting and distorting the opportunity for *individual* choice in treatment decisions.

This is causing critical challenges today, which have relevance for all of us tomorrow and into the future. We are inadvertently creating a threat to the very supply of new medicines our lives may one day depend on. Instead of the serious discipline of science, cancer drug development is increasingly characterised by the irrational idiosyncrasies of a mediaeval monastery.

As a consequence, perfectly promising new drugs are disappearing or dying, physicians, along with patients, are being penalised and companies are collapsing. It's not exactly a happy state of affairs.

There is little appreciation of this malaise in the wider community. In large part this is because the world of biotechnology is an enclosed one, protected by the arcaneness of language and the abstraction of science. These are barriers preventing easy entry. This book hopefully improves accessibility, by opening the door a bit wider.

Trying to cure the disease is a tough gig. Much of this book is cancer *noir,* charting setbacks rather than celebrating success. Whilst it deals with the darker depths, it also tries to capture a brighter side too. There is a sub text of unquestioning optimism and determination. The protagonists at Antisoma ultimately lose their last bet. In the end, their remaining drug is good but not good enough. They've played their cards with a steady hand but their luck has been less steadfast. However, theirs is a story of people who won't give up.

This book is about all those who, despite the frequent disappointments involved, keep coming back for more. However many times they lose at the tables, they crave one more stack of chips, one last round with the croupier. This is because working in cancer biotechnology is as addictive as any form of gambling. It's the adrenaline rush of James Bond and rock and roll, all in one. The newest drugs are easily the equal of the implausibly incredible gadgets at Bond's disposal. And as in his escapades, biotechnology is a constant adventure up against an evil enemy seeking to destroy mankind.

Except of course that Bond always prevails in the end. That isn't what usually happens in cancer medicine, where your adversary most often seems to come out on top. But on those occasions when you do get the upper hand and score a victory, it's the best feeling there is. It's playing Wembley. It's being Mick or Keith for a moment or two. You are fleetingly Kings of Cancer. At least until the next setback dethrones and deposes you.

This book tells that story.

PROLOGUE

She was a number now. Not a name. Number 01305. Although she was still allowed initials. JDW in her case.

It was an unlucky number. It had to be. No one could call *this* good luck. It was to protect her anonymity. They couldn't use her full name. It was the same with the others involved too. But it added to her already overwhelming sense of humiliation. As though she were too embarrassing to be associated with. As if *she'd* done something wrong. Very wrong.

And she definitely wasn't free. A prisoner now. She wasn't *actually* locked up but she was just as captive as if she had been. She could in theory get up and walk out. But then she would die. Not right away but probably within days. Definitely a week at most.

She lifted her left arm to scratch at the itch caused by the stiff starchy sheet of the bed she was lying in. The sharp constraining tug told her that she was effectively tethered down. She examined, for the hundredth time, the slow drip, drip, drip, of the reddish tinged fluid, as it percolated from the bag above her head all the way down to the vein in her arm.

Her life was hanging not so much by a thread but rather a length of plastic tubing. The surrounding skin of her forearm was flushed and dusky mauve. Perhaps that was a good sign.

As her arm was pulled back down to the bed it banged against her left breast, reminding her, as if she needed it, of the surgery which was, even now, sometimes still sore to the touch.

At the time, she'd thought that had to be the worst thing. You never got over losing most of a breast but maybe you could learn to just get on with it, to put your life back together. You could start looking towards the future, rather than remaining forever in an unforgettable past.

But now seemed even worse than then. And she'd never imagined that could possibly be the case.

Most frightening was the speed of it all. Maybe she'd been feeling more tired than normal for a month or so but the visit to her family doctor had only been a week ago. She suddenly seemed to be bruising easily. It wasn't painful but big dark blotchy discolorations kept coming up on her arms and legs, almost overnight. Her husband made her go. She hadn't wanted to, fearing deep down, knowing deep down, that it wasn't going to be good. When you'd been through something like cancer once, you *knew* when bad news was back in town.

She was only twenty nine when it had been diagnosed, back in 2004.

Hardly any life at all. She was living in Houston at the time, working in IT for Exxon. She'd been sent to the world's largest cancer hospital. It was right on her doorstep, the MD Anderson Centre, part of the University of Texas. There hadn't really been any choice over the operation and the subsequent gruelling rounds of chemotherapy. That's what they'd told her. And even worse, there had been no way out of the radiotherapy. It had left her so exhausted, she wondered why she was bothering to put herself through all this. But Professor Hortobagyi was confident things had been caught early. Her chances, in the future, were very good with aggressive therapy now.

And he'd been right. That was five years ago and she'd remained disease free ever since. Get to five years and you can begin to think about being cured. Start entertaining an idea you'd been forced to banish from your mind, up until that point. No guarantees but with time, it could progress from being just a remote possibility towards becoming a definite probability. You might just have beaten the fucker.

But that was a week ago.

That was before her visit to the Hollings Cancer Centre and the appointment made for her to see Professor Stuart. Her own doctor hadn't said very much but the speed with which he'd arranged the referral seemed to tell her all she needed to know.

Rob Stuart was a highly regarded leukaemia specialist at the Medical University of South Carolina, in Charleston, where she lived now. And he *really* knew about leukaemia. Not only did he treat patients day in and day out, other people's husbands and wives, fathers and mothers, sons and daughters. He'd also treated his *own* wife, who'd been diagnosed with acute leukaemia some five years previously. She had survived though. Thanks to him.

And that's what she had now. He'd told her it was leukaemia. Apparently it could occur in up to twenty per cent of patients receiving the sorts of cancer chemotherapy she'd endured back in Houston. It usually took about five years to manifest itself. Which was nature at its very cruelest. Delivering a potentially fatal blow, just when you were entitled to think you might be in the all clear from your first dance with death.

Leukaemia was a cancer of the blood cells in the body's bone marrow. Most commonly it singled out the elderly. There was nothing to explain why it would suddenly arrive one day on their doorstep. But having turned up, it was there to stay. Usually it was rapidly fatal.

But it could also occur as a consequence of something else from the past, in people like her. People who seemed destined never to have the chance of a future.

A number of the drugs used to treat tumors, such as breast cancer, could have a long term side effect in a proportion of survivors. They developed a particular type of leukaemia called *secondary acute myeloid leukaemia.* No one was really clear why some people, a minority, were singled out to be stabbed in the back like this whereas the rest, the majority, escaped. But what everyone was clear about was that it meant bad news.

It was July 2009 now, the humid height of the South Carolina summer and without treatment it was unlikely she'd see Christmas. Even with treatment, there was a distinct possibility she still wouldn't see Christmas. That's how difficult a condition it seemed to be.

Professor Stuart still had more tests to do but that's what the initial results were suggesting it was. He'd insisted she come into the Leukaemia Unit straightaway for further investigation and urgent treatment. Apparently you didn't hang around with something like this.

But now that was all she had to do. Hang around. Almost in limbo between life and death itself. Neither could decide which one wanted her.

Left to its own devices, the leukaemia would carry her off in days. Bleeding to death, or overwhelming sepsis were the commonest causes. Fungal infections were the most feared though. She'd heard stories of people's faces falling apart. They had to be taken for surgery every couple of days, to scrape out the infected bone. That was a life worse than death.

It didn't bear thinking about. Better to put it out of your thoughts. Otherwise, you'd probably go out of your mind.

Maybe the drugs, which at that very moment were permeating throughout her body, would help. Maybe they would get to the bone marrow and take out the leukaemia lurking there. Maybe they would be ineffective. Maybe she'd be one of the twenty per cent actually killed by the powerful side effects of treatment, in the first few weeks. Whatever happened, it was clear though that in order to give you a chance of life, these drugs had to take you to the brink of death first. Just hopefully not over the edge.

The therapy she was getting was experimental. That made her situation sound as bad as it was. Normal drugs couldn't touch this cancer. The new drug was known as AS1413. Unlike her, it was also allowed a name. Amonafide. Which sounded like a kitchen cleaner. It came from a small cancer company in London, England called Antisoma.

She'd never even heard of them a week ago. But by now the name was as familiar as her own. Except she couldn't use that. Patients in clinical trials were never identified personally. 01305 was her number now. 013 was the hospital and 05 was her. The fifth person Professor Stuart had tried this on. Although he hadn't said what happened to the other four. But she just had to trust him now.

That's all she could do. Put herself in the hands of others. And they had put her in a test tube. She was part of their experiment and nobody seemed to know exactly what was going to happen next. Whether she lived or died, pulled through or passed away, was now all down to this unknown drug, belonging to those unknown people.

She couldn't have known it but their existence was also as inextricably bound up with the drug as her own. Whether they survived or not partly depended on whether she did.

Better if she didn't realise that though.

ONE

PAINT IT BLACK

**Setting the scene. An introduction to Antisoma Research.
An unexpected death in the family.**

I

The biotechnology industry is worth three hundred and fifty billion dollars worldwide. That's a lot of money. There are some very valuable companies out there. Antisoma Research wasn't exactly one of them though. In fact, we accounted for less than one third of one thousandth of one per cent of the total. Which wasn't very much at all. And now it looked as though even that was about to disappear.

We were in biotechnology and cancer was our business. That most feared agent of death was our lifeblood and our livelihood. It's what consumed us. We thought we had cancer cornered and covered. We told ourselves we controlled it, because we understood it. But now, it was about to prove us wrong.

When they get the cancer diagnosis, most patients want to know *how long*. Not how long have they got left but how long has *it* been there. How long have they been harbouring their own killer and just when did their life start stopping. It was never possible to give an exact answer, although invariably it was longer than they might have imagined.

But with us it was different. We could point a finger at the moment we started dying. It was nine o'clock in the evening in London. Ten at night in Basel. And three in the afternoon in Chicago. Three far flung places. One fatal problem. The day was March 25th 2010. It was a Thursday.

II

It was bitterly cold in Chicago that day. The sky was overcast and a fierce wind was blowing up East Superior Street from Lake Michigan. People scurried along the pavements with their heads down, constantly clutching at flapping coats. It was a day for being inside. Lucky Lara certainly thought so, as he looked out of the window of the fourth floor meeting room in the Peninsula, one of Chicago's best hotels.

He studied the milling street below, deep in thought. It was looking bleak outside. But then it was looking bleak inside too. It was only ten in

1

the morning but already the day had turned out dramatically different from anything he was expecting.

The Peninsula Hotel was quiet, restrained and understated. The exact opposite of Lucky in fact. Professor Primo Lara was a lung cancer specialist from the University of California, up in Sacramento. He was short but incredibly dynamic and energetic. If he were any taller he'd probably explode, because there would be too much energy, all in one place at the same time. Young and charismatic, he was universally known as Lucky Lara.

No one could remember where the name had come from but it had somehow stuck. Which had always seemed somewhat inappropriate, given his particular line of work. The fact that he looked like a member of the early Osmonds probably didn't help either. If you met him for the first time, you might have him down as occupying a Saturday night game show slot, rather than a position at the top of the world oncology rankings. He had the genial affability and effortless charm of the best compères. Everyone enjoyed his company. Even his patients, although he was the last person they really wanted to find themselves getting to know. Something has gone badly wrong, when you are on first name terms with an oncologist.

Lucky was chairing a committee meeting that morning with four other US cancer experts. They all had proper names though. The group had gathered in Chicago, to look at data from an ongoing multinational lung cancer clinical trial. It involved a new drug, which was reaching the final stages of testing.

Even with the best available treatment, the average lung cancer patient was fortunate to survive much more than a year, following the diagnosis. Most didn't even make it that far. For some it was only weeks, for many just months. It wasn't a good position to be in. There weren't exactly any cancers you'd choose to suffer from. But if you had to, lung cancer would be very low down on the wish list. That's why most of them didn't bother to give up smoking, even then. There wasn't enough time left for it to make any difference.

There was a real need for new drugs to improve the outlook and many people had high hopes of this one. The trial wasn't over yet but the committee members had been asked to review how well the drug was working and how safe it appeared to be. It was a precautionary check, to make sure it was worthwhile carrying on.

Things had looked enormously promising in earlier trials, producing some of the best results ever seen in lung cancer. And so no one was expecting any surprises from the latest data. It should confirm that the drug was maintaining its exceptional potential.

Lucky turned around to face the room. The dark wood and muted brown leather of the boardroom, where they were meeting, added a suitably sombre note to the atmosphere around the table. Things had not gone according to plan. The five experts looked at each other and then one more time at the piles of paper, scattered in front of them.

On the basis of what they were seeing, they had just decided to kill off what had, until then, been one of the world's most promising experimental drugs. Now it was about to join countless thousands of others in the chemotherapy cemetery. Lucky knew he was going to have some unlucky news to deliver, later that morning.

III

In Basel, it had been a beautiful spring day. Even in the late afternoon, the sunlight was still pouring through the windows of the extraordinary Frank Gehry designed building. It occupied a prominent position in the middle of the St Johann Campus, located in the north west of the city, right on the banks of the Rhine.

The light cascaded through the roof and down the five upper stories, all the way to the massive underground auditorium and Learning Factory, located in the three basement levels. Here almost a thousand people could gather at a time, for meetings and events. Completed in 2009, on the site of an old chemical factory, this epitome of architectural expressionism sprouted out of the ground in all directions, in an exuberance of unrestrained growth.

It was like a huge glass tumor dividing out of control. That however was a suitable visual metaphor for the activities of the people who worked inside it. Along with other buildings on the Campus, it was home to thousands of employees of Novartis, the enormous Swiss pharmaceutical company.

One of them was Hervé Hoppenot, the urbane and charming President of Novartis Oncology. Many thought he bore more than a passing resemblance to Bill Gates. His organisation was however slightly smaller than that of the Microsoft boss. But with nearly a thousand people, it was still impressive. He was based in New Jersey in the US but also had an office at the Basel headquarters.

In keeping with the weather, Hoppenot was in a cheerful mood. It was five in the afternoon. He was waiting for a phone call but he was confident the news would be good.

IV

By nine in the evening, it had stopped raining in London. Thunderstorms had been erupting intermittently all day long. But now they had eased off and moved on. The weather had caused widespread traffic problems. In South East London these weren't helped by road works, repairing a burst gas main at the junction of Dulwich Road and Half Moon Lane, one of the major routes through the area.

Even at this time of night, cars were backed up all the way along the edge of Brockwell Park. A dark blue Mercedes had just pulled out of the traffic jam and into the side of the road, outside the Lido Cafe. That was dark and deserted now.

But the car's driver wasn't after light refreshments. She'd just received a deeply disturbing phone call. It would turn out to be one of the most important of her professional life.

Ursula Ney was the normally combative Chief Operating Officer of Antisoma Research, a small biotechnology cancer company based in Chiswick, West London. She was widely regarded as one of the best in the biotech business. She'd been on her normal route home. But now she suddenly felt lost. She couldn't quite take in the conversation she'd just had. It was almost impossible to believe.

For a couple of minutes she sat there, staring into the darkness. Then she slowly picked up the cell phone from the seat next to her and pressed a speed dial number.

V

She should have called this afternoon.

Instead, it was dark outside now, as the phone started ringing. That didn't bode well. Ursula was never late. Even Time itself didn't dare get in her way.

I answered the call. Her normally booming voice sounded drained and distant, even though I knew she was only a few miles away, in another part of London.

"Novartis have just got back to me and it's bad news I'm afraid…very bad news."

At least it was straight to the point. This was clearly no time for niceties.

She was strangely subdued. And she was never like that. Normally, as with nature abhorring a vacuum, Ursula would expand with effusiveness to fill any space she was in. She was one of those eternally effervescent larger women, both physically and as a personality, tending to dominate any situation she was involved with. But then I guess she hadn't been confronted with one quite like this before.

It wasn't exactly a *promising* start to the conversation.

"OK," I heard myself squeaking, from somewhere seemingly very far away. For the last four years I had been Antisoma's Chief Medical Officer, in charge of their experimental cancer programmes.

"I've been talking to Hervé in Basel and the ATTRACT I clinical trial is a bust," she continued. "There's no difference between either of the treatment groups, absolutely none. They've been checking it all evening, that's why I'm so late."

4

I slowly sank on to a chair. *Did you really just say what I thought you did?*

"Are they *sure*?" I asked, even though I knew they would be.

"Well, according to Hervé, Novartis heard from the Data Monitoring Committee in Chicago about four hours ago. And they've had their own people working on it ever since. It doesn't look like there are any obvious screw ups anywhere. Our drug, ASA404, doesn't seem to have made any difference, compared to the standard treatment for lung cancer. The tumour response rates were the same and the patient survival was almost identical for each group.

Hervé reached me as I was on my way home and I nearly drove off the road. I just can't believe it."

Neither could I.

ATTRACT I was a tortuous acronym for *A*nti vascular *T*argeted *T*herapy: *R*esearching *A*SA404 in *C*ancer *T*reatment. Big cancer studies always have a name and the more contrived the better. It's a kind of insider joke. Not a particularly amusing one but then you tend to have rather limited material to work with in cancer medicine.

ATTRACT I was a clinical trial of over a thousand patients with lung cancer from every corner of the world. They had all been followed for at least twelve months, to see if their tumours would shrink and how long they managed to live for.

More importantly, it represented a trial with ASA404, the code number of our flagship cancer drug. This was a novel and revolutionary compound, which acted in a different way from most cancer chemotherapy. Rather than attacking the tumor directly, it destroyed its blood vessels instead.

Deprived of essential nutrients, the cancer starved to death. Most cancer drugs target the tumor itself but also inadvertently kill off other rapidly dividing healthy cells too. That's why patients' hair falls out and they spend all day stuck on the toilet, because the lining of their gut has been shredded to pieces. ASA404 avoided all of that. It had exceptional promise in a number of malignancies but had been outstanding in earlier clinical trials in lung cancer.

As well as being a very good drug, it was the only real one we had. It was certainly our pride and joy. If it had been a poem, ASA404 would have been that one by Auden. It was our North and South and East and West. It was the corporate compass by which we orientated ourselves. Without it we would be directionless.

We were developing ASA404, with Novartis, as an exciting new treatment for lung cancer. This wasn't *exactly* the news we'd been expecting from Hervé. What he'd effectively told Ursula was that our biggest and most important drug, the only one anyone really cared about, had just hit a brick wall. At a hundred miles an hour. And it didn't sound as though there were any survivors in the wreckage. The data from the trial had shown ASA404 just wasn't doing anything extra, when added on top of the usual treatment for lung cancer.

There were two groups of patients in the study. One had been treated with a combination of two standard established drugs, whilst the other received the same two drugs but with ASA404 added on as well. The proportion of patients whose tumours were shrinking was the same figure of about twenty per cent, whether or not ASA404 had been given. And the ASA404 patients weren't living any longer. On average it was about fourteen months for both groups.

In other words, ASA404 wasn't doing anything at all. It wasn't destroying a greater number of tumours and it wasn't eking out anyone's existence. It was, in fact, a complete failure. Which just didn't seem possible. Up until now it had been too outstanding a drug for that. Previously, it had produced some of the best results ever seen in this disease.

This was bad. *Cancer* bad. There had been a lot riding on it for us. Everything in fact.

Although Antisoma was small, we managed to support a number of experimental cancer programmes. But ASA404 was by far and away the most important, accounting for over three quarters of the company's value. We weren't big enough to develop it alone and so counted ourselves fortunate to have secured a partner in Novartis, the world's second largest pharmaceutical company.

If it came anywhere in the world size rankings, Antisoma was probably around about the five or six thousandth sort of level. It was a very imbalanced partnership therefore. Rather like the Coca Cola Company cosying up to a corner shop. But a lot of cancer drug development was done like that. The biggest and the smallest, somehow rubbing along together.

ATTRACT I was the culmination of ten years of work and represented a seventy million dollar clinical study. It should have been the last step on the way to ASA404 becoming a blockbuster drug for the world's commonest cancer. That made it a very big deal, even in Novartis's book. For us, it was like Jason finding the Golden Fleece.

VI

Drug development is nearly always carried out in a sequence of progressively more demanding steps. With a novel drug, like ASA404, you start out with small simple clinical trials, just to get a feel for the new agent. You're not asking too much of it at this point. To begin with you just want some understanding of whether it might work and what sorts of side effects it may produce.

After that, the drug gets put through progressively larger and more demanding clinical trials. At each stage, it has to perform better and meet more stringent criteria, in order to progress to the next one. It's like a TV quiz show. It could be the malignant mutation of *Who Wants To Be A Millionaire?* Your new drug has to survive ever more demanding questioning, as it moves ever nearer to the top prize.

With ATTRACT I, ASA404 had been about to answer the very final question. The one for the million pound prize. And it had seemingly given the wrong answer. And as in *Millionaire*, if you didn't get that one right, all the earlier correct responses didn't matter anymore. They couldn't help you out now. One wrong answer and everything was lost. All the previous promising and positive clinical trial results with ASA404 wouldn't compensate for it failing at this last hurdle and in this final trial. Those were the rules of the game. It was all or nothing at this stage.

At least on TV, the contestants usually left with a consolation prize of some sort. But there was nothing like that in biotechnology. There were no rewards for failing. And it hadn't been a million pounds at stake either. It was more like several billion. That was the size of the reward, if you managed to win the drug development contest. There were big stakes being played for here.

VII

A shot at the top prize had been a long time in coming for Antisoma. The company had already been around for over two decades, after being founded in 1988 by two maverick individuals from the Hammersmith Hospital in London. Nigel Courtenay Luck was a renowned cancer immunologist, and Agamemnon Epenetos, an equally distinguished cancer clinician and researcher.

They began with a single drug and some money borrowed from the Leventis brothers. They were Greek Cypriots, who'd made an enormous fortune from businesses in Nigeria and elsewhere in Africa. These were Greeks bearing a welcome gift though. Their funding gave the company a vital jump start.

For years afterwards, Antisoma was incongruously based at *West Africa House*, just off the Hanger Lane gyratory system in North London. The Leventis family had given them some space there, in their own office block. It never seemed the right address though. Not when all the other biotechnology companies were in California and places like that. We wanted to be in the sunshine with them. We wanted to be with the hippies, not the hoodies.

The only drugs normally associated with Hanger Lane were those sold in the shadows of the underpasses. But when we talked about shooting up, we mainly had our share price in mind. Mercifully, we moved to a much more upmarket office park in Chiswick, not that long after I joined.

I didn't know Aga, as everyone called him. He'd largely disappeared from the scene by the time I arrived. But he remained beaming out from any number of photographs, looking like a particularly self-satisfied satyr.

Nigel was still very much there though. Short, squat and rugged with a bristle brush moustache, he looked exactly like an RAF squadron commander, in the midst of a Battle of Britain foray. Down to earth and with a colourful turn of phrase, he possessed an encyclopaedic knowledge of immunology and also a heart of gold.

In fact, he was almost too good for his own good, mainly side stepping the political tensions and manoeuvrings within the company. He now spent much of his time travelling the world, on Antisoma's behalf, lecturing at various conferences and seminars. His expertise was very much in demand. It wasn't a bad life.

If he had a fault at all, it was that he snored horrendously. I remember once flying back with him overnight from Texas. The sound of Nigel sleeping was loud enough to drown out the drone of the two jet engines on either side of us. Getting ready to land in London and with only twenty minutes to touchdown, the cabin crew couldn't get Nigel to wake up. I ended up having to hit him on the head with a plastic bottle of water to rouse him. When awake though, Nigel was one of the best things about Antisoma.

Nigel and Aga's work had been in the then emerging and exciting area of cancer antibodies. At the time, these were referred to as the so called *magic bullets.* This was in the belief that they would home in on cancer cells, rather like a guided missile seeking its target, whilst steering well clear of other healthy tissues. Hence the name chosen for their fledgling company. *Antisoma,* Greek for "against the body." It wasn't a very good name really, especially as we didn't have many antibodies left now.

But many biotech companies for some reason seemed to derive comfort from such classical connotations. Eleos for example is a small US cancer company, whose name is based on the Greek god mythically personifying compassion and mercy. The fact that they are located in Omaha, Nebraska presumably partly explains why they felt the need to invoke this particular deity.

ARIAD is a very innovative Boston based oncology biotechnology company, named somewhat implausibly after the Greek heroine Ariadne. She mythically fell in love with Theseus, giving him a spool of thread that enabled him to trace his path in and out of the labyrinth, as he set off down it to kill the Minotaur. According to ARIAD, the labyrinth was supposed to symbolise the complex system of molecular pathways within the cell. The spool of thread represented the signalling mechanisms that would lead scientists to the discovery of new cancer therapies. Fucking ridiculous really.

Antisoma wasn't that pretentious, although it had definitely lost the thread early on, with its initial antibodies all failing in the clinic. The company had subsequently been through a fair share of ups and downs, its fortunes ebbing and flowing like a particularly vigorous tide running up and down a beach. But it had survived, despite at one point, several years ago, being only about three weeks away from running out of money altogether.

Inevitably, Antisoma had changed a lot over the years. It had evolved from that early dog and pony show into something more like a thoroughbred racehorse. It was sleek and powerful. And more than capable of going the distance. Especially with ASA404 in the running.

There were now about a hundred people altogether, which was an average size for a European biotechnology company. Most were based in Chiswick. Our offices were a dramatic display of glass and chrome. We were located in a high tech park containing every conceivable facility. All the buildings encircled a large central plaza. On Friday lunchtime there would be events there, to herald the forthcoming weekend.

Usually, these were the normal fare of bands and barbeques. But now and then, there would be something out of the ordinary. One Friday it was camel racing, with real sand and real camels. It was like looking out of your window onto the fall of Tobruck.

We had an outpost of about fifteen or so scientists, at our laboratories on the campus of St George's Hospital in South London. Mostly they remained locked away behind their biohazard barriers. We left them to their task of manipulating nature and rewriting the laws of biology.

There were also another fifteen people at our recently opened offices in Boston in America. The US was the centre of gravity for the biotechnology world and you had to have a presence there.

Antisoma was run by the ten members of the senior management team. But three of them really wielded power.

Glyn Edwards was the Chief Executive Officer and top of the tree. He was very tall and seemed to almost walk with a slight stoop, as though tacitly acknowledging that he was just a bit taller than he was really comfortable with. Despite this, for some reason he always managed to wear trousers which looked too long in the leg. His background was pharmaceutical sales and marketing and he was perhaps strongest as a steadying pair of hands. Glyn had skillfully managed to steer Antisoma down a safe channel over the years, avoiding most of the rocks along the way.

He was though, an inveterate optimist and dreamer. His mind was full of potential deals which would never quite happen and opportunities which somehow failed to materialise. Biotechnology was like that most of the time. But he was never embarrassed when these schemes came to nothing. He would move straight on to the next one. You had to admire him for his sheer *chutzpah*.

Having been at Antisoma for over a decade, Glyn was shrewd enough

9

to have the Board all sorted out. He was very comfortably ensconced and had things just as he liked them. He seemed fairly bulletproof.

In his spare time, Glyn had an allotment he looked after in Maidenhead, where he lived. Somehow this leisurely activity seemed to epitomise his relaxed approach to life. He drove a Porsche 911 but you suspected it would never be fast. He was affable, genial, ever cheerful and always approachable. He also had a well developed dry sense of humour. He was going to be needing it fairly soon, by the look of things now.

Eric Dodd was Antisoma's Finance Director. He was blunt and brusque, brimming with cost cutting energy and business efficiency. He had an almost military precision and rigour to him, which was something of a contrast to the unstructured informality which often prevailed at Antisoma.

Eric had only been there a couple of years, having previously worked for the enormous GlaxoSmithKline. He didn't always seem that settled at where he'd now found himself. It was as though much of the time, it took all his effort to patiently tolerate most of the rest of us. He was like a headmaster, frustrated at no longer being allowed to whip out a cane and unleash six of the best, to drum up a little discipline.

Eric was a seasoned senior corporate executive. If Glyn had fallen under a bus, Eric could have taken over as captain at the helm. Although it would be a very different vessel we'd now find ourselves travelling in.

Glyn was like a gondolier, wafting along the canals of Venice with an impressive economy of movement and efficiency of pace. Eric was more akin to white water rafting in a kayak, probably with a hole smashed in one end where he'd taken a lump of rock in his stride somewhere along the way.

Either would have kept our head above water though. Up until now at least.

But Eric was the more demanding of the two to deal with. In most small biotechnology companies, there is inevitably a tension between the clinical group, which always accounts for the largest slice of expenditure, and the finance department. Their natural inclination is to conserve cash wherever possible. And often even where it isn't. But there seemed more to it with Eric. When he had to sign off an invoice you could almost imagine him wincing, as though he were passing a kidney stone or something worse.

This was especially so when it came to travel. Developing modern cancer drugs has become an international undertaking. You nearly always end up with clinical trials running in a number of different countries and continents, all at the same time. This means you have to keep on top of things. You need to stay in contact with the people using your drug on a daily basis. You can't just leave them to it. Things are too complicated for that.

Because of this, you have to be prepared to travel a lot. In the clinical group, we would think nothing of popping down to Australia or New

Zealand just for a day or so. Or anywhere else in the world, if it were necessary. Which it frequently was.

Often you'd go all that way, only to meet a cancer clinician in his hospital for an hour. Maybe an hour and a half at the most. They were busy people after all. They didn't have the time to take a week off and go vacationing with you. But on occasions, it was necessary to make the effort and undertake those sorts of journeys. Sometimes nothing else, except sitting down around a table, would do. Even if it were only for an hour. We were, after all, dealing with advancing the frontiers of medical science. You couldn't always sort that out, from the other side of the world, with Twitter.

These trips in particular often seemed to drive Eric apoplectic with inner rage. He was the Finance Director after all and there were big sums of money involved. But there was also an unstated accusation that these might be partly pleasure trips, undertaken for the sybaritic indulgence of those involved. Which in fact was in sharp contrast to the gruelling and unglamorous slog they really were. There was little that was appealing about finding yourself in the milling crowd at Singapore's Changi Airport at three in the morning, resembling nothing more than the cast of extras from Shaun of the Dead.

Once or twice, when confronted with an invoice from Fares Fair, our travel agent, he almost turned a dusky mauve, rather like a fine claret. He might have been just moments from a stroke. At six or seven thousand pounds for some of these trips, he may well have had a point. But it wasn't worth the risk of putting yourself in a wheelchair over it.

Although he held the purse strings and could have made life difficult, had he felt like it, Eric nearly always nodded these things through in the end. He wasn't the kind of person to constantly question his colleagues' judgement, however perplexing it may have seemed to him on occasions.

The bad news about ASA404 wasn't exactly going to give Eric a warm glow though. An awful lot of Novartis money, which should have been coming our way, had just been firmly halted in its tracks.

And then there was Ursula, the Chief Operating Officer, in charge of the day to day running of the company. Ursula was larger than life and endearingly domineering. She also laughed a lot. So much so in fact, that she actually had *two* laughs. One was a sort of cackle, stopping just short of being strident. You could normally work out where she was in the building, by listening out for the next raucous outburst, which was never very long in coming.

The other laugh was softer and much more melodic. That's the one you didn't want to hear. It was invariably the prelude to a forcefully direct display of displeasure, which you *really* didn't want to be on the end of. When she was angry or annoyed, Ursula never raised her voice or shouted. She didn't need to. That laugh number two was enough to grab your attention and brace you for whatever was coming next.

11

Ursula had been a scientist originally, before working her way up through project management and into senior executive positions. She had spent years at Celltech, one of the few UK biotech successes, before it was acquired by the Belgian UCB Group in 2004. After that, she'd arrived at Antisoma.

Bold and blustery, she was direct, no nonsense, down to earth and ready to take on anyone she felt needed to be corrected. Which was most people most of the time. Many of us were a bit on edge when she was around but in a positive way. We'd mentally up our game a notch or two, to try and keep up with her.

She had a prodigious energy for work and was that rare mixture of someone capable of adopting a strategic analytical approach, at the same time as having an exhaustive grip of operational detail across all areas of the company's activities. Ursula really was the glue which held everything together at Antisoma.

But now, with the unfolding failure of ASA404, she and the rest of us were going to have our work cut out, to prevent things from becoming unstuck and rapidly falling apart.

VIII

"The problem is the Data Committee and that bloody interim look," I continued, on the phone. "We should never have allowed it. Someone ought to get their legs cut off over that." At this, she burst into a fit of raucous laughter. I hoped she didn't have me in mind, when the chopper eventually came out.

Lucky and the rest of the Data Monitoring Committee had the job of looking at the data from the ATTRACT I trial when it was about *half way* through. So although not complete yet, it was sufficiently advanced to give you a good idea of what was going on. The intention was to make sure that things were looking as they were supposed to. In other words, that ASA404 seemed to be providing some extra benefit, in terms of patients living a bit longer. This would make the trial worth continuing to the end.

On the other hand, if it didn't look as though ASA404 was stacking up and doing very much, then the members of the Committee had the ability to halt the trial then and there. If that's what they felt was best. They also had the authority to do this independently of what we or Novartis might think about it.

And that's exactly what they had just done. Which wasn't something anyone had been expecting. Certainly no one in Antisoma, or in Novartis and most probably it came as quite a surprise to Lucky and the other members of the Data Monitoring Committee too.

To say no one was expecting this turn of events was something of an understatement. We considered it slightly less likely than Mullah Omar and the rest of the Taliban emerging from a cave to announce they were embracing world peace. Even in our wildest dreams, of which we had many, we'd never anticipated ASA404 failing at this point.

Large cancer trials, like ATTRACT I, often ended up recruiting well over a thousand patients and sometimes many more. This made them big and therefore very expensive undertakings. They also exposed a lot of patients to a drug you might not know much about, at that point in its development.

Because of this, it was normal to schedule a look at how the trial was doing at about the half way mark. This was known as an *interim look*. The phrase was as unimaginative as it was self-explanatory. But then this was cancer medicine after all. It would probably have been inappropriately facile, although arguably more accurate, to refer to this exercise as *Spin The Wheel, Open The Box, Turn The Card*, or something along those lines.

IX

Usually these early inspections showed that things were progressing pretty much as expected, thus justifying running the trial through to its natural conclusion.

Occasionally, the results at this stage were so unexpectedly better than originally anticipated, that the trial was stopped there and then. There was no need to carry on. You'd already proven the point. That didn't happen too often though.

Conversely, in a small proportion of cases, an interim look suggested that there was no merit in carrying on with the trial to its completion. On the basis of what you could see already, there was little hope of the drug in question showing any benefit, however many more patients you might put into the study. The odds were just too low.

Technically this was called *futility*. It was futile to carry on. And that now appeared to be the case with ASA404. At least according to the people in Chicago. Overnight, this most promisingly potent of drugs had gone from being fertile to nothing more than plain futile.

The advantage of an interim look was that it helped give an early warning of events that were going in an unexpectedly positive or negative direction. It thus allowed you, if necessary, to stop a hugely expensive and time consuming clinical trial, at an earlier stage than would otherwise have been the case.

The downside was that, by the very nature of it being an *interim* inspection, the data was nowhere near as complete as it would be at the end of the trial. This made it harder to base reliable conclusions on.

It was like reading only half a book and trying to guess what happened in the rest of it. The risk was that by stopping early, you might actually be missing out on more promising data, which could have emerged if you'd allowed the trial to go all the way to completion. A useful new drug could thus have been strangled at birth.

But on the other hand, if things weren't looking too encouraging at this midway point then they could get even worse, if you allowed the study to continue. This could potentially expose more and more patients to an ineffective or dangerous drug. Or worst of all, one which was both. And that was something you definitely wanted to avoid.

Interim looks were therefore far from perfect and carried the liability that they might be misleading you. You might guess the wrong ending to the story. But they were part of the game we all played and everyone accepted the dangers involved. Gambles like that were a normal part of our world.

Drug development is all about judging these sorts of risks and beforehand, we had estimated the likelihood of ASA404 not surviving the interim look to be minimal. Less than that even. If it crossed our minds at all, it was simply to savour the impossibility of such a thing ever actually happening. There was always a chance it might fail at the end of the trial but surely not now. The previous data with the drug were just too good for there to be any real possibility of it stumbling at this first hurdle.

Which was in fact a very low one anyway. For technical reasons and also because you only have a limited amount of information (compared to what there will be when the trial has completed) interim looks allow a drug to perform much less well than would be the case at the end of the study. The drug can get away with producing a smaller effect half way through, than it will need to demonstrate when the trial is complete.

It's a bit like climbing a foothill on the way towards eventually scaling the mountain. On the basis of how it had performed in the past, ASA404 should easily have passed this test. Strolled through it in fact.

And so what we had been expecting and waiting to hear all afternoon, was that Lucky's committee had given the nod for the trial to carry on, leaving it to come to a natural end in about eighteen months' time. Not that everything had been stopped now for futility. For lack of potential. For lack of hope. A failed audition, a flunked exam, an unsuccessful job interview, a rejected advance. All rolled into one. ASA404 had turned out to be all mouth and no trousers. And as a consequence, we were probably now going to lose the shirts off our backs.

Ursula and I both knew it was a disaster of indefinable dimensions for us. There was just too much that depended on ASA404 remaining alive and healthy. Like the survival of the company for one thing. Most of what we were, how we were seen and how we were valued, rested with this one drug. It was like the heart pulsating at the centre of our corporate body. If it stopped beating, everything else would surely shut down and die. It shouldn't be like that but unfortunately it was. That's just how things had turned out.

Having a knife plunged in your back like this was bad enough but the unexpectedness of it was the real killer for us. Cancer trials like ATTRACT I typically have at best a sixty to seventy per cent chance of a successful outcome, when they are completed. So we had always known there was a possibility things might fall apart. But that was supposed to be a year and a half away. Not now.

We weren't ready. We weren't prepared. We hadn't had time to work out a Plan B, to deal with a meltdown like this. It would admittedly have to be *some* plan but we'd have thought of something surely. We'd have found a get out of jail card from somewhere.

The interim look now should have been a formality. Instead it had become a visit to the doctor for a routine check up, only to be told you had three months left to live. Up until that moment, you had all the time in the world. Now, there was none left. It was too late for all those plans you hadn't yet made. Maybe that's how the patients in the ATTRACT I study had felt, when they got the diagnosis. We now seemed as doomed as they were.

That was biotechnology though. The risks, as with the potential rewards, were enormous. Like any gambler, you needed luck as well as skill to survive. And your luck could turn at any time.

But we were the Kings of Cancer. Up until now, we had reigned supreme over all we surveyed. Our good fortune shouldn't be running out just yet.

How could it have gone so wrong?

TWO

START ME UP

The life and death of a drug. An introduction to the world of biotechnology. The players assemble.

I

Biotechnology is a strange mixture of medicine and magic. Science, by itself, often isn't enough. You need to conjure up some luck too, now and then. But there aren't that many lucky breaks going around. ASA404 was one of them though. It was a new type of cancer drug. There wasn't anything else like it out there. Up until now, it had offered huge promise and potential as a novel approach to treating some of the most difficult and intractable of malignancies.

As with all new drugs, it started off life with just a code number rather than a name. Originally it had been AS1404, *AS* standing for Antisoma and 1404 for probably nothing in particular. For inexplicable reasons, now long forgotten, it became ASA404 upon passing over to Novartis. A name would come later on. In the case of ASA404, that turned out to be *vadimezan*. It wasn't exactly eloquent but then cancer wasn't a condition known for its finesse.

It belonged to a class of compounds collectively described as *vascular disrupting agents*, or VDAs for short. Its novelty lay in the fact that it acted through destruction of the blood vessels to a tumor, rather than on the tumor cells directly. Cancers are very active, expanding and dividing at a rapid rate. A new tumor can't grow much beyond a diameter of about two mm, without laying down new arteries and veins to support itself. And so right from the outset they have to create a copious bed of blood vessels, to provide them with the oxygen and nutrients needed to sustain this kind of pace.

ASA404 wiped all of those out, thus disrupting the tumor's supply lines. Because tumors are expanding at such a frantic rate, they don't have time to form new blood vessels in the structured manner that normally characterises biology. Instead they create a vascular network with a highly aberrant architecture. The blood vessels are arranged in a haphazard way, with little obvious order or organisation. This is in marked contrast to the much more precise arrangement usually found in normal non-malignant tissue.

This lack of structure in the tumor vasculature helps create a chink in its armour. The abnormal blood vessels are more fragile than they should be, as they've not had time to develop properly. They are also burdened with inefficient metabolic processes, within the cells of which they are composed. These two liabilities make them vulnerable to physical and chemical attack.

Which is exactly what ASA404 did. It damaged the already weakened walls of the tumor blood vessels and also disrupted the cells' metabolic pathways, so that they started poisoning themselves. The end result was collapse of a blood vessel and the subsequent death of those parts of the tumor it had been supplying.

If you gave ASA404 to animals with various cancers, you could see the blood vessels disappearing and the tumors shrinking away in front of you, over the next twenty four hours. That's how dramatic the effects were. ASA404 didn't exactly hang around to do its stuff.

Because normal tissues had a normal pattern of blood supply, ASA404 should be selective for the tumor itself and so not cause damage to other parts of the body. The idea was that if you combined it with conventional cancer chemotherapy, the stuff that acted through killing the actual cancer cells, you would get a much better outcome, than by using chemotherapy alone.

Because ASA404 and chemotherapy drugs were acting by different mechanisms, you should be able to safely add them together. They wouldn't have overlapping side effects, which would otherwise make such a combination too toxic for the body to tolerate.

This would allow you to attack the tumor from two different directions at the same time. This double edged assault should produce much more dramatic efficacy than either approach alone. At least that had been the theory.

Antisoma had stumbled across ASA404, sometime after it had emerged from the test tubes of the Cancer Society Research Centre, at the University of Auckland in New Zealand, where it had been discovered in the late 1990s. They had handed it on to the charity Cancer Research UK (CRUK) in London. The chemists down in Auckland weren't really in a position to do much more with it by themselves.

CRUK acted as a kind of clearing house, which took promising new agents from academic and other sources. It would then complete an initial clinical trial or two, before subsequently packaging the drugs up and passing them on to pharmaceutical companies for further development. They eventually transitioned ASA404 on to Antisoma, in return for some future royalties if the drug eventually succeeded.

No one was sure, at that stage, if this new approach of vascular disruption would actually work in the clinic. Whilst it might have been novel and unprecedented, it was also utterly unproven. Because it didn't exactly come with a guarantee, Antisoma had managed to acquire a potential breakthrough compound at a bargain basement cost.

From there, they had then moved it through the early stages of the pathway of progressively larger tests and trials that new drugs have to undertake. Usually, you start off in a handful of patients and then slowly increase the numbers to whom it is given, as you get more confident with the drug. Often, it's a painfully protracted process. You just have to learn to be patient. Sometimes though, it's worth the wait.

II

Around about Easter 2006, we started to receive data from a study of about eighty patients with advanced lung cancer.

This was normally treated with a combination of two conventionally acting chemotherapy drugs. The sort that tended to poison everything in sight. This usually produced only modest effects at best though. And so increasingly, newer drugs with different mechanisms of action were being added in as well. Many patients were now treated with three or even four drugs, assuming they could withstand the toxicity and that someone was prepared to pay for them.

Our study showed that adding ASA404 on top of carboplatin and paclitaxel (two very well established and widely used cancer drugs) markedly improved how long the patients were surviving. Those receiving the combination including ASA404 were living on average about fourteen months, whereas those who didn't survived only about eight months.[1]

Incredible though it may seem, at the time these were just about the best survival figures ever reported for this type of patient with lung cancer. It was an outcome which was better than anything we could have hoped for. In fact to begin with, the data seemed almost too good to be true. No one got that lucky. We certainly never had before.

We were working on other drugs, apart from ASA404. These were being examined in a variety of malignancies, including breast, kidney and skin cancers, as well as in certain leukaemias. Some of them represented very advanced technologies, which had never been tried out in the clinic before. It wasn't a bad development portfolio for a company of Antisoma's size. But none of these other drugs were showing the sort of potential ASA404 seemed to be dangling in front of us.

Results that outstanding and this early on in the development of a cancer drug, were rare occurrences. It was like a bright light shining in a dark room. Whereas usually the best you could hope for, at this stage, was a dim glimmer that left you feeling around in the shadows, fumbling to find your way.

Our initial disbelief rapidly dissipated though, to be replaced by a sense of detachment from reality. This wasn't how things usually went in biotechnology. What kind of parallel existence had we suddenly found ourselves projected into?

However, the more we looked at the data, the more persuasive it became. The clinical trial was too small to be conclusive. That would have to come later. But the signals were so strong that we had to believe them. It looked like we were on a roll here and might just have the beginnings of a winner on our hands.

Having a drug that extended the lives of people with lung cancer from eight months to basically just over a year, might not seem a huge difference. But successes in cancer medicine are usually measured in such small increments. A couple of months here, a couple of months there. When you haven't got many left, it can make a big difference.

For the fortunate few, chemotherapy can actually cure a limited number of malignancies, even when widespread. Examples include cancer of the testicle, Wilm's tumor (a kidney cancer of children), Ewing's sarcoma (a rare type of bone cancer) and a number of blood cancers including particular types of leukaemia and lymphoma.

But these are the minority. There are over two hundred different types of malignancy and most remain incurable, unless caught very early on. Sooner or later they will spread, like an army mobilising and invading. For the majority of cancer sufferers once this happens, the time their treatment buys is limited to months for many, or a year or two perhaps for the luckiest.

A graphic example of one of the hardest tumors to deal with is cancer of the pancreas. This is a large gland near the liver, in the abdomen. Pancreatic cancer is one of the most feared of all malignancies, terrifying physicians almost as much as patients. There is only about a four per cent chance of surviving the diagnosis. Finding out you have this particular disease means it is definitely time to book that cruise, right now. You're not going to get another opportunity.

Fortunately, it is one of the less common cancers, affecting about forty thousand people a year in the US. Which is just as well, because despite being one of the most intensively investigated malignancies of modern times, it has remained stubbornly resistant to even the most advanced and innovative of experimental treatment approaches.

With this disease, patients' lives are typically extended by a month or so at most, even with the best new drug therapies. That's just *four* extra weeks between diagnosis and death. Not even enough time to see it through to the quarter finals of *X Factor*. And that's without taking any account of how the quality of that extra time might be eroded by the inevitable, often distressing side effects that all cancer drugs produce to varying degrees. Four weeks of lying in a pool of puke isn't much of a therapeutic advance.

And so, if there were any kind of pecking order within the tumor types, a hierarchy of hopelessness, as it were, the patients with lung cancer could almost count themselves lucky to be getting an extra six months

19

improvement in survival with ASA404. That was a lot of television. A whole football season if fact. By the awful standards of cancer comparisons, it didn't get any better than that.

It's an outcome we were certainly ecstatically happy with. Maybe the patients didn't share that sense of unbridled enthusiasm. But they were in fact getting the best deal on offer in Cancer City. It wasn't much, but there wasn't anything better anywhere else.

The ASA404 study had involved about eighty patients. That was quite a decent size, in biotechnology terms. It was typical for a drug at that stage in the development process. Which in the case of ASA404 was about the half way mark.

In this particular instance, the study had taken over two years from start to finish, had cost about ten million pounds and involved collaborating with lung cancer specialists in three continents. And that's not even beginning to include the complexities of dealing with the various governmental agencies, which very tightly regulate any type of clinical trial. Or the myriad local hospital committees, which also need to clear everything which involves any sort of experimentation on their patients, within their own hospital facilities.

Overall, seven very different and disparate countries were involved, each with their own seemingly mutually contradictory requirements. The ensuing endless permutations and pirouetting often resembled the chaotically inefficient proceedings of a United Nations Assembly, trying to steer a contentious issue through to some semblance of a resolution. But somehow, despite having only a handful of people to deal with all of this, we managed to get through everything and had a hugely promising trial result on our hands.

At the same time, we were also seeing some early information on how ASA404 was doing in two other clinical trials we were still running. These were in ovarian and prostate cancer. Both studies involved patients who had *already* been treated with some sort of initial therapy and whose disease had subsequently progressed. So they represented an even tougher group than the lung cancer patients, who had all been receiving treatment for the first time, following on from the diagnosis of their condition.

Despite these more difficult and intractable patient types, the results from both trials were looking good at this stage. This added to our overall sense of optimism, that we had something special with ASA404.

III

An experimental cancer drug that appeared to be working was a rare commodity. After all, the vast majority didn't. For every one that made it even this far, there were countless others that had fallen by the wayside. It was like trench warfare. The progress was painfully slow. The casualties along the way were too horrific to contemplate.

Drug development in general, and cancer drug development in particular, have a hugely high attrition rate. The chances of a compound making it all the way, from discovery to approval for marketing, are less than a tenth of one per cent. Cancer is a formidable enemy. It has been around since at least the dinosaurs. There has been plenty of time for it to develop almost impregnable defences.

We have only been fighting back for the last hundred years or so. It's been a very unequal struggle so far. About three quarters of new drugs have failed and fallen by the wayside before the stage ASA404 was currently at. And that meant ending up with nothing to show for the twenty five to thirty million pounds you would have spent overall to get to that point.

To have a drug looking good in three different tumor types was that much scarcer still. It didn't happen very often. It was about as common as having your own personal unicorn. So all things considered, we were in a very good position compared to many of our biotech brothers, lumbered with much less promising projects as they often were. And we knew it.

So we were feeling good with ourselves. We had a warm glow, that only the lucky touch can bring. You need that luck, to have any hope of ever joining the ten or so large and successful biotechnology companies which are in existence.

Names such as Amgen, Genentech, Genzyme, Biogen Idec, Cephalon and Celgene weren't exactly household ones. But within the closed cloisters of the biotechnology fraternity, they were revered for having managed to get drugs from the clinic and on to the market. In our religion, that was a transformation every bit as miraculous as the transubstantiation worshipped by others. It allowed them to start making money, rather than simply consuming it in development costs, like the rest of us.

But they were the exception. The industry is more typically characterised by hundreds, if not thousands, of small cancer biotechnology outfits similar to Antisoma, all struggling to come up with successful new agents. These are companies who would have given almost anything to be in the happy position we were, of having a drug that appeared to work. A drug with promise. A drug with a future.

IV

Most of our fledgling peer group were in North America but with a reasonable number in the UK and the rest of Europe too. Few have any drugs on the market and so make no money. Most are furiously engaged in discovery and development, consuming prodigious amounts of cash in the process. The majority of them evolve though the same life cycle Antisoma had followed. Which is basically driven by the never-ending struggle to acquire money, in order to survive.

A small biotechnology company is like an infant. It needs constant feeding, in this case with funding, seemingly at all hours of the day and night. As it gets older, its appetite becomes less frequent but much larger, having to consume more and more, to prevent it from eventually starving to death.

Biotechnology companies typically start small, with a handful of people based around one idea or technology. This is usually still in the test tube, often arising out of someone's life research in a university department or other academic environment. And without very much cash at all. What money there is, typically consists of a sorry mixture of the odd grant or two and the proceeds of re-mortgaged houses, belonging to those involved at the start up of the company. Houses still belonging to them for now at least.

Importantly, one of that small group of hardy pioneers typically includes a founding scientist with a passionate and proselytising belief that their innovation will succeed, where so very many have failed before. And who are prepared to risk the very roof over their head to prove it. That's the kind of spirit needed at this stage in the game.

Over the next year or so, if the science holds up and those involved appear to have been tapped by the lucky stick, then the research may just move sufficiently far forwards to attract an initial round of external investment. This is usually from specialist venture capitalists (abbreviated to VCs) who make their money out of trying to spot tomorrow's winners, based upon today's less than complete information.

The VC art is much more arcane than that, as it isn't even *tomorrow's* winner they are sifting around for but the best bet for three or four years down the line. That is the minimum sort of time period a new cancer technology needs before starting to look promising, given the huge odds of failure each and every day. It is a bit like looking at a clutch of new born foals and trying to guess which one to put money on, as a winner of the Derby in five years' time. There's not much to go on. You have your instincts and you have hope. That's about it.

Traditionally, VC funds were raised from a wide range of general healthcare investors. More recently, the larger pharmaceutical companies have also been establishing their own venture capital funds, known as CVCs (corporate venture capital), to invest in promising early stage companies. Organisations with such vehicles include Novartis, GSK, Pfizer Lilly, Roche and Takeda. Collectively, they account for over a billion dollars of investment annually.

One example is GSK's venture fund, known as SR•One, which has so far placed over six hundred million dollars into the biotechnology arena, currently involving over thirty companies. It's a clever way of becoming involved at an earlier stage, and therefore lower cost, with some of the most exciting emerging new science. It's a slightly more sophisticated way of buying options on the future potential of promising new technology.

If the luck and the science stay steady, even though probably by now far short of the original messianic predictions of the founders, then a company may be able to raise some more private funding. It can then expand, through recruiting extra people and progressing additional technologies. These can either arise from other in-house research, or as a result of science acquired from external sources. This is often from other less fortunate companies that haven't managed to keep all their balls in the air, for whatever reason, and have to start selling off assets in order to pay the bills.

Eventually, after many stops and starts, disasters and recoveries, setbacks and steps forward, a biotechnology venture may reach the stage where it has managed to sufficiently advance its technologies to be able to raise a *significant* sum of money for the first time. This could be through effecting a trade sale of itself to another (ideally much larger) pharmaceutical company.

Alternatively, it could maintain its independence, by floating on one of the public stock exchanges. These are usually the London or New York ones, although some of the European companies seem to elect for one of the *pot pourri* of local bourses. This is known as *IPOing* (standing for Initial Public Offering), the technical term for the transition from private (VC) investing to issuing shares which are available for purchase by the public at large.

If a biotech company goes down the former route, of selling itself to a larger pharmaceutical organisation, then it tends to have one of two fates. It could be swallowed up and subsumed into the leviathan acquirer, or alternatively left alone and intact, being managed at a distance from the mother ship. This is in the belief that innovation can be best maintained and fostered in a creative smaller environment, rather than a claustrophobic larger one.

Either way though, the effective consequence is access to extensive future funding to progress the drugs and the science to the point where they either come to fruition or finally fall apart. There is also usually a handsome financial return for those holding shares in the company at the time it is sold.

This is the route by which, in recent years, many of the largest drug companies have acquired some of their most innovative and promising new early stage cancer agents. The biotechnology world was buzzing, not so long ago, over the *billion dollar* deal in January 2011 by which Amgen acquired a privately owned company in Woburn, Massachusetts

23

called BioVex. This had a cancer destroying virus (called *OncoVex*) it was developing for a particularly fatal skin cancer known as malignant melanoma. That is a horribly lethal disease. It starts as a mole and rapidly ends up in the mortuary.

OncoVex had only completed a fifty patient clinical study at the time of the sale. Which meant that Amgen was effectively paying about twenty million dollars per patient, to get its hands on this new technology. That's not bad in anyone's book, especially BioVex's.

If however a trade sale weren't possible, or a company wanted to maintain its independence, then it could instead attempt an IPO in the UK or US. In this case, it would expect to issue new shares to raise a sum of money typically around about thirty million pounds. The exact amount though depends on how promising the company's pipeline of research products looks. And just how willing potential investors are to hand over their cash. For the original founders of the company, who probably put themselves under personal financial duress to get things going, the IPO can also be a big pay back time. A shareholding which has been there since inception, can have increased in value by many multiples at the time of a company flotation.

Usually biotechnology IPOs involve the newly issued shares being taken up by a mixture of larger general institutional investors, such as pension funds, and also specialists set up to invest solely in health care. The shares are typically allocated to the investors in advance, through the investment bank handling the IPO. It's unusual for private individuals, the so called retail investors, to be able to acquire shares prior to the actual flotation itself.

If a biotechnology company manages to successfully sell all of the shares it was planning to issue at the IPO, and at the price it was intending, then the flotation has obviously been a success. These though have been few and far between recently. In the last couple of years, many biotechnology IPOs have turned into complete failures. This has been due to the generally debilitated state of financial markets in the US and elsewhere, combined with disillusionment over the large number of biotechnology setbacks there have been recently. VCs have started referring to companies wanting to IPO as entering "The Valley of Death." Your chances of getting out alive aren't that good.

In many cases, the whole process has been abandoned, often at the very last moment on the day before the intended IPO itself. These dashed debuts have usually been the consequence of last minute reservations by potential investors. They have had a wobble or lost their nerve at the moment of being asked to put their hand in their pocket and actually get the cheque book out.

In the US in 2010, there were only about a dozen biotechnology

IPOs out of the thousands of queuing companies. In Europe there were none at all. Five years earlier there would have been hundreds in a typical year. Many investors are increasingly being tempted to put their money into social networking sites and the like, rather than unreliable drugs. Why waste money curing cancer when instead you can create a chat room with much less risk.

Even if biotechnology IPOs have managed to avoid collapsing altogether recently, they have usually ended up with share prices very much less than the company was anticipating. Endocyte is a small cancer biopharmaceutical company based in Indianapolis in the US, which managed to raise about eighty million dollars from an IPO at the beginning of 2011. That doesn't sound like a bad sum but they could only raise it by selling shares at seven dollars. They had been planning to do so at double that, until they realised investors weren't going to touch them at such a price.

On the very same day, BG Medicine, which was a fledgling medical diagnostics company based in Waltham, Massachusetts, had an IPO which raised about fifty million dollars. But that was only after they too had slashed their selling price by fifty per cent to seven dollars a share. There's nothing existing investors dislike more than selling on the cheap. But if you're desperate enough, you have to take what's on offer. Even biotech beggars can't be choosers.

However they do it though, the trials and tribulations of securing funding are definitely worth it, for those companies lucky enough to pull it off. Because it gives them the financial firepower to progress promising compounds to the sort of position we were then at with ASA404. Which was about the midpoint. Half way to where you want to be.

A lot of money is needed to get to this so called *End of Phase II* stage of development. If your drug is still working, then this is your happy place on the cancer highway. This is where you want to be. You get a rush from even thinking about it.

It's like having spent the last few years pushing an enormous rock up a steep, seemingly never-ending hill, at last reaching the summit where you are then poised on the edge, ready for that final heave which will send it crashing down the other side. *That's* your end of Phase II point. On top of a mountain, with the wind in your hair and suddenly in control at last of something that's been constantly threatening to roll back and crush you for as long as you can remember.

V

Conventionally, new drug molecules pass through three sequential stages of clinical evaluation during the development process. If they are lucky enough to make it all the way that is. These are described, rather unimaginatively, as Phase I, Phase II and Phase III. In practice, it's becoming increasingly difficult to divide what is effectively a complicated continuum, into three discrete steps. It's almost like trying to reduce a Tintoretto painting to its constituent colours. They are too interwoven to separate out. It's also a rather pointless exercise, as the picture would be destroyed in the process.

But it's a simplification everyone still adheres to in drug development. Maybe it made sense thirty or forty years ago, when drug molecules were all simple and similar. But in the current era of complex molecular diversity, this is a reductionism which has probably lost its rationale.

Phase I trials are small scale ones, involving limited numbers of patients, normally about twenty to twenty five. These intrepid individuals are given a new drug (which has only just recently escaped from the test tube in the laboratory) for the very first time, usually in slowly and cautiously incremental doses.

The main purpose of this is to find out the probable side effects in humans. And to get some idea of what sort of dose level is likely to be best tolerated. You also want to make a guess or two about how frequently the new drug should be given (once a day, twice a day or whatever) and for how long (for a week, a month, only once ever, continuously and endless other permutations). At this stage, you are also looking for initial hints or clues that the drug may have the anti-cancer properties expected of it. But that can often be difficult to detect this early on.

About ninety per cent of drugs never make it beyond Phase I, usually due to excessive toxicity or because there is no hint of any efficacy of any sort. For a scientist in a biotechnology company, this sort of failure can be a devastating demolition of years of arduous work. And the end of a huge expenditure of hope and hype to have progressed the drug to even this initial stage.

And worse still, it's also probably what will happen with the next drug, and the one after that, until at last one of them somehow makes it through. Phase I trials involve pushing a lot of boulders part way up the hill, only for them to then roll unstoppably back down again.

It's *Le mythe de Sisyphe*, written large and loud. In early stage cancer drug development, the experimental often seems to merge with the existential.

Phase II trials are the most important for smaller companies, such as Antisoma and all the other myriad hungry hopefuls out there. They can mark the transition from an ever present probability of early failure to some sort of possibility of future success. These are clinical trials on a larger scale than the preceding Phase I undertakings. They often involve around a hundred or so patients and are designed building on the information obtained from the earlier studies.

They are intended to gain a first clear impression of the possible efficacy of a new drug, in a particular disease. These trials are based on the best guess available of the likely dose. You need one which will be big enough to maximise the chances of the drug working, whilst not being so large that it causes overly unacceptable toxicity and side effects. This balancing act is as much an art as a science. Especially in cancer medicine, where the traditional approach has been to select a dose of a drug which stops just short of killing the patient, whilst hopefully still killing most of the tumor.

Although there are an infinite number of variants around the actual design of Phase II trials, the broadest distinction is between *controlled* and *uncontrolled* ones. Uncontrolled trials are the simplest and therefore always the least expensive choice. They involve just one group of patients who all get the same treatment, your new drug.

Controlled trials are where patients are divided into two or more groups, usually consisting of one group which receives your drug and another group which receives something else. This is usually the best available established treatment around at the time. It therefore allows you to make a direct comparison of how your drug does, in the same sort of patients recruited over the same period of time and in the same hospitals, as the standard of care drugs.

Controlled trials are considered to be a much more robust and powerful assessment of how a new agent is performing. But by virtue of involving two or more groups of patients, they tend to be significantly more expensive and to take longer to complete, than uncontrolled ones. Given that time and money are always the two things in shortest supply in any biotechnology company (hope being the most abundant), there are difficult decisions which have to be taken when it comes to Phase II trials.

You need to consider the trade off between how much to spend and how long to take, versus the robustness and credibility of the data you end up with. In clinical trials, you tend to get what you pay for. The more elaborate, expensive and time consuming a trial is, the more likely people are to believe the results coming out of it.

And credibility is the key consideration at this stage in the development process. Phase II trials are generally intended to generate data which is strongly suggestive but usually not yet confirmatory, that a drug does actually work. Although a supreme and sublime moment for companies like Antisoma, the arrival of positive Phase II results is unfortunately only a prelude to the true determinant of whether a drug will survive. That test is the Phase III trial.

In cancer medicine today, Phase III projects are frequently huge undertakings, typically involving a thousand or more patients, who are often in the study for periods of a year or longer. These trials are so big, they usually develop an uncontrollable momentum of their own. You have to press the start button and then patiently wait for them to eventually come to a halt some years later, when they have at last run their course. It's very difficult to influence them along the way.

Initiating a Phase III study is like pushing the boulder over the edge of the mountain. After that, you have to watch it career on its way, hopefully coming to a final resting place, somewhere near to where you were originally aiming for. Whether it does or not, is beyond your control though. It's all down to the forces of nature. There's not much you can do, except watch and wait. And pray.

It's very important to get these big studies completed in a manageable period of time, with most companies normally aiming for two to three years. To achieve this, it's usually necessary to run the trial in a number of different countries and continents, all at the same time. This inevitably adds massively to the complexity and cost of the whole process. For this reason, a Phase III trial can easily end up consuming sixty or more million pounds of investment. And that is assuming only one Phase III trial is required, as sometimes there is a need to undertake two or more, to be really sure what is going on with a new drug.

The aim of this sort of study is to ensure that a sufficiently large number of patients are treated across a wide enough range of different hospitals and clinics. This then gives a clear idea of how the drug is likely to behave, once it reaches widespread use in normal clinical practice. The Phase III trial is considered the only really definitive data to confirm that a drug actually works and that its side effect profile has been adequately characterised.

Positive results from a Phase III trial allow a company to submit the data to the relevant governmental regulatory authority in each particular country. They subsequently use this information (and all the earlier Phase I and II results) to decide whether to approve the drug for general clinical availability. This then allows doctors to use the drug as and when they want to, rather than just within the tight constraints of a clinical trial.

And it is only at this point that the company finally begins to receive some money back, from being able to sell the drug at long last. They can thus start to recoup their enormous preceding investment, which has probably spanned a period of about a decade or so by now.

The stakes are so high that negative data from a Phase III study frequently leave a smaller biotechnology company struggling to survive from that point onwards. As Antisoma was shortly to so graphically demonstrate.

Disconcertingly, despite all the encouraging data which have been generated along the way from earlier clinical trials, only about thirty to forty per cent of oncology drugs actually make it through Phase III. The rest fail at this final hurdle because they don't manage to prove, beyond all reasonable doubt, that they work. Or they turn out to have hitherto unsuspected side effect liabilities. Or often a combination of both.

Cancer is a disease which never gives up. Even at the very last moment it can still take a new drug down.

VI

Considering these odds and the massive investment a Phase III trial represents, the Phase II data upon which it's based needs to have as much credibility as conceivably possible. There's too much at risk here. Even the largest pharmaceutical multinationals have problems funding and managing more than a handful of Phase III trials at any one time. For a smaller company, one alone represents a formidable challenge to resources. And a potentially fatal risk, if the bet goes the wrong way at the end of it all.

So you have to be as confident as you can that you're doing the right thing by jumping on the Phase III rollercoaster. This decision, based upon the inevitably incomplete and less than conclusive data available from a Phase II trial, is always a daunting proposition. It's like marrying someone you've never met or buying a house you haven't seen. It requires a huge leap of faith and supreme confidence. Or mind-numbing stupidity. All of them probably.

To make that decision, a company is going to want the most credible Phase II data it can lay its hands on. And in oncology, that comes from the *randomised double blind comparator Phase II trial.* This is a trial in which the patients are randomly allocated, a bit like the toss of a coin. This is the *randomised* bit. They either go into a treatment arm which contains your drug, or to a separate treatment arm with an alternative drug. This is so that you can directly *compare* the two. Neither the doctors involved in the study nor the patients themselves know who got what, until after the trial is over. Which is the *double blind* part. You disguise all the drugs to look the same, so their true identities are hidden. Hopefully it stops any potential assessment bias creeping in, against one drug or the other, from the doctors involved.

This type of study is the most powerful and best designed clinical trial technique you can have. It's like flying Concorde rather than Aeroflot or driving a Bentley instead of a tractor. This approach is generally regarded as giving the best chance of the Phase II data predicting what is likely to be the eventual outcome of larger scale Phase III trials. It's the kind of information which gives a company the greatest degree of confidence, when contemplating spending its own money on further clinical development. And often more importantly, it is also the best lure there is for enticing larger pharmaceutical companies to step in and help out with their cheque book.

And *that* was precisely the sort of data Antisoma was sitting on, with its ASA404 Phase II lung cancer study. Some of the best results ever seen, showing the drug prolonged survival by a substantial period of time, in the world's commonest and most deadly malignancy. Data from a robust randomised comparator Phase II trial.

In the world of the small biotechnology company, that was alchemy. You'd turned a chemical in a test tube into pure gold in the clinic. This was a drug you would want to take into Phase III, even if it meant risking the shirt off your back to pay for it. Because the odds were that you would soon be able to afford a wardrobe with more clothes than you could possibly count.

That left only the small issue of the seventy or eighty million pounds it would cost to get to the end of Phase III.

VII

Antisoma had about thirty million itself but a lot of that was already committed. We had three other cancer drugs in earlier stages of development to pay for and also those two other ongoing trials with ASA404. That wouldn't leave a lot left over. Hardly anything in fact. Not with all our running costs on top.

We were therefore faced with a classic biotechnology dilemma, of huge promise and nowhere near enough potential with which to realise it. The possible solutions were however fairly simple. We could either raise the money ourselves and plough on regardless. Or, we could try in effect to sell the drug in its entirety, by finding a partner in another, much deeper pocketed, company. Assuming of course there was one out there willing to pay whatever we thought our treasure trove was now worth.

Many small biotechnology companies reaching this divergent point, would like to go down the path of self-sufficiency. They'd prefer to progress by themselves, all the way through Phase III.

Holding on to a drug for longer allows the company to generate a lot more value with it. If you are sitting on a successful Phase III clinical trial, then the drug is ninety per cent of the way there. Most of the risk is behind you now. The rock has rolled down the mountain and landed more or less where it was expected to. All that remains is the hurdle of governmental approval, as the final barrier blocking the way to the market place and the money.

Obviously, with an asset this advanced, a company can command a far higher price from a potential partner than at an earlier stage, when the risks are so much higher and the rewards so much more distant.

Tantalisingly there is also the possibility, if the Phase III data are really good, of being able to raise the money to create a marketing and sales infrastructure. This would allow a company to go on and actually commercialise a drug itself, thus reaping and retaining all the rewards.

This successful progression, from a molecule in a test tube all the way through to an actual medicine on the market, represents the zenith of many a corporate ambition. It was certainly ours. The dream is to become a *VIPCO*. To turn into a *v*ertically *i*ntegrated *p*harmaceutical *co*mpany, presiding over a drug from the cradle of chemistry to the ultimate grave of generic competition. It's a prize aspired to by most and yet attained by very few. So many dreams and ambitions are shattered along the way, by the capricious vagaries of the drug development roulette.

But it is certainly a prize worthy of the desire attached to it. A move to the market represents the transition from promise to product. And this can often increase a biotechnology company's value by a disproportionately large increment. Something which is otherwise almost impossible to attain.

Cell Therapeutics was a small biotechnology company based in Seattle and about the same size as Antisoma. Like us, it was struggling to get cancer drugs through development. Also like us, it had experienced a big Phase III failure in 1999, which left it languishing almost unnoticed by the financial markets. However, in the summer of 2000, Cell Therapeutics suddenly rocketed to become one of the best performing stocks on the entire US NASDAQ exchange. And all because it had a single drug, which was about to be approved for use in the US and make it on to the market there.

Called *Trisenox* it was actually nothing more sophisticated than old fashioned arsenic (although in a particular chemical variant, called arsenic trioxide). Arsenic was used extensively in traditional Chinese medicine and appeared to be a highly effective treatment, for a rare variant of an already rare group of leukaemias.

In the case of Trisenox, the disease was called *acute promyelocytic leukaemia*. There are only about two hundred new cases a year in the US and so many physicians will never actually even see a patient with it. Despite this microscopic market, the Cell Therapeutics' share price had spun out of control, because it now had something that set it apart from so many of its struggling biotech rivals. That being an actual approved *product*.[2]

Possession of such a mythically rare entity allows a company's valuation to defy the known laws of motion. It's as though it has slipped on to a stock exchange, in a parallel universe to the real one. This desperation of the markets to respond to positive news was a reflection of how little of it there was at the time. At least as far as cancer biotechnology companies were concerned.

Cell Therapeutics' high jump had established a corporate precedent the rest of us were keen to follow. But at Antisoma, the attraction of taking the risk and trying to get through Phase III ourselves was more than just the return it might give to our long suffering shareholders. It was also the fact that it would give us *currency*.

The more your company is perceived to be worth in the stock market, the more you can use your shares and the value they represent, to do additional deals. Those could be acquiring extra drugs or even entire companies, either way further increasing your value. This can create a self-perpetuating cycle of one value enhancing deal permissively facilitating the next, in a kind of chain reaction that could seemingly continue almost indefinitely. Or at least up until the point when one of them blows up in your face and then everyone steps back and pauses for breath.

There are a number of biotechnology companies which started from nothing, before progressing to become substantial entities through acquisitional sprees, often catalysed by one initial lucky break. The US oncology company Cephalon was started twenty years ago by one man, Frank Baldino.[3] That meant it had been in existence as long as Antisoma. Whilst it may share a birthday though, Cephalon's destiny has been dramatically different ever since. Its history has been characterised by a seemingly never-ending sequence of deals, resulting in an eventual market value of four billion dollars.

Frank Baldino just kept following his instincts, discovering undervalued and overlooked assets, which others had discarded or discounted. Each deal he did served to increase the value of what had been there before and thus paved the way for what was to come next. Corporate circles don't get more virtuous than that one.

And we at Antisoma, sitting there with ASA404, wanted to become a Cephalon. We wanted that very much indeed. So if we could, we intended to hold on to the drug and take it all the way by ourselves, without having to hand it over to a partner. By doing that, we could get enough value into the company to start building our empire.

The only thing standing in our way was all that money needed to get us to the end of Phase III. Along with the fact that we just didn't have the structure or people resources within our company to support an endeavour of that enormity. And of course, the requirement for ASA404 to hold on to its phenomenal potential.

And also, there was the small matter of our relationship with Roche.

VIII

Roche is a Swiss based pharmaceutical company and one of the biggest in the world, in its own right. But significantly, it also owns California based Genentech. It had acquired just under fifty five per cent of the company in 1990, at a time when Genentech had established itself as the largest and most successful of all the biotechnology brethren.

As its South San Francisco address of *One DNA Way* attested, Genentech was without any doubt the number one biotechnology company in the Universe. Subsequently, Roche would acquire it entirely, in early 2009, in a forty seven billion dollar deal.

Enormous though that sum is, it wasn't actually the biggest pharmaceutical merger, in what turned out to be a bumper year for such transactions. It was pipped to the post by Pfizer's sixty eight billion dollar acquisition of Wyeth.

Nevertheless, it showed the sort of financial firepower Roche could bring to bear when they wanted to. These people played in the big league.

Importantly for us Roche, through Genentech, had what was easily the world's bestselling biotechnology drug. This was an antibody called *bevacizumab*, perhaps more easily pronounced by its trade name of Avastin.[4] Like ASA404, Avastin also worked by attacking a tumor's vasculature, rather than the tumor cells themselves. It did this however in a slightly different way, by destroying the newest and most recently formed blood vessels in a tumor. Unlike ASA404, which targeted the older and more established ones.

No one knew yet which would turn out the better approach in the end. But Avastin was already widely used for lung cancer and for colon cancer. It would, in due course, be approved for use additionally in kidney and breast cancer and also a particularly virulent and intractable form of brain tumor, called a glioma. It was, quite simply, an enormously successful drug, despite the fact that it came with a severe series of side effects. Avastin was like a beacon guiding other biotech companies, providing them with a point of reference.

Through Avastin, Roche were clearly a natural and obvious potential candidate for ASA404 at some point, given the overlap between the two drugs. Of even greater relevance though, Roche already had a long standing partnership with Antisoma. This effectively gave them first right of refusal on any drug we were considering finding a partner for, or developing into Phase III ourselves. Roche therefore seemed to have a pretty watertight grip on ASA404 and its future destiny. They could almost claim it as a birth right, by virtue of owning Avastin and on top of that, they had a marriage certificate with us.

The origin of this lay in a deal the two companies had signed back in 2002. This gave Roche access to pretty much everything in Antisoma's pipeline, for the next five years, in return for staged payments from them to us. This situation worked for both sides as it obviously gave us money and also an effective sense of validation, from one of the largest of all the world players in the pharmaceutical arena.

Clearly, compared to something as enormous as Genentech, we were nothing more than a minnow, probably even something smaller, like plankton. Despite this, Roche had hundreds, quite possibly thousands, of similar arrangements with companies like Antisoma, scattered all over the world. They were like a huge whale, gliding through the biotechnology ocean, sifting up marine morsels by the giant mouthful.

The advantage to them was that through these collaborations, their development teams gained potential access to a wide range of new drugs and technologies, without having to go to the trouble of actually inventing them themselves.

By 2006, Roche and Antisoma were quite extensively intermingled. Roche were even running an early stage Phase II clinical trial with one of our antibodies, this one numbered AS1402. It was intended as a novel treatment for patients with breast cancer and the fact that Roche were looking at it, in this particular tumor type, had substantial symbolic significance for us. This was because their stable of antibodies also included *Herceptin,* which was widely acclaimed as a major advance in the management of patients with breast cancer. It was used in combination with normal chemotherapy and dramatically improved results in suitable patients.[5]

In fact so outstanding was it, that when the Herceptin clinical data was unveiled, at one of the world's largest cancer conferences, there had actually been cheering from the audience. This wasn't an occurrence usually observed within the markedly undemonstrative and cynical oncology community who frequent such events. Carnival time didn't come that often for the cancer clinicians.

We weren't in a hurry therefore to disabuse anyone of the impression that, if Roche were going to the trouble of looking at AS1402 in breast cancer, it was because they believed it might just be the next Herceptin in the making. In fact, the Roche study ultimately turned out to be disappointingly negative and they subsequently quietly handed the drug back. We would go on to complete another failed study in breast cancer ourselves, before dropping AS1402 altogether. But it was a good story, while it lasted.

In a similar vein, were Roche to exercise the option they now effectively held over ASA404, the inference would have to be that they saw an Avastin-like potential in it. With all the associated promise of enormous sales and huge commercial success.

All things considered therefore, we seemed to be sitting right in the middle of the Swiss sweet spot. The only problem with this pleasing and promising future was that Roche had just told us, unbelievably, that they were going to say *no* to ASA404. Despite the Phase II data, they were actually going to *pass* on their option.

Where the hell had *that* come from? And why now? It wasn't exactly welcome news, just when we were in the middle of happy hour with ASA404. It was certainly something of a surprise, when they decided to share that one with us.

The timing of their decision couldn't have been worse. Instead of everyone else basking in the glow of our good fortune, they would all now be wondering where things had gone so wrong. What, they would question to themselves, had Roche uncovered that had seemingly sent them running for the hills? Or the Alps, more accurately.

We would need to carefully explain this one away. Without creating the impression we had been dumped. We had to protect our asset's unblemished reputation. And that was going to be far from easy.

Admittedly, Roche running away might potentially be good in one sense. It would give us an unfettered reign over our destiny again. If we wanted to develop ASA404 ourselves, we would be free to do so.

By turning their back on us, Roche would be untying our hands in the process. They would have relinquished their right to snatch our goods and chattels out of our grasp. However, they could definitely have picked a better moment to rain on the parade we were planning.

As a partner, they had obviously been able to preview the ASA404 data in lung cancer, even though we hadn't yet shared it with the rest of the world. That particular debut was planned for the beginning of June, when we were hoping to make some waves at that year's American Society of Clinical Oncology (ASCO) meeting. In the world of cancer medicine, this was Saturday night prime TV. It was the show *everyone* tuned in to watch.

IX

Most industries have their own particular yearly showcase – the Detroit Car Show, the New York Book Fair, the Paris Fashion Week. In the case of oncology, it was ASCO. This year, 2006, thirty thousand oncologists, from all around the globe, were descending on Atlanta Georgia for the annual five day information fest, which characterised the world's largest annual cancer get together.

Clinicians, academics, research scientists, pharmaceutical companies of every size, government regulators, members of the trade press, financial analysts and just about everyone else with an interest of any sort in cancer, come together in this traditional summer pilgrimage, running from a Friday to the following Tuesday, at the beginning of June. Even the odd patient makes the journey, presumably in the hope of staying one step ahead of their own physician.

So big has this event become, that there are a limited number of cities with a convention centre and hotel capacity large enough. Unlike other annual events, such as those in Detroit or New York or Paris, which had a fixed location, ASCO was peripatetic. It usually shuttled between Chicago, Orlando, and unfortunately, Atlanta. Which had to be one of the most culturally bleak and spiritually deficient places, just about anywhere in the world. If cancer were a city, it would surely be Atlanta.

Orlando wasn't much better though. How could you seriously expect to hold a cancer convention in a *theme park*? At ASCO time, the city was full of the incongruously inconceivable sight of darkly suited droves of oncologists, gathered at breakfast, whilst engaged in earnest conversation on epigenetic gene silencing, or some other aspect of cancer molecular biology. And all the while, splendidly surrounded by a rainbow of holiday making Hawaiian shirts, Bermuda shorts and sun burned rosy red skin.

35

Along with life-size Mickeys or Goofys, shuttling from table to table, clutching enormous barrel sized breakfast bread baskets and generally getting in the way of vital cancer research.

This celebration of human diversity was thrown together in Smokey Joe's Breakfast Bonanza Bar, or whatever the name of the dining room, in the particular resort hotel the vagaries of fate had chosen to deposit these lost delegates in. It was the most bizarre possible mix of vocation and vacation.

But then again, in Orlando the incongruous is always just around the corner. Florida Hospital, on North Orange Avenue, is after all home to the Walt Disney Memorial Cancer Institute. Only in Orlando could cartoon and cancer coexist in such happy harmony.

But Atlanta didn't even have the distraction of all human tragedy, which Orlando so richly displayed at every twist and turn. A vast, vapid, anonymous sprawl, it was as depressing for visiting oncologist conventioneers as the disease itself. The only features of note were the Coca Cola Museum and the headquarters of CNN, neither of them having much to feature and even less to take note of. Probably the most interesting thing in Atlanta was the UPS Store, which featured a wide range of packaging items and other stationery essentials.

In amongst all this nothingness, was the hugeness of the Georgia World Congress Centre, home of the ASCO meeting. Spanning an incredible area of four *million* square feet, the Centre consisted of a seemingly endless succession of meeting rooms, auditoriums, restaurants, cafeterias, internet access points, briefing rooms and slide preparation areas. Followed by more restaurants and cafeterias. The prevailing philosophy of the organisers was clearly that the body needed feeding in parallel with the mind.

Everything was laid out around an enormous central hall. Here attending companies promoted huge exhibits featuring information on their established drugs and the potential riches of their development pipeline. Often these stands boasted elaborate multimedia displays, with sophisticated animations depicting the complex molecular events through which a particular cancer agent was thought to be working.

All this came with lavish leather sofa seating areas, refreshments and much more. Some had golf putting greens, to provide a brief respite from the serious business of curing mankind's greatest affliction. Others touted competitions and quizzes, usually based around some aspect or other of cancer medicine.

Often, particularly at the more popular times of day, stands featured a guest speaker. Someone pre-eminent in his or her area of expertise. This would be a celebrity name, a real big hitter, who could rapidly draw an admiring crowd, with the insouciant ease of a film star inadvertently attracting attention in the middle of Oxford Street, on a Saturday afternoon.

To someone outside this arcane world, a talk on *Current controversies in the management of node positive triple negative breast cancer,* or *The role of salvage chemotherapy in advanced relapsed/refractory non APL acute myeloid leukaemia in patients over the age of sixty,* might not seem like a top end gig. But this was the very stuff the ASCO attendees had flown half way round the world for.

Until recently, it was possible for companies at exhibit stands to hand out any manner of free gifts, in an effort to entice attendees over their threshold. Books, computer mice, organisers, pens, pads, desk tidies, clocks, barometers, mugs, paper weights, stress balls, timers, rulers, calculators, paper clip holders, folders, gonks, key rings. Trivia of every variety and shade of banality, all prominently branded with the name of some drug or other, which could actually represent the difference between life and death, for someone it might be given to. They were showered around like confetti.

It was as though it were Christmas time and they had to fill your stocking for you. This would result in the unedifying spectacle of hordes of oncologists groaning under the weight of their amassed booty, as they struggled to drag it from the room. There must be a limit to how many Post-it Note pads one clinician can cope with but it never seemed to stop them coming back for more. Unfortunately though, recent rules cracking down on promotion to physicians have virtually eliminated this munificence, leaving the average exhibition stand more Spartan than a monk's cell at Lent.

All of the conference activity is connected together by mile after mile of moving walkway, running from one end of the labyrinthine layout of the convention centre to the other. Hapless delegates seemed to spend most of the day trudging from one meeting or presentation to the next, constantly barging into one another with conference back packs containing voluminous amounts of literature. And with conference passes swinging around their necks, like hard earned medals from some bitterly fought campaign.

Many individuals were speakers or presenters, members of some particular faculty or another, or just long serving ASCO attendees. They actually did have coloured ribbons, red, yellow or green, attached to their conference passes, like battle distinctions. This combined with the general air of frenetic and yet seemingly purposeless activity, to create the impression of an army in disarray and retreat. Falling back, under the onslaught of the enormous tidal wave of information and data with which it was being attacked.

Information is everywhere at ASCO. Scientific sessions, plenary sessions, meet the professor sessions, oral presentations, written poster presentations, working groups, faculty meetings, state of the art lectures. The daily scientific programme starts at about seven in the morning and often continues on until ten or so at night. People are here to gorge on data from dawn to dusk, eating it up from gargantuan platters, served up in an endless procession.

Each day consists of thousands of different activities, many occurring simultaneously, scattered across the convention centre and often spilling over into adjacent hotels. And that is before you even take account of all the pharmaceutical company sponsored educational events and meetings. These are crammed into every availably vacant slot in the already stuffed and strained schedule.

It's a never-ending oncological orgy of information, with instant gratification at every turn. And the participants never seemed to be sated. They could carry on for days on end. The pathology of cancer had become the pornography of the clinician.

The American Society of Clinical Oncology, sponsor of this extraordinary extravaganza, is a not for profit organisation dating back to 1964. It is widely regarded as the pre-eminent driving force of oncology education in the US, publishing prestigious medical journals, as well as organising the annual ASCO meeting. The quality, integrity and reputation of ASCO make it *the* place where everyone, whether a pharmaceutical company or an academic researcher, wants to present their new data. It's guaranteed the biggest and best audience, thus producing the maximal possible impact.

Information presented at ASCO is formally captured in the highly regarded *Journal of Clinical Oncology* (JCO), thereby creating an important point of academic reference and accessibility. But perhaps more critically, a lot of what is shared at ASCO makes its way into the wider world, due to both the extensive specialised, and also wider more general, media coverage of the annual meeting. ASCO even has its own television station, ASCO–TV. The cancer channel was more entertaining than most reality shows.

Cancer progress makes good news and even quite small advances announced at ASCO, or subsequently published in JCO, can receive surprisingly generalised coverage. One recent study presented there involved a potential new prostate cancer drug called abiraterone, from the evocatively named Los Angeles based Cougar Biotechnology. A study in just twenty one patients with prostate cancer led to BBC news headlines of *"Potentially the most significant advance in the field in seventy years."*[6] The main clinician involved in the trial, Dr Johann de Bono from the Institute of Cancer Research in the UK, even appeared on the *Today* programme to talk about it.

Cougar had definitely captured its prey this time.[7]

And so ASCO was definitely the place to present our ASA404 data. There would be a global audience watching. If there were potential investors out there somewhere, who might be prepared to come up with the sorts of sums of money we were looking for, they would hear the message most loudly and clearly via ASCO. Alternatively, if there were a large pharmaceutical company keen to take ASA404 off our hands, then they too would have people there, looking and listening.

And so the situation with Roche didn't exactly help things, because it had the potential to become a damaging distraction from our main event. If they were rejecting a drug which looked this good, there must be a very sound reason for it. And everyone would want to know what it was. We wouldn't have minded finding out ourselves.

X

Roche had actually told us a few months earlier, after seeing the initial ASA404 data, that they probably didn't want to move things forwards. But they hadn't told us *why*. In fact they never actually did. Of course, we had asked them. But they just wouldn't reveal what must have suddenly become commercially sensitive information for them. From having been a close and comfortable collaborator we had clearly already, in their minds at least, become a potential competitor.

Speculation naturally was rife within Antisoma. The general consensus was that they must have some competing project internally, which had won the battle for resource allocation. In a company of that size and complexity who knew how many myriad diverse candidates were all vying for funding. And what byzantine internal political pressures were brought to bear in this decision making process.

Another idea, fashionable for a short while around the coffee machines, was that the decision had something to do with protecting the Roche/Genentech Avastin franchise. It all depended on how you looked at things. On the one hand, ASA404 could be a superbly complimentary fit with Avastin. It worked through a similar but still sufficiently distinct mechanistic pathway and targeted the same lung cancer tumor type.

Alternatively, it could be perceived as a potential competitor and hence probable threat. There was a lot of overlap between the two drugs. Both occupied the same conceptual space of attacking tumor blood vessels and again both were intended for the same tumor type. Maybe they were in fact too similar. Perhaps, therefore, Roche were worried that they would be unable to expand the usage of one drug, without constraining the prospects for the other.

This made some sense but still left the problem that whilst Roche might wash their hands of ASA404, this didn't make the threat to Avastin go away. Instead it left it still there but in the hands of someone else and, if anything, more than ever outside of Roche's control. If they were having problems accommodating both Avastin and ASA404, then why not simply acquire the latter and thereby contain the risk?

It wouldn't be the first time a large company had got its hands on a development candidate perceived as a threat, only to then sit on it and effectively slowly suffocate the potential usurper. Fears of one drug cannibalising the other didn't therefore quite add up as a convincing explanation for Roche going AWOL.

There was also one other company which was developing a vascular disrupting agent, similar to ASA404. Maybe Roche were planning to link up with them, so the conspiracy theories ran, abandoning us along the way. OXiGENE was a small company, possibly even smaller than Antisoma, with facilities in Oxford in the UK and Waltham Massachusetts in the US. They had a VDA which, at the time, was called *combretastatin*. This name was to subsequently evolve into the even more ineloquent *fosbretabulin*, for reasons best known to OXiGENE.

Combretastatin was being developed by them for a comparatively rare form of cancer, affecting the thyroid gland. This certainly didn't have the huge commercial promise afforded by ASA404 in lung cancer. About fifteen hundred people a year in the UK are diagnosed with thyroid cancer. That's compared to the approximately forty thousand with lung cancer. This is a huge difference, probably explaining why most people don't even know where their thyroid gland is, or what it does. They can go their whole life through, without it causing any trouble and certainly not threatening to kill them.

It just wasn't in the same league as lung cancer. Combretastatin also appeared to be quite a toxic drug, with a lot of side effects, involving the heart and the circulatory system in particular. This was another disadvantage of it relative to ASA404.

But what we didn't know at the time, was that OXiGENE were planning a trial with combretastatin, in lung cancer. They were also going to combine it with both Avastin and ordinary conventional chemotherapy, in an unprecedented quadruple approach.

This was exactly the kind of proposition which must have crossed the mind of Roche at some point for ASA404. It was certainly something we had been thinking about. OXiGENE had rather vauntingly designated it the FALCON study. It was as though they were about to swoop down and snatch the prize out of our own hands.

Unfortunately though, rather than soaring on high, FALCON subsequently plummeted to earth.[8] Combretastatin seemed to be bringing very little to the party. Its addition to the other drugs didn't produce any obvious improvement in outcomes. Four drugs appeared to be no better than three.

Although it ultimately failed however, at the time this study was first mooted, it must have generated a lot of interest back in Basel. Assuming of course that Roche had somehow become aware of it. Maybe they wanted to be free to swap horses half way through the race.

We never did find out whether Roche and OXiGENE dallied with one another. Certainly nothing subsequently happened between the two companies. In fact, OXiGENE struggled on alone, almost going over the edge itself, a few times along the way.

With all these different possibilities, there was no way we could work out what was really going on at Roche. And therein lay our biggest dilemma. We couldn't actually point to a specific explanation for them turning away from our most prized asset. And so the natural assumption, amongst other people, had to be that Roche knew something about the ASA404 data that we weren't revealing. Something which cast a sufficiently dark shadow over the drug's future prospects to make it too big a risk. Even for a company the size of Roche. That was a big liability to have out there. A fucking enormous one in fact.

It would be like a black cloud hanging over us, when we should have been bathed in sunshine. The fact that it wasn't true didn't matter. Because it easily could have been. There were any number of places where, theoretically, things could have gone badly wrong and we just hadn't let on yet. Apart from the clinical progress, there are all sorts of other components of the development process where a drug can potentially fall apart, however promising it is looking in the clinic.

Whilst new drugs are being tested in patients, there are also a whole series of animal toxicology studies which are being carried out in parallel. These are designed to look at the possible damage a new agent might cause, once it is in widespread clinical use. Obviously all drugs, however useful they eventually turn out to be in man, will cause a variety of side effects in animals. This is particularly true if they are given for very long periods of time and at dose levels which are much higher than those ever likely to be used in the clinic.

And that is exactly how new drugs are actually administered in animal testing. The idea is that if you give much more, and for much longer, you will maximise the chances of seeing anything untoward and unwanted. So if an experimental medicine is being given to patients in a clinical trial at a daily dose of say ten mg, you might give it to animals, usually rats and dogs, at one thousand mg or even five thousand mg per day. If in the clinic patients are receiving a seven day course of the new medicine, then in toxicology testing you might try giving it to animals every day for a month at a time.

By doing this, you are bound to elicit some side effects of one sort of another. There is a spectrum ranging from something relatively trivial, such as a little bit of diarrhoea, all the way through to death itself. However, a rat and a human, whilst both mammals, are at very different stages of the evolutionary process. What happens in the former is not necessarily a strong predictor of how things will turn out in the latter.

In drug testing, rats are particularly prone to kidney damage for example, whilst dogs have a very high propensity for vomiting. And so both species tend to overestimate the likelihood of these things happening in man. On the other hand, neither the rat nor the dog were able to predict the effects of thalidomide on the developing fetus in humans.

There is therefore an art to toxicological science, which lies in trying to estimate the likelihood of findings, seen with animals, also happening in the much more complex biological system represented by human beings. This guesswork also has to take account of the very much higher dose levels that are used toxicologically, compared to clinically.

It is a little bit like requiring safety testing for a new family car model to include artificially accelerating it up to say two hundred miles per hour. And then having to decide whether to fail it because the steering and braking turned out to be less than adequate at this sort of massively excessive speed.

As with new car safety, drug toxicology testing standards are tightly regulated by governmental requirements in the US, Europe, Japan and elsewhere. Although in the case of new medicines, these are often based more upon outdated historical precedents, rather than contemporary common sense. What this means for potential new agents, such as ASA404, is that toxicology testing is one of the unavoidable regulatory requirements of the overall drug development process.

But rather than producing black or white easily interpretable data, it often results in outcomes which are much more nebulous, sitting firmly in the grey area of the spectrum. So maybe people would think Roche had uncovered something worrying in the toxicology data for ASA404? Not a finding so dramatic that it would have killed the project stone dead. But something in the grey penumbra. Something that was still sufficiently disturbing to raise questions over the longer term viability of the whole thing.

Drugs that make it all the way through Phase III clinical testing and on to the market, have usually had any toxicological liabilities resolved along the way. But nearly all drugs at the earlier Phase II stage of ASA404, would still have a number of ambiguities and ambivalences needing to be explained away. And any one of these could potentially still turn out to be sufficiently serious to eventually lead to the abandonment of the whole programme.

But that didn't seem to be the reason for Roche's reticence. Of course ASA404 had its own issues, within the complexity of the entire series of animal testing experiments it was going through. In fact, it would have been surprising if that hadn't been the case. But we were certain there were no potential showstoppers in there. That couldn't be the explanation.

Obviously there are very many other dimensions to the challenge of developing a new drug, which could have given Roche the jitters. One area that is often overlooked is whether or not a drug can be physically manufactured, at a cost that allows a pharmaceutical company to actually make a profit. Many new drugs, especially cancer medicines, are hugely complicated molecules which require very elaborate chemistry, using very expensive starting materials, to be able to make them on an industrial scale.

For most drugs the costs involved in manufacturing can be reduced over time, as more experience is gained with the process. But sometimes this just isn't possible and the expense remains prohibitively high. As a general rule, the costs of actually manufacturing a drug have to be less than ten per cent of the final selling price, in order for it to be commercially viable. This is because of the overwhelming range of other expenditures that also need to be covered in formulating, packaging, warehousing, distributing, marketing and generally supporting a new product, before any sort of profit can start to emerge.

There are a surprisingly large number of drugs which never make the light of day, simply because, despite a company's best endeavours, there is little prospect of getting manufacturing costs down to that key cut off level.

But there were none of these problems with ASA404, which is what's generally known as a *small* molecule. Technically *small* refers to a compound's *molecular weight,* measured in the arcane physical unit of the Dalton. To be precise, actually 282.290660 Daltons in the case of ASA404. The molecular weight, in turn, is determined by a compound's chemical structure.

In practice, small tends to be used as a generic designation for simple, straightforward, synthetically derived chemical molecules. As opposed to *large* ones such as proteins, antibodies or complicated DNA sequences.

These all typically have molecular weights running into the tens of thousands. The molecular weight of the antibody Avastin is one hundred and forty nine *thousand* Daltons. This obviously makes it enormous, even within the minute world of the molecule, compared to say ASA404.

The relevance of this is that generally the smaller and simpler a molecule, the easier and therefore cheaper the process of manufacturing it tends to be. Which makes sense intuitively, as a larger compound will obviously need more components, with which to build it, than would a smaller one. And the more steps there are in the process of putting a molecule together, the more frequent are the opportunities for things to go wrong and for the costs to mount up.

43

However, ASA404, with its measly molecular weight of under three hundred, was an easy drug to make. So simple in fact that if you were to Google the technical name for the specific molecular structure of ASA404, which is *5,6-Dimethylxanthenone-4-acetic acid,* at least eleven companies come up in China alone, who can manufacture the drug for you. At least to a laboratory grade, if not better. Right there and then. Almost while you waited.

So if it wasn't the manufacturing process, what else could Roche possibly be worrying about? The only other area that crossed our mind was that of the patent protection surrounding ASA404.

Obviously, by the time a pharmaceutical company has managed to get a drug from the test tube to the market place, it will have invested an awful lot of time and money along the way. Current conservative estimates are probably something like ten years and five hundred million dollars respectively.

The company will need to recoup *all* of that money through sales, before it even begins to see any kind of actual profit. And so it has to be sure that it will have the marketplace exclusively to itself for a reasonable period of time, in order to justify the risk of that size of overall investment. Which is why it is so important that a new drug has as strong a patent, or intellectual property (IP), position as possible. You need to be able to block anyone else from being able to jump on the band wagon without having done all the preceding hard work.

There are broadly two types of IP which apply to new drugs. These are called *composition of matter* patents and *use* patents. The former is a patent protecting the actual molecular structure of the new drug. As long as it is in force, it effectively prevents anyone else from manufacturing that same molecule, or anything very closely related to it. This is the best sort of IP to have, because it is the easiest to define and defend and so every time trumps the other sort of IP, the use patent.

This is a form of protection which relates to the way a drug is used. A company could try to patent the use of a new drug XYZ for the treatment of, say, advanced breast cancer. By itself, this kind of IP wouldn't prevent another company from actually making XYZ. But it would prevent any attempts at selling it for use in the treatment of that particular disease.

Obviously this is a more specific and much narrower level of protection, compared to the composition of matter patent. This is because it only applies to the use of the drug in one particular context. It is also often difficult to get a use patent because the granting of one depends upon being able to demonstrate something *novel* and not immediately *obvious* about the proposed usage. This frequently requires the submission of supportive clinical trial data, which the company may not yet have generated.

Furthermore, what actually constitutes *novel* and *unobvious* is somewhat subjective. This frequently leads to protracted dissent and disagreement between the applicant company and the relevant patent authority, often resulting in a refusal to grant the requested use patent.

And so composition of matter patents are nearly always preferred over use patents, as a form of IP. However once granted both patents have only a finite duration. It varies from country to country but is typically around about twenty years. After that, a company is relatively defenceless against marauding interlopers who may want to get in on the game.

Twenty years may sound a long period of time but it can take about ten years from discovering (and patenting) a new molecule to getting it to the market place. That is half the protection already gone, even before a single dollar has been earned in revenue. And then there is that five hundred million or so dollars of development costs to recoup.

Given that it usually takes a drug about five years of being on the market before it reaches peak sales, there isn't really very much of that twenty years left over, in which to actually make a profit. That's why companies tend to take out new patents along the way, whilst that twenty year clock is ticking with alarming rapidity. Even a few extra years of overall IP coverage can still make a huge commercial difference. It can prolong those golden final years when sales effectively equate to profit.

ASA404 was a drug which had been around for long time already. It had been discovered at the University of Auckland, in a period when academic institutions didn't always transfer promising assets to outside organisations with quite the rapidity they employ today.

When the people in New Zealand did decide to do something with it, they eventually passed it on to Cancer Research UK (CRUK), on the other side of the world. By the time CRUK had completed their evaluation of ASA404 and eventually passed it on to Antisoma, some of that protection period had obviously been eaten into.

We had taken out a raft of use patents for ASA404, which certainly usefully extended its life. Despite that though, the overall mix of IP was perhaps more like a patchwork quilt than the cashmere blanket Roche would have preferred to be bedding down in.

It was difficult to believe though that any potential IP issues would be enough to account for Roche's negative stance. What we had was good enough. It could have been better but both we, and we were sure Roche, had made do with much less in the past, with other compounds on other occasions.

Despite all the potential pitfalls, we were pretty confident about the robustness of the overall ASA404 package, whether it were the clinical data, the animal testing, the manufacturing, the intellectual property, or whatever else. But there was still a problem. Externally people would continue to harbour the suspicion that Roche had found a skeleton in the ASA404 cupboard. One that was banging loudly to get out.

Thinking through how best to deal with this, we decided eventually to simply link together two announcements. One would be the very encouraging Phase II data with ASA404. The other that Roche, very encouraging data notwithstanding, weren't going to be staying for the rest of the party. Whatever the reasons for that may have been.

The best course now was just to report events as they had unfolded and then try to put the best subsequent spin on things. The sooner we had the news out there, the sooner we could start trying to limit any damaging speculation.

If we had been a private company, one whose shares weren't traded on a public stock exchange, then maybe we could have sat on the news of Roche reneging for quite a while longer. We could have waited, until it suited us better, before making this turn of events more generally known externally. But being public, we were much more constrained than that.

All public companies labour under the obligation to promptly release any information they may have, which could be deemed to be *price sensitive*. This is news which could have an influence on the share price, were it known publically. It is a measure intended to protect existing and prospective shareholders. In theory, it prevents them from buying or selling shares in a company, without knowing all the facts that the management might be in possession of.

Obviously though, the interpretation of these provisions is an act of judgement. Arguably anything a company does is potentially price sensitive. And it would be impossible to disclose everything, particularly things that were actually commercially confidential. Similarly, the definition of *prompt* is in practice an infinite exercise in ambiguity and prevarication. However, even the most creatively imaginative reading of the regulations would still leave one with the conclusion that the Roche situation required disclosure. And sooner rather than later.

Taking this into account, we decided upon June 6th as the date we would issue a press release. Right in the middle of the Atlanta ASCO meeting. Our hope was that the positive impact of the findings with ASA404, particularly in the context of the annual ASCO event, would somehow neutralise the adverse impression created by the developments with Roche. At worst the two events could turn out to be neutral overall, one effectively cancelling out the other. With a bit of luck though, the combined impact would still be positive, although obviously less so than might have been the case without the loss of our corporate partner.

For biotechnology companies like Antisoma, which don't yet make any profits, the share price is effectively determined by the sentiment with which the financial markets respond to good or bad news from the company.

Whilst encouraging news is never a guarantee of a share price rising, bad news will always depress a company's shares. And often by a disproportionately large amount. All companies therefore use their share price as the barometer, by which they assess the outcome of any new developments they release into the public domain.

We didn't know what overall impact our news would have, but we were about to find out.

XI

We issued our press release, innocuously entitled *Antisoma reports survival advantage for AS1404 in lung cancer and regains product rights*, at seven am. This is the time everyone puts out their releases, just before the London Stock Exchange opens for business. The Roche bit was mentioned, almost in passing, tucked away in the second paragraph:

"Antisoma also announces that is has regained all rights to AS1404 from Roche, and plans to take the drug forward promptly into a Phase III trial in lung cancer. Extensive preparations have already been made to allow seamless progression to the next stage of development."[9]

It ultimately turned out to be almost two years later, in the middle of April 2008 before the first patient received any ASA404 in the Phase III trial. The use of words such as "promptly" and "seamless" may in retrospect have been somewhat ambitious. But who was to know at the time. We had to be optimistic and actually believe our own aspirations, otherwise how could we hope to persuade anyone else?

However, you can't just put out an announcement like that and then sit back to watch your share price oscillate like a yoyo. You have to phone up the people whom you really want to get your message through to. Those are mainly the stock analysts who cover your company, your larger institutional shareholders and the financial press. That means manning the phones from the crack of dawn and trying to get hold of people who don't really want to be got hold of.

It's then a case of reciting a well rehearsed script, whilst trying to maintain an even level of enthusiasm. Usually in the face of a reception of reticence, reluctance and resistance. Given that we were all in Atlanta, there was the added burden of doing it in the middle of the night, to take account of the five hour time difference.

But whilst often dispiriting and difficult, ringing around does at least afford a degree of latitude and licence. You could say things that you'd rather not have printed, in black and white.

"*Yes*, the data with ASA404 was very encouraging and we were definitely going to pursue it into Phase III. *Yes*, the clinicians actually involved in the trial agreed with this. *Yes*, the data was being very positively received at ASCO. *No*, we really didn't know why Roche had elected not to maintain their involvement with ASA404. *No*, we didn't believe they had found anything that was of concern to them in the programme. *No*, we hadn't shown them any new data about ASA404, from the ongoing trials in prostate and ovarian cancer.

Yes, the Roche decision referred to all clinical trials with ASA404. Not just the lung cancer one. *No*, Roche's decision over ASA404 didn't affect their relationship with us over the rest of our programmes, where they still had an option. *No*, we didn't believe that their pulling out of ASA404 would turn out to be a setback for us. Instead it would free us up to go it alone. Or to look for alternative, and maybe even more favourable, deals. *Yes*, that meant we would be considering other partners going forwards. *No*, we weren't talking to anyone at the moment – we had only announced the news half an hour ago after all. *Yes*, we'd like to do Phase III by ourselves. *No*, we weren't in a position to discuss how much this might cost. *Yes*, we believed we could raise the necessary financing though.

No, this wouldn't lead to us having to abandon any of our other programmes. *Yes*, we would be adequately staffed and resourced to run all of them. Even if we were saddled with the Herculean task of a Phase III commitment. *No*, we weren't yet in a position to say when we would be announcing our next steps. But it probably wouldn't be before the end of the year at the earliest."

Overall it didn't actually sound too bad a story. We might even start believing it ourselves. The lung cancer data was compelling and ASA404 was now clearly a strong Phase III candidate. There was also some considerable truth in the proposition that we may actually be able to turn the shorter term Roche setback to our longer term advantage.

When the original deal with them was negotiated back in 2002, ASA404 was obviously at a much earlier stage than was currently the case. There was now a real chance of us being able to pull off an even better bargain, starting again with someone else. Our hand would be strengthened through having *actual* clinical data to negotiate with. And very good data at that.

This was much better than the conjecture and speculation which would inevitably have characterised those earlier Roche negotiations. And so we should have a very good chance of extracting more from a new partner now. If we couldn't do the Phase III study by ourselves, then at least we should find a partner on much better terms than before.

But our position was also weakened by the negative perceptual overhang of the Roche rejection. And by the fact that any potential investor, or commercial partner, would know that time was not now on our side. We may have completed Phase II but we had to get the drug into Phase III trials as soon as we could.

In drug development there is a real need to maintain a momentum in clinical testing. Otherwise energy, enthusiasm and commitment on the part of all the hospitals involved tend to rapidly dissipate. Or one of your competitors gets a foot in through the door ahead of you. Then suddenly their drug is everyone's new best friend and you can't get a look in. Once this happens, it is doubly difficult to get things going again.

Additionally, the drug development process is a hugely complicated scaffold of individual components, each intimately interrelated and intertwined. Delays in any one part can exponentially compound delays elsewhere. And all too often seemingly everywhere. The whole edifice can rapidly start to come apart.

Given this, there was clearly a need for us to get on with resolving the future of ASA404. We couldn't afford an interruption of any duration. The longer things dragged on, the less favourable might be any eventual deal we could strike, as we were increasingly seen to be running out of time.

And so after the press announcement went out, our eyes were glued to the computer screen. It showed the minute by minute movements in Antisoma's share price, in amongst that of all the other companies on the London Stock Exchange. There was a sea of black, yellow and red fonts charting the rise and fall of various shares, according to the vicissitudinous predilections of the market on that particular morning. It was a corporate chromatogram of success and setback.

XII

Throughout the preceding five months of 2006, our share price had remained fairly constant, gently swaying between about nineteen pence and twenty three pence. It had been slowly drifting towards this upper limit over the last six weeks or so, probably in mild anticipation by the markets of some sort of encouraging announcement about ASA404.

If the price now went up, anywhere above say forty pence, this would be highly encouraging. Probably sufficiently so to mean that investors would be receptive to being touched for some of that extra sixty million or so we were looking for. This would therefore allow us to hold on to the honey pot for a while longer and extract even greater value further down the line.

If, on the other hand, the share price fell by any significant amount, then it would be fairly clear that things hadn't gone down too well. It didn't have to be that big a price drop either, given the unwritten rules that appeared to apply to small company valuations. Larger positive changes and smaller negative ones seemed to have equivalence, in terms of their impact on the market's view of a company's overall merits. And whether to buy or sell their shares.

An unfavourable response now would almost certainly preclude us, in the shorter term, from securing any additional investment. And the problem for us was that we only had the shorter term left.

Alternatively, the share price could choose to do neither of these things and remain more or less where it was. It might go up or down by a manageable amount but not to dramatic extremes.

None of us really knew what avenues would be open to us, faced with such lacklustre ambivalence. Would we be able to raise more money or not. Could we retain control of our destiny, or would it be swept out of our hands by the need to find a partner. It wasn't an ideal situation to be in.

But maybe we would have quite enjoyed this riskiest of all creeks to be paddling up. Not quite knowing where we were going and whether our luck would be in or out when we eventually got there. It represented that element of risk, the gamble, the inherently unquantifiable unpredictability of drugs and biotechnology. It was what attracted many of us who had ended up in this world.

Sir David Jack, a dour no nonsense Scot, was for very many years Head of Research for what used to be Glaxo, before it assumed its current guise of GlaxoSmithKline. He was a brilliant scientist, who could rightly claim the credit for a number of drugs which have become household names, such as *Ventolin* for asthma and *Zantac* for stomach ulcers. Both are hugely successful products.

However, when asked what he did, at the various cocktail parties, finger buffets, dinners and other functions which he was doubtlessly obliged to attend on a regular basis, he'd invariably reply "Professional Gambler."

Which is what he was really. Although an extraordinarily successful, or at least extraordinarily lucky one. And that's what we were too, at Antisoma. Although in a different and much lower league than Sir David. We were gamblers, hustlers, card sharps, dice jacks, casino jockeys. Just chancers really. We masqueraded under the guise of science, with all the associated connotations of precision, exactness and predictability. But in reality, our world was often the exact opposite of all those things. We revelled in that paradox.

However, the random roulette of drug development alone wasn't enough of a gamble for some of us. We were attracted by the double jeopardy of the uncertainty of biotechnology companies and their parlous prospects too. A Molotov cocktail would have been less volatile.

And it is just as well that we were like that, happy to take potluck and live with the uncertainties involved. Because by the close of the markets on that Tuesday, our share price did indeed find itself mired in the middle territory. It neither rose precipitously nor crashed catastrophically either, ending up at about eighteen pence. That was a fall of around twenty per cent, compared to where it had been before we began picking up the phones at the start of the day.

The Roche element appeared to have predominated but not disastrously so. So the good news was that we weren't dead. But although still alive, we weren't quite sure just how injured we were. Could we limp on and get our hands on the money we were looking for, to keep ASA404 moving forwards. Or would it soon become apparent to everyone that we couldn't keep up the pace by ourselves and would need the support of a partner to get us going again.

Could we take the ride alone, or would we need someone to hold hands with.

XIII

Our share price remained depressed for most of the rest of the summer, in part at least due to the traditionally sluggish nature of the financial markets over the holiday period. This was particularly so in August, when nothing much happens in most of the European centres, including London. Instead swarms of bankers, brokers and analysts disperse all over the globe. They need a well earned rest from creating or destroying the dreams of others. And lining the pockets of themselves.

But after the summer sojourn, a greater appreciation slowly developed of the promise and potential of ASA404. This was helped by encouraging early data from the still ongoing trials in ovarian and prostate cancer.

The disappointment many had initially felt, when Roche walked away, also inevitably started to subside somewhat. It was doubtlessly assuaged by increasingly promising noises coming from us, about potential suitors we were entertaining as a replacement for them. Recognising that we were handicapped by our share price and so might not be able to go it alone, we had started looking around for suitable partners.

And there were many possibilities. The autumn months were a whirlwind of activity with potential companies coming and going. Most of the serious players came knocking at our door anyway. These were the companies with both an established interest in oncology and also the requisite depth of pocket. Well developed Phase II drugs, with good *randomised* clinical data, just like ASA404, were exactly the sort of proposition any large company would give serious consideration to.

Phase I compounds were much more abundant but represented substantially greater risk, by virtue of being so early. On the other hand, unpartnered ones already in Phase III were very much rarer and hugely more expensive to acquire, should they actually ever become available. On any drug dating site, ASA404 would therefore have stuck out as an enticing prospect. It should tick all the boxes.

And so people came to look at what was on offer. As with most commercial discussions, we followed a structured process. It was like dating in many ways. We'd meet up casually to begin with. If we seemed to like each other we would start spending some time together. We'd gradually tell each other more and more about ourselves. Until you reach the point of knowing whether there's something there or not. And then eventually you have to decide whether to take the plunge and move in together.

That awkward first date would usually start off with us giving whichever particular company it was, a presentation of non-confidential information about ASA404. This basically consisted of telling them only what was already available in the public domain. And which they could probably have found out for themselves, had they been so minded. But we liked to think we presented it with an elegance and élan, which made the journey worthwhile for them. After we'd set out our stall, they would then modestly present their credentials and why they could be trusted with our family jewels.

The main purpose of an initial exercise like this seemed to be to play a game whereby they tried to catch us out. They'd attempt to get us to reveal something which we hadn't yet made public and which we probably didn't want to tell them, at this stage. Similarly, we would almost inevitably let something slip we weren't supposed to. And then we had to try and prevent them seizing on it.

There was an importance to sizing each other up like this. We needed a round or two of sparring, to see how well matched up we might be. As potential partners for the three or four years a Phase III trial might take, each side had to feel they could trust and get on with the other over such a protracted period. You had to make sure there was a cultural fit of some sort.

We liked to see ourselves as a small flexible and almost anarchically innovative company. Well, occasionally. However, most of our prospective partners were larger multinationals, with none of those characteristics.

Smaller companies attract more entrepreneurially minded, flexible types. People who thrive on risk and are willing and able to turn their hand to a wide variety of differing roles and responsibilities. Large companies by and large don't. They tend to mould individuals into more constrained and defined positions, within a much better delineated organisational hierarchy. Usually this doesn't overly foster innovation and imagination. They squeeze the individuality out of their people.

That's exactly why many big pharmaceutical companies end up acquiring their most promising science from much smaller biotechnology ones. The latter can manage the "chaos" of unfettered scientific thought and originality so much more effectively than the former.

Neither approach is better or worse, just different. But it did mean we sometimes found ourselves experiencing a cultural divide, when meeting prospective new partners. One of the earliest examples was a date we had that autumn with a reasonably high ranking group of senior executives, from one of the largest of the US pharmaceutical companies. The meeting was on a Sunday morning, during the fag end of a cancer conference in New Orleans. It was the only way we could get our respective calendars to work.

Despite the bohemian, voodoo, genteelly distressed, weekend ambience of the old French Quarter hotel we were meeting in, they all arrived in seemingly identical blue suits, white shirts and red ties. Along with a little corporate button badge pinned to the left jacket lapel. For some reason, they seem to love those in America.

Most were weighed down by the oversized black document bags that you see airline pilots lugging around airports. I'm sure there were small rolled up travel umbrellas poking out of one end. They were the flight crew from Airline Anodyne.

They wanted to sit together on the same side of the conference table. They didn't want to mix. I don't know what was wrong with us. But they obviously thought it was catching. Arrayed in front of them were yellow legal note pads and a neat row of company embossed pencils. There was a kind of collectivist culture, whereby they seemed to need to think and act in concert, rather than separately. It was as though the Moonies had moved into mainstream pharmaceuticals.

Which threw us a bit. It wasn't what you'd call a promising start. It also quickly became apparent that they couldn't make any decisions. They would need to refer back to others, who were presumably still in the headquarters mother ship. Which was a bit surprising. There were so many of them in the room, it was difficult to imagine anyone left back at base.

It wasn't our way of doing things. There was a glass wall running down the room, in between them and the four or five of us, ranged around the other side of the table. It was like watching enormously lumbering marine creatures, through a tank at the aquarium. But if we saw them as overly constrained, maybe one or two of us came over as unnecessarily cavalier, possibly even uncouth. However we both gave it our best shot over the next few hours. Each side after all potentially had something the other wanted. But despite the mutual self-interest, it never really got off the ground.

Walking back out into the September sun later that Sunday, we hoped they wouldn't want to pursue things. It hadn't been a happy date. More like an arranged marriage, between two ill-conceived and incompatible partners. But we needn't have worried, because after extensive internal consultations, they decided that they didn't actually want to see us again. We'd never been so happy to be dumped. Maybe our entire corporate history would have been radically different, if only we'd combed our hair before going into that meeting.

XIV

As it happened, we were turned down by a number of other companies, many of whom seemed to be much more culturally compatible. Some of those who passed at this initial stage were almost certainly time wasters in the first place. They were just on a fishing expedition, to see if they could find out more about ASA404 and what we were up to. We assumed this was probably because they had a competitor drug of their own, tucked away in the wings somewhere. You get quite a lot of people who mess you about like that.

Others may have baulked at the realisation of the size of the investment needed to move the programme forwards. Or the sorts of financial terms we were looking for. It was amazing how little certain people expected us to consider accepting. For some, it was too risky at this stage, despite how good our data was. They'd prefer to wait until the end of Phase III and accept having to pay a much higher price then. Maybe one or two just didn't like the look of us. Nothing you could put your finger on but still enough to stop things in their tracks.

However, there were quite a few companies who were sufficiently interested to move to the next stage. This was to sign a *confidentiality agreement* (CDA) between us and them. With this in place, we could reveal information that wasn't yet in the public domain. It allowed the other party to make a more realistic assessment of the programme. In return, they were obligated not to use this for any commercial purposes of their own, should an eventual transaction not take place between the two sides.

Whilst a normal part of negotiations, this is quite a serious legal undertaking, which companies tend not to enter into lightly. They want to avoid inadvertently tying their hands for the future. And so it is usually indicative of a reasonably significant level of underlying interest.

Having put a CDA in place, then an expanded team from whichever company it was, would descend upon us. This usually involved individuals from the labs, the clinical group, drug manufacturing, patents, regulatory, legal, marketing and business development. Just about everyone in fact. With all their people and all ours, it would often be a squeeze to fit everybody into one room.

This amassed corporate cacophony always served as a reminder of just how complicated the drug development process had become. On a typical day, there were probably more people gathered there, just to *talk* about moving ASA404 forwards, than had been involved in the entire story of discovering, developing and distributing penicillin, during the Nineteen Forties. Life had been a lot simpler back then.

These meetings would start off with presentations including information omitted from the earlier non-confidential briefing. This usually related to commercially sensitive aspects of the manufacturing process. Along with detailed estimates of the costs and timings of the clinical studies which still needed to be undertaken. Most importantly, we shared our projections for how we saw the sales potential of the drug, once it made it to the market. And just when the cash would start to roll in.

We were revealing all the things we normally kept hidden from public view. It was like taking our clothes off in front of them.

After that moment of intimacy, everyone would divide up into smaller groups, to go through specific areas in more detail. We'd then all coalesce again at the end of the day, to exchange mutual endearments and encouraging pronouncements on subsequent steps.

Usually these events seemed to go well and we would end them with a quiet sense of optimism. Our new best friends would soon be coming back to play again.

But quite often, we never saw them after that. Despite us baring all. A week or two later, we would receive back a message that they weren't interested in proceeding. To start with, this confused us and then after a while it began to concern us. It didn't seem to quite make sense. Maybe Roche did know something after all. Something which we still didn't but clearly everyone else apparently did. However in reality, there probably wasn't one specific reason for this reticence. In fact, it may not even have had that much to do with ASA404 *per se*.

Even for the largest pharmaceutical companies, the decision to take on a Phase III proposition, such as ours, wasn't one which could be made lightly. After all, we were talking about not far short of a hundred million dollars here. That was for the clinical trial alone. We would be looking for a similar additional sum for ourselves, as a reward for our investment and risk to date. We'd carried ASA404 this far all alone and we'd need a payback, before handing it over to someone else.

Any organisation has only a finite amount of finance and people which it can allocate to this kind of commitment. And so a substantial proportion of the pot going to ASA404, meant that there would be that much less left to go around the other projects. And doubtless there were many internal voices clamouring for their own vested interests, within the companies who were now turning us down. The more realistic and imminent ASA404 was looking as a proposition, the shriller these voices presumably became.

Sometimes, they couldn't agree with us on the sales figures for ASA404 we shared with them and how much money it might make. And just as importantly when. There was a definite art to that anyway. You were trying to guess what state the cancer market would be in five years into the future, when ASA404 reached that happy place.

The biggest influence on how much revenue you thought a drug might make, was the price you believed it could command. Market share was a distinct second. Some cancer drugs were being sold at impossibly high prices. Dendreon, for example, was a Seattle biotechnology company with an advanced, cellular based, drug for prostate cancer called *Provenge*. It was priced at ninety three thousand dollars per patient. That was a lot of money. Particularly as you didn't get a huge amount in return. It provided three or four months of benefit at best. Provenge wasn't a drug which cured anyone.

Many new cancer drugs were routinely costing thirty thousand dollars per month. This was only viable because, even with treatment, most patients weren't living long enough to get through more than a couple of cycles of therapy.

Even so, it was clear these sorts of costs weren't sustainable and probably all cancer drug prices would be subjected to radical surgery over the coming years. Particularly with all the turmoil over healthcare economics. Which made it exceptionally difficult to know what price ASA4004 might command, when the time came. You might just as well get out a set of Tarot cards, as try any more rational projections.

It wasn't surprising therefore, that some potential partners couldn't make our sums add up. They didn't think there was enough profit in it for them, to justify paying the sort of price we were asking. There really wasn't much left for us to talk about in that case.

There was also an element of individual psychology and self-preservation at play too. The decision to proceed with a deal would be made by a small number of individuals within a company. The business development and marketing people were going to have the loudest voices and the greatest say. If they went ahead with it, then their own corporate futures would forever be intimately intertwined with the success or failure of ASA404. And that element of personal fate often made people more than a little nervous about reaching positive recommendations.

The dilemma lay in there being no such thing as a risk free proposition in drug development. It was a huge leap of faith to take on that kind of commitment. There were nearly always as many reasons to say *no* as there would be to say *yes*. And there was a lot less risk in saying no. A positive decision however, meant living with the ever present possibility of things falling apart, at any time in the future.

It all depended on what state of health your own current pipeline was in. And how much you might need to take a risk with a new drug, to give things a boost. What sort of bet did you want to make and how much might you be prepared to lose, if it went wrong. When there were bills to pay, mouths to feed and careers to protect, the element of *personal* risk, in taking on an as yet unproven new drug, could seem disproportionately large.

And that could be the case even for drugs with the sort of robust randomised Phase II data that ASA404 possessed. There was still a long way to go in Phase III. And an awful lot of money that could be lost along the way. If you want a guarantee, buy a kettle, as they say. And many of these larger companies were populated by those of a relatively risk averse disposition. Given a choice, they would probably prefer a kettle to the bubbling cauldron of investment risk that ASA404 represented in their eyes.

But obviously not all corporate individuals were like that. Deals get done every day of the week, throughout the pharmaceutical world. Although, admittedly, usually of a smaller magnitude than the one under consideration here. There were definitely people out there with the appetite for the risk and the financial ability to place the bet. People who wanted to have a *really* big punt at the casino.

And some of those clearly resided within one of the biggest pharmaceutical players of them all. As we were soon to find out.

XV

Headquartered in Basel, on the banks of the Rhine and just metres from the Swiss-French border, *Novartis* was created in 1996 from the merger of Sandoz and Ciba-Geigy. It employed over a hundred thousand people, scattered over one hundred and forty countries throughout the world. More than half of them worked in pharmaceuticals. The rest were spread out over other divisions such as vaccines, diagnostics, consumer health and the Sandoz generics business.

The Pharmaceutical Development Division, responsible for drug development within Novartis, had over seven thousand employees *alone*. Which was about a hundred times more people than in the whole of Antisoma.

They had locations in Basel, New Jersey and Cambridge in the US, Horsham in the UK, Hyderabad in India, Tokyo in Japan and Shanghai and Changshu in China. The Novartis Oncology Business Unit was in Florham Park, New Jersey. Clearly this was a big operation in anyone's book. They were just about everywhere.

At the tip top of the pyramid, overseeing this enormous organisation was the Novartis CEO, a Swiss medic by training, called Daniel Vasella. He had originally been the CEO of Sandoz, at the time of the formative merger. Underneath him somewhere in the hierarchy was the American born Head of Novartis Oncology, David Epstein. He'd started life as a pharmacist and then moved, via strategic consultancy, into a number of high level managerial positions within Sandoz, prior to the Novartis transformation. Novartis and David Epstein were interested in ASA404, so it seemed. Very interested indeed.

Overall, Novartis had about fifty products actually on the market. These were broadly divisible into cardiovascular, respiratory, neurological, immunological, infectious and cancer conditions. About six or seven of these were cancer drugs, mostly an unexciting and slightly dated collection. But with one *very* notable exception.

Imatinib was a drug for one of the commonest types of leukaemia. Chronic myeloid leukaemia (CML) is a disease characterised by too many immature white cells in the blood and bone marrow.[10] A millilitre of blood from a healthy person would contain somewhere between four thousand and ten thousand white blood cells. The same volume of blood from someone with CML would have up to twenty five times that number. That was a lot of cancer cells. The condition affects about five thousand people each year in the US alone.

Known as *Gleevec* in the US and *Glivec* in Europe, imatinib had set the world of oncology on fire when it was initially approved in 2001. Which was no mean achievement, given the inflammable resistance normally displayed by the discipline.

Prior to its advent, about thirty per cent of patients with CML would be expected to survive for five years or longer. With Gleevec this was increased to an extraordinary ninety per cent, a figure unprecedented in the annals of cancer medicine. Gleevec didn't actually cure CML, because if you stopped taking it then the disease would recur. But it did turn it from a fatal into a chronic disease, which you could hold at bay. It became a condition you were more likely to die with, rather than of. Which was an outstanding achievement by the usual standards of cancer medicine.

But what made Gleevec *really* remarkable that it was both the end of a journey, which had begun over forty years earlier and also the beginning of a new revolution in cancer treatment. It was the pharmaceutical equivalent of the first man landing on the Moon.

Back in the late nineteen fifties two scientists, Peter Nowell and David Hungerford had discovered that diseased cells from patients with CML possessed an unusually small and atypical chromosome. This became universally known as the *Philadelphia chromosome*, after the city in which it was discovered.

Nearly twenty years later scientists in Chicago worked out the structure of this distorted chromosome. They deduced that it was actually made up of two separate bits taken from two other normal chromosomes (numbers nine and twenty two) in the body.

Whatever was causing CML was doing it by mixing up normal

chromosomes to produce abnormal hybrids. For the next ten years scientists at the US National Cancer Institute in Bethesda and at Erasmus University in Rotterdam tried to work out what this meant. Eventually they pieced together that the Philadelphia chromosome was itself squeezing together two normal genes, usually kept apart by nature on different chromosomes, to create one abnormal one. This was called the *bcr-abl fusion gene*.

From there the story subsequently travelled to Los Angeles. In 1990, researchers at the University of California identified the abnormal *protein* produced by the abnormal *gene* arising from the abnormal Philadelphia *chromosome*. This protein turned out to be a mutated form of a naturally occurring enzyme called *tyrosine kinase*. The normal enzyme plays a key role in regulating cell division.

The problem with the mutant form was that it caused the enzyme to be active for inappropriately long periods of time. It couldn't switch itself off like its normal counterpart could. This was forcing white cells to proliferate at an abnormally high rate. In turn this resulted in accumulation of huge numbers of immature white cells. Which was the exact underlying disease process in CML. Everything suddenly seemed to be fitting together.

The last leg of the journey was northwards from sunny Los Angeles to snowy Oregon and an oncologist called Brian Drucker at the Oregon Health and Science University. He turned out to be holding the key which would eventually unlock the door to the Novartis Gleevec treasure trove.

Scientists now knew precisely what was causing the abnormalities within CML. It was all due to the aberrant form of the enzyme tyrosine kinase. It should therefore have been a small step to develop a drug which could block this enzyme. This would arrest the overly zealous cell proliferation it was causing and thereby stop the disease in its tracks.

The big problem they were facing though was that tyrosine kinase turned out to be one of literally *hundreds* of kinase enzymes in the body. Each one was responsible for regulating a slightly different but still essential process of some sort or another within the cell. And all acted through a similar mechanism. They worked by adding a chemical (*called a phosphate group*) onto proteins within the cell, thus switching them on or off.

Although subtly different from each other in function, all these enzymes were structurally very similar. It was therefore conventionally held to be impossible to come up with a drug which would be specific for just *one* enzyme alone. An enzyme such as the CML tyrosine kinase. And if you couldn't come up with a drug targeting one particular kinase you would inevitably end up blocking a whole range of them.

Given the importance of these enzymes to the normal functioning of the body, it was feared that the resulting side effect profile would be fatally toxic. You would be killing the patient as well as the disease.

But Brian Drucker thought he had seen a way through this impasse and ended up tracking down Ciba Geigy, the Novartis forerunner. At that time it was one of the few pharmaceutical companies tinkering with tyrosine kinase inhibitor research. Collaborating with a scientist there called Nick Lydon, Drucker started screening Ciba Geigy's tyrosine kinase blocking compounds.

He was looking for anti-cancer activity in bone marrow samples obtained from patients with leukaemia. By 1996, the very year that Ciba Geigy and Sandoz came together to form Novartis, the Oregon group had identified one particularly promising compound, ST1571.

This acted by blocking a specific region of the CML tyrosine kinase enzyme. It prevented the transfer of phosphate groups to other proteins, thus effectively paralysing the enzyme. But critically, it left all the other tyrosine kinase enzymes untouched. ST1571 was the code number for what would ultimately become imatinib and Gleevec.

Two years later, Drucker ran a small Phase I trial with Gleevec in just over thirty patients with CML. The results were astonishing. Each and every patient went into remission. Furthermore, Gleevec turned out to be extremely well tolerated thus negating any residual fears about the safety of this approach.

As if that weren't enough, it transpired that in a number of patients the abnormal Philadelphia chromosome had disappeared altogether. Treatment had essentially reversed the entire underlying disease process of chronic myeloid leukaemia. That was magic.

In the years between 1998 and 2001, almost six thousand patients with CML were studied in clinical trials with Gleevec. Incredibly, the initial promise held up through these subsequent larger scale studies. It really was a revolutionary drug. Eventually it rode into the market place at the beginning of the new millennium, on a tidal wave of enthusiasm.

And that exuberance was generated in large part by something *even* more exciting than the clinical promise Gleevec was showing in a disease as intractable as CML.

By interfering specifically and exclusively with a single enzyme, which was itself solely responsible for a whole disease process, Gleevec was seen as heralding the beginning of the era of truly *targeted* cancer medicines.

These were drugs which would selectively home in on unique pathways implicated in causing specific types of malignancy. This had been the dream of so many for so long. To use these *magic* bullets rather than the napalm of the past. Cancer treatment would in the future be much more destructive to the tumor itself and with far fewer side effects resulting from collateral damage to normal tissue. So beginning with Gleevec, the belief was that new agents would become increasingly effective and progressively less toxic.

Originally, these hopes had been pinned upon antibody therapies, which had already been around as established cancer treatments since 1997. That was when an antibody called Rituximab had become the first to be approved, for use in a particular type of blood cancer called non-Hodgkin's lymphoma. However, antibodies had turned out to be relatively ineffective by themselves. They had to be combined with conventional cancer chemotherapy to work. But this then largely negated the original proposition of specificity and selectivity.

Maybe it would all be different with Gleevec. The signs were encouraging. Daniel Vasella even found the time in 2003 to write a whole book about the Gleevec story, *Magic Cancer Bullet. How a Tiny Orange Pill May Rewrite Medical History.* The title seemed to capture the optimism of the moment.

If sales were anything to go by, the Gleevec success story was clearly a sustained one. The drug was producing revenues of over three billion dollars a year by the time we started talking to Novartis.

So all in all, Novartis would be a fantastic partner for us. They had the best cancer drug on the planet. They could also easily afford whatever price we might want for ASA404. We definitely wanted to be part of their world.

But could we actually pull it off?

XVI

Novartis had turned up as a potential partner for ASA404 quite late in the day, during the last few months of 2006. They certainly knew how to make a late entrance.

We were of course still talking to other companies. A few of these had pushed themselves into quite a detailed and advanced level of negotiation with us. Although not at a particularly rapid pace it must be said.

Typically, given the complexity of everything, deals involving drug development take about six months to get sorted out and finalised. That's from initial contact between two companies to ink actually drying on the signature page of a contract.

Anyone involved with biotechnology knew these were the sorts of time frames. And everyone was aware we must have been talking to potential partners since the early summer. People were beginning to figure, around about October or early November time, that a deal might not be that far off. In anticipation of this, our share price started to creep up. By the end of November it had actually reached nearly thirty five pence, having flat lined at about fifteen pence for most of the summer.

Our banking advisers were confident that we should seize this window of unexpected opportunity and raise some more money before the end of the year. The fact that we were still far off signing a deal with anyone, let alone Novartis, didn't seem to bother them in the slightest.

And so we did just that, issuing a press release on December 15th proudly announcing that we had raised twenty six and a half million pounds. Not bad going for a day's work.

In the current climate of financial distress, securing that amount of money would be little short of a miracle. Lazarus coming out of his tomb would have been less remarkable. No one talks about those sorts of sums anymore. But at the time, we hardly gave it a second thought. With ASA404 in the family, it seemed more like an inheritance we were entitled to.

Nearly twenty seven million pounds sounded a lot of money. But it still wouldn't be anything like enough to get ASA404 through the Phase III programme by ourselves. It strengthened our negotiating hand and gave us funds to advance earlier stage drugs and bolster our portfolio. It was never good to look like a one trick pony. But it also served to reemphasise the importance of securing a partner for ASA404. There was no realistic way we could do it alone.

By this stage, just days away from Christmas, we were actually nearing the final stages of negotiation with a very reputable US based pharmaceutical company. One we had been talking to for the last four months or so. It may not have been quite in the top five but would undoubtedly have been a catch to be proud of. And more importantly, they had the depth of pocket we were looking for. They also didn't appear to have arrived by spaceship from another planet. We could get on with them.

But it wasn't Novartis. Who were simply bigger, better and just more successful all round. They seemed to have that touch of luck, at least as evidenced by Gleevec, which was such an important asset in the drug development lottery. There was also a certain pleasing irony at the symmetry of Antisoma being jettisoned by one major Swiss company, only to be embraced by their rival across the road.

But more desirable though they may have been, Novartis were also that much further behind. They were only now completing the last stage of their evaluative process, the so called *due diligence*.

This was an exhaustively painstaking exercise of not taking our word for anything we might have said, either during non-confidential or confidential discussions. Instead it involved going though as much of the documentation for themselves as they could possibly manage, before physical exhaustion and mental collapse overtook them. The other company in the running had already completed this arduous undertaking a while ago. Fortunately without coming across anything that seemed to cause too much consternation.

And so now, just before Christmas, teams of technical specialists from Novartis were spending three feverish days locked away in one of our office blocks. They were surrounded by mountainous piles of clinical reports, audit findings, data listings, laboratory workbooks, regulatory correspondence, manufacturing files, toxicology summaries, expert reports from intellectual property lawyers, financial accounts and forecasts, commercial market analyses and various other assorted documents. Collectively these all attested to ASA404's provenance and propriety, from its origins in a New Zealand laboratory right up to the present moment.

In amongst the brightly coloured baubles and Christmas decorations, they toiled away. They were there from early in the morning until trudging back through the snow to their horrible Hanger Lane Holiday Inn late at night. All the time trying to catch us out. To find that smoking gun. The one being held by a skeleton, hidden in a closet.

Then finally, the day before Christmas Eve, they were done and we all convened, in the gathering gloom of the winter's afternoon, for a final festive wrap up. And generally, they were happy. There were a few outstanding issues with some of the clinical data and parts of the manufacturing process but nothing substantive. The intellectual property position remained a bit of a worry. But they had been aware of this beforehand and it didn't seem that the level of concern was any greater now than it had been then.

Now they had to go back to Basel and New Jersey, produce a comprehensive report on all of this and then feed it into the Novartis machinery. But it looked as though the cogs would continue to turn and negotiations would progress further once the New Year arrived.

They headed off to the airport and we headed into a huddle to speculate on what might happen next. We just couldn't believe how near we seemed to be. We also wondered how much longer we could carry on stalling our other erstwhile partner. Just in case it didn't work out with Novartis.

And then we all went our separate ways for the holiday period. Our share price had climbed up to almost forty pence by the end of the year. It was a nice Christmas present from the financial markets.

Starting the New Year, it seemed as though all our Christmases had come at once. We had a great drug asset with ASA404, an awful lot of money in the bank, a share price soaring so high we were struggling to keep sight of it and a potential multinational commercial partner of whom we could be proud. On top of all that, there was the distinct prospect of a deal with Novartis, of all companies.

XVII

As it turned out, it took another four fraught months to finalise a deal with the Swiss giant and we lost the other party somewhere along the way. We nearly lost Novartis once or twice too.

But eventually, almost a year after we had been forced to announce that we had been jilted by Roche, we were able to issue a press release in April, letting the world know that we had fallen into the arms of Novartis. We had finally signed the deal with them around ASA404.

And what a deal it was. In return for us granting them a global licensing agreement, we received an immediate payment of one hundred million US dollars. And there was a further *eight hundred million* dollars in staged payments if everything went according to plan and the drug made it all the way. On top of that eye watering sum, Novartis were additionally going to pay for the entire Phase III programme in lung cancer. That represented another seventy million dollars. And they would cover our outstanding costs for the still ongoing Phase II ovarian and prostate trials.

It infinitely exceeded what we could have expected under the terms of the original Roche arrangement. And it was also substantially better than anything anyone else had been prepared to put down on the table. If we'd ever been disappointed about not going it alone, this more than made up for it.

News that the deal was about to be signed off within Novartis had reached us a day or two beforehand. We were stuck in a dismally dull Antisoma senior management off site meeting. It was being held for some reason in Stoke Poges, in Buckinghamshire. No one seemed to know how on earth we'd ended up there. But it didn't matter though, because the excitement of the imminent Novartis completion washed over us like a tidal wave.

It led to proceedings being more or less abandoned for the afternoon. The immediate prospect of all that money suddenly bonded us together in a way no team building exercise could ever achieve. We all wandered, slightly shell shocked, around whatever country club we were holed up in.

But exhilarating though that initial intimation of the impending consummation was, it couldn't really prepare us for the euphoric feeling two days later. The announcement went out early in the morning on Thursday April 19th 2007, just as the markets in Europe were coming to life.[11]

The reception was massively positive, with the press coverage being particularly acclamatory. Congratulatory messages were coming in left, right and centre. Including from a number of those companies who had turned us down over the last twelve months. Even our former colleagues from Roche chipped in with their best wishes. Our share price, which had been steadily climbing for most of the year, reached almost sixty pence. This left us, for a while at least, as one of the most valuable biotechnology companies in the UK.

At long last we were most definitely the Kings of Cancer. This was our coronation. We were riding the crest of the tidal wave which had started in Stoke Poges a couple of days earlier. It had rapidly reached an unstoppable momentum. On that Thursday morning in 2007, it seemed as though we were never going to fall off.

XVIII

But now, three years later, we had definitely come off, with a big fucking crash. We were already struggling to keep our heads above water. There was a distinct danger of drowning.

That's certainly how it seemed on that Thursday evening of the Data Monitoring Committee's interim look, as I sat there in the gloaming and the gloom, talking to Ursula.

"What happens next?" I asked her, staring at my cell phone as though she were about to emerge through it.

But we both knew the answer to that. During the three years since the Novartis deal, we had managed to consume a large proportion of our cash. And along the way we had been forced to drop two of our earlier stage compounds, AS1402 in breast cancer and AS1409, intended for use in both melanoma and kidney cancer. They weren't doing enough in the clinic. At least as far as we could see.

Furthermore, the Phase II ovarian and prostate results with ASA404 had turned out to be less promising than the lung cancer data. It wasn't that ASA404 hadn't worked. Just that it hadn't worked well enough to justify continuing further. At least for the time being. And so Novartis had parked these two possibilities for the foreseeable future. And with it any extra payments we would otherwise have received.

More positively, in 2008 we had bought Xanthus Pharmaceuticals, a cancer company based in Boston in the US. Like Antisoma, their name had a classical Greek origin, this time in the mythology of *Xanthus*. This was the immortal horse ridden into battle by Achilles and who saved him from death in the Trojan War, by forewarning him of his impending fate. We could have done with someone like him to have flagged up ATTRACT I in advance. But it's unusual, in drug development, to have a talking horse on your team.

There was however a bit more synergy between the two companies than just the classical derivation of their names. Xanthus would provide us with some much needed North American infrastructure, in terms of people and facilities.

They also had an interesting collection of cancer drugs in development. This would complement our own dwindling portfolio of compounds. In the middle of 2009 we had even managed sell a Xanthus drug called *fludarabine*, to French based Sanofi, for sixty five million dollars. That was a lot more than we'd paid for the whole company in the first place.

Xanthus had the rights to *oral* fludarabine and this had just been approved in the United States, for use in a type of blood cancer called chronic *lymphocytic* leukaemia.[12] This was a close but less treatable cousin of chronic *myeloid* leukaemia, where Gleevec had done so remarkably well.

Fludarabine was already a well established drug in the US but only when given as an *injection*. The intravenous form was already marketed there by Bayer. In Europe, it had been available for over a decade in both injectable and oral forms, with over eighty per cent being prescribed as a convenient tablet rather than a cumbersome injection. The Xanthus achievement had been to finally get the oral version of fludarabine approved in the US.

This had been quite a neat piece of fast footwork on their part. There hadn't been a need to undertake large and expensive clinical trials in the US with oral fludarabine. Instead they simply gathered up the last ten years of data from using the drug in Europe and repackaged it in a way which the US regulatory authorities could no longer ignore.

Despite the obviously greater convenience to patients, there had been a surprising reticence in the US to approving the oral version of the drug. There was a supposed concern that taking it by mouth might not be as effective as injecting it. This reservation had persisted even though extensive European experience, in tens of thousands of patients, had shown this wasn't the case.

Cynically, some thought the issue had more to do with the fact that in the US, oncologists were paid a fee for giving a drug as an injection. They didn't receive this simply for writing out a prescription for some tablets. This kind of remuneration could add up to quite a sizeable sum of money, when spread out over enough patients. There was therefore something of a vested interest in keeping the oral form safely on the other side of the Atlantic.

However, Xanthus had finally managed to breach the defences and have oral fludarabine made available in the US. It was now down to Sanofi to take on the oncology community and start depriving them of part of their income. That was a struggle they were welcome to. There wouldn't have been a similar degree of French involvement in conflict on American soil since the War of Independence, two centuries earlier.

We were now burning through money at a rate of about two million pounds a month. And so despite that cash injection from Sanofi, we were steadily depleting our formerly substantial financial reserves. There were two predominant reasons for this. We now had a more complicated and extensive organisation to fund, spread over three sites. There were our headquarters in West London, our laboratories based at St George's Hospital in South London and of course the recent addition of our US outpost in Boston.

On top of that, we were also grappling with another Phase III programme, apart from ASA404. And moreover one we were having to fund ourselves.

AS1413, better known as amonafide, was another of the compounds we had acquired from Xanthus. It had started life many years earlier as a drug under investigation in a number of different solid tumors, such as breast and prostate cancer. But it hadn't worked in any of them. However, a set of fortuitous laboratory experiments had suggested it might instead work in blood malignancies. Subsequently some early clinical work had shown highly promising results in a particularly virulent form of leukaemia called secondary acute myeloid leukaemia (sAML).

This was a fairly rare disease, with about seven thousand people being diagnosed with it each year in the US. But it was becoming more common and was devastatingly difficult to treat, with most people dying within months. The relative rarity of the disease was matched only by the scarcity of luck in the lives of those afflicted with it.

Secondary AML was typically caused by chemotherapy given for some earlier cancer the patient had suffered from. Increasingly, women who had been successfully treated for breast cancer four or five years previously were now developing secondary AML, due to the original treatment they had received.

The chemotherapy or radiotherapy killed off the breast cancer but in the process also damaged the DNA of normal cells in the blood and bone marrow. This then became a time bomb ticking away over the years until it eventually exploded with such catastrophic consequences.

Just as one fatal disease appeared to have been overcome, the next one arrived out of the blue. Eradicating one cancer, only to create another, wasn't really much of a cure.

Because it was relatively rare, sAML had limited commercial potential. However, the lack of any effective existing treatments and the apparent promise of amonafide just about justified developing the drug in this otherwise borderline disease. Xanthus had managed to get amonafide to the end of Phase II. But they hadn't been able to afford a randomised trial and so instead had done one with just amonafide by itself. After that, they had run out if money and so couldn't progress things any further forwards. Until Antisoma came into the picture. We arrived just in time, like the cavalry, with wads of cash stuffed in our saddle bags.

But compared to ASA404, this time we knew we would be alone. Unlike lung cancer, the commercial opportunity with sAML was too circumscribed for a large company to take the risk of involving itself. At least until we had the Phase III results. Also, we lacked any *randomised* Phase II data with amonafide, making any Phase III trial that much more risky. It put people off.

As if that weren't enough, acute myeloid leukaemia was widely and rightly regarded as a graveyard for new drugs. There had been very many failures and very few successes over the years. Little had made it through.

With all that against us, the only way forwards was to have the courage of our convictions and fund things from our existing resources. We weren't going to persuade anyone to come along with us for this ride. The risks at this stage were too high and the rewards too uncertain. And so we found ourselves digging deep into the pockets which had been so recently well lined by Novartis. We had to get out the money to pay for what would eventually turn out to be the world's largest ever randomised trial in the treatment of secondary acute myeloid leukaemia.

The amonafide Phase III programme was a four hundred and fifty patient study. That's for a condition where many major cancer centres would only see two or three new cases each year. Each patient would also need to be followed for up to two years after entering into the trial. This meant that we had to get over one hundred leukaemia centres involved. Otherwise there was no hope of ever finishing the study in a manageable period of time. In turn this required running the trial in over thirty different countries. These ranged from South and North America all the way round to Australasia and included most points in between.

All this international enterprise came at a huge cost. The trial consumed about forty million pounds. And this time it was forty million pounds of our *own* money. That was a big drain on our war chest. It meant our cash reserves were markedly diminished.

But the predicament we now found ourselves in was likely to get even worse still. Although completely different development programmes, the futures of ASA404 and amonafide, were intimately intertwined. And with ASA404 having just gone down, it was quite likely it could take amonafide with it.

The origins of this double jeopardy lay with our vaunting ambition to be a company like Cephalon or Celgene. One with products of our own on the market. This had led us to negotiate a provision in the original contract with Novartis, whereby we would be able to *co-market* ASA404 with them in the US.

Co-marketing is a common arrangement within the pharmaceutical industry. It's where two separate companies market the same drug, but under different brand names. Rituximab for example has gone on to become one of the world's bestselling antibodies. It is marketed in the US by Biogen Idec under the brand name *Rituxan* and in Europe and Canada by Roche under the name *MabThera*.

For the product owner, which was Biogen Idec in the case of rituximab, co-marketing offered the advantage of increasing sales penetration whilst retaining ownership of the all important proprietary brand name. Co-marketing ASA404 provided similar advantages for Novartis. But for us it was a godsend.

It would be a huge step forwards in that we could finally put into place a sales and marketing operation. Novartis were even going to pay for our own sales force for the first five years of the co-marketing period. We could establish the whole thing by piggy backing on the extensive expertise of Novartis and even better, at their cost.

One problem with this however was that sales forces need a range of products to go out and talk to cancer doctors about. There is only so much mileage you can get out of one drug, however good it is. Sooner or later there comes a need to have something else to put down on the table in the oncologist's office, when you drop by. Other than a pile of Post-it Notes that is. There is, after all, only so far a gonk can get you.

And that was where amonafide fitted in. We could get the ball rolling with ASA404, which would undoubtedly keep us going for a while. Then along would come amonafide, which we could use our new Novartis funded sales force to commercialise for us. It would give them more things to talk about. And make sure they were busy all day long. And help us wring as much profit as possible out of amonafide.

And this was how we had been able to justify funding the hugely expensive amonafide Phase III programme. If we were going to market it ourselves then there would be no need to find a commercial partner, thus allowing us to keep all the proceeds. That made the drug a lot more profitable for us. It was how the sums eventually added up to make sense, despite the limited overall size of the commercial opportunity.

The only small problem now was that without ASA404, there would be *no* Novartis funded sales force. And without that, the commercial viability of amonafide had just fallen over the edge of a cliff.

It wasn't exactly going to help us, in the troubled times ahead.

XIX

"What happens next," said Ursula, in answer to my question, "is that we have to put something out about it by Monday at the latest. Tomorrow, Friday, is too soon to double check everything with Novartis and make sure all the facts are completely correct. After that, the markets are closed for the weekend. And so we will have to wait till Monday."

After that, we would be in the financial intensive care unit. People would be gathered around, wondering what a decent interval would be prior to asking about the possibility of any of our organs becoming available for donation.

"I'd better carry on phoning the others I haven't managed to get hold of yet."

Ursula's measured tones penetrated into the pessimism of my mental imagery. She had returned to her characteristic brusque efficiency. The

69

collapse of our world had clearly occasioned only a momentary diversion from her normal iron discipline and determination.

"Talk tomorrow then."

I heard her car start up and then the phone went dead.

As I walked down the corridor of the house, the disappointment started to turn to anger. With myself and the rest of us. Maybe we hadn't considered this possible outcome seriously enough. We had been too confident and too complacent.

It wasn't as though there hadn't been any warnings. Just the month before, Pfizer had announced the failure of *three* Phase III programmes, all in one day. One of them was with a very promising new agent for lung cancer, a drug called figitumumab. Which was possibly an even more intimidating name than vadimezan. And there had been many other failures in the recent past too.

But if there had been warnings we hadn't heeded them. We'd blithely taken it for granted that we had another year or so until the end of the ASA404 programme. It had seemed plenty of time in which to mitigate the risk of the drug failing at that point. Maybe bring in another advanced stage compound, acquire another company altogether, even merge with someone else. They were amongst the strategic options we had been considering for the future. All of which were opportunities now firmly consigned to the past.

Like all gamblers at some point, we had made the fatal mistake of forgetting that our luck would run out sooner or later. We may have been the Kings of Cancer once, but now we'd been well and truly dethroned. We'd been left with nothing more than a fiefdom of futility over which to rule.

I went into my office, which was full of stuff that suddenly didn't matter anymore. My eyes swept over the bookshelf looking for Daniel Vasella's *Magic Bullet*. The story of the Gleevec success that ASA404 could now never become. It was more like *Tragic Bullet,* in our case.

My mind started racing with questions.

Why do so many cancer drugs fail, compared to the tiny proportion of successes?

What stacks the odds so badly against us, making this disease such a formidable enemy? Was it the drugs themselves, or something about the way we were evaluating them?

And, of course, was there anyway Antisoma could survive this drastic setback?

THREE

HEART OF STONE

How a cancer drug is developed. The rules of the game. Why it is so difficult to work out who is winning and losing. An entrance to Wonderland.

I

Live and Let Die is a James Bond adventure about the illegal drugs trade. Obviously in biotechnology you try to stay on the right side of the law. Bond's antics in New Orleans with Mr Big don't at first sight have much of relevance to cancer drug development. With the exception however that in the book, the heroine *Solitaire* possesses the ability to foretell the future.

That was a skill we could have really done with at Antisoma, along with many other biotech companies. A bit of necromancy. Never mind all the scientists, pharmacologists, clinicians, project managers or whatever that we already had. What we *really* needed was someone who could find their way around a Ouija Board. Because trying to predict the future of a cancer drug and whether it seemed to be working or not, was far from straightforward. As we were finding out. There was definitely a bit of voodoo involved somewhere. It certainly wasn't black and white. In fact, little in cancer medicine ever was. Except for death itself.

The ATTRACT I Data Monitoring Committee had killed off ASA404 because it wasn't working. But how had they actually reached this decision and why had we so signally failed to see it coming? And more importantly, could they have got it wrong? What would Solitaire have been able to tell us?

Was there any possibility, however slim, that this was a nightmare which we may one day be able to wake up from? This seemed remote though. An enormous number of drugs before ASA404 had failed too. There was a never-ending cavalcade of cancer catastrophes, which seemed to characterise man's struggle against this most formidable of foes.

Back in February 2009, President Barack Obama called for a renewed effort against cancer, "to conquer a disease that has touched the life of nearly every American, including me, by seeking a cure for cancer in our time."[1] But he wasn't the first American President to take a stand against the disease, with Richard Nixon having launched his much vaunted *War on Cancer,* in 1971.[2]

In the intervening years between Nixon and Obama, and putting to one side antibodies, proteins and so on, a staggering five hundred thousand chemical compounds alone were tested for anti-cancer activity. With only about *twenty five* having survived to be in widespread clinical use today.

The vast majority were abandoned along the way, because they appeared not to work. And so it would seem that ASA404 was in good, or rather bad company as it were, in the chemotherapy cemetery. That's where most new agents were destined to end up. The prognosis for the drugs was even worse than for the disease they were intended to overcome.

However, all those failures and fatalities imply that there is some straightforward and objective way of determining whether a cancer drug actually *works* or not. But in fact, it is far more complicated and controversial than that. That's where the black magic comes in.

Deciding on the utility of a new drug is a balance between the beneficial efficacy and the unwanted but usually unavoidable side effects. Obviously though, this judgement will be influenced by the clinical context within which it is going to be used.

A more dangerous disease will lead to acceptance of a greater degree of serious side effects than would be the case for a much less significant one. A condition as hopeless as cancer is going to tolerate much higher levels of toxicity with a new drug than would be the case for say asthma or indigestion or, come to think of it, pretty much anything else, other than cancer itself.

II

Government regulatory authorities keep a careful eye on drug toxicity. Between 1992 and 2011 for example, twenty eight drugs were withdrawn from the US market due to safety issues emerging after they had originally been approved[3]. It doesn't look like getting any better any time soon.

The reasons for this ranged from the relatively commonplace to the much more arcane. The heartburn drug cisapride was withdrawn, due to concerns over an issue as straightforward as heart rhythm disturbances. By contrast, the multiple sclerosis drug natalizumab was implicated in something as exotic as *progressive multifocal leucoencephalopathy.* This is a rare and usually fatal viral disease which attacks the brain. It really is as bad as it sounds.

But *none* of these were cancer drugs, despite the fact that many result routinely in much worse side effects than those which finished off the drugs having to be withdrawn.

Cisapride was approved in the US in 1993, to treat heartburn and other indigestion related disorders. It's a drug which increases gastric motility and tightens up the muscle sphincter at the junction of the stomach and oesophagus. Nearly ten million Americans were prescribed the drug, before its availability was severely curtailed in 2000.

This was after discussions between the manufacturers, Johnson and Johnson, and the US Government's drug regulatory body, the Food and Drug Administration (FDA). Safety concerns had arisen over a particular type of heart rhythm disturbance, called *QTc prolongation,* which was occurring in a very small proportion of people taking cisapride.

QTc prolongation is a phenomenon whereby part of the heart muscle's normal electrical cycle, which is what keeps it beating so rhythmically, becomes prolonged, as the name suggests. This can occur due to many different causes, including a variety of drugs.

The danger lies in the fact that occasionally, QTc prolongation can unpredictably provoke a kind of electrical epileptic fit in the heart muscle, causing it to suddenly stop working. This prevents it pumping altogether, usually leading to instant death. The greater the degree of QTc prolongation, the higher is the risk of this happening.

It's a big price to pay for a bit of indigestion relief though. And so despite the drug generally having an excellent safety record, the risk of sudden cardiac death, tiny though it was, just couldn't be justified by the undoubted benefits of cisapride.

By contrast, a whole host of widely used cancer medicines have all been implicated as *major* causes of QTc prolongation. These include various classes of drugs, both old fashioned ones (such as the DNA damaging anthracyclines and alkylating agents) and also a number of the newer biotechnology advances. With some anti-cancer drugs, the effects are so severe they even have what is called a *Black Box Warning* attached. This is the strongest form of safety message issued by FDA about a drug and is a final step just short of removing it from the market altogether.

A Black Box designation requires that all printed material about the drug, both inside and outside the actual drug packaging, and any materials developed for prescribing physicians, must carry a warning about the side effect in question. All surrounded by a prominent black box. This is intended to provide a clear signal that the drug has substantial associated dangers.

In practice, it doesn't influence physicians that much. If you were designing a fair ground ride intended to scare the living daylights out of people, it probably wouldn't be called *The Black Box*. It just doesn't have much punch to it. But then it's difficult to imagine anyone at FDA, the very epicentre of federal bureaucracy, ever having dreamed about running away to join a carnival.

However, despite its limited impact, people try to avoid being issued with a Black Box Warning, if at all possible. It tends to make medical malpractice lawyers extra keen. Also, if potential competitors have a cleaner drug, it gives them a head start on the promotional front. They can make a little bad publicity go a long way. In most medical disciplines therefore, a black box is the kind of luggage which generally slows you down.

But in cancer medicine, Black Box Warnings are routine occurrences. For example, Cell Therapeutics' *Trisenox* (arsenic trioxide for the treatment of acute promyelocytic leukaemia) produces very prominent QTc prolongation. It carries a detailed Black Box Warning advising on the risks of this. Trisenox also causes other heart abnormalities with names such as *complete atrioventricular block* and *torsade de pointe type ventricular arrhythmias*. That's a lot of warnings. You need a very large black box to fit them all in.[4]

But it doesn't stop Trisenox being very widely used in the treatment of leukaemia, every day of the week. This is because it's a universally fatal disease, if left untreated. And so the risk of substantial toxicity is going to be acceptable as the price you have to pay, in return for some sort of benefit from a drug like this. Particularly if there aren't that many other treatments available. And if you have acute promyelocytic leukaemia there aren't a lot of alternatives to Trisenox. Apart probably from being carried off in a black box yourself. You don't exactly have much of a choice here. It's the same with most other cancer therapies too.

Trisenox is a good example of one of the most difficult challenges in cancer medicine, which is that many of the drugs have side effects as dangerous as the disease itself. And often these can affect a large number of the patients who are treated. Also, very few drugs actually cure cancer. At best, they will slow down progression of the disease and so buy some extra time. Usually though, this is in only a small proportion of patients.

There is therefore, a need to define the point beyond which the substantial *risk* of toxicity with a new agent is no longer outweighed by the more modest *chance* of deriving a benefit from it. In other words that it doesn't *work*, in the sense of providing a clinically useful outcome for the patient.

This high wire balancing act is a clinical art, usually generating more controversy and contention than consensus. It is conceptually equivalent to determining how long a piece of string is. Which is frequently an exceptionally difficult measurement to make in medicine.

You have to decide, for example, whether a drug with a twenty per cent possibility of a fatal side effect is worth the risk, if it provides a forty per cent chance of prolonging survival for another six months in those getting through the treatment. Especially if there were a ten per cent chance of living that long untreated anyway. The question you are left facing is whether the potential reward is worth the palpable risk.

Each new drug brings its own different set of permutations. You need the mental agility of a bookmaker's runner to assimilate the odds. These are the sorts of calculations which usually complicate the assessment of new cancer agents. That's just how it normally is.

Occasionally however life is simpler and it can become a fairly straightforward equation. For example, when it emerges that more patients are dying *with* a new drug than *without* it then you don't really need to have been to medical school to reach the conclusion that it isn't working very well.

And that's exactly what happened recently with a very promising new drug called *elesclomol*.

<h1 style="text-align:center">III</h1>

Elesclomol was being developed for the very difficult to treat skin cancer called advanced melanoma. This is a highly feared disease where patients are lucky to survive much more than about six months. It usually starts innocuously enough with an itchy mole on the skin. But it's rapidly downhill from that point onwards. The melanoma train is a non-stop express to the hopelessness of the hospice.

Elesclomol was a cancer drug which appeared to work by escalating the amount of so called *oxidative stress* cancer cells were subjected to, pushing it beyond a point which they could tolerate and so resulting in cell death. Oxidative stress occurs when the cell's normal biochemical processes produce more particular toxic chemicals (called *reactive oxygen species*) than the cell can get rid of. By increasing these oxidative toxins Elesclomol was acting in the opposite way from the *antioxidants* widely promoted in everything from vitamin supplements to skin care creams.

Melanoma tumors were believed to be in a particularly high state of oxidative stress already and so this seemed a logical starting point for an agent working the way elesclomol did. It was a neat idea, effectively turning the body's own detoxifying mechanisms against the cancer and poisoning it to death.

The drug belonged to a small US biotechnology company called Synta Pharmaceuticals. This was about the size of Antisoma, and located in Lexington, Massachusetts, just beyond Interstate 95, not far from Boston. The company's technologies were built around work originating from their scientific founder, Lan Bo Chen a Professor of Pathology at Harvard Medical School and its associated Dana-Farber Cancer Institute.

They styled themselves as combining *"the high energy culture and exciting growth opportunities of new biotechnology with the drug development assets and expertise of a mature pharmaceutical company."*[5] The Synta team must have been pulsing with energy and excitement when they announced in November 2007 that the first patient had been treated in their elesclomol Phase III melanoma trial.

An earlier Phase II study had compared a standard but largely ineffective melanoma drug, paclitaxel, against a combination of paclitaxel and elesclomol given weekly to patients with advanced melanoma. These were patients who'd already had treatment in the past and failed on that. They were therefore desperate to try anything new. The results were very encouraging, with three times as many patients in the elesclomol group showing tumor shrinkage.

Furthermore, patients in this group were taking on average a hundred days before their disease started to progress again, compared to just fifty days in the group getting paclitaxel alone.[6] Those weren't bad findings for a rapidly fatal disease such as melanoma.

Although it only accounts for about five per cent of skin cancers, melanoma is responsible for over seventy five per cent of skin cancer deaths. This is largely because there are very limited treatment options, which, until very recently, haven't really improved in over three decades.[7] At the time, there was basically nothing out there which worked. Elesclomol looked as though it might introduce a bit of hope into an otherwise hopeless situation.

The Phase III trial was given the acronymic title SYMMETRY, standing for **S**ynta **M**etastatic **M**elanoma **E**lesclomol **Tr**ial. Although that didn't seem to account for the **Y** at the end. Maybe that should have been a warning. Failing to pull off an overly ambitious acronym probably wasn't a good sign of things to come.

As in the Phase II trial, patients were randomised to either paclitaxel or the combination of paclitaxel and elesclomol. Eventually this study would recruit a total of six hundred and fifty one patients, from one hundred and fifty hospitals, spread over fifteen countries. This was a big study. They weren't messing about here.

Synta didn't reveal how much the SYMMETRY trial was costing them but a conservative estimate would have to be at least fifty million dollars. It presumably helped therefore that the programme was funded by Glaxo Smith Kline who had signed a collaboration deal to develop elesclomol in October 2007. This was potentially worth up to five hundred and eighty five million dollars if things went well. Synta had received an upfront sum of eighty million dollars in December, shortly after the first patients had been entered into the study. There was therefore a lot riding on the SYMMETRY trial.

But if elesclomol kept its promise and looked as good at the end of Phase III, as it had at the end of Phase II, then it was almost certain that the drug would be nodded through by FDA. This would be the first time in thirty years that a small molecule had received approval for the treatment of melanoma. Success in SYMMETRY would therefore provide a significant new treatment option for patients and physicians. It was ground breaking stuff.

The good news around elesclomol continued in 2008. In January the drug was granted *Orphan Drug Designation* by FDA in the US, for use in advanced melanoma. Orphan drugs, as they are rather whimsically described, are intended for use in rare diseases, defined in the US as those having less than two hundred thousand patients.[8] In Europe, rare diseases are classified as those disorders occurring in less than five per one hundred thousand of the population.[9]

There are somewhere between six and seven thousand different diseases which meet this criterion and they affect about thirty million people in Europe alone. Up to a third of cancers overall and pretty much all paediatric malignancies fall within this group. Although melanoma is in fact now growing at a faster rate than any other cancer, the number of patients being diagnosed each year is still only about sixty thousand in the US. And so it is well within the threshold of the orphan drug limitations.

The granting of orphan drug status confers certain regulatory benefits on a drug and also has some financial advantages in terms of refunding of regulatory fees and tax credits. But most importantly, it also gives seven years of market exclusivity, for that particular drug, when used for the particular orphan disease in question.

These measures are intended as incentives for pharmaceutical companies. The idea is to encourage them in the effort to develop new therapies for conditions which might otherwise be too rare to make it worthwhile financially. In the case of elesclomol, orphan drug status probably wouldn't have had any impact on its commercial prospects. But it always sounded good in a press release and shareholders seemed to like hearing about developments such as this. It somehow made them feel virtuous.

During 2008, recruitment of melanoma patients into the SYMMETRY trial continued at a steady pace, in line with everyone's expectations. Things were going so well that in November of that year Synta started a second, earlier stage, clinical trial with elesclomol in advanced prostate cancer. This was another tumor type with supposedly high levels of endogenous oxidative stress.

In December, the Data Monitoring Committee (charged with reviewing ongoing safety and efficacy information from the SYMMETRY trial) gave the green light for the study to continue. Patient recruitment was duly completed a few months later in February 2009.

That same month the first patient was recruited into a *third* elesclomol clinical trial in patients suffering from advanced disease with a variety of different tumor types. Synta were throwing everything they had into the drug, so convinced had they become that this one was a winner.

In what was turning out to be a very busy February, they also received a ten million dollar payment for the completion of recruitment into the SYMMETRY trial. This brought the total received so far from GSK to one hundred and thirty million dollars, including the eighty million received in 2007 and another forty million received in 2008. That was enough money to relieve a lot of stress, oxidative or otherwise. Not bad going for a company which was less than seven years old and with a drug which although promising, was still far from being proven.

And then, just two days away from the end of this hectic month, the tsunami struck. The Data Monitoring Committee had looked at additional recently arrived information coming out of the SYMMETRY study. And this time they didn't like what they were seeing. They didn't like it at all. In fact, they felt compelled to suspend the trial immediately, thus preventing any of the remaining patients receiving further treatment with elesclomol.

The reason for this dramatic turn of events was that the new data now showed a *smaller* number of patients surviving in the elesclomol and paclitaxel arm of the study compared to paclitaxel alone. Elesclomol appeared to be somehow contributing to the death of more patients than it was actually helping. Although the explanation for this may have been unclear, the need to act wasn't. Synta were forced to put an immediate halt to all three of the elesclomol studies. They probably didn't know what had hit them.

"Our first concern is for the safety of patients and therefore we acted promptly to halt the SYMMETRY trial once it was evident that there were serious safety concerns," said Eric Jacobson, Synta's Chief Medical Officer.[10]

"This is a considerable setback," added Dr Safi Bahcall, Synta's CEO, as something of an understatement.[10]

Synta subsequently undertook a more intensive analysis of the data.[11] In particular they were looking at those melanoma patients who had lower levels of a blood marker called *lactate dehydrogenase* (LDH). This is an enzyme normally produced in the liver, but detectable in the blood.

For reasons which aren't fully understood, many cancer patients with elevated levels of LDH have a much worse prognosis than those with lower levels. That applies to a number of malignancies, not just melanoma. LDH levels are widely used therefore as a rough and ready way of separating out the patients most likely to respond to a new drug.

In the SYMMETRY trial, those patients with lower levels of LDH appeared to be deriving benefit from elesclomol. It was still delaying the time before the tumor spread. At least the drug was doing something. But it wasn't enough. This positive finding in a fortunate few couldn't counteract the greater mortality in the majority. Especially as no one could come up with an explanation for why the patients were dying. Which made it impossible to work out how to prevent it.

But that's how it was in biotechnology. One minute you were flying high above the clouds, the next a burning wreck in the middle of a field. Synta were rapidly becoming an example of what can happen to a small company when it suddenly loses a big asset.

In March, just weeks after the suspension of the SYMMETRY trial, they announced a major restructuring with a significant number of redundancies. The *high energy culture and exciting growth opportunities* had just come to an end. Maybe this was an unwelcome portent of things to come for Antisoma, after the failure of the ATTRACT I trial. Who could tell. Anything was possible when your biotechnology bubble had just been burst.

In June, GSK formally ended the collaborative arrangement, handing the worldwide rights back to Synta. A few days later Dr Jacobson, the Chief Medical Officer left the company. That was always a bad sign. All this in less than four months after having been on the crest of wave at the beginning of the year. We knew how they felt.

Synta had no immediate place left to go with elesclomol. When you have an agent like this, one associated with *excess* mortality, that is obviously a toxicity too far and no amount of efficacy advantage is going to cancel it out. You then have a drug which clearly doesn't *work*, at least in that disease and with those particular types of patient.[12] It doesn't provide enough clinical benefit. Quite the opposite in fact. The risks are far too high, without the counterbalancing possibility of any benefit.

And there have been any number of other cancer drugs like this. Ones which get the balance sufficiently wrong, that they tip over the line and end up doing more harm than good. That's the experimental knife edge you are often so precariously poised upon. Something you'd hoped would delay a patient's disease instead ends up accelerating their demise. Usually though it isn't that straightforward, as a cancer drug will typically have significantly awful side effects but stop short of actually causing excess deaths. There is then a need for that almost biblically difficult judgement of weighing up the usually limited efficacy and the normally extensive toxicity. The benefit versus the risk. Had he been an early oncologist, even King Solomon would have been challenged most of the time.

And matters are made worse still by the problem of exactly how to measure the efficacy of a new cancer drug, in a way everyone else will agree with. Because that isn't clear cut either, creating difficulties for even the biggest of biotechnology companies. Never mind the smaller ones such as Antisoma or Synta.

IV

With annual revenues of over four and a half billion dollars, Genzyme is one of the powerhouses of the biotechnology industry. Founded in 1981, it is located in Kendall Square in the middle of Boston, not that far from Synta in Lexington as it happens. Although any similarities between the two probably stop there. Right next door is the world famous Massachusetts Institute of Technology, with Harvard Medical School just across the other side of the Charles River.

The three hundred thousand square foot Genzyme Centre, opened in 2005, features cutting edge technology such as computer controlled window blinds and hanging mirrors to decrease reliance on artificial lighting. Not that it needed much of that. It's such a successful company the sun could almost have shone out of Genzyme itself. Employing over twelve thousand people worldwide it was one of the big boys on the block, more than capable of looking after itself.

One of the company's drugs is called *clofarabine* (Clolar). This is widely used as treatment for a particular type of childhood leukaemia called acute lymphoblastic leukaemia (ALL).

Broadly there are four main types of leukaemia. These are acute lymphoblastic leukaemia (ALL), acute myeloid leukaemia (AML), chronic lymphocytic leukaemia (CLL) and chronic myeloid leukaemia (CML).

As the names imply, the acute leukaemias tend to develop with dramatic urgency whilst the chronic ones have a more indolent, smouldering course, at least initially. It's the acute leukaemias which kill off the patients so quickly. The chronic variants take their time and it may be several years before the patients destabilise and become as unwell as those with acute disease.

The acute leukaemias tend to strike at the two extremes of life, predominantly affecting the youngest (ALL) and the oldest (AML). There are about five hundred cases of childhood acute leukaemia each year in the UK, with about eighty per cent of these being ALL. This makes it the only leukaemia and one of the few forms of cancer overall, to be more common in children than adults. It occurs most commonly below the age of five years.

For most, childhood ALL is treatable, indeed often curable. However those not responding to initial treatment attempts often end up on clofarabine and it is an important drug in this group of patients. It's usually used after most other available therapies have already failed. It often therefore represents a last chance to do something for these tragically afflicted children.

Whilst patients at this stage are unfortunately beyond cure, clofarabine can often keep the disease at bay for a bit longer. Maybe get them well enough for that trip to Disneyland. Or Lapland. Or wherever. Pretty much every parent would take that chance, if it were offered to them. Quite often, clofarabine was the only hope they had left to cling to.

However, out of Genzyme's annual revenues of over four billion dollars, clofarabine only accounts for about one hundred million, because childhood acute lymphoblastic leukaemia is a rare condition. It affects only about 0.0001 per cent of children overall each year. And so whilst clofarabine might be a worthy drug, it is not a very weighty one in terms of Genzyme's overall business.

Which is why, for a number of years, Genzyme had been trying to develop the drug for use in adult acute myeloid leukaemia (AML) as well. Success here could boost revenues to six hundred million dollars a year or more. Out of all the leukaemias, adult AML was the obvious commercial place to take clofarabine next. It represented the largest number of patients for whom effective therapies were currently lacking. The other leukaemias either had much smaller patient populations, or were already relatively well served with treatment options.

Whilst there aren't any cancers you'd exactly look forward to having, AML is one you'd try the hardest to avoid. If you actually had any choice in the matter that is. It's essentially a disease of the elderly, becoming increasingly more common over the age of sixty. Although it affects only about twelve thousand people a year in the US, AML accounts for one per cent of all cancer deaths.

Patients with AML under the age of about fifty do relatively well with treatment and for those with the most favourable disease characteristics, even a cure is possible. However for all the rest, which is by far and away the vast majority, the outlook is bleak with a survival prognosis of less than a year.

And that's despite aggressive chemotherapy using a combination of drugs. Even with this kind of intensive approach, many patients fail to respond at all. Or if they do it's only for very short periods of time, typically a couple of months. Unfortunately, many older patients are unable to tolerate this sort of demanding treatment schedule. Often, they end up ineligible for any kind of intervention at all and are effectively consigned to the hospice from the outset. It's not a good fate.

There is therefore a clear need for new drugs in AML, both to help patients who have failed on conventional chemotherapy and those for whom it is not a treatment option in the first place.

AML, like most leukaemias, is a disease of the white cells which are present in the blood. These are the main weapons for fighting infections in the body and for providing immunity. The white cells themselves are formed from *haematopoietic tissue* (literally *blood forming* tissue). This is found primarily in the bone marrow which occupies a honeycomb like structure in the middle of the pelvis and the longer bones of the body.

Normally these haematopoietic cells divide in a controlled and regulated manner, producing a steady stream of new white cells. These replace the older ones, which usually die away after three or four weeks. However in leukaemia this normal regulation is lost and the production of white cells goes into overdrive. New cells are formed and pumped out at hundreds or even thousands of times the normal rate.

This leads to a flood of immature functionless cells, which haven't had enough time to develop properly. These poorly formed abnormal cells eventually crowd out all the normal ones in the bone marrow, preventing it from working properly.

Along with the absent normal white cells, there is a progressive depletion of the red blood cells (which carry oxygen) and the platelets (which stop bleeding). This results in the symptoms of bone marrow failure, which are usually anaemia (due to the loss of red cells), bruising and bleeding (due to the loss of platelets) and a massively increased susceptibility to infections (arising from the depletion of normal white cells). If left untreated, these complications prove fatal to the patient with AML, often within weeks.

Conventional anti-leukaemia drugs are very powerfully poisonous to bone marrow. The hope is that by giving high enough doses, a patient's entire bone marrow, including all the diseased leukaemic parts, can be wiped out. If all goes well, when the haematopoietic cells regrow (which occurs about a month or so after treatment) they will be normal again and effectively disease free.

In practice however, leukaemic cells appear to have evolved ways of "hiding" from the chemotherapy. This means that whilst they may appear to have disappeared after initial treatment, they often recur again, typically within six months or so. When this happens it is a condition called *relapsed AML*.

This carries a particularly grave outcome, as a cure is exceptionally unusual in these circumstances. In about twenty per cent of these patients you can successfully treat them a second time around but it's usually only a short lived response. Hence there is a very real need for new therapies to deal with what is effectively a swift death sentence for patients at this stage of the disease.

There are many overlapping similarities between ALL and AML, the differences mainly relating to the particular subtype of white blood cells affected by the leukaemia. And so if clofarabine worked in one sort of leukaemia, then it would seem reasonable to expect that it might work in the other type too. Indeed initial clinical trials in AML, given alone and in combination with other drugs, appeared promising. Therefore, with high expectations, Genzyme initiated in April 2006 a three hundred and twenty five patient trial called CLASSIC I.

This was in adults with *relapsed* AML, whose disease had come back, after initially responding to treatment with conventional leukaemia therapy. Once you relapse with this condition, time is rapidly running out. These are the sorts of patients who really need to have their affairs in order and to start saying their final farewells. There aren't going to be too many happy endings. There just aren't effective drugs to treat this stage of the illness.

These desperate patients were therefore eagerly entered into the trial. Anything was worth a go. They were randomly allocated to treatment with either the standard anti-leukaemia drug cytarabine (given by itself at a very high dose) or to treatment with a combination of cytarabine and clofarabine.

Never a company to hang around, in September of the same year Genzyme followed this up with the commencement of the CLASSIC II study. This was a smaller trial of clofarabine alone in elderly patients aged sixty or older who'd recently been diagnosed with AML. They were being treated for the first time but were judged by their doctor to be unsuitable for aggressive standard chemotherapy. Clofarabine was thus a welcome alternative to no treatment at all, which would otherwise have been their fate.

Between these two trials therefore, Genzyme seemed to have AML pretty much covered. Given the history of many previous drug failures in this disease, it might have been a bit of a long shot to expect both trials to hold up. But many people were confident clofarabine would make it through one of them.

The first trial to complete was CLASSIC II, the study in elderly patients. Preliminary results were presented at the June 2008 American Society of Clinical Oncology meeting in Chicago, by Professor Harry Erba from the University of Michigan.[13] He was a prominent and highly regarded leukaemia specialist who had previously trained at Yale, Stanford and Harvard.

Professor Erba was able to report that one hundred and sixteen patients (with an average age of about seventy years) had been entered into the trial and that excitingly, just over forty five per cent had responded to treatment with clofarabine. That seemed pretty good in a group with such a dreadful prognosis. It also compared highly favourably to the proportion of paediatric patients with ALL responding to the drug, which was much lower at twenty per cent.

Further information from the study was revealed later in the year, again by Professor Erba, at the American Society of Haematology Meeting in San Francisco in December.[14] His opinion on the data was very clearly that "given the prognosis of older AML patients treated with standard chemotherapy, these results are *truly impressive.*"[15] Most leukaemia specialists agreed with him. This looked like a useful drug for a group of patients with a very bleak outlook.

V

With CLASSIC II apparently looking good, everyone was now wondering how well clofarabine would do in CLASSIC I, the study in relapsed AML, the even harder to treat condition. This was a more complicated trial, taking much longer to complete and the preliminary results didn't become available until two years later in October 2010. This time Genzyme turned to an even bigger name to front the occasion.

Hagop Kantarjian was the undisputed doyen of US leukaemia thinking. He was the biggest beast in that jungle, with one of the loudest roars. Born in Lebanon, he'd progressed from studying medicine at the American University of Beirut, all the way through to being Chairman of the Department of Leukaemia at the University of Texas MD Anderson Cancer Centre in Houston. There weren't any pinnacles higher than that one. There is nothing like MD Anderson anywhere else on Earth.

Covering more than eleven million square feet, it is the world's largest dedicated cancer centre, employing over seventeen thousand staff, with an additional thirteen hundred volunteers. It's so vast that it even has a public transportation system *inside* the hospital. Over one hundred thousand patients a year are treated there and the Centre has its own research budget of five hundred million dollars, with around eleven thousand patients participating in clinical trials annually.

The early work on the combination of clofarabine and cytarabine, as used in the CLASSIC I study, had been undertaken at MD Anderson. This was by Stefan Faderl, a physician within Professor Kantarjian's group, who was actually the main clinician involved in the trial. He would also formally present the results the following year, at the June 2011 American Society for Clinical Oncology meeting, again in Chicago.[16]

With all the might of MD Anderson behind him, Professor Kantarjian's words carried a lot of weight when he summarised the October public release of the CLASSIC I results. Even if he'd been reading out the telephone directory, people would still have sat up to take notice of what he had to say.

"Of importance, the Clolar (*clofarabine*) combination *doubled* the remission rate to forty seven per cent," he explained, in a Genzyme press release.[17]

"Also, we see a thirty seven per cent improvement in event free survival, a particularly important measure of clinical benefit *(this is the probability of a patient's leukaemia worsening, or them dying)."*

Given that these patients had relapsed AML which was notoriously difficult to treat, it was a significant achievement to see a *doubling* of the response rate.

Prior to the advent of clofarabine, a trip to Lourdes would have been as good a bet as anything else available to them. Management of these cases was so difficult it was usually impossible for clinicians to agree on the best treatment. There were twenty to thirty different chemotherapy regimens in use. The diversity of these approaches simply attested to the lack of efficacy with them all.

With the results from both CLASSIC I and CLASSIC II apparently looking so good, Genzyme ought to have been feeling pretty pleased with themselves. The sun should be shining even more brightly than normal on the Genzyme Centre. All those computerised blinds and mirrors would have been in overdrive. But they weren't.

Instead, the outlook for clofarabine was suddenly looking cloudy at best, possibly even with storms on the way. Uncertainty was beginning to emerge about the chances of clofarabine being approved by the US regulatory authorities for use in relapsed AML, despite the seemingly outstanding results.

And this was all down to differences of opinion about how to actually measure the efficacy of clofarabine in this trial. Fairly profound differences, it must be said. Pessimism over the fate of CLASSIC I hadn't exactly been helped by the fact that a year earlier, in October 2009 and just nine months after the impressive results with CLASSIC II had been unveiled by Professor Erba, FDA had refused to accept the results of that study too. Again because of disagreements over how the efficacy of the drug should be measured.

But why should there be such controversy about a drug like clofarabine. After all, either you had leukaemia or you didn't? You'd responded or you hadn't. Wasn't it that simple? Unfortunately leukaemia, like most cancers, made itself much more difficult to deal with than that. It was often very complicated to work out what was going on with new drugs, as far as this particular disease was concerned.

However, to understand the complexity involved here, you first have to grasp the rules of the game being played.

VI

Because leukaemia is a condition predominantly of the bone marrow, it is possible to take a sample of this from a patient, before and after treatment. By comparing the two, you can then see how the disease is responding. Whilst doctors find this sort of information immensely helpful, the patients usually have a different view of things. For the individual concerned this is a painful and unpleasant experience.

Trephining or *trepanning* is the medical term for making a hole into bone. It's a procedure dating back to Galen, Hippocrates and beyond. It hasn't improved much over the centuries though.

A *bone marrow biopsy,* which is a form of trephining, involves having to force a wide bore needle, about the size of a drinking straw, right through to the middle of a patient's bone, the hip being the most common site. After that, you attempt to suck out some marrow through the needle (called an *aspirate*), also obtaining a small section of bone (called a *biopsy*) if possible.

Despite the use of extensive local anaesthesia this is a procedure which patients rapidly come to dread, because of the pain involved. It's the same sort of sickening visceral pain as when you actually break a bone. In fact it's not uncommon for them to refuse altogether, unless they are given a general anaesthetic. *Nothing* in the life of a leukaemia patient is pleasant or easy any more.

But one way or another, you need to get that sample. Because once obtained, it is easy to then examine the bone marrow and simply count the number of abnormal leukaemic cells present. This is possible because they have a distinctive appearance when stained with special dyes and looked at down a microscope. This is a process called *histomorphometry*. Some people devote their whole lives to it.

It might not sound that glamorous but this kind of specialist pathology is now awash with high technology diagnostic aids. Techniques such as flow cytometry *(which measures disease markers on the cell surface)* and DNA amplification *(which can track down genetic abnormalities on chromosomes in the nucleus of the cell)* are making it much more *CSI* than ever before. But despite this, the microscope is still the mainstay.

Typically, the bone marrow from an untreated patient with leukaemia will contain anywhere between twenty and one hundred per cent abnormal leukaemic cells (referred to as *blast cells*) which are present in amongst all the normal ones. After treatment has wiped out the diseased bone marrow, a patient is considered to have responded if a sample from the recovering bone marrow shows less than five per cent blast cells. If the blast count is five per cent or higher, then they are classified as treatment failures.

This is of course an arbitrary division. Four point nine per cent blasts is a success and yet five point one per cent isn't. But that's just how it is and how it's done. It's a way of working which has become widely used to assess the effects of both the standard treatment of patients with acute leukaemia and also to see how well new experimental drugs are doing.

Despite the more sophisticated techniques now available, counting abnormal cells under a microscope at least has the distinct advantage of being simple and easy to do. It has become established as the gold standard for determining the clinical course of patients with leukaemia and for assessing the efficacy of anti-leukaemic drugs.

Patients with less than five per cent blasts in their bone marrow (and who have no signs of leukaemia anywhere else in the body) are called *complete responders* (CRs) and their disease is said to have gone into *remission*. This usually occurs within thirty to sixty days of treatment being given.

Today, about eighty per cent of younger patients with AML can now be expected to achieve a CR with modern therapy. However the figure drops dramatically with increasing age over sixty and for those patients of any age with relapsed AML. In these two groups CR rates are usually only about twenty to thirty per cent.

So there is a straightforward and quantifiable way of measuring at least *one* effect of anti-leukaemia drugs such as clofarabine, through determination of the CR rate. This also has the advantage of not having too much variation in measurement or controversy in definition. Such a measurable parameter is called an efficacy *endpoint* in clinical trial terminology.

For clinical trials though, as well as being measureable, an endpoint for a drug also has to be *relevant*. Which means that is must document something about the disease which is of significance, in determining how well or badly the patient is likely to do in the longer term.

CR rate in leukaemia for example, is considered to be a measure with some degree of relevance. This is because patients who do not respond to initial treatment and who therefore do not achieve a CR are known to do very badly. They die much more quickly, compared to those who do go into remission. So obviously a new drug which increases the CR rate is probably doing something to improve patient outcome, at least in the short term.

Which makes sense. If you are getting rid of the diseased bone marrow, you would expect that to translate into some sort of clinical benefit. Patients in remission have fewer symptoms of bone marrow failure, such as anaemia and bleeding and infections. This can markedly improve their quality of life. For an eighty five year old patient with AML, an extra three or four months like that can represent a significant clinical benefit. Even if it's all they ever get out of being treated.

However, the situation is usually more complicated than this. With AML, failure to achieve a CR means that the patient is going to die rapidly and have virtually no chance of bringing the disease under control. That's a given. Going into remission is essential to any possibility of having a longer term outcome. But actually achieving a CR after initial treatment is *not* by itself enough to prevent the disease from coming back again, from *relapsing*.

AML is a very difficult malignancy to deal with, because the abnormal leukaemic cells are highly adapted to avoid treatments used against them, by hiding away in the body, where they can't be detected. Even for a patient who has achieved a CR after treatment and who has absolutely no leukaemic blast cells detectable in a bone marrow sample, in the absence of doing anything further that patient will relapse. Sooner or later they will come back with fifty or sixty per cent blast cells in the bone marrow again.

This is because even in someone who appears to have no visible leukaemia left following therapy, there will in fact still be *at least* a million undetected leukaemia cells present, hiding away deep in the bone marrow throughout the body. Invisible. Like sleeper cells, waiting to be activated. That's how cunning cancer can be.

This secret army of malignant marauders in AML is called *minimal residual disease* and if left untreated, it will rapidly start to recover and divide again. This inevitably results in a relapse of the leukaemia and a rapid downhill journey from that point. Which is why achieving a complete response, as a measure of how a drug is affecting the disease, only tells part of the story.

The other part is that after a patient has achieved a CR and gone into remission, they need to receive additional intensive treatment almost immediately. There is no time to hang around. You have to keep one step ahead of the leukaemia. Otherwise, they have no hope of a cure or at least a longer term remission. Without further treatment, death is their imminent destiny. The initial therapy given to a patient to get them into remission is called *induction* therapy. Treatment they receive subsequently is known as *consolidation*. Both are essential to having any chance of a future.

Consolidation treatment can take the form of further very high dose drug chemotherapy, or increasingly often a bone marrow transplant from a suitable donor. Today this more commonly involves a *stem cell transplant* which consists of giving specific purified cells derived from bone marrow, rather than the whole thing itself. Undertaking these kinds of post remission treatments is highly skilled and hugely dangerous. Something not far short of twenty per cent of patients can die of complications of the treatment itself, in even the most experienced of centres.

But without undergoing such interventions the only certain outcome is disease relapse and death anyway. And on the positive side, there is a real prospect of an actual cure, for a proportion of patients at least. The chance of an end to the living nightmare their lives have descended into. Most patients would clutch at that straw, given the opportunity.

This kind of staged approach, whereby patients get a series of treatments one after the other, can however create enormous difficulties in trying to work out the particular contribution of different drugs to a patient's eventual outcome.

Consider someone on the CLASSIC I trial who achieved a CR and went into remission, after receiving clofarabine and cytarabine. They then went on to have post remission consolidation therapy with a stem cell transplant and lived for twenty six months after that.

Then compare that patient with someone else on the trial, who also achieved a CR and went into remission after cytarabine alone. They subsequently received post remission therapy with a mixture of high dose anti-leukaemia drugs (because a stem cell transplant donor wasn't available) and died twelve months later.

The first patient lived fourteen months longer than the second one. But the difficulty lies in trying to work out whether that was due to them receiving clofarabine and cytarabine at the outset, compared to cytarabine alone. Or how much of it might have been because they subsequently underwent a stem cell transplant, rather than the alternative of high dose chemotherapy, which the second patient received. You just don't know. And that is the dilemma in assessing the role a specific cancer drug plays in the overall outcome of a disease with a hugely complicated treatment course.

It becomes hard to compare patients, because differing things are happening to them. This is particularly the case with malignancies where the patient might survive for quite a few years. Women with advanced breast cancer for example, might receive five or six different treatments in the three or four years between diagnosis and death. And to varying degrees, each patient's treatment course will be different from all the other patients. If one patient lives longer than another, it's hard to work out exactly which of the treatments was responsible for it.

In the case of the CLASSIC I trial, if more patients had a CR and went into remission straight after receiving clofarabine and cytarabine, it must be due to the effect of clofarabine itself. There is nothing else at that point which is different from the group receiving cytarabine alone. And so comparing CR rates is an *accurate* measure of the effect of clofarabine. However, CR by itself has only a limited *relevance* to the patient and their eventual clinical course. Because without further treatment, the leukaemia will inevitably come back.

A more important outcome might be how long patients survive, depending on whether or not they received clofarabine at the outset. After all, that's what the patient is ultimately most interested in. They're probably not overly bothered about the precise percentage of blast cells in their bone marrow. They just want to know if they will make it to the end of the year or not.

But looking at survival is complicated by the fact that each patient may have received markedly different treatments, in between going into remission and eventually dying. And so it is much harder to work out the unique contribution played by clofarabine itself. In technical terms, the effect of clofarabine is *confounded* by all the other things going on.

When developing a new drug, patients and physicians are most interested in knowing whether it will prolong survival. That's what matters more than anything else. And yet this is the hardest question to convincingly answer in clinical trials, because of all these complicating factors. They can drown out any contribution of the drug.

With all cancer studies it is much simpler to measure the short term actions of a new agent. But it is much harder to show a longer term effect, even though that is what you really want to know about. You end up with the unsatisfactory conflict that the greater relevance an endpoint has, the harder it becomes to measure it. The more you want to see something, the more easily it seems to be able to hide away from view.

VII

With CLASSIC I, Genzyme were caught out in the end through exactly this difficulty. Their particular problem was that clofarabine and cytarabine together had shown a much higher CR rate than cytarabine alone, with twice as many patients going into remission. But critically they hadn't seen *any* difference in survival between the two groups, irrespective of whether they did or didn't receive clofarabine.[18]

So the drug was clearly doing something, there was no doubt about that. Getting patients into remission was certainly better than nothing at all. It improved patients' symptoms and quality of life, getting them out of hospital for a while at least. But it didn't seem to be translating into a longer term advantage. Patients weren't living for any greater period of time.

There were two possible explanations for that. Either clofarabine genuinely had no longer term effect in patients. All its actions were limited to the first couple of months. Or, it was actually helping some people live longer but it was impossible to *prove* it in a clinical trial, due to all the other noise going on around the patients and their treatment. No one could tell for sure which was the real explanation.

Despite this conundrum, you somehow still had to answer the question of whether there was enough evidence of efficacy to justify the considerable toxicity associated with the drug. Which included bone marrow suppression, cardiovascular disturbances, skin lesions, liver and kidney damage. All in all, it had some very nasty side effects.

Did it have the right balance of good and bad? How did you decide whether clofarabine *worked* as a cancer medicine? Just how long a piece of string were Genzyme holding here?

And trying to fathom that out, if it weren't hard enough already, was made doubly difficult by two additional complexities. The first was a consequence of the strange and often bizarre rules of the game by which cancer studies such as CLASSIC I and II are conducted.

The second arose from the unpredictable way regulatory authorities sometimes behave when analysing the results of trials such as these. When assessing the relative risks and counterbalancing benefits, they often seem to be playing according to a set of rules all of their own.

VIII

The techniques for interpreting clinical trials and the idiosyncrasies they engender are almost a world of their own, set apart from the rational rules that govern normal daily activity. This can create no end of difficulties for those involved. The problems start with the fact that most clinical studies, whether in oncology or other areas of medicine, tend to measure a number of different things about how a drug is working, each of which is an *endpoint*.

With cancer medicine, trials usually look, amongst other things, at how many patients have tumor shrinkage, how long this lasts and how long the patients live. These are called *hard* endpoints, not because they are difficult to achieve but because they are supposed to be easy to measure in an objective quantifiable way.

Other endpoints might include the effects of a drug on a patient's level of pain. Or on their overall quality of life, looking at things such as how well they are sleeping, are they able to do normal daily activities including getting dressed, doing the housework and so on. These kinds of outcomes tend to be more difficult to measure in a standardised way and so are called *soft* endpoints.

For example, prostate cancer often spreads to the skeleton, causing serious problems with bone pain. However, one person's determination of severe pain might only be moderate pain to another individual, which in turn it might be quite mild pain to a more stoically minded third patient.

So it is easier to determine that a prostate tumor has shrunk by say three cm, because that would be the same amount whatever patient it was measured in. Whereas trying to work out a fifty per cent reduction in cancer pain is more complicated, because each patient may be starting off from a different place and have differing values for measuring an improvement.

Often in clinical studies there is a desire to include as many endpoints as possible, both hard and soft ones. You want to fully characterise the potential efficacy of a new drug and to minimise the risk of missing something useful about it. This is important because not all drugs produce the same pattern of effects.

Many older chemotherapy cancer drugs will both shrink existing tumors (*e.g.* a big lump of lung cancer in the chest) as well as delaying the appearance of new ones and thus the spread of the disease. So the effect of the drug could be picked up by looking at the *response rate* (number of patients with tumor shrinkage) alone. That would be enough to know you had a drug that was doing something.

But many newer targeted cancer agents and immunotherapy approaches don't appear to shrink existing tumors very much, if at all. And so they have very low response rates. But they still delay the time to when the disease starts spreading (or the patient dies anyway). This is technically called the *progression free survival (PFS)* and is a very important measure of how drugs are working. For example, the recently arrived kidney cancer drug sorafenib (Nexavar) acts on a very specific enzyme pathway implicated in the growth of the tumor. It has revolutionised the treatment of this particular disease as it *doubles* the progression free survival period from three months to six months.

That's a big improvement. And yet it only causes tumor shrinkage in one or two per cent of patients. If you looked at just response rate alone for sorafenib, you would erroneously conclude that it didn't really work.

So the greater the number of endpoints you measure, the more you would seem to have things covered, in terms of picking up effects of your drug. That's why many clinical trials can end up with ten or more endpoints, each measuring a different *aspect* of how the drug is working. These typically include response rate, progression free survival and overall survival. But there are many others which you could also include.

In leukaemia for example you could look at how many patients, with chromosomal abnormalities at the outset, have these return to normal after treatment. Or how well the bone marrow recovers, by counting the numbers of red and white cells and platelets. You can also repeat some of the endpoints in a trial by measuring the same thing in all the patients together and then again in selected subgroups (such as those with high and low LDH levels, amongst many others).

Crucially however, a conflict arises within clinical trials when you do this. The more endpoints you include, the greater the number of times you are effectively looking at whether a drug might be working. If you measure ten different things about a drug, you are really having ten separate looks at whether it has any activity. And the more frequently you do this, the more likely it becomes that you will actually see something simply due to *chance*, rather than because it really exists. The paradox of clinical studies therefore is that the more often you look, the more likely you are to see something that isn't really there.

This means that in practice, clinical trials are all about firstly, comparing two drugs (or a drug and placebo) to look for differences in efficacy and then secondly, trying to determine whether any difference seen is a *real* one, or just a *random* occurrence.

And this can end up having big implications, when trying to decide whether a cancer drug works or not. If you're not careful, a clinical trial can give you the completely *wrong* idea about how a new drug is doing.

These problems arise because all clinical trials involve human beings, who are inherently biologically variable. They also involve measuring responses to drugs, which tend to differ from person to person.

When you are setting up a clinical trial with a new drug, you can't really test it on every single person in the whole world. Although that would be the only way to fully characterise the effect of a drug on humans. Instead you have to use a *sample* of people, maybe a hundred, maybe a thousand, maybe even ten thousand but it won't be *everyone* on the planet.

And any one sample of people will respond differently to a particular drug, when compared to another sample of the same size. The difference in response between the two samples may be small or it may be big but it definitely won't be exactly the same.

This means you end up with *variability* in responses to a drug each time you do a clinical trial, each time involving a different sample of patients. And this is one of the biggest issues when running studies in cancer medicine. Because if you're not careful, variability can lead to the random occurrence of misleading results.

Imagine you lived in a town with a thousand green cars and a thousand red cars. So the numbers of each colour were actually the same. Every time you drove around town along the same route, if you were to compare how many red or green cars you saw, the numbers would differ a bit on each occasion. It would depend on how many car drivers of either colour were also out and about in the same part of town as you, at the same time.

The only way you could be *certain* of counting exactly the same number of red and green vehicles on any particular journey would be if you were to see all thousand red cars and all thousand green cars out on the road at the same time. Which would be incredibly unlikely to happen.

It's just the same with clinical trials. You will get a different answer every time you make a comparison between two drugs. Because on each occasion you are only looking at a *proportion* of patients and not all of them. (*Just as the numbers of red and green cars you see will vary each time you count them, because you're not including every single car in the town*).

On those journeys around town, most of the time you would see roughly the same proportion of green and red cars. However sometimes by *chance* you would see a lot more green than red. This might mislead you into thinking that the town now had more green cars than red ones, even though the total number was actually the same. And the more journeys you made, the greater the chance that sooner or later you would see more of one colour than the other and reach this misleading conclusion.

This same issue of random chance applies to clinical trials between any two cancer drugs. Say we have drug A which has *genuinely* better efficacy than another drug, drug B. There is however always the possibility that a clinical trial comparing the two could reach a different and false result (either that B appears better than A or that A and B appear the same).

The chances of this happening depend upon how large the real difference between the two drugs actually is. It also depends on how many patients you have included in each group receiving drug A or drug B. And on how many endpoints you are measuring.

Putting endpoints to one side for a moment, the *smaller* the real difference between the two drugs, and the *fewer* the number of patients in each treatment group, then the greater is the risk of a misleading result occurring by chance.

Sticking with the car analogy, say the town has one thousand red cars and only ten green ones. In that case it is very unlikely that you will see more green cars than red ones. And that's whether you make very short journeys around town or very long ones. So there would be a low risk of you reaching the false conclusion that there were more green cars than red ones.

This is because the size of the difference between the colours is very big. If the difference were smaller (say one thousand red and five hundred green cars) then you would still usually see more red than green, especially on a longer journey. On a shorter journey though there would be a greater probability of you coming across more green than reds, just by chance. The shorter the journey, the more likely this would be. You wouldn't have the opportunity that a longer trip would afford to reverse the chance imbalance.

In clinical trials, the length of the journey is the equivalent of the number of patients in your trial. Shorter journeys equate to a smaller number of patients. And a higher risk of something occurring by chance.

In trials, including an endpoint (whether it is response rate or progression free survival or overall survival or whatever else) is like making an individual car journey. So, even if there are one thousand red cars and only ten green ones, if you make enough journeys, sooner or later by chance you are going to see more green than red cars. It might take a very long time, but it will happen eventually. Especially if you are making short journeys all the time.

The same thing applies to clinical trials. For any given real efficacy difference between two drugs, the bigger the number of endpoints and the smaller the number of patients you include, then the greater the chance of coming up with a finding which isn't really there. You're going to see something misleading, just because you are making a large number of short journeys.

All clinical trials therefore become a *compromise*. You want to include as many endpoints as you can, to maximise the chance of measuring an effect of your drug. However, you also want to avoid having so many that inevitably some turn out positive by chance, thus leading to potentially erroneous conclusions.

The smaller the difference between two drugs really is, the more important these considerations of multiple endpoints and random occurrences become.

One way of tackling the potentially misleading nature of clinical studies is to designate one particular endpoint as the so called *primary* endpoint in a clinical trial. This then becomes the most important parameter of efficacy for that drug, in that particular trial. It takes precedence over *all* the other endpoints.

All the statistical mathematics involved in the design of a study are then intended to minimise the possibility of a positive or negative finding with the primary endpoint occurring by chance.

After defining an endpoint as the primary one, all the other efficacy measures included in the trial then become *secondary* endpoints. So in a cancer trial, the primary endpoint might be specified as survival. Secondary endpoints would probably include response rate and progression free survival (although all sorts of other ones are possible too).

When designing a clinical trial, complex statistical techniques exist to calculate in advance the possibility of a difference in the primary endpoint being due to chance alone. These use a mathematical model which takes account of three main things. The first is the *number of patients* going into the study. Second is the *size of the difference* you are expecting to see for one drug compared to another. The final one is an estimate of how *variable* the results would be, if you were to repeat the trial on a number of different occasions, with differing groups of patients.

For most studies, the usual minimum requirement is that the mathematics predict at least a ninety five per cent chance of a result with the primary endpoint being genuine. In other words, the probability of it having occurred by chance is no greater than one in twenty. For any given comparison between two drugs, the smaller the difference you expect to see, then the larger the number of patients you need to put in each group to achieve this level of probability.

The primary endpoint chosen for a trial is a very big deal. It's one of the most important decisions a company ever takes. This is because if the drug fails to show a difference here, the trial is automatically written off as a failure. It doesn't matter how many secondary endpoints the drug does well in. If it falls short on the primary one, it's game over. Especially as far as any regulatory authority is concerned.

You can think of it as a relay race. However fast you are and however many of the early stages your team wins, if you lose the final one, then you have lost. Period.

So when we say that a drug has *failed to meet* the primary endpoint in a trial, this can mean one of two things. Either *no* difference was seen between the two drugs being compared. Or alternatively, if there was a difference, the statistical testing applied to the results showed that this could have occurred by chance, with a probability greater than one in twenty. In other words the likelihood of the result being genuine is less than ninety five per cent.

Either way, the trial is a failure and if it is a big study then you may well have just said goodbye to the better part of fifty million dollars or more.

This may seem very arbitrary. It's certainly contentious. Regulators in both the US and Europe appear to be immutably wedded to this threshold of ninety five per cent, even if a drug has only just missed it and all the supporting secondary endpoints are strongly positive. It is rather like running that relay race and coming first over the finishing post, then being disqualified from winning on a technicality.

But those are the rules of the drug development game and if you infringe them, you *will* be disqualified and sent off. If not approached sensibly, this can easily create an excessive extremism, whereby the statistical means have become an end in their own right. And many promising drugs which undoubtedly have efficacy have been disallowed because of this methodological mindset.

Which was exactly the problem for Genzyme with CLASSIC I. The primary endpoint was overall survival and the clofarabine group had just failed on this.[18] The fact that every other drug in AML for the last twenty years had also been unable to show a survival advantage didn't matter. Neither did the fact that the clofarabine combination had done better on four other important secondary endpoints (overall remission rate, complete remission rate, event free survival and four month event free survival). Nor, as Professor Kantarjian had originally pointed out, that nearly one in two patients achieved a CR and went into remission.

The trial was still, technically at least, a bust. Genzyme looked like they were out of the game. FDA wouldn't spend too much time looking at the study, if it hadn't met the survival primary endpoint.

This was the end of the road, for now at least, for clofarabine in relapsed AML, certainly as far as regulatory approval was concerned. Incredible though it may seem, a drug which clearly worked would be going no further forward. For many people there would seem to be little method evident in this madness. Just evidence of madness in the methods of clinical trials. But those were the restrictions we lived under and the contract we had all freely entered into. We all knew that and we all accepted it as part of our way of life. It's just how it was.

But it was doubtful the dying and desperate patients, from whom clofarabine had just been snatched away, would be so accepting. If they actually had any say in the matter that is.

As it turned out, FDA hadn't much liked clofarabine in the CLASSIC II study in elderly AML too much either. But at least they did get as far as formally reviewing this particular trial. It wasn't rejected out of hand like CLASSIC I. Somewhat improbably, the future of clofarabine in the elderly would eventually be determined over two days in September 2009, in a depressingly beige basement ballroom of the Hilton Hotel in Silver Spring, Maryland.

This turned out to be an event which would show just how much drug regulators could struggle with reaching consistent judgements for new cancer agents. And how this sometimes led them to behave with a courtly capriciousness that would have put even the worst historical Habsburg despot to shame.

IX

Located on the I-495 Beltway surrounding Washington DC, the Maryland Hilton sits in an anonymous sprawling suburb, about thirty miles northwest of Washington. It's just a few miles from the home of FDA in Rockville, another depressingly soulless satellite of the capital.

FDA (Food and Drug Administration) are the US federal body responsible for protecting public health. They are often referred to as just *The Agency*. Their trans-Atlantic equivalent would be the European Medicines Agency (EMA) based in London.[19]

FDA are an enormous organisation of over eleven thousand employees, in a bizarre and byzantine world all of their own. It's a place populated by an extraordinary collection of individuals, most of who appear to have lost touch with normality many years ago. They live a strangely hermetic existence in their citadel fortress, eschewing contact with the outside wherever possible.

And yet it is impossible to avoid dealing with them. They have a very firm grip on regulating clinical trials and are backed up by the full force of the law. This includes the ability to send people to prison if necessary. Whilst having all the agility of a lumbering dinosaur, they also have the muscle and mass of those extinct creatures.

They have to be taken seriously therefore and treated with caution.

The extraordinary Middle-earth world of FDA is explored in much greater detail in Chapter Nine.

FDA regulates a vast array of things, including animal and veterinary products, cosmetics, dietary supplements, food, tobacco products, radiation emitting substances, medical devices, vaccines, blood and biological products, and of course, drugs. Overall, they oversee items accounting for twenty five per cent of American consumer spending.

On a typical day, their website included announcements warning about an *E coli* bacterial outbreak associated with *Bravo Farms Dutch Style Gouda* cheese, the approval of a drug called duloxetine hydrochloride for musculoskeletal pain, the reclassification of certain digital mammography devices for breast X-ray imaging, an initiative to help food producers access food safety educational materials more easily and a warning about safety issues associated with *Brazilian Blowout,* a professional hair straightening product.

FDA had their fingers in many different pies. Working there, it helped to be an octopus.

To assist in their wide ranging remit, FDA utilise forty nine advisory committees, one of which is the Oncologic Drugs Advisory Committee (ODAC). FDA are not alone in this, with external oncology advice being routinely sought by other regulatory authorities around the world. Similar committees regularly guide the European Medicines Agency, Health Canada, the Japanese Pharmaceuticals and Medical Devices Agency and the Australian Therapeutic Goods Administration. However, the American system is the most organised and most transparent.

ODAC consists of a core of thirteen voting members, with FDA getting to pick and choose who goes on to the committee. It typically includes clinically practicing oncology experts, a biostatistician, a representative of patients' organisations and usually a non-voting representative from the pharmaceutical industry. The composition changes to a certain extent, depending on which particular types of cancer the committee is considering drugs for.

The job of ODAC is to review applications which have been submitted to FDA for marketing approval and provide a recommendation about whether or not to grant this.

FDA decide which drugs they feel in need of advice from ODAC but they aren't required to automatically submit every drug application to them. Likewise, they are not obligated to accept an ODAC recommendation, although they do so in about eighty per cent of cases. The two exist a little bit at an arm's length but it would be difficult to describe ODAC as being independent of FDA. No regulator is going to bind their hands like that.

Many believe FDA use ODAC to float issues and defuse decisions which would otherwise be too contentious, were they to come from them directly. For practical purposes therefore, FDA and ODAC can be considered points on a spectrum, rather than two discrete entities. Or maybe Siamese twins would be a better analogy still.

Between them, they represent the Scylla and Charybdis that have to be navigated by hapless companies seeking cancer drug approvals. However, unlike Odysseus, who could choose which sea monster to take on, biotech companies are usually confronted with both at the same time. The ensuing battles are often on an equally mythical scale.

The Committee usually meets four times a year, for two days on each occasion. It typically considers one drug application in the morning and one in the afternoon, on each of these days. It's a routine which never seems to vary. Regulators like an orderly existence. They also seem to prefer meeting in drab downbeat Hilton hotels, spattered around the greater Washington area. Maybe it helps create an appropriate atmosphere of forlorn hopelessness, given the subject matter usually under consideration.

The sessions are open and televised. Members of the public are able to attend as part of the audience. Provided they have applied in advance, they can also make spoken submissions to the panel. This is usually about their experiences as a previous patient in a clinical trial with the drug in question. Written transcripts of the meetings are subsequently made available on the FDA website.

The proceedings are run along fairly adversarial lines, with presentations about the drug to the panel from both FDA and the relevant pharmaceutical company. It's like the prosecution and the defence. Members of the Committee hear these statements, and then cross examine the presenters. They also receive comments from patients and any other members of the public who have turned up. After that, the ODAC members vote individually in favour of approval or rejection of the drug. It is then up to FDA to go back to Rockville and decide what they are ultimately going to do.

Considering the seriousness of the subject and the augustness of the panel, ODAC meetings tend to have a surprisingly outdated and almost amateurish feel to the proceedings. It's like watching some terrible mixture of *The Antiques Road Show* and *Britain's Got Talent*. But FDA seem to love it. And so it keeps running from one season to the next, like some sort of lynchpin of the TV listings.

X

The meeting to consider clofarabine and three similar drugs was held on September 1st and 2nd 2009. It was chaired by Dr S.Gail Eckhardt, who was Head of the Division of Medical Oncology at the University of Colorado in Denver and a colorectal cancer specialist. Why she had been chosen to lead a meeting looking at four drugs all for blood cancers was a little unclear.

But then this was the world of regulatory review, where nothing was exactly what it seemed. In the course of those two days ODAC considered four drug applications, all in the area of haematological malignancies, voting in favour of two and against two others.

At Antisoma we were avidly watching the proceedings, as they were broadcast. With two drugs of our own in leukaemia, we were naturally interested to see how events unfolded. If our luck held out with one or both of them, we might well find ourselves in a couple of years' time standing on the same paisley patterned carpet in the same Hilton meeting room, before our very own ODAC hearing. So we wanted to get a sense of what might be in store.

We were also interested to see how the other companies involved in the show performed. A little bit of professional peer appraisal. It was always good to keep an eye on what the competition were up to.

On the first day of the meeting, ODAC had considered and eventually voted in favour of two drugs, one called *pralatrexate* and one called *romidepsin*. If the names of the drugs weren't complicated enough, the diseases they were intended for were worse still.

Pralatrexate had been developed by a small biotechnology company called Allos Therapeutics based in Westminster, Colorado, just northwest of Denver. It was for a rare cancer called peripheral T cell lymphoma (PTCL). Allos had conducted a single non-randomised study called PROPEL.[20] The company probably deserved approval just on the basis of the ingenuity they had displayed in coming up with a pronounceable acronym for the trial (*P*ralatrexate in patients with *R*elapsed *O*r refractory *PE*ripheral T cell *L*ymphoma).

A Google search for the term PTCL will come up with Pakistan Telecommunications Company Ltd and you will actually have to work quite hard to find mention of peripheral T cell lymphoma. Which emphasises the relative rarity of the disease. PTCL is a type of blood cancer affecting about nine thousand Americans each year, usually manifesting itself as swollen lymph glands. It is normally treated with aggressive chemotherapy but is fairly resistant and so generally carries a poor prognosis. Hence the need for a new treatment such as pralatrexate, which is a chemotherapy drug blocking one of the key metabolic pathways important for cell survival.

The PROPEL study included just one hundred and fifteen patients but was still the largest ever conducted in PTCL. That's how small the field was. All the patients had received previous treatment for their disease and were generally in quite a poor state by now. Despite this, a commendable twenty seven per cent showed a response to pralatrexate, in terms of a reduction in measurable disease, lasting on average about nine months. The drug did appear to be quite toxic though, with nearly half the patients having a serious side effect of one sort or another.

However, ODAC were clearly suitably impressed, eventually voting ten-four in favour of the drug. Three weeks later, FDA granted pralatrexate something called *accelerated approval*, based on the response rate and duration of response. This was on condition that Allos undertake additional clinical studies, to characterise the effects of the drug on survival.

Full approval is given to drugs where FDA believe there is sufficient safety and efficacy data to approve it without having any conditions attached. This is the way most drugs get through on to the market. However, in certain circumstances, usually serious and life threatening illnesses which are lacking existing satisfactory treatments, FDA can grant a *conditional* approval to a drug. This is when they have decided that additional information is going to be needed but where they don't want to reject it outright.

The idea is to avoid unnecessarily depriving seriously ill patients of a potentially useful new treatment approach, when they have nothing else to turn to. It's an initiative which arose in the early nineteen nineties, largely as a response to very vocal criticism from AIDS activist groups. They claimed that FDA were taking too long to approve new drugs, with large numbers of patients dying needlessly as a consequence. Which is exactly what was happening.

Reluctantly, FDA were eventually forced by Congress to grant this concession, although they would doubtless have preferred to carry on at their normal glacial pace. In their view a major public health catastrophe was no reason to change the way they did things.

This accelerated approval, as it is called, is based on the concept of what is known as a *surrogate* endpoint. This is something which is quicker and easier to measure and is reasonably predictive of something *else* that you would really like to know about but which is more difficult and time consuming to examine.

FDA define a surrogate endpoint as something which is "reasonably likely, based on epidemiologic, therapeutic, pathophysiologic or other evidence, to predict clinical benefit."[21]

Although not exactly widely used in oncology, a useful way to think about it would be to imagine an egg timer. This provides a surrogate measure of how well cooked an egg is. It is much simpler to look at how much time has gone by, than it would be to get the egg out of the pan, break it open and then throw it away and start again if it wasn't well done enough. Most of the time, the egg timer reasonably predicts how well cooked the egg will be. One is a surrogate for the other.

With AIDS drugs, many were approved by measuring their effects on the actual levels of AIDS virus detectable in the patient's body. Either that, or effects on levels of cells in the blood known to be targeted by the virus. These surrogate markers were considered likely to predict how long the patient might live. And so improvements in the former should lead to increases in survival too.

Obviously survival is a more relevant indicator of how useful a drug might be but would take very much longer to measure than do simple blood tests. So by using a surrogate endpoint, a drug can be made available to patients much more quickly. That is of course provided you are confident that the surrogate endpoint really is somehow linked to a more useful clinical outcome, such as increased survival or improved quality of life.

With cancer drugs, surrogate endpoints are basically those which fall short of measuring mortality itself. Effects on parameters such as response rate or progression free survival are believed by some to be predictive of similar effects on overall survival. In other words, to be surrogates for it. Others disagree and believe you can't put any reliance on anything other than survival itself. By and large, there is no real consensus on this. FDA seem to have changed their mind fairly frequently in the past, which can make life difficult for everyone, themselves included. The truth is, no one really knows.

As discussed later on, this is in fact one of the most contentious and controversial areas of cancer medicine and drug development, where there is currently little agreement on the relevance or predictability of endpoints other than survival itself.

Despite this, a number of cancer drugs have received accelerated approval. The first one was as far back as 1996 and involved a drug called docetaxel in metastatic breast cancer. It was based on effects on tumor shrinkage and response rate. Another was actually clofarabine itself in paediatric ALL. This was given accelerated approval in 2004, based on the number of complete responses (CRs).

Overall, there have been about twenty five or so accelerated approvals in cancer. And pralatrexate was about to become the latest addition to this list.

One of the main requirements of accelerated approval is that a company also commits to undertake additional confirmatory clinical studies, after the drug is actually on the market. These have to show an effect on the ultimate endpoint for which approval was given on a surrogate basis. If these studies turn out negative then there is every possibility of the original approval being withdrawn. The drug would then disappear from the market.

Until recently, pharmaceutical companies would often effectively ignore this requirement. Or if they did pay at least lip service to it, do so by initiating studies that never seemed to actually finish and from which no data emerged. After all, they had little to gain and potentially everything to lose by taking the risk of conducting additional clinical trials. Which might well turn out to be negative. That was one boat you definitely didn't want to rock. Not with the money already rolling in.

For years FDA were surprisingly powerless in the face of this abuse and could do little other than try to shame recalcitrant companies into compliance. Which was unlikely to get them very far. However, a change to the law in 2007 gave them a much greater ability to enforce these requirements, so that they essentially became mandatory rather than optional.[22]

Therefore pralatrexate wasn't yet out of the woods. Allos would still need to conduct another study, with survival as the primary endpoint. But in the meantime, the drug would be out there on the market and the cash would be pouring in.

Which is exactly what Gloucester Pharmaceuticals were hoping for with romidepsin, the next drug reviewed by ODAC. Gloucester was a small oncology company, based in Cambridge Massachusetts. It basically only had this one drug. So there was a lot riding on this for them.

Originally known as FK228, romidepsin was a natural bacterial product, first identified by the Japanese Fujisawa Pharmaceutical Company. Their scientists had isolated it from a bacterium called *Chromobacterium violaceum*.

In turn, they had discovered this in a soil sample taken from the Yamagata prefecture, in the mountainous and volcanic Honshu region, Japan's largest island. A number of drugs, for cancer and many other diseases, have their origins in soil samples collected from around the world. These could literally turn into *pay dirt* if a promising chemical was subsequently extracted from them.

Clinical trials with romidepsin in cancer were originally conducted in the US by the government's National Cancer Institute and Gloucester Pharmaceuticals picked up the drug in 2004. So romidepsin's journey from an Asian mountain had already been an epic one by the time it reached its final destination in front of ODAC in Maryland.

Romidepsin is what is technically called a *histone deacetylase inhibitor* (abbreviated to HDACi, pronounced "ach-dac"). It is part of an exciting new generation of cancer drugs, collectively described as *epigenetic* agents. These act to reverse functional changes in key regulatory genes, which have somehow become inappropriately activated or deactivated during the cancer disease process.[23]

There was one HDACi ahead of romidepsin and already on the market. This was called *vorinostat* (Zolinza) and belonged to Merck. Ironically for us at Antisoma, this was a drug which had failed an interim look in a Phase III lung cancer trial, just a year before the same fate befell ASA404. But despite that setback, vorinostat had gone on to demonstrate dramatic activity in the treatment of yet another rare blood cancer, called cutaneous T cell lymphoma (CTCL).

This is a condition where abnormal cancerous blood cells collect, mainly in the skin. It tends to follow a somewhat indolent course and carries a better prognosis than PTCL. But it can still severely impair peoples' lives, with the intense and incessant itching it causes sometimes driving patients to suicide. CTCL is a rare disease, with only about one thousand new cases each year in the US. But despite the small market size, the pathway already forged by vorinostat seemed to be one that Gloucester were happy to follow with romidepsin.

There were two single arm studies with the drug in CTCL, which landed in front of ODAC that September in 2009. One comprised ninety six patients who had failed *at least* one previous treatment for CTCL.[24] The other consisted of seventy one patients who had failed *more than* one previous therapy.[25]

Overall, about thirty per cent of patients in the two trials responded to treatment, as defined by the amount of tumor disease which could be detected and measured. The responses also lasted for quite a long period of time, on average about two and a half years. Romidepsin seemed to be well tolerated too, with only about two per cent of patients experiencing serious toxicities.

It therefore looked like a good drug for an unpleasant and undertreated condition. And so after due deliberation, ODAC voted ten-zero in favour of romidepsin (with one abstention). FDA subsequently granted *full* approval on November 6th.

In terms of interpreting clinical benefit, it seemed inconsistent to many that FDA gave only *accelerated* approval to pralatrexate. This was a drug for PTCL, which is both a much more common and usually a more serious condition than CTCL. And one for which no other approved therapies are available.

Yet they granted *full* approval to romidepsin for use in CTCL, which is a much less common and less aggressive disease. And one for which three approved therapies already exist (vorinostat, along with two others called bexarotene and denileukin diftitox).

Pralatrexate would need to go on and demonstrate a survival advantage to confirm its efficacy. Otherwise it might be withdrawn from the market. Romidepsin however was home and dry, with its usefulness seemingly established. And that was despite the absence of any information on whether it increased, decreased or had no effect on survival.

However, if that appeared inconsistent, these double standards of regulatory review were to become more contradictory still, when ODAC eventually got round to considering Genzyme's clofarabine.

But before that, it had to review a third drug, laromustine (formerly also known as Cloretazine but now with the trade name Onrigin). This was also a new AML agent but not, with the best will in the world, the strongest of ODAC applications. It was however a drug which was later on to play a role in influencing our own final destiny at Antisoma, although we couldn't have known this at the time.

XI

Laromustine belonged to a small New Haven Connecticut company called Vion. And to be honest, Vion was always going to have its work cut out with this particular drug.

The company had submitted an application for approval in elderly patients (by which they meant over sixty years of age) with AML. These were patients considered to have particular risk factors, suggesting they wouldn't do very well with normal intensive chemotherapy. And so they were precluded from receiving it. Their doctors just thought it was too dangerous to give it to them, as they wouldn't be able to tolerate the side effects. So instead, they were given the chance to try out laromustine.

Vion had conducted two single arm studies. One included eighty five patients with AML[26] and the other had a subset of fifty five similar patients.[27] These seemed to show that about thirty per cent of patients were responding by achieving a complete response (CR). A thirty per cent response rate in these sorts of patients wasn't bad, particularly considering they probably otherwise wouldn't have been given any treatment at all. But the remissions weren't lasting very long. It was less than six months on average before the leukaemia started returning in most patients. This was Vion's first problem.

As ODAC member Ronald Richardson would later put it, "half of these remissions were shorter than six months in duration and about a third of these I think you could measure with your watch."[28]

The situation wasn't helped by their second problem, which was that the majority of patients in either study had also received additional active AML drugs during the trial. They had been given cytarabine in one study and a drug called hydroxyurea in the other. This made it difficult to work out the exact contribution of laromustine in isolation. Although an issue which complicated many other cancer clinical trials, it definitely wasn't helping out Vion in this particular instance.

But by far and away the biggest challenge they were grappling with was the safety data from the studies. According to an FDA analysis of the data, about twelve per cent of patients who received the drug were dying of lung damage, which seemed to be due to the laromustine itself. A further twenty per cent were getting lung problems which weren't that far short of being fatal.

That was a lot of toxicity to balance against what was effectively a one in three chance of getting a short lived respite from your disease. You'd have to be feeling pretty desperate before taking that kind of risk. But then this was AML. As if that weren't bad enough, there was worse news to come. FDA knew about even more disturbing results from an earlier Vion trial.

This was in younger patients with relapsed AML, where laromustine and cytarabine combined were being compared with cytarabine alone. Here the study had been suspended in July 2008 because about five times more patients in the laromustine arm were dying in the first thirty days of treatment, compared to the cytarabine alone arm. Overall, forty per cent of patients in the laromustine arm were experiencing a fatal adverse event of some sort compared to only thirteen per cent in the cytarabine arm. Survival had been *reduced* to about four months with laromustine, compared to six months without it.[29, 30]

When your experimental drug has a mortality rate involving nearly one in two of the patients receiving it, that's not a good position to be in. Vion had subsequently changed the trade name from Cloretazine to Onrigin at the end of 2008. Maybe they'd been hoping for a fresh start. But when you have a problem that big, it stays around and haunts you from the past. Like a serious criminal record. There aren't many places left to go with a conviction of that sort hanging over you. Especially when you're standing in front of an advisory judge and jury which is notoriously conservatively cautious when it comes to drug safety.

With the odds stacked against them, Vion still managed a spirited defence bringing along a number of their own outside leukaemia experts as character witnesses. These included heavy hitters such as Professor Bob Löwenberg from Rotterdam, the prolific Professor Alan Burnett from Cardiff and the urbane Professor Gary Schiller from UCLA. However, even with this papal triumvirate, the thirteen-zero ODAC vote against laromustine was probably a foregone conclusion from the moment the meeting had actually started a couple of hours earlier.

The Committee were unanimous that a *randomised* trial was needed to better characterise the potential efficacy and definite toxicity of laromustine. They needed more information to understand the risk-benefit trade off of this drug in elderly patients. Something which appeared to be very much in the balance at the moment.

For once, it was difficult to disagree with them. With a slightly more benign clinical profile, laromustine would have definitely filled a medical gap. The elderly with leukaemia were by and large very poorly served. But on the basis of the evidence presented, the drug was just too toxic. It was also unlikely that randomised data would make much difference to this interpretation. But ODAC had passed the buck back to Vion and left them to sort the mess out.

As it turned out though, they never had a chance to consider another trial with laromustine. Vion simply couldn't withstand the ODAC rejection and eventually filed for Chapter 11 Bankruptcy a couple of months later, with debts of sixty million dollars. They became one more biotech blow out and laromustine turned into one more dead drug. That was obviously one big headache for Vion's management and investors.

What we didn't know at the time, as we sat watching events unfold from London, was that laromustine would cause us some big headaches of our own, just a year later. FDA's experiences with it would in turn come to adversely influence their views on one of our own leukaemia drugs.

The little bit of shameful schadenfreude, inevitably occasioned by laromustine unravelling, would come back as big time karma for us a bit further down the line.

But at the time, we weren't giving laromustine too much thought. We were much more interested in what ODAC would make of clofarabine. When its turn finally came, this drug seemed to have a lot more going for it than laromustine. Not least was the fact that most people believed it was actually a useful drug which worked.

Like Vion, Genzyme's CLASSIC II study was intended to support approval for the use of clofarabine in elderly patients with AML. The study had selected out patients who would be unable to tolerate the more aggressive chemotherapy which was usually employed. And so the ability to receive clofarabine represented an important treatment option for them. Particularly as the alternative was no treatment at all.

The trial consisted of one hundred and twelve patients, aged over sixty and the final results showed a very creditable forty five per cent complete response rate. Furthermore, the average survival was about ten months.[31] Again that wasn't at all bad for a group of patients this old. The toxicity appeared to be acceptable too, certainly compared to what the committee had seen for laromustine. Looking at the CLASSIC II data overall, most ODAC members felt the drug worked.

This was a sentiment summed up by the views of panel member Dr Lodovico Balducci, who was Division Chief at the H. Lee Moffitt Cancer Centre and Research Institute in Tampa Florida. He had a particular interest in cancer of the elderly. Dr Balducci was chairman of the Geriatric Oncology Consortium, which conducted nationwide clinical trials in older individuals. He was also chairman of the committee on guidelines for management of the older individual of the National Comprehensive Cancer Network. So he knew a thing or two about cancer in the elderly. Or the *older individual,* to adopt the more currently correct term.

"I have a special stake in management of cancer in older people because that's the focus of my research and my life," he told the assembled audience.[28]

"And right now, I think we have virtually no information on what is happening to the majority of our cancer patients, since fifty per cent of them are seventy and older. And we have virtually no information about these people. So we have to find a way to study what is going on in this population.

This trial (*CLASSIC II*) might not have been perfect...but for me the most important question it addresses (*is that*) we are dealing with a drug which has a very high complete remission rate, in a group of patients that otherwise would have had a very low complete remission rate. I'm impressed by the fact that fifty per cent of the patients with complete remission did not receive other treatment. And those who did receive other treatment, maybe (*it was*) because their pathological condition was improved by the drug."

The impression that clofarabine was really working in these older patients was obviously important. Particularly as much discussion at the meeting revolved around the fact that the elderly often end up missing out on active treatment for cancer altogether. The committee heard a presentation on AML and the elderly from the cerebral and charismatic leukaemia expert Professor Eli Estey, from The Fred Hutchinson Cancer Research Center in Seattle. This is something of a spiritual home to haematologists, because it's where bone marrow transplantation was originally developed.

His startling finding was that Medicare data showed only thirty per cent of people aged over sixty five received *any* kind of chemotherapy for cancer in general, never mind leukaemia in particular. Unbelievably, this meant that nearly three quarters of elderly patients weren't getting treated.

In the case of AML, there was a clear belief that the elderly did badly with conventional therapy. This was either because they couldn't tolerate the side effects or they had disease which had evolved to become resistant to standard chemotherapeutic approaches, as Professor Estey explained.

And yet this prejudice was often misleading, as individual patient experience suggested many of the elderly could do very well. This was particularly if an initial drug like clofarabine improved them to the point where they could actually then withstand more intensive treatment approaches.

"I actually gave the education sessions at ASCO this year," explained panellist Gail Roboz, the young and dynamic leukaemia specialist from Weill Cornell Medical Centre in New York, up on 69th Avenue and First Street. This is where the hospital towers over the East River, like some enormous menacing metropolitan structure straight out of Gotham City.

"And I decided as a little experiment to photograph my seventy five year old father in law, who is a math professor and I had him all spiffy and looking really great in a tie. And I took a picture of him," she continued.

"And then for the second slide I messed up his hair and put on a patient gown. And I told him to look dishevelled, which he did very well. And it was shocking how different they looked.

And I think that's what happens with older patients – this amazing ability to actually look better after treatment. And to take somebody who initially does not give you at all the impression of even possibly being able to undergo chemotherapy, let alone a stem cell transplant. And then ultimately realise how great they look in remission," concluded the always great looking Dr Roboz.

"I completely agree with Dr Roboz," Dr Balducci continued.

"In geriatrics, there is a concept of *frailty*, which means a person who was still independent, but is on the edge of dependency, as soon as some major stress occurs. And many of these people (*in the CLASSIC II trial*) are in exactly that situation. And by relatively gentle treatment, you have in this case (*with clofarabine*) the opportunity to reverse a condition and make them available (*for more intensive*) treatment."

AML is a disease predominantly of the elderly. Given that apparently the elderly weren't by and large actually receiving any treatment, clofarabine surely seemed to be a useful step forwards, with its nearly forty per cent response rate. Especially if it subsequently opened the gateway to more aggressive approaches.

And yet despite the obvious points in favour of clofarabine, the committee seemed hung up on the absence of a randomised trial.

"I think we all understand that there's *well documented* activity (*with clofarabine*)," confirmed committee chairman Dr Eckhardt.

"But really the vote is based on whether or not a randomised trial is indicated."

It was a controversial issue. The drug seemed to work. Why waste more time on another trial, randomised or not. However, at least one committee member had a clear view on this and was ready to nail his colours to the mast.

"The issue being raised here is that with the absence of a randomised trial, we don't have an evidence based justification that alternative standards of care wouldn't be better, when considering overall benefit to risk," opined Professor Thomas Fleming.

He was a statistician and biometrician at the University of Washington in Seattle. He'd already been off at a similar tangent, in the earlier deliberations on pralatrexate.

He also seemed to be completely missing the point here, that there *weren't* any accepted alternatives. As Dr Roboz patiently pointed out.

"Which standard of care was that you're referring to?" she interjected, asking what was to turn out to be the key question in the subsequent deliberations.

"It would be the standard...it would be...it would...well...do we want to design the trial now?" struggled the floundering Professor Fleming. "The single arm trial doesn't allow us a proper understanding about clofarabine's contribution to the overall outcome as well. And that's, in essence, what a randomised trial is needed to address," he continued, in a characteristically dogmatic and determined way.

Although he may have overstated the point, some appeared to be in agreement with his basic tenet.

"Maybe this drug will be better. We don't know that," said Professor Wyndham Wilson, from the National Cancer Institute in Bethesda, Maryland. "But I think in the absence of a randomised study with just a small Phase II study, I think we are opening ourselves to approving a new (*and less demanding*) standard."

Others weren't having any of that though.

"It's probably career suicide for me to say anything against a randomised trial," began Dr Roboz "but what are we looking to randomise it to and to what end? It's difficult for me to imagine what could be learned, barring that it is substantially worse than doing nothing, which is awfully tough to accomplish in AML."

Dr Balducci agreed. "Unlike Dr Roboz, because of my age, I really don't have to worry about my future career and so I can argue against (*randomised*) clinical trials." Which he then proceeded to do, suggesting that there was sufficient evidence already in favour of clofarabine, given the impressive response rates and acceptable toxicity profile.

The debate continued backwards and forwards, in favour of and against the need for a randomised trial, in a seemingly almost random fashion itself. Eventually, Dr Richard Pazdur decided to put the boot in.

Since April 2005 he had been Director of the Office of Oncology Drug Products at FDA. He was therefore their main man. Thin and wiry, he was a serious person with a serious job. He was highly intelligent, hugely experienced and widely respected.

It wouldn't be surprising if he occasionally enjoyed the attention willingly afforded by audiences to someone in his position of power and authority. He now reminded everyone in the room that FDA had pretty much told Genzyme of the need for a randomised trial, in a meeting the two had held, back in December 2007.

"Quote," he declaimed, somewhat theatrically, reading from the minutes of the meeting between FDA and Genzyme. He just happened to have them to hand.

"Generally, approval of new drugs for initial treatment of AML is based on results of randomised controlled trials. It will be difficult to interpret the results of this trial without a control. We recommend that you conduct a *randomised* controlled study. Unquote."

He followed this up with a right hook, by reminding the audience that the European regulatory authority, the EMA, had also come down on the side of randomisation. This was when Genzyme had submitted data on clofarabine to them a year earlier. He'd landed a significant punch and it was a dramatic example of the Machiavellian mastery that marked the way all the best regulators presented data.

The truth was that in March 2008, Genzyme had withdrawn a clofarabine application originally submitted to the EMA by their then partner, a company called Bioenvision. However, this hadn't included *any* of the CLASSIC II data, as that study was still ongoing at the time. Instead, the application was based largely on one small trial in the elderly, known as BIOV121.[32]

Even with the best will in the world, which wasn't exactly a defining characteristic of most regulators, it would have been a stretch too far to expect the EMA to approve clofarabine on the basis of this limited data alone. Genzyme had therefore sensibly concluded that their best bet was to bide their time and wait for CLASSIC II to run its course. Which meant that ODAC now had a significantly more substantial package of clinical data, compared to when their European counterparts had made up their minds. What the EMA had decided in the past, based on different data from now, didn't therefore seem that relevant to the current deliberations. However, this historical inconsistency didn't appear to be holding Dr Pazdur back.

"The population seems far too heterogeneous, regarding unsuitability for intensive chemotherapy," the EMA had decided, as he unhelpfully now pointed out. "In the absence of randomisation, no conclusion can be made regarding a potential benefit related to the treatment with clofarabine."

He left the message hanging in the air for a moment or two. The implication was clear. If the Europeans had already come down in favour of randomisation, who were FDA to come along and rock the regulatory boat now.

It was a fancy piece of footwork, especially as, in addition to the dubious validity of calling the EMA to the witness box, the Agency also seemed to be overlooking the small fact that Genzyme *had* already tried to do a randomised trial. However, they'd found it a well-nigh impossible struggle to get off the ground.

"I doubt there's anyone in this room who wouldn't say that a randomised trial is preferred," said Dr Michael Vasconcelles, the Group Vice President and Global Head of Oncology at Genzyme, as he stood up and stepped into the ring.

"The question is whether it's *feasible.* I'd just like to take you back a few years to when this study was designed, when Genzyme submitted a protocol to FDA for review. As Dr Pazdur mentioned, there was agreement between Genzyme and FDA on the comparator for that study, for this population."

Dr Vasconcelles argued that before the start of CLASSIC II, Genzyme and FDA had sat down and talked about doing a randomised trial. However the problem they were facing was the lack of any widely used alternative clofarabine could be compared to.

The study was aimed at patients who were unfit for standard aggressive therapy. In these cases, there was no agreement among clinicians about whether there was any other worthwhile treatment at all. Which is why so many patients ended up getting nothing. In the absence of an acknowledged approach for these patients, there just wasn't any other obvious drug to match clofarabine against. There was no existing standard of care.

However FDA had remained fixated, insistent almost, on the idea of a randomised trial, whatever the difficulties. And so Genzyme had eventually agreed to try to include a comparator for CLASSIC II. But the best they could come up with was just a very low dose of cytarabine by itself. This would be about a tenth of the dose that was used as standard aggressive treatment in fitter patients.

This was an approach occasionally used by some clinicians, in selected

111

older patients. It could be given as a subcutaneous injection and usually managed on an outpatient basis. By the standards of AML, things didn't come any more simple and straightforward than that.

Usually it was an attempt to offer some hope and a sense that at least something was being tried. It was psychologically better than doing nothing. Whilst there was some data in favour of low dose cytarabine for the least unfavourable types of elderly AML,[33] many regarded it as little better than nothing, as far as most patients were concerned. The justification though was that whilst it was unclear if it was likely to do much good, the dose was so low that it was equally unlikely to do *too* much harm. It wasn't really much of a justification.

You had to sympathise though with the contortions the Genzyme people must have put themselves through. They had a new drug uniquely intended for patients for whom there was no current treatment and yet they were being forced to find a suitable current treatment to compare it to. It was like some kind of philosophical question on the nature of non-existence, which FDA were expecting them to resolve.

As Dr Vasconcelles went on to explain, "When Genzyme moved forwards with AML experts and potential study investigators to consider enrolment into that trial, there was a refusal to enrol patients (*into the low dose cytarabine comparator arm*). And further there could not be agreement reached (*sic*) on an alternative. It's on that basis that Genzyme moved forwards with the study that I've shared with you today, on the recommendation of our outside experts."

So there it was. Leading US AML experts from all parts of the country, who had participated in the CLASSIC II trial, had been reluctant to enter patients into a comparator arm. There was nothing out there which was considered any better than placebo. Surely, they reasoned, patients had nothing to lose, and most likely potentially a lot more to gain, by all of them going into the clofarabine arm.

And you could readily see it from the patient point of view too. Why would you want to take a chance on receiving a treatment which was quite possibly no better than nothing at all. Not when you could receive something which seemed to work, although no one was sure just how well and at what cost in terms of toxicity.

Clofarabine might have been a bit of a lucky dip but at least you'd be more likely to come away with something. It was better than not being taken to the fair at all, which was pretty much the situation if you were in a trial and randomised to low dose cytarabine.

It was a graphic demonstration of how few treatment options were available to these desperate patients. Everyone wanted a shot at the new experimental drug. However bad it might turn out to be, it couldn't be worse than any of the alternatives.

Many patients who take part in cancer clinical trials are surprisingly altruistic in their motivation. But few would be inclined to stretch this to the point of taking an ineffective comparator medication, simply to satisfy the regulatory fixation of a group of faceless federal employees up in Maryland. But FDA clearly didn't see it that way. In their minds a randomised trial was the only sensible thing to do. The fact that no one was going to take part just didn't come into it.

So Genzyme found itself stuck in the middle, between the desire of FDA for randomised data at any cost and the refusal of clinicians to do any such thing. The dilemma was summarised by Dr Gregory Curt, who was an oncology expert from Astra Zeneca and the pharmaceutical industry representative on the committee.

"I'd like to say that the sponsor's in something of a bind here, because they really did plan to do a randomised trial. And when they brought it through to experts in the leukaemia field, they were told that the trial could not deliver. So, there appears to be a disconnect potentially between regulatory and expert opinion."

Dr Curt had here touched on one of the fundamental issues of contention in oncology drug development. Namely that FDA and other bodies frequently seemed to insist on regulatory requirements which were simply inconsistent with current clinical practice. Too often they appeared to be out of date, out of touch and unable to keep up with the ever increasing pace of medical advances.

And even worse, they didn't seem to care. It wasn't their problem. Along with ODAC they were judge, jury and jailor. Their job was to lay down the law and it was up to others to try to find ways of implementing it. As we were to find out at Antisoma almost exactly a year later, when dealing with FDA ourselves.

Despite the impossibility of what they were insisting on, Dr Pazdur was still ready to fight his corner, as far as clofarabine was concerned.

"This is not the first time from sponsors that we've heard they cannot do a randomised study, because investigators don't agree to a particular comparator arm. This is a common, common, common comment that is presented to us."

If it was such a common problem, maybe it should have been telling him something but clearly the message wasn't getting through. However many times he'd heard it before, he clearly didn't care about the difficulties FDA's intransigence created. His line in the sand was clear.

"The importance here is the process of randomisation, okay. And that's what we're really interested in."

FDA wanted randomised data, come what may. They were manning a randomised redoubt and they weren't about to have it breached. It was as though they'd rather see a good drug go down, than surrender any ground on this point of principle. To many observers it was impossible to understand

FDA's insistence on data comparing a drug clearly as active as clofarabine to something, in fact *anything* else, almost for the sake of it. Particularly as Genzyme had already tried this and hit a brick wall of resistance from clinicians and patients alike.

It was a typical example of regulatory extremism, whereby the means had become more important than the end. Randomisation was seemingly of greater significance than the results themselves.

We were certainly scratching our heads, as we watched from London, whilst the proceedings lumbered on. It was as though we'd inadvertently tuned into Crazy TV. But FDA lived in their own introspective world and played by their own idiosyncratic rules. And unfortunately most of the time the rest of us had no choice but to fall in line with them.

XIII

To be fair to FDA and ODAC however, the results from the CLASSIC II trial were more complicated than the issue of randomisation alone. Although that was generating more than enough controversy by itself.

The trial was originally intended to recruit patients who were *unsuitable* for standard intensive chemotherapy, for the initial treatment of their leukaemia. That was the whole point of the study. However in practice, about a *third* of the patients went on to receive precisely this treatment, sometime *after* having been treated with clofarabine.

This resulted in another debate raging in and out of all the other strands of the ODAC meeting. Some members argued this was because a proportion of the patients, originally selected at the beginning of the trial, were in fact in much *better* shape than they were supposed to be. With the inference that they should never have been entered into the trial in the first place. This, they claimed, was shown by the fact that these patients were subsequently judged to be able to withstand aggressive treatment.

Others held the view that the patients were genuinely in a poor condition and could never have tolerated intensive treatment at the outset. They were able to do so later on only because clofarabine had markedly improved their condition, to the point where they could now cope with more aggressive interventions.

Sometimes clinical results were a perfect example of Newtonian Laws. For every opinion, there was an equal and opposite reaction. Obviously the former interpretation weakened the whole point of the trial, whilst the latter analysis added strength to the argument that clofarabine was really helping these patients out. The problem was that no one could work out which was the correct explanation.

This extra level of complexity about the trial results didn't help the already contentious differences of opinion over the need for randomisation.

114

And maybe this helped at least partly explain why, when the vote eventually came, ODAC surprisingly and unexpectedly came out nine-three in favour of the need for a randomised trial with clofarabine, prior to approval. Despite everything presented to them, they had actually voted *against* the drug.

The three votes opposing a further trial came from Dr Roboz, Professor Balducci and also Professor John Barrett, who was Head of Bone Marrow Transplantation at the National Institutes of Health in Bethesda.

Although the majority had voted in favour of the need for another trial, many had struggled with this decision, mainly because they recognised that clofarabine did actually work.

"I had a difficult time with this *(the vote)*," said Michael Link, who was a paediatric oncologist from Stanford University School of Medicine in Palo Alto, California. "There's no question to me, in my mind, that this drug is active."

Margaret Tempero, Deputy Director of the UCSF Cancer Centre in San Francisco was also in two minds. "I also had a difficult time with this vote. This is clearly an active agent."

Gary Lyman, from Duke University Medical Centre in North Carolina, who had argued fairly consistently against clofarabine throughout the meeting, was also a little less certain when it came to voting. "I voted "yes" *(in favour of another trial)* although I likewise had a very difficult time with this given the clear activity of the drug."

Virginia Mason was Executive Director of the Inflammatory Breast Cancer Research Foundation and the consumer representative on ODAC. "I voted "yes" and it's hard since I'm a cancer survivor *(and)* I'm sure not everyone would agree with my choice."

Dr Thomas Flateau was the patient representative, having himself had AML and undergone intensive chemotherapy and a bone marrow transplantation. "I also voted "yes" and I'm still having difficulty with that vote. Clearly, as others have said, it has activity."

Seemingly, only the overly self-assured biostatistician Professor Tom Fleming was in no doubt. "I voted "yes" and I think I can be brief with my reasoning," he boldly stated. Before then going on to expound, at great length, his immutable views on clinical trials methodology and the need for a randomised trial with clofarabine.

And so the future was looking decidedly bleak. Clofarabine at ODAC suddenly looked as out of place as an Eskimo at the Equator.

XIV

Of course, the final decision still rested with FDA. But everyone in the room at the Hilton knew they would follow the ODAC recommendation and deny approval. As they eventually did, a month later.

And that was despite the fact that most of the ODAC panel seemed to agree clofarabine worked, one way or another. And in a frail and elderly patient group, who didn't have other treatment options. These were people whose prognosis was extremely grave, with a life expectancy measured in months at best.

AML was a dreadful affliction. Richard Pazdur himself had described it as "a devastating form of cancer."[34] And he should know. Over the years, he'd seen more malignancy than most. There hadn't been a new drug approved for use in the disease for almost a decade. Now both patients and physicians were crying out for additional treatment approaches. Maybe that was why the three ODAC members who actually voted for the approval of clofarabine were the only ones with direct clinical experience of treating the older AML patient group.

Given the depressingly fatal nature of AML and the dearth of effective treatment options, it seems unduly capricious for clofarabine to have been rejected so decisively. And mainly because of a lack of more rigorous randomised data. The rejection seemed even more unreasonable as two other drugs, pralatrexate and romidepsin, were approved in the same meeting, by the same Committee, for broadly similar haematological malignancies. Certainly for conditions which weren't any more serious or fatal than AML in the elderly. And each on these was on the basis of only single arm *non-randomised* data.

There was simply no consistency of approach to the interpretation of data for the different drugs. Which made it exceptionally difficult for those actually trying to develop them. They just didn't know where they stood and what would ultimately be expected of them by a regulatory system which seemed to be constantly changing its mind.

Overall, Genzyme's foray into adult AML didn't seem to have much to show for all the time and money thrown at it. Unlike Vion, they were easily big enough to absorb a setback like this but it was still a blow. Clofarabine hadn't made its case persuasively enough in CLASSIC II, in the elderly, just because the study hadn't been randomised. In CLASSIC I, in relapsed and refractory patients, it had fallen short of meeting the primary endpoint of a survival advantage. Which was an automatic disqualification.

And yet clofarabine had been rejected not because it *didn't* have efficacy but simply because no one could agree exactly how to define and measure it. In reality, it wasn't so much the drug that had failed but rather the regulatory review it had been put through. And this seemed to have resulted largely from a collision between clinical complexity and regulatory rigidity. This is a conflict which increasingly characterises and impedes the clinical drug development process. It is the leitmotif to the lives of those who play the biotechnology game.

Clofarabine's demise was in the end due to disagreements with FDA-ODAC about endpoints (survival) and trial design (randomisation). Whilst many saw this as an injustice to the drug, it didn't ultimately result in that much controversy, outside of the oncology community. AML is a relatively rare disease and the elderly with cancer aren't that newsworthy. They tend not to speak with a very loud voice and mostly go unheard.

But young women suffering from breast cancer are a different proposition altogether. That's much more emotive and much more evocative. A year later, in 2010, the exact same disagreements over trial design and survival endpoints arose again, when FDA and ODAC came to review the use of Genentech's blockbuster Avastin antibody, in patients with advanced breast cancer.

But this time, the issue of whether to approve the drug would go on to provoke a nationwide furore, involving everyone from cancer clinicians in prestigious institutions, to cyber-columnists on popular internet sites. It would starkly demonstrate how little agreement there was on assessing the clinical usefulness of new cancer drugs. And just what an important issue this had now become.

Most disturbingly, it would reveal how the future availability of new cancer medicines appeared to be at the mercy of a regulatory process which often seemed to have more in common with the irrational idiosyncrasies of a mediaeval monastery than the serious discipline of scientific discovery.

The Avastin controversy crystallised many of the difficulties and dangers cancer medicines are facing and has implications for everyone involved with novel agents. It would go on to threaten the credibility of FDA and the potential viability of future cancer drug development. In the case of clofarabine, the cancer juggernaut had suffered an engine failure. With Avastin, it was involved in a fatal head on motorway collision. The wreckage is covered in detail in Chapter Eight.

XV

Avastin aside, those leukaemia ODAC debates, at that September meeting, showed how cultural, clinical and social issues inevitably come to each play a part, in the assessment of new cancer drugs. All the inconsistency in interpretation of clinical trial data simply attests to the fact that, ultimately, the determination of whether a cancer drug *works* or not is as much subjective art as objective science.

That, after all, is how treatment decisions are made at the individual patient-physician level. A doctor has an objective framework of his medical knowledge of the disease and the treatment choices available. But he also makes a subjective determination of what is best for an individual patient. This is based on, amongst other things, his impression of how well they might be able to withstand treatment, what their own views and desires are and also the physician's perception of the outcome of different treatment approaches in his own hands.

Whilst that works at the level of an *individual* patient, the problem with clinical trials is the *collective* nature of the results they generate. Here you are dealing with *averaged up* data. This might overlook extremes of, at one end, patients who are doing very well and deriving exceptional benefit and at the other end, those who are faring particularly badly and being harmed. But these groups risk being missed, because you are only looking at what happens in the middle.

Clinical trials tend to dampen down and mask out the range of individual patients responses to a drug. And this is where the regulatory process potentially falls apart. It is difficult to make these risk-benefit assessments, at the regulatory level of protecting *public* health, without compromising the *private* individual physician–patient ability to make the exact same determination.

To resolve this, it would make more sense for drugs, such as clofarabine, to be approved on the basis of some measure which showed on *a balance of probability* that they possessed some useful activity. This would be much more appropriate than the current requirement of having to prove this *beyond all reasonable doubt.*

We should be applying a test of civil, rather than criminal, proof to our new cancer drugs. This would act as a safety net but still allow us, on a case by case basis, to accommodate anomalies, such as whether trials were randomised or not. And to accept drugs which fall short on important endpoints, provided the overall picture of efficacy is a consistent one. After that, it would be down to the doctor and the patient to do the difficult balancing act of deciding whether the potential benefits outweighed the undoubted risks.

These are after all drugs which are only ever used by highly trained physicians, who really know what they are doing. They aren't exactly the kind of thing you can get over the counter at the supermarket pharmacy. There's hardly a risk to the general public, through making these agents less regulated and more widely available. And so for cancer drugs, there should be a devolution of responsibility away from regulators and down to the practicing oncologist in the clinic.

But that would require FDA, and other regulatory bodies to let go of a power they clutch so tightly, they probably couldn't release their grip even if they wanted to. And so, for the foreseeable future, we seem destined to remain mired in a sea of confusion, with drug assessments influenced as much by capricious chance as any sense of clinical credibility.

XVI

If there is any clarity emerging from all this confusion, it is the simple conclusion that no one *really* knows how to interpret how well or badly a cancer drug is actually working. And how much benefit it's really providing. It's just not something you can write down in black and white. The risk-benefit assessment is so subjective and shapeless that it frequently defies definition.

Developing a cancer drug is like preparing a complicated dish. You can have a recipe and make sure there are all the right ingredients, mixed in the correct way. But sometimes when you eventually bring it out from the oven and serve it up, people simply can't agree on whether it's actually cooked properly and how well it tastes.

This makes drug development an impossibly complicated and unpredictable task, meaning that sometimes you end up getting your fingers burned. Which is exactly what had happened to us with ASA404 and the ATTRACT I study. The conclusion had been reached that the drug didn't work. But we still weren't really sure what recipe the Data Monitoring Committee had been using and whether they'd followed it properly. That's what we still had to find out.

When it came to cancer drugs, all we did know for certain was that no one could really work out which to let live and which to let die. But we had to find a way to stay alive ourselves. We had to know just what shades of grey had coloured the decision around ASA404. And whether there was any room for manoeuvre.

FOUR

NOT FADE AWAY

**Where does Antisoma go next? Does it have what it takes to survive?
Life at the coal face of drug development.**

I

Like a patient when they hear the diagnosis, we needed a mental straw to cling to. There must be something we could focus on, which might mean things weren't as awful as they obviously were. Was the decision that ASA404 hadn't worked the correct one? Was there a seam of controversy we could mine? Might there be some ambivalence or ambiguity we could exploit?

Any little glimmer would do. After all, it wasn't exactly straightforward making that sort of determination. It would be easier to pick the winner of the four fifteen at Wincanton. For a race in two years' time.

These were the thoughts running through the minds of the Antisoma senior management team, as we sat ranged around the expansive Boardroom table on Friday lunchtime, the day after the DMC had dropped its bombshell.

The video link fluttered into life and we were connected to our colleagues over in the Boston office. It was eight am there, one pm in London. But we might as well have been in a time warp. Everyone seemed to be acting and thinking in slow motion, so disorientated were we still by the events of the night before.

"Right," said Ursula. "We need to act swiftly and decisively." Eric has been doing some back of an envelope calculations."

Eric had clearly spent most of the morning on the back of an enormous envelope of one sort or another. He did, after all, now have a very big task ahead of him. Given the enormity of what had suddenly hit us, he had somehow managed to undertake an impressively detailed initial analysis of the situation. Eric was very good in a crisis. He had a calm and unflappable air of assurance that allowed him to focus on the issue in hand with an almost Vulcan intensity.

"In the situation we're now facing, we have to assume there will be no additional revenues, prior to the amonafide Phase III data," intoned Eric, with all the animation of a funeral usher. Given the context of the meeting, it seemed the right tone of voice to be adopting.

"It's possible Mike may be able to partner the DCAM programme and we could get three or four of million for it but we can't afford to take that possibility into account at the moment."

Mike was Mike Boss, a British expatriate who'd been based in the US for years. He'd come with the Xanthus acquisition, having been their business development manager. If you were meeting him for the very first time, it would come as absolutely no surprise to learn that his main hobby was bird watching. He might even have had a cupboard at home, full of bells and sticks and other essential paraphernalia of the modern day Morris Man.

Since the merger, Mike had transformed into the General Manager of our *autoimmune disease programme*. Up to this point we had exclusively been a cancer company, which didn't have an autoimmune programme. But now we suddenly appeared to be the proud owners of one.

Symadex was one of our oncology drugs. Unfortunately, it wasn't doing very well in the clinic. In fact it wasn't doing anything at all, in any of the tumors we tried it in. But our chemists had been working away at the molecule and using it as a prototype to invent different new structural variants.

No one could quite remember why they had started doing this. But despite that, they had come up with some novel molecules which appeared to have interesting effects. They were damping down the overactive immune system, which characterises diseases such as multiple sclerosis (MS) and rheumatoid arthritis. These are conditions where the body effectively starts attacking itself, using immune cells as weapons of self-destruction. Hence the name, *autoimmune* disease. They are often very difficult conditions to treat.

We had tried out one of these molecules in a guinea pig model of multiple sclerosis. Incredibly such things do exist. You can use chemicals to create an allergic reaction in the brain of the animals, which closely resembles the disease findings in MS.

The guinea pigs had subsequently performed the equivalent of jumping out of their wheelchairs and going on to win a four hundred meters hurdle race. Whilst running backwards. We took this as an encouraging sign that there might be a promising new drug here. It was however a very long way from the clinic. Somewhere along the line, this programme had acquired both the acronym Dendritic Cell Autoimmune Modulator (DCAM)[1] and also an impressively large valuation, both of which seemed to be creations of Mike's.

Eric projected an Open University graph, showing just how much we were spending each month (a lot) and how long it would last if we didn't cut back (not very long). He didn't say anything but an air of collective recrimination hung in the room.

The obvious problem was that at our current rate, we would run out of cash in the middle of next year. Which was before we'd really know where we stood with FDA, over the potential approvability of amonafide. It would be very unlikely we could raise more money before we knew we had a viable drug. We'd have our work cut out even then. There was therefore a pressing need to reduce expenditure and tease out another six or so months of cash lifeline.

Eric explained that we would have to reduce staff numbers substantially, freeze any planned pay rises and of course, there would be no bonuses this year for any of us.

"Hold your horses...no bonus," we screamed mentally. Well, at least some of us did.

Hurriedly and less selfishly, I thought about how bad it would be to have a round of redundancies right now. We had only recently lost a number of people, including Nigel Courtenay Luck, our very popular Chief Scientific Officer. There had been a belt tightening after the banking crisis and liquidity crunch. It had been a very big blow at the time. We really didn't need another now.

"We're also going to have to consider shutting down the labs, or maybe the Boston office and perhaps moving to somewhere cheaper to rent here in London," continued Eric cheerfully, like a story teller at a children's party. At least he was trying to put a brave face on things. Eric was helping to mentally steer us towards the harsh realities he realised we were now facing.

II

Up until now, we had been planning to commercialise amonafide ourselves, at least in North America. Faced with the loss of the Novartis support infrastructure, that plan had become redundant, overnight. We had also been talking to companies about partnering amonafide in Europe, although there hadn't been a huge amount of enthusiasm from them so far.

Nick Adams was our Head of Business Development and he had been feverishly working away at this. Both a lawyer and a scientist, he was an Antisoma ten year veteran, who'd been with the company through most of its previous ups and downs. He always seemed to have a slightly bewildered look, as though the vagaries of everyday life were a constant puzzle to his exceptionally intelligent mind. You couldn't hope to meet a kinder or more considerate person though. He also knew the Pharma industry backwards and could reel off obscure deal terms from years ago, involving companies that probably didn't even exist anymore, at the drop of a hat.

The problem he faced with amonafide was that the commercial potential in Europe by itself was too small to interest many companies. Ideally, we needed to find someone already in haematological malignancies, who could easily assimilate amonafide into an existing portfolio. But there weren't very many of those around. Also, the ones we were talking to seemed to be markedly risk averse. It was unlikely we'd be able to pull off a deal, until we had the headline results from the Phase III study.

The dismal history of drug failures in AML was such that most people would want to see something a little stronger than the current non-randomised Phase II data. Everyone was familiar with that ODAC meeting in September the year before, when clofarabine and laromustine had been torn apart.

Also, people in other companies could work out for themselves that, as time went on and our cash dwindled away, we might become more desperate to sell amonafide on less favourable terms. And so we were unlikely to be thrown a lifeline in the shape of a deal, when we needed one most. Which was any time right now. However, on the positive side, we would now be offering worldwide commercial rights. There was no way we could hold on to North America for ourselves. Maybe the bigger opportunity this represented might spark a bit more interest. We could but hope.

There was always the possibility of abandoning amonafide altogether at this point. Someone actually suggested it. Fiona McLaughlin was head of our non-clinical research. She was a very experienced pharmacologist, normally based up at our laboratories at St George's Hospital in South London. She had only been with Antisoma a couple of years, having joined to take over the running of our day to day scientific activities. Fiona had a powerfully analytical brain which always helped focus any debate. This was certainly an idea which captured everyone's attention. It wasn't as crazy as it might first have sounded.

Amonafide was a risky project, in a very difficult disease and one which we had always justified by virtue of it being counterbalanced by the seemingly less risky ASA404. The Phase III study was about three quarters of the way through. But we could still save an awful lot of money if we stopped it now. It would also allow us to avoid any of the costly regulatory and other work we would need to do at the end of the clinical programme.

Taking everything into consideration, we could probably save about ten million pounds. Once that would have been an almost insignificant sum for us but now it could keep us alive for almost another half a year. It was a reminder of just how much our circumstances had changed overnight.

If we stopped amonafide, perhaps we could spread the savings over a wider range of earlier stage bets. So that we weren't backing just the one horse as it were. And a very temperamental horse at that. The only problem was that we didn't have anything else in our own cupboards to place a bet on. There weren't exactly a lot of promising projects squirreled away. Instead, we would need to go out and find a few interesting new propositions elsewhere. This would both take a long time and be fraught with uncertainty. Ten million pounds didn't buy you very much at the oncology boot sale.

It would also be a very bold move for a company which had just suffered the failure of one Phase III programme, to then go and jettison another. Especially considering just how much time and effort had gone into getting it that far. Shareholders were unlikely to be receptive to something like this. They would probably ask the not unreasonable question of just why we had spent so much of their money on it in the first place.

However, in the sepulchral gloom of that Friday afternoon, it was as though all the normal rules had been dispensed with and everything was up for consideration.

"What about Inflazyme," I suggested.

"Who or what is *Inflazyme*?" asked Sharon.

Sharon Grimster was in charge of manufacturing, project management, regulatory, quality, all sorts of things. Her department was like a brica brac shop, full of all the odds and ends which didn't quite fit anywhere else. She and Ursula went back a long way, having worked together for years at Celltech, Britain's first ever biotechnology company. She was very structured and organised and was perhaps most comfortable with process and procedure, rather than the impromptu and impetuous. Which meant we probably shouldn't have got along. But in fact we did.

Sharon could find a way of working with almost anyone. She was a natural mediator and often helped find the compromise solution that appeared to be eluding the rest of us, whenever a particularly controversial subject was on the table. She could probably have sorted out most of the more intractable problems the Middle East was saddled with, if only she'd had the time to get round to it.

"Inflazyme was a Canadian biotech company, based in Vancouver," I went on.

"They hit a brick wall at the beginning of 2007, when an asthma drug they had their hopes pinned on fell apart. Pretty much everyone left and by the middle of the year they were flogging off research equipment to get cash. But then they sold the remaining assets to a Swedish company called Biolipox (*it must sound better in Swedish*). Inflazyme took the cash, bought a saw mill and turned themselves into a lumber company, betting on a recovery in the American house building market."

Which had indeed been a bold and brave mood. Although they were still waiting for the recovery.

"That would be an interesting one to communicate to the markets," added Daniel Elger, with the eager enthusiasm that characterised everything he said. Daniel, who appeared to be the product of a Home Counties middle class upbringing and who'd been to Oxford, had the incongruous habit of prefacing statements with the phrase "*eh by gum,*" pronounced in a quite credible Yorkshire accent. He was Head of Communications and another Antisoma long-timer, with a similar period under his belt to Nick.

"So maybe we could stop everything, take the cash and go into something that has nothing to do with drug development," someone else continued. "What about computer gaming, copper mining something like that?"

Little did we know at the time how prescient this would actually turn out to be, less than a year later.

"You could buy a lot of lottery tickets for ten million quid," offered Chris Smyth drily, over the video link.

Chris was Head of Clinical Operations and based in Boston. He was British and had originally been in London, before being sent over to the US to set up a North American office. We had briefly established one in Princeton New Jersey, prior to acquiring Xanthus and moving everything to Boston shortly afterwards.

He was tall and thin, undertaking Ironman triathlons in his spare time. There was an air of quiet, unforgiving determination about him, which other less committed individuals could find unsettling. Chris would rather die in the attempt, than fail to deliver on a commitment he had made. He was definitely the kind of person you wanted on your side. His idea didn't seem a particularly bad one to me.

"Can we get back to ASA404," said Ursula, as ever blunt and to the point. "Gary, Lucky Lara was Chairman of the DMC. You know him quite well don't you."

It was more an accusation than a question. She continued, without waiting for a reply.

"Phone him up and find out what their view was on things. You never know – it may not have been as clear cut as it looked at first sight.

Now, is there any more we need to do at the moment? Our own statistics people are going over the data, just to make sure that nothing really obvious has been missed. Wouldn't put it past someone to have got the groups mixed up."

At this, she burst out laughing, as she was prone to do at the slightest opportunity.

We spent the next hour or so knocking around increasingly improbable explanations for why ATTRACT I had failed. Other than that ASA404 just didn't work. We didn't like that one. But no one could come up with anything convincing.

It was time to check out Lucky.

III

"We're in deep trouble now Lucky," I said to the Chairman of the ATTRACT I DMC. I had managed to get him on the phone a few days later, as I was driving along somewhere or another.

125

He was in his office at the UC Davis Medical Centre, located on the imaginatively named X Street in Sacramento, Northern California. Compared to other parts of the Sunshine State, it's a dreadfully desiccated city with no soul. It was no surprise they couldn't even manage to name their streets after anything more interesting than the letters of the alphabet. But Lucky seemed happy enough there. Maybe being Professor of Medical Oncology was sufficient compensation.

Lucky's voice pulsated with intensity over the Bluetooth speaker, as though he were sitting in the passenger seat, gripping me by the arm.

"I know Gary. And on top that, it's been a terrible twelve months for cancer Phase III failures generally hasn't it? We've just had figitumumab and vandetanib fail in lung cancer and then there's been Avastin in prostate and stomach cancer, Sutent in breast cancer, in two separate trials, as well as in colon cancer and now 404 too. It's awful really."

No, no, I thought. I know all this already. Tell me something *lucky*, Lucky.

"How did the DMC see 404 Lucky. Was it as clear cut a decision as it seemed to be, looking at it from outside? It can't have been that straightforward, surely."

"Yeah, pretty much so. It was quite open and closed," he energised over the airwaves, unwittingly dashing our lingering hopes. It didn't sound from Lucky's tone of voice that they'd spent hours disagreeing over whether they had the right endpoints to determine if ASA404 was working. The controversies swirling around the rest of the oncology community had clearly passed them by.

"There just wasn't a difference between the groups for any of the outcome parameters. Nothing for response rate, or progression or survival. But what really swung it for us was the lack of any significant extra side effects in the ASA404 group. It's as though it just wasn't doing anything at all, good or bad," he continued.

"Otherwise, we might have said...well...OK...the survival data is a bit immature at the moment...and the side effects show it has activity of some sort at least...and so maybe it wouldn't have been so clear cut.

But 404 wasn't doing anything though. You didn't forget to add the drug to the injection kits did you?" he joked.

At least I hoped it was a joke. The thought of a fuck up on that scale was too awful to contemplate. Especially as it wasn't beyond the bounds of possibility.

It was time to move on swiftly.

"So Lucky...the control group...you know...the patients who got just the carboplatin and paclitaxel...they seemed to do a lot better in the ATTRACT study than they did in the Phase II trial. In ATTRACT, they were surviving about fourteen months on average, the same as the ASA404 group in fact. Whereas in the earlier study, it was only about nine months. Did you have any ideas about that?"

"Staging creep," he shot back, fast as a bullet. At least I think he meant "staging- creep" rather than "staging...*creep.*"

"Staging-creep and greater use of second and even third line agents," he expanded.

Staging was a technical term which described the extent to which a tumor had spread from its initial site of origin. It was important in working out the likely prognosis and best treatment approach.[2]

There were five main tumor stages for lung cancer.

Stage 0 also known as *carcinoma in situ*, was the earliest stage at which lung cancer could usually be detected. The tumor would be present in only a few layers of cells and wouldn't yet have grown beyond the inner lining of the lungs. At this stage, the tumor would be considered non-invasive.

Stage I was where the tumor had not spread at all and so was still localised to its site of origin within the lung. This stage was further broken down according to whether the tumor was bigger or smaller than three cm.

Stage II occurred when the tumor had encroached onto nearby structures, either adjacent lymph nodes (glands) or other tissues. These could include the chest wall or the linings of the lung or heart. Again this was subdivided according to the size of the primary tumor.

Stage III disease was said to be present when the cancer had spread further afield. It was now invading other parts of the chest, which were at some distance from the original site of the tumor. This stage was further broken down into IIIA or IIIB, depending on the exact pattern of how the tumor had spread within the chest.

Stage IV, which was the most advanced, was when the tumor had travelled outside the chest to other areas of the body, such as the liver or the brain or the skeleton.

Obviously the more advanced the stage of the tumor, the less likely it was to respond well to treatment. Stage I disease, caught early on, could often be surgically removed, with the patient subsequently remaining disease free and effectively cured. On the other hand, Stage IV disease was always incurable and an inevitable death sentence.

Tumors were staged usually using imaging techniques such as CT (*computed tomography*) scanning or MRI (*magnetic resonance imaging*). Both construct computer generated images of the inside of the body, from which tumors could be detected by their characteristic appearance. MRI and CT are very good at detecting most tumors and represent a huge advance over anything that was available previously.

However, they do have limitations. They can miss very early stage metastatic malignancy. CT and MRI also sometimes struggle to distinguish between active tumor remaining after treatment and what may now just be dead tissue. Additionally, it's sometimes difficult to distinguish between malignant disease and more benign abnormalities that could be occurring at the same time. Fibrocystic changes in the breast for example, can look very similar to a breast tumor, when the scan images are examined.

And so other techniques are being adopted, to try to sort out this kind of problem. One of these advances is called PET (*positron emission tomography*) scanning. This involves injecting a small dose of a sugar type substance into the patient. The sugar molecule has a small radioactive "label" attached, which allows it to be detected with a special camera held over the body.

Because cancer cells are normally a lot more metabolically active than normal cells and so use up a lot more energy, the radiolabelled sugar tends to accumulates selectively in cancer tissue. This results in a strong localised radio signal, helping to distinguish the active cancer tissue from more quiescent normal structures. By combining this *functional* image from PET with the *anatomical* image from MRI scanning, it is possible to generate a much more accurate picture of any cancer that may be present.

And this is what Lucky was referring to when he talked about staging-creep.[3] Both the original ASA404 Phase II trial and the ATTRACT I Phase III study had been limited to patients with Stage IIIB and Stage IV disease. This is collectively referred to as *advanced* lung cancer. These are usually the sorts of patients you seek out for a new experimental drug. The ones with nothing to lose.

However, recruitment of patients into the earlier Phase II study had taken place three of four years before recruitment into the subsequent Phase III trial. There hadn't been much PET scanning around then and so few patients had undergone it.

But in those intervening few years, technology had moved on apace, with PET scanning becoming much more widespread. This resulted in a significant number of the ATTRACT I patients having been staged using the more advanced technique.

There were therefore a number of patients with PET scans showing them to have sufficiently advanced disease to be classified as Stage IIIB or IV. However, some of this cancer spread would have been missed with less sensitive CT or MRI scanning alone. In which case the patients would have been classified as Stage II disease. Which would have meant they were excluded from the study.

So effectively, over the time between the two ASA404 lung cancer studies, the stage of some patients' disease classification was *creeping* from Stage II to a more advanced Stage III or IV. Simply due to the use of better imaging techniques.

This was leading to patients being recruited into the later ATTRACT I study with *earlier* stage disease and less obvious tumor spread, than had been the case with patients in the previous Phase II trial. They were simply being "reclassified" as later stage, due to the more sensitive imaging being used.

However, and this was the important bit as far as Lucky was concerned, because these later patients effectively had less marked disease, they were likely to be more responsive to chemotherapy. And maybe, in part, that was why the patients in the ATTRACT I study were doing better with conventional treatment, than had been the case in the Phase II trial.

If Lucky was correct, it would mean there were basically different types of patients in the two studies. The difference may have been quite subtle but it could still be enough to account for the variation we were seeing between the two trials. Small changes could sometimes have much bigger consequences.

Plausible though this sounded, it still didn't explain why there appeared to be no *extra* contribution from ASA404, when added on to chemotherapy in the ATTRACT I study. That was still a mystery. The creeping should have affected both arms, giving each an equal boost. But it did illustrate the moving target cancer medicine could sometimes be.

Changes in clinical practice and medical technology could complicate the interpretation of clinical trials, undertaken at different times, with the same drug or drug combinations. An entire clinical trial programme might well take six or seven years. Medical advances could often occur more rapidly than that. There was therefore a real potential for these kinds of methodological complications to pop up and throw a spanner in the works now and then.

The other big problem Lucky had referred to was the greater use of second and third line treatments in the ATTRACT I study. Normally in a cancer trial patients continue treatment, with whatever it is they have been assigned to, until their disease has clearly started to progress and get worse. This is a sign that they are no longer deriving any benefit and so it is pointless carrying on with that particular approach.

When this happens, they may be able to undergo subsequent chemotherapy with a different sort of cancer drug or drug combination. This may buy them a little more time, by getting their disease back under control for a bit longer. When that failed, maybe there would be a third or even a fourth possibility to try out.

Just what happens to an individual patient after failure of initial (first line) treatment is a complicated decision. It's influenced by many things, not least whether there are actually any alternatives available. And increasingly importantly, whether there is funding to pay for them. Other factors which come into play include how well the patient is likely to tolerate further treatment, given the battering their body would inevitably have received from the first round of chemotherapy. You have to be confident their quality of life is likely to be improved by treatment resulting in only a modest prolongation of disease control at best. And almost certainly at the cost of substantial toxicity.

In some diseases, adult AML being one very good example, once patients have failed on initial chemotherapy, there is very little agreement about whether subsequent treatment is likely to provide any additional benefit. It may even end up doing more harm than good. In many instances these patients may not receive any further active drug therapy. Particularly if they are elderly, which most are.

Conversely, younger patients with advanced breast cancer might receive anything up to eight or nine different sequential chemotherapy approaches during the course of their disease. This is particularly so in countries such as the US, where that level of health care funding would normally be available.

Lung cancer was somewhere in between these two extremes. For non-small cell lung cancer (NSCLC),[4] the type ASA404 was aimed at, everyone seemed to agree that a combination of at least two, increasingly three and sometimes even four different drugs was the best approach to the initial, first line, treatment of the disease.

There was however little agreement about which exactly were the best drugs to combine. US clinicians preferred cisplatin and paclitaxel, usually combined with Avastin. Most Europeans opted for two completely different drugs, gemcitabine and vinorelbine, again combined with Avastin. There were quite a few other possible permutations as well. Exactly which patient received what, was more down to local custom and physician preference than anything else. There was no real rhyme or reason here.

There was no clinical evidence that any one of these combinations was any better than any other. And yet physicians remained immutably wedded to their particular favourite. Trying to get them to change to something else was like trying to persuade a child to hand over its sweets.

For second line treatment, the choices were more limited and mainly single agents were used. Combinations seemed to produce greater toxicity but no extra efficacy. For a long time, the commonest two drugs had been docetaxel and another one called erlotinib (Tarceva). More recently a third drug, pemetrexed had also become widely available.

In general about forty per cent of patients went on to receive one of these second line therapies. The benefits however were usually modest, with the drugs only slowing the disease down for a month or so at best. Very few received any subsequent third line treatment. They tended not to live long enough. Or they just couldn't face it any more. You couldn't really blame them.

The ASA404 Phase II study had been conducted in Europe, Australia and New Zealand where the use of second line treatments hadn't been that extensive. This was partly because in these countries, the cost of the drugs was often considered too high, relative to the modest benefits. Tarceva for example prolonged progression free survival by just two weeks and overall survival by only two months, when compared to placebo. And yet it cost about two and a half thousand dollars per month. That's paying out a lot for very little in return.

The ATTRACT I trial on the other hand, had been a worldwide study conducted in many countries, including the United States, where cost considerations weren't such big constraints. Additionally, by this time pemetrexed had become established as a much more widely used drug than had been the case for the earlier Phase II trial. Whilst still producing only modest benefits, in certain types of NSCLC it increased survival by an extra five or six weeks, compared to erlotinib or docetaxel. It wasn't a great improvement but in cancer terms it wasn't bad either. If it were you, you'd want that extra month or so.

This additional firepower in the second line armamentarium helped increase the number of patients who went on to receive something further after their initial therapy failed. If this resulted in a small but nevertheless significant extension of their survival, it could partly explain the longer life expectancy we were now seeing in the ATTRACT I study.

However, the number of patients with second line or subsequent therapy seemed to be very similar between the group that received ASA404 and the group that didn't. There was therefore still the problem, as there had been with staging-creep, of explaining why ASA404 wasn't doing something a bit extra, on top of all the chemotherapy.

Lucky seemed to have a clear explanation for that.

"Well, maybe ASA404 just doesn't work. That would explain everything wouldn't it," he added helpfully.

I involuntarily looked nervously over my shoulder, as though there might be someone sitting in the back, who could have overheard this blasphemy.

From listening to him, it seemed as though the deliberations over ASA404 had been very simple for the DMC. Their decision had all the conviction of a catholic priest in a confessional. There was nothing like an ODAC level of controversy, by the sound of it.

It wasn't exactly the conversation I'd anticipated having with him. From what Lucky was saying, it didn't sound as though there was much need for a coroner's inquest into the death of ASA404.

IV

What we'd been hoping Lucky would say, was that they'd been at each other's throats, so divided by disagreement were they. And that he'd never been comfortable with the decision they'd eventually reached to stop the trial. In fact, he'd been hoping we'd call, just so that he could get it off his chest. To exonerate his guilt as it were. But that didn't sound the kind of conversation we were going to be having any time soon.

We'd have settled for him telling us that maybe there was something about the conduct of the trial, which made it hard to interpret the results. Perhaps there were a whole group of hospitals from Kazakhstan, or some other far flung region, where for some reason hundreds of patients in the ASA404 group had been deprived of any second line treatment. Whilst all the patients in the other group had been pumped full of extra drugs.

Unexpected imbalances like that happened from time to time in clinical trials. Physicians sometimes reasoned that patients who'd received an additional experimental drug had been given a lucky break, compared to those who hadn't. And so if subsequent therapy was in short supply, the latter group would get first choice with it.

It wasn't uncommon to have one region in a large trial behaving differently from all the others and sticking out like a sore thumb as a consequence. If something of that sort had occurred, it could play a part in skewing the survival results *against* the ASA404 arm. It wouldn't have been a fair comparison between the two groups, if one were being treated differently from the other.

But there appeared to be nothing underhand in the Urals to help us out. According to Lucky the trial was tip top, through and through. It had after all been double blinded and so none of the doctors could have known who'd received which treatments anyway.

Even if there had been some glaring problem, making the results unfairly biased against ASA404, there wasn't a huge amount we could do about it now. The findings of the trial would remain as they were. At best, we'd have been able to argue that maybe the study was flawed rather than the drug. If we wanted to do anything about it though, we would almost certainly have to repeat the trial all over again. But nobody was going to give us the money for that.

The world was full of failed Phase III trials, with apologists peddling explanations for why it would all be different the next time around. These protestations were usually as credible as an addict promising that this time they really were going to stay clean. So ASA404 was probably even more dead than Elvis, as least as far as ATTRACT I was concerned.[5]

"But Gary, what about ATTRACT II. When will that be available?" Lucky enthused.

ATTRACT II. *Of course.* Perhaps there was a life after death. After all, many were convinced it was only a matter of time before the King made a comeback from his rhinestone repose.

ATTRACT II was another ASA404 study which Novartis were *still* running. This was roughly the same size as ATTRACT I, consisting of about one thousand patients altogether. It was comparing ASA404 combined with docetaxel, to docetaxel alone. These were being used as *second line* treatment of lung cancer.

Novartis had been so certain ASA404 was a winner that they'd set up these two enormous studies to run concurrently. They wanted two throws of the dice. They were convinced they would more than double their money.

ATTRACT II. *That's* more like it Lucky.

After all, there were examples of cancer drugs which had failed as first line therapies and yet went on to work, when used as second line treatments. But they were few and far between. Erlotinib was one in fact. It hadn't shown any extra benefit, when *combined* with other drugs, as initial treatment of NSCLC. But it was a useful second line therapy when used by *itself.*

At first sight, it doesn't necessarily make sense that a drug which is ineffective when a malignancy is at an earlier stage, would actually work when the disease has progressed even further. But sometimes the biology of a cancer appears to change as it becomes more advanced, rendering it responsive at a later stage to drugs which couldn't touch it earlier on. That was cancer for you though. Forever capricious and unpredictable.

All the second line drugs which worked in lung cancer did so as single agents. They were most effective as *mono-therapy.* Our problem was that ASA404 didn't work very well by itself. We knew that from animal studies. It needed to be given in combination with something else to exert its full potential. It was being used with *paclitaxel* in ATTRACT I and *docetaxel* in ATTRACT II.

These were very similar drugs, both being members of a general class of cancer compounds called *taxanes.*[6] These all act in the same way, by poisoning the scaffolding which keeps the nucleus of a cell intact. This in turn causes the cell to collapse and die.

Our worry was that paclitaxel and docetaxel were just too similar to expect much difference between them. If ASA404 hadn't worked with one, we weren't sure how likely it was to do so with the other, despite the fact that they were being used at different stages of the disease.

When Novartis had originally put together the ATTRACT I and II trials, they had stayed with the general ASA404-taxane combination, which had been so outstandingly successful in earlier studies. With that formula having now failed in ATTRACT I, it could well become a liability for ATTRACT II as well. Only time would tell.

ATTRACT II had a different DMC from ATTRACT I and there was a different chairman. This one was a statistician from Washington DC. And an academic statistician to boot, with an interest in the *architecture of multisite clinical trials.* Whatever that meant.

Dealings with statisticians were often unpredictable. Many were all too often dangerous enthusiasts, especially the ones with an academic background. These were people who tended to see clinical trial methodology as an *end* in itself. Rather than what it should be, which was simply an expeditious *means* to determine whether or not a drug appeared to be doing something useful.

This usually meant that they lacked the insight, which clinicians such as Lucky tended to possess, into the pragmatic compromises required of real life clinical trials. Having said that, it was difficult to imagine anyone coming up with a worse decision than Lucky had over ATTRACT I, at least as far as we were concerned.

"They have an interim look scheduled for that study but it's not until towards the end of this year Lucky."

"Well, it's slim but there is a chance that ATTRACT II might survive the interim look and go all the way to the end."

It was a long shot at best. But not completely impossible. In drug development anything can happen. We'd all learned that over the years. People still spot Elvis after all.

I said goodbye to Lucky and left him to go and shine some sunlight into the gloomiest corners of the dark world his patients inhabited.

V

Despite Lucky's optimism, we had to assume ASA404 was dead and gone. We couldn't afford the luxury of pinning any remaining slim hopes on ATTRACT II. Besides, we didn't have the time to give it any thought. Although ATTRACT I had come off the rails, there was still a huge amount needing to be sorted out, to bring it to a halt.

Managing a large Phase III oncology programme was like being in control of an oil tanker. Even after you had shut down the engines, it would take a long time to come to a stop. And you still had to make sure you didn't hit anything, whilst that was happening.

So we had to meet with our counterparts at Novartis, to work out what to do next. It wasn't exactly going to be a fun meeting but in many ways it made a welcome break from the funereal atmosphere prevailing in London. It had been bleak and black there ever since the enforced redundancy programme had started to take effect.

That was bad enough. It had however been made incalculably worse by the sudden and dramatic departure of Ursula.

In the immediate aftermath of the interim look fall out, the Board had decided we could no longer justify the cost (and a considerable salary expense it was) of both a CEO and a COO. Given our newly straightened circumstances, that was probably an unavoidable outcome. The Board had to be seen to be doing *something*.

So Ursula was going to be the one to go. She had drawn the short straw. Or rather *we* had.

When the news of Ursula's departure was released, the next day's London broadsheets all crowed, in their business sections, that this was just the beginning and there would be more casualties to follow, as we desperately tried to cut costs and conserve cash. You could almost feel the journalists rubbing their hands with glee.

Barry Price, the Chairman of the Board, issued a statement.[7]

"Ursula has made an enormous contribution to Antisoma and its board. I would like to thank her for all she has done to build a world class development team and regret profoundly that she and other talented individuals are leaving because of the news we have received this week."

That seemed a bit disingenuous of the Board. Barry was a great bloke, with a background in pharmaceutical manufacturing for Glaxo, after which he'd put together a clutch of non-executive directorships with companies like Antisoma. He had an avuncular air about him and wouldn't have been out of place propping up the bar of any country club anywhere in the world. He was very down to earth and usually in touch with what was going on around him.

But the Board didn't seem to grasp just how fundamental Ursula's place in the organisation was. Because in reality, she had contributed more to the company than many of the rest of us combined. And they should have been tuned in enough to know that. The money would have been much better saved by jettisoning a handful of the non-executive directors instead.

She'd initially agreed to stay for three months and sort out the restructuring we now needed to undertake. That hadn't worked out though. There was still resistance in some quarters to too much change too rapidly. Recognising this, Ursula had decided to cut her losses and make good her escape. She clearly still had her wits about her.

And so we were left with a need for a huge structural revision of the company, at the same time as the loss of the only person who could really make it happen. We certainly knew how to take a bad situation and make it worse. But one way or another, we would have to soldier on without her now.

And first up, that included going to the US to arrange a funeral. Now we had a death certificate from the DMC, there was no reason to delay the ceremony any longer.

VI

On the last Tuesday in April, we found ourselves gathered around the conference table in Meeting Room 4 at Novartis's Florham Park, New Jersey complex. You reached it from New York, over the George Washington

Bridge, north west to the quaintly named town of Parsippany and then via Route 10 East to the Columbia Turnpike.

There wasn't much of any interest in Florham Park. Apart from it being the training ground of the New York Jets. But then we weren't exactly there for rest and recreation.

Meeting Room 4, on the second floor of one of the many wings of the enormous building, was long and narrow. The Novartis contingent were already gathered as we trooped in. James Kirshaw,[8] from their product strategy group, was the most senior Novartis person there. He was a serious man with a serious demeanour. He looked and sounded like an investment banker, confronted with a nasty case of sub-prime liability.

James expressed condolences over the fate of ASA404 and the subsequent battering our share price had taken. We all paused for a moment of reverential reflection. Then it was down to the serious business of dissecting a dead drug.

Tim Logan,[9] their Global Program Team Director, young and eager like a bouncy puppy dog, had first go with the scalpel. They had contacted all investigators in ATTRACT I by e-mail, letting them know of the DMC decision. There were plans to follow this up with a number of regional webcasts, to discuss issues of individual concern with clinicians.

One of the main problems was what to do with the large number of patients who were still in the trial and receiving ongoing treatment. That was quite a big loose end to tie up. Novartis were going to inform clinicians which particular treatment arm their patients had been originally randomised to. Up until now, the individual investigators were blinded to this and so didn't know whether their patients were receiving ASA404 or not.

Given that the DMC had effectively concluded ASA404 wasn't working, the logical thing might have been to stop all remaining patients receiving any further treatment with it. However it was unlikely to be that black and white in practice. There were bound to be a substantial number of *individual* patients who appeared to be benefitting from ASA404. In these cases, it would be difficult to deprive the patients of something that seemed to be helping them out. They didn't exactly have a lot else to turn to.

ATTRACT I had been looking at the *overall* results with ASA404, averaged across everyone in the trial. But that could well disguise pockets of patients who were doing better than the average. Which is to say better than nothing at all. There may well have been certain types of patients in whom ASA404 was actually working. They'd just been drowned out in the noise of everyone else in the study.

Often with new drugs, there were a proportion of patients who did well, in amongst the overall negativity of a failed trial. Normally the problem was trying to identify them and work out why they appeared to be different from everyone else. If a clinician in ATTRACT I felt they had a patient benefiting from ASA404, then it would be extremely hard not to carry on supplying it. This would need to be sorted out on a case by case basis though. Which was going to take considerable time and effort.

Additionally, there remained a whole pile of operational issues to be resolved. These included obligations such as informing local hospital ethics committees, government regulatory agencies and also the insurance companies in each country, who provided cover against being sued over possible side effects.

There would be a need to contact each hospital pharmacy. They would have to destroy remaining supplies of ASA404 in a controlled way, so that ultimately the fate of every vial of drug released at the outset of the study could be accounted for at the end.

Radiology facilities, pathology departments, laboratories, patient record units, even administrators at each hospital would need to be appraised of events.

It was like dealing with the aftermath of someone who'd lived a particularly chaotic life and then died suddenly, without leaving a will.

And of course there remained the task at every centre of gathering all the paperwork from the trial. The records of each individual patient would still need to be completed and then collected for forwarding to Novartis. They would still have to construct the huge database of the gigabytes of information generated by ATTRACT I overall. This was scheduled for July.

After that, Novartis would need to analyse all the data and then write up a detailed report of the study. There was a regulatory obligation to document negative clinical trials, as well as ones with a successful outcome. You had to put your dirty linen out for everyone to see. The intention was for that to be available sometime in the autumn.

Importantly, there was also the delicate challenge of communicating the findings from ATTRACT I to the hundreds of clinicians involved in ATTRACT II. This had to be done in a way which hopefully still maintained their enthusiasm for ASA404 and the latter study. Undoubtedly some would conclude that the failure of ATTRACT I made continued participation in ATTRACT II less attractive. It was very difficult to argue against that position, if someone chose to adopt it. Especially as it was what some of us already believed deep down.

Maintaining the momentum of ATTRACT II was going to be an issue but cancer clinicians were inveterate experimenters. They'd all learned a long time ago that you could never guess what the dice were going to show, until they stopped rolling. Maybe ATTRACT II would surprise everyone. We all knew that in cancer medicine, the only certainty was uncertainty. There was a good chance enough clinicians would stay the course, thus allowing the trial to proceed more or less according to plan.

One other big remaining issue was Novartis's intention for all the additional ASA404 activities they had been planning. The ones beyond ATTRACT I and ATTRACT II. Any drug development programme is a myriad of interrelating events. There were six or seven other clinical trials Novartis needed to undertake at some point, to support the lung cancer studies.

These consisted mainly of small studies, looking at technical issues, such as what happened to ASA404 in patients with liver damage or kidney damage (they were the organs through which ASA404 normally made its escape from the body). Or what happened when it was given at the same time as other drugs, which might potentially interfere with the way the body handled ASA404 itself. These were standard studies that most drugs went through as part of the routine work up of a new agent, during the clinical development programme.

All of these would have to be completed by the time of any regulatory submission, for either ATTRACT I or II. On top of that, there had been enthusiastic plans for a number of clinical trials with ASA404 in other malignancies. When you had what looked like a clear winner, you didn't want to hang around.

Additionally, there were proposals for a series of clinical studies to be run by organisations outside of Novartis. These mainly involved collaborative investigator groups and encompassed a range of tumors. Trials like this, generically known as *investigator initiated studies*, always presented something of a dilemma to all pharmaceutical companies.

They were studies run by clinicians individually, or gathered together in collaborative groups. They usually originated the idea for the trial themselves and ran it through their own organisations, largely at their own cost. The pharmaceutical company's main contribution was to provide the drug supply.

The advantage of this arrangement to investigator groups was that they could quickly and easily get their hands on new experimental drugs they were interested in. For companies it represented an opportunity to have their drug evaluated in a range of different tumor types, without having to incur very much cost along the way. The big disadvantage however was that once the pharmaceutical company handed over the drug, they had no real influence over the conduct of the trial or the timing of data emerging from it.

Investigational groups often took significantly longer time to run a trial than a company would. But more importantly, they often exerted less rigorous control over exactly how and where the study was conducted. There was therefore a greater liability for things to depart from both parties original expectations. And this was something that made companies very nervous, especially with drugs that had not yet received regulatory approval.

The unexpected or the unanticipated were the last thing you wanted, especially if it had anything to do with side effects or safety. Particularly when you had a regulatory body like FDA breathing down your neck and looking for any opportunity to start asking difficult questions. Investigator initiated trials carried *exactly* that kind of risk.

Understandably, given the failure of ATTRACT I, Novartis were now considering closing down all of the studies in the pipeline. They would effectively be cancelling everything to do with ASA404, except for keeping the ATTRACT II study going, at least up until the scheduled interim futility look towards the end of the year. It seemed the only obvious way to proceed. In the unlikely event that the study survived that key intermediate point, then Novartis could always press the button again.

Although no one from their side said anything, some of us had a strong impression that Novartis would have preferred to just shut down *everything* to do with ASA404 there and then, including ATTRACT II, and move on to something new. After all, they were a huge organisation, who must have any number of promising projects on the go.

It was always better to be working on a drug which was still on the up, rather than one that appeared to be most definitely on the down. Once a drug suffered a major setback, it was always going to be a struggle to maintain momentum from then on.

Inevitably, there were also personal elements at play. A small number of people within Novartis, including one or two who were there in Meeting Room 4, were closely linked to the decision and the deal to bring ASA404 into the company.

Up until this point it had been a valuable corporate asset, featuring prominently in Novartis's oncology pipeline. They'd made a big play of the drug at last year's ASCO. It wouldn't have been doing anyone any harm to be associated with it. But now, although no one could really be blamed for things having fallen apart, there were probably a few people who would prefer to put some distance between themselves and the drug and the sooner it went away, the happier they might be.

However, one way or another, ASA404 seemed destined to linger on for months to come, at least as far as ATTRACT II was concerned. It was trapped in a ghastly nether world, between the living and the dead. Which was a situation which pretty much summarised Antisoma's overall prospects.

VII

Leaving Florham Park, it felt as if we were in one of those relationships where you *know* the other person wants to end it but they don't seem able to find the right time or place to do so. And you can't find the right words to bring it up either.

Knowing this, we returned to London to take a long hard look at where we thought we now stood. And whatever it was we were standing on, it was definitely more than a bit wobbly.

We did still have amonafide. And that was a Phase III asset. Not many companies got that far in the first place and so things could be worse. The amonafide trial was on track to complete recruitment in August. We should be in a position to have a first look at the data at the end of January the following year. However, the big problem with amonafide was that even if things looked good in January, it was very far from certain whether we could survive long enough to capitalise on this. Even with Eric and the Board's enthusiastic cost cutting, the cash would run out in the autumn of next year. By then we would only be about half way through the FDA review process, never mind getting to the ODAC turkey shoot.

To stay alive, we had to get more cash before then and the sooner the better. However in January, the best we could hope for was data on the response rates we were seeing in the amonafide study. Data on how long the patients were living, the overall survival, wouldn't be ready until later in the year, around May or June time. And we knew this was going to be an important part of the jigsaw for FDA and other regulatory bodies. We may not have to *prove* that survival was better with amonafide but we certainly needed to be able to demonstrate that it wasn't any worse.

Given this, the big question was whether we'd be able to get our hands on any money in January, on the back of the initial and very incomplete amonafide results. There was a considerable diversity of opinion within the company over this. The clincher was whether anyone would pay out a large upfront payment in January, when more crucial data would be revealed just months later.

Those all important final results wouldn't however become available until just a few months before the Antisoma coffers ran dry. Given how long it took to court potential suitors and then consummate a deal, we may well still run out of cash before anything was signed.

If the worst happened, in a situation like that, with a deal potentially on the table, it was likely that our long suffering investors would divvy up. They'd find some money to keep us afloat, until a contract had been nailed down. But no one wanted to get that desperate. It was like borrowing money from a friend. You just knew it was a mistake you'd live to regret. Especially if you found you couldn't pay it back later on.

Even if the final data with amonafide looked good, everyone knew nothing could be taken for granted until ODAC had been given a chance to throw its opaque hand into the ring too. If amonafide made it that far, an ODAC meeting might not take place until the middle of 2012. There was a real possibility of our worst nightmare coming true, whereby potential partners would stay their hand and more importantly their chequebook, right up until then.

That for example was exactly what happened to Gloucester Pharmaceuticals. Celgene, one of the large US biotechs, eventually bought the whole company but not until very shortly *after* ODAC voted in favour of romidepsin, for use in cutaneous lymphomas. Gloucester however had somehow managed to find enough money to keep going that long. We simply weren't going to be able to do the same. It was just too protracted a period to be living hand to mouth, with no guarantee of things going our way at the end of it all. And so it looked like amonafide by itself was unlikely to offer us any certainty about our future.

VIII

That left our other remaining asset, AS1411. We had been working away at this compound for the last six years. It sometimes seemed as though we didn't really understand it any better now than we did then. Many small companies might have given up with it ages ago. But sometimes in drug development you come across a molecule out of the *Living Dead.* It just won't die, however many ways you try to kill it. AS1411 was one of those. In our hands, it was to have more resurrections than a bookshelf of bibles.

It belonged to a class of compounds known as *aptamers*.[10] These were short sequences of either DNA or RNA nucleic acids which, depending on their particular length and the precise nature of the constituent nucleic acid building blocks, adopted very precise three dimensional shapes.

This allowed them to bind to other molecules, with the same sort of specificity and selectivity as an antibody. However, they were very much easier to manufacture and also didn't provoke the sorts of allergic immune reactions which antibodies could do, when given to humans repeatedly.[11] AS1411 consisted of twenty six DNA units linked together. This resulted in it adopting a conformational structure causing it to bind to something called *nucleolin*.

Nucleolin is an important protein, found in pretty much every cell in the body. It's usually located in the middle of the cell, within something called the *nucleolus*. This in turn is located within the *nucleus*, the very centre of the cell. Normally nucleolin stays within the cell, where it shuttles around doing all sorts of things associated with control of DNA and the creation of proteins from RNA templates.

However, it appeared that cancer cells for some reason also sprouted nucleolin on the surface of the cell, as well as having it internally.[12] This didn't happen on normal cells. Usually nucleolin inside cells was isolated from the environment outside. It was sequestered within the nucleolus, itself within the nucleus. That in turn was enveloped by the cell membrane surrounding the cell. The whole thing was like a set of Russian dolls, stacked one inside the other.

If there were nucleolin stuck on the surface of the cell, this would be accessible to all sorts of things floating around in the blood, including drugs like AS1411. And so in theory, AS1411 would be able to target cancer cells, by binding to their cell surface nucleolin, whilst leaving normal cells alone. This in turn should reduce any damage to non-cancerous tissue, with fewer side effects as a result.

Whilst that was all well and good, there also had to be a way in which AS1411 could actually go on to kill the malignant cell, once it had bumped into it. Just tagging along on the surface wasn't going to disrupt a determined cancer cell too much. Somehow it had to find a way inside the cell, in order to fatally disrupt its survival mechanisms. Otherwise, there was no obvious way in which it could kill the cancer. And so there had to be more to AS1411 than just binding to nucleolin.

However, trying to find out what that might be would eventually turn into our greatest ever drug development challenge. If we had been trying to cure cancer in ancient times, the AS1411 development programme would easily have counted as one of the Seven Wonders of the World. It could comfortably have displaced The Colossus of Rhodes or the Hanging Gardens of Babylon, so vaunting was the ambition and so awesome the expenditure of time and effort. But that was drug development for you.

<h1 style="text-align:center">IX</h1>

AS1411 had started life at the James Brown Cancer Centre in Louisville, Kentucky. That's not James *Godfather of Soul* Brown but James *Graham* Brown, who'd been a Louisville property developer responsible for buildings such as the Brown Hotel, the Brown Theatre, the Brown Garage and the Martin Brown Building.

The colour brown summed up Louisville. Situated on the Ohio River and describing itself as *the northernmost southern or southernmost northern* city in the US, either way it was drab and colourless. It only came alive on the first Saturday of each May when it was home to the world famous Kentucky Derby.

It was the sort of place where you could imagine people stopping in the street, with whichever close relative they happened to be married to, and pointing at planes in the sky. There used to be a book in the common room of the Antisoma labs at St George's Hospital in London entitled *Landmarks of Louisville,* doubtlessly discarded in disgust by someone returning from a visit there.

The James Brown Cancer Centre had been around since 1978 and was dedicated to providing state of the art cancer services to the residents of Kentucky. They, for some reason, seemed to suffer from a higher rate of malignancy than many other parts of the US. Maybe boredom could cause cancer.

Not surprisingly therefore, the mission of the Brown Cancer Centre was to "help relieve the disproportionate burden of cancer borne by Kentuckians."[13] To help achieve this, it had a flourishing research facility which amongst other things had resulted in the world's first cancer vaccine to be produced by tobacco plants and the world's first ever clinical trial of the use of coloured berries to prevent cancer in high risk individuals. It was, if nothing else, an interestingly eclectic portfolio.

It had also produced AS1411, known then as AGRO100, which had come out of the laboratory of two scientists there, the husband and wife team of John Trent and Paula Bates. They had noticed that AGRO100 inhibited the growth of pretty much *every* type of cancer they looked at in the test tube, which was a fairly unusual finding. Normally it was hard enough finding new agents which looked active against one or two tumor types. Let alone the whole lot.

The excitement around this led them to initiate a Phase I clinical trial at James Brown, undertaken by an Argentinean born oncologist called Damian Laber. Also involved was Dr Don Miller, who was the Cancer Centre Director and a specialist in treating melanoma.

Like most Phase I clinical trials in oncology, this one was aiming to recruit patients with a whole range of different types of malignancy, such as lung, breast, melanoma, colon, kidney and so on The hope was that if patients with one particular sort of tumor started responding, this would give a clue about where to focus subsequent clinical trials. These sorts of early clinical signals can end up being misleading, as often as they are accurate. But at least it gives a place to start.

As the AGRO100 trial progressed, Dr Laber and Dr Miller noticed that out of the first ten or so patients there was one with advanced kidney cancer who appeared to have some tumor shrinkage. There were possibly also effects in a patient with lung cancer. Based on this, they narrowed down the rest of the trial to either kidney cancer or lung cancer. After another twenty or so patients had been recruited, there were twelve with kidney cancer and two of these had shown a response.[14]

That may not sound much but in these early exploratory trials, it's just the sort of thing you are looking for. After all, any patient entering a Phase I study is going to have already been through pretty much every other treatment option. These are people with end stage disease. They have run out of road. That makes it surprising when you see anything at all with a new experimental drug. So one or two responders is usually considered quite good going. That is what a lot of cancer medicine is about – tiny little signals rather than glaring great signs.

One of these patients had a *partial* response, meaning that their disease had shrunk down but was still detectable. The other patient appeared to have experienced a *complete* response, which meant that his disease had entirely disappeared. He'd started off with an enormous tumor mass in his abdomen and this had shrunk away, as had deposits in his skin and elsewhere. There was nothing left to detect. This was despite him having previously received three or four other kidney cancer drugs, which hadn't had much effect at all.

This sort of extensive disease regression was highly unusual in advanced kidney cancer, which was notoriously resistant to therapy. It occasionally occurred following treatment with a very unpleasant immunological agent called IL-2 (interleukin-2) but otherwise hardly ever.

X

There probably isn't much to report on in Louisville most of the time. Maybe that was why in November 2004 the local TV station, WHAS News, ran the story of the "*Louisville Miracle.*" This was a piece documenting the dramatic recovery of the patient with the complete response to AGRO100. The patient, Bill Sebree, was seen in various hospital settings within the Brown Cancer Centre, positively glowing with good health in each scene. Bill's daughter, Melody, was pictured lurking around the outpatient clinic, apparently for the sheer fun of it.

Damien Laber was filmed in a variety of doctorly poses doing various doctorly things. Whilst he was doing that, Paula Bates was interviewed in her laboratory expounding the virtues of nucleolin. And Don Miller appeared in a dark suit, his hair an apogee of the coiffeur's art, looking like a particularly compelling TV evangelist. Which in a way is exactly what he was doing, as he talked about the future potential of AGRO100, in a suitably reverential tone.

The Louisville Miracle was certainly an interesting clinical signal. But it was hard to know just what to make of it. There are certain types of malignancy, kidney cancer being one and melanoma another, which are known to very occasionally go into remission. This happens, seemingly out of the blue, with the disease apparently spontaneously diminishing or disappearing altogether. This occurs in the *absence* of any treatment. However, cancer doesn't just disappear all by itself. *Something* must be helping it on its way. In the case of kidney cancer, it is one type of malignancy which tends to be more susceptible than many others to attack by the body's own immune system.

One of the many remaining challenges of cancer medicine is to figure out how to turn the body's immune defences against cancer cells, in the same way they attack other abnormal threats such as bacteria, viruses and parasites. In theory, cancer cells should be capable of being destroyed by immune attack, because they are abnormal and effectively foreign. However, in practice they have learned how to "hide" from immune surveillance, by producing substances which suppress the immune system in the immediate vicinity of the tumor. Cancer cells have adapted to shelter themselves from the rest of the body, by creating their own unique *tumor micro-environment*.

But every now and then, for reasons no one fully understands, the tumor's defence shield seems to break down in kidney cancer patients, making it "visible" to the immune system. This then attacks the malignant cells, leading to a spontaneous cancer clearance mimicking the sort of response seen in the AGRO100 kidney cancer patient. It doesn't happen that often but still frequently enough to be a recognised phenomenon.

The problem now was to work out whether the Louisville miracle was genuinely due to AGRO100, or simply one of those random occasions when the immune system was given a chance to do its stuff.

It was however impossible to know. Either explanation was credible. If you believed in the drug, as the people in Louisville clearly did, you could argue it was entirely due to the effects of AGRO100. It was just too big a coincidence otherwise. Alternatively, you could favour the view that it was all down to Mother Nature finally deciding to fight back. It was less likely that story would make it on to WHAS though.

There were other things about the study which were also puzzling. The two responses that were seen occurred only after a delay of some months following the drug treatment. That wasn't what you would normally expect to see (except with some of the newer immunotherapy agents). Usually, if a malignancy is going to respond, it starts doing so more rapidly than this. With some types of cancers, called lymphomas, you can actually see the tumors visibly shrinking in front of your eyes, within hours of giving the patient the right sort of chemotherapy.

Admittedly, few tumor treatments are associated with such dramatic urgency. But not that many act at the leisurely pace seen in the James Brown study either. With AGRO100, events seemed to take a perplexingly long time to happen. Like most things in Louisville. You apparently had to sit back and be patient, something in short supply when you were running out of time with terminal cancer.

Also, because the amount of drug which had been available was very limited, all the patients in the study had received one, or at the most two, seven day cycles of AGRO100 treatment. There just wasn't anymore to go around. The shortage of drug supply itself wasn't surprising. That sort of thing is very common in the early stages of drug development. It can be very difficult to work out how to manufacture something as complicated as a new medicine. In the early days the available supply could often be severely restricted, until you got on top of this.

However, with most cancer drugs, if you didn't have enough available to continue with repeated cycles of treatment, the cancer would rapidly breakaway again and start progressing. It was like pressing down a button to keep a light on. As soon as you took your finger off, it would go out again. And yet this hadn't been the pattern with the two responding patients. They'd received only one or two cycles of treatment with AGRO100 and yet maintained prolonged subsequent responses. Here it was more like flicking a switch. Once you'd done that, the light would be on all the time, until you switched it off again.

It wasn't what you would expect to see and there didn't appear to be any obvious explanation for why AGRO100 should behave in this way. Maybe it was just a manifestation of its novelty, as an exciting new cancer agent. That was the optimistic explanation. The alternative interpretation was that this was another piece of evidence in the prosecution case, that AGRO100 didn't really have anything to do with the tumor responses. It had been behaving too oddly for that. They were instead nothing more than the false signals which sometimes complicated Phase I clinical trials.

Another unanticipated finding from this study had been a complete lack of any side effects, or other signs of toxicity, in any of the patients. It was very unusual, in fact almost unprecedented, to have something as powerful as a cancer drug which didn't also produce unwanted toxicity of some sort. Usually the only time you saw that was with molecules which weren't doing anything at all, either good or bad. But at face value, AGRO100 appeared to be a new exception to this rule.

So all in all, there were a number of aspects to this initial Phase I study with AGRO100 which didn't fit with what you might normally expect to see. This might have meant nothing, as a novel drug acting through a novel mechanism might well produce a novel pattern of results. You had to keep an open mind, otherwise progress would never be made.

However, after a while in cancer medicine you learn to be cautious when confronted with the unexpected, especially when it appears to be better than you were hoping for. In reality, nature is rarely that helpful.

In an ideal world, the next step might have been to repeat the Phase I study and see whether or not the same findings occurred a second time around. Given the vagaries and unpredictability of early stage clinical trials, it was a sensible rule of thumb to undertake two or three initial studies more or less at the same time. Reproducible outcomes gave you much more confidence that the results were reliable.

But sometimes, when you are trying to build a company, you can't hang around to hedge your bets like that. You have to follow your instincts and take the deal while it is still there to be done. Before someone else snatches it away. You have to take the risk and hope for the best.

XI

In an act of commendable corporate opportunism therefore, Antisoma had swooped in and bought Aptamera, the company which owned AGRO100, in January 2005, for just over twenty million dollars.

It was a big gamble though. The exploitation of novel technologies obviously offers huge potential and is the very *raison d'étre* of biotechnology companies. But there is a difference between a technology which you have invented and originated yourself, in the case of some biotechnology approaches maybe something you have devoted most of your academic life to perfecting and a technology you have gone out and acquired "off the shelf."

In the former case you know the devil of the detail, all the nuances and which cupboards the skeletons are hidden in. In the latter case, you don't. And AS1411 seemed to have more skeletons tucked away than an average sized cemetery.

On the other hand, however well you know it, no drug is ever perfect. There is always a reason to walk away, if you are so minded. Sometimes though, you just have to take the risk. And Glyn's instincts appeared to be correct. The financial markets seemed to like the Aptamera news, with the Antisoma share price shooting up massively from fifteen pence to twenty four pence.

And it was *very* big news in Louisville. The mayor, Jerry Abramson, even made a trip to London to visit the Antisoma offices. It was his first official duty, on a five day visit to the UK. He was keen to persuade Antisoma to locate a North American office in Louisville. Why he thought anybody in their right mind would want to do something like that was never really made clear though.

However, even with this overwhelming civic endorsement, AS1411, as AGRO100 had now become, would eventually turn out to be a difficult and frustrating drug to develop. Every aspect of it seemed to be like a slippery bar of soap in the bath. No sooner did you think you had a firm grip on it, than it jumped out of your fingers and sank out of view. But being at the forefront of science was never exactly going to be easy.

The first big problem was that we had no idea about the way in which it might be working. Just how did it actually kill cancer cells? We knew it appeared to bind to nucleolin on the surface but we needed to find out what happened after that. This was important for two reasons.

Knowledge of the actual molecular mechanisms which caused many cancers was expanding almost exponentially. There was therefore an increasing necessity to understand just how a new drug worked, in order to marry it up to the right type of cancer. If a particular malignancy was caused by overactivity of pathways A, B and D within a cell, it wouldn't be worth trying out your drug, if it worked only by blocking pathways C and E for example. But you couldn't make that assessment without knowing just where on the cancer highway your drug had set up the roadblock.

Also, because most approaches to cancer treatment involved combining drugs together, there was a distinct advantage in knowing how each drug worked. That helped in choosing the combinations which were most likely to complement each other, rather than potentially cancelling one another out.

Try as we might though, AS1411 refused to give up its secrets. We had academic collaborations with five or six leading cancer research centres in the US, Australia and the UK. They were all looking into different aspects of how AS1411 might conceivably exert an anti-cancer effect. All they seemed to do however was come up with experimental results which were largely inconsistent, if not incompatible, with one another.

Although we shouldn't have been surprised, as that was often the case with early stage drug development. It was like starting to put together a complicated jigsaw puzzle with none of the pieces seeming to fit at the beginning, although the finished picture on the box told you that they somehow had to.

For starters, we couldn't actually confirm, in our own hands, that nucleolin was detectable on the surface of tumor cells. Either it wasn't there, in the tumors we were looking at, or we were using different techniques from others, who had seemingly easily managed to detect it in the past. One of the problems after all was that this sort of experimental work was exquisitely sophisticated and often there was almost a degree of art involved as well as the science.

This sometimes made it difficult to come up with the same results, when the same experiment was repeated in different laboratories. It was quite often like that when you were trying to get to grips with a new drug. It was still another layer of complexity though, in a story that already had enough twists and turns.

Without convincing and reproducible evidence for the nucleolin hypothesis, a lot of the AS1411 story would have just fallen away. And along with it our ability to develop the drug, in any rational or planned manner. We'd end up stumbling around in the dark. Even more than we were already.

This kind of uncertainty wasn't that uncommon however, in the early stages of drug development. There was also the comfort of a large body of literature from academic groups around the world, all of which appeared to confidently attest to the presence of nucleolin on the surface of tumors. If you read those papers you'd leave with the impression that tumors were covered with the stuff, like warts on a goblin's face. But it didn't exactly help reduce a growing sense of unease over other aspects of AS1411's complicated character.

We were, for example, trying to understand what was happening to AS1411, when you injected it into patients. Normally, the body doesn't want bits of DNA or RNA floating around and so has developed highly efficient means of getting rid of these substances. Enzymes called nucleases are present in the bloodstream and rapidly break down DNA or RNA fragments to harmless materials.

AS1411, as a string of DNA, should have been an ideal target for attack by nucleases. To overcome this, the people in Louisville had especially chemically engineered AS1411. They had bolted on extra bits, at each end of the length of DNA, in a way which should block the nuclease from getting to it.

Without this protection, once it was in the bloodstream AS1411 would be disintegrating more rapidly than an ice cream in an inferno. On the assumption that the Louisville chemical wizardry was working, the key question we then had to answer was just how much of the drug did you actually need to give to patients, for it to start exerting an effect against their malignancy.

It is one of the earliest and most fundamental questions you ask about a new agent. It's also often one of the most difficult to answer. AS1411 was no exception to this.

XII

Cell lines are sheets of a particular type of cancer cell, a breast cancer cell, a lung cancer cell, a leukaemia cell or whatever. They are originally derived from an actual patient with that particular cancer and have been propagated in a test tube ever since. Some of these cell lines can date their history back decades, to the patient who provided the tissue in the first place. The patient may have died but their cancer has lived on, immortalised in research institutes from San Francisco to Shanghai.

In the laboratory, cancer cell lines are bathed with a new drug, such as AS1411, at varying concentrations, to see whether the cells survive or die. This gives you a rough and ready idea of what might be suitable future cancer targets and how much of a new drug you might need to use on them.

Cancer cell lines grown in a glass dish have limitations though. They don't have the blood supply or any of the other complexities of a three dimensional tumor in situ in the human body. Drugs could therefore be killers in a cell line but go on to prove ineffective, when confronted with the much more sophisticated architecture of an intact tumor.

And so agents which show promise in a cell line are usually subsequently evaluated in a xenograft model. This is an animal, nearly always a mouse, in which a human tumor has been grown, usually on the animal's back. This is achieved by injecting human tumor cells and then getting them to grow and establish themselves, just like a spontaneous malignancy would do.

Once the cancer is growing steadily, you can treat the animal with your drug and then examine its effects in exactly the same way as you would in a clinical trial, by measuring response rates, progression free survival and even overall survival. This is obviously a more elaborate way of looking at the potential of a new cancer agent but still has only limited predictive ability of any clinical promise.

This is partly because of the incredible complexity of human cancer and also because of the inevitably artificial nature of a mouse with a human lung tumor, or whatever else, growing out of its back. For xenografts to work, you have to effectively wipe out the animal's immune system, to prevent it rejecting the foreign tissue of the human tumor. That complicates the clinical relevance of any findings you might see. The mouse model is biologically very different from the clinical situation.

Despite the drawbacks of these various experimental systems, however many of them we examined with AS1411, the answer was always the same. It seemed to have an effect on pretty much every tumor we looked at but only when the concentration of the drug exceeded a certain threshold. Nothing happened when the drug levels were lower than that. We also found we needed to keep the concentration of the drug above this dividing line for about four to five days for it to start working, although no one knew why.

Our challenge therefore was to be confident that we were able to reproduce these levels of drug exposure in patients being given AS1411. This was complicated by the fact that it is often difficult, early on in development, to have an accurate way of measuring very small quantities of a drug in the human body. It's made even harder as the drug is mixed in with something as enriched as blood, which obviously contains a very large number of other chemicals and substances. It takes a long time to perfect the assays used to undertake this kind of precision work. They need to be able to recognise the drug molecule, AS1411 but ignore all the other chemical distractions surrounding it. It's a bit like a laboratory version of playing *Where's Wally.*

Which means that in early clinical studies, you are often unsure of how much drug is really around, when you try to look for it in patients. If you can't see it, is it because the drug isn't actually there, or is it because you are using a tiny torch in the dark when really you need a floodlight that you don't yet have?

With AS1411, the waters were muddied further because there was some animal data to suggest that it became more intensely concentrated in the tumor itself, compared to the levels in the blood. Some drugs did that over a period of time, following injection into the bloodstream. AS1411 could therefore be exceeding the necessary threshold where it mattered most, irrespective of what was happening in the blood, which was the only place we were able to measure it. There was however no way we could confirm that.

These various complications meant that at best we had to rely on a rough and ready estimate of how much AS1411 was actually reaching the eventual destination of the tumor. And therefore whether we were giving enough of the drug or not. It was like driving on a remote road with the petrol gauge having packed in, whilst trying to guess how much fuel was left and whether you could reach where you were aiming for. There was a lot of hope involved. And the ever present danger of miscalculating and being caught short.

Even if there was enough drug getting into the tumor, we weren't certain how easy it would be to administer the sort of prolonged infusion it seemed to require. The animal experiments suggested you needed four or five days of constant exposure. Anything shorter and the drug just wouldn't do its stuff. The Louisville Phase I study had even managed to exceed this, due to AS1411 being given as a continual infusion, twenty four hours a day for seven days in a row.

You can just about get away with that sort of thing in a cancer trial, with end of the road terminally ill patients. These are people who have run out of other choices. Being tied to a bag of drug for a whole week is a price many are willing to pay, in return for some hope of living a little bit longer. Or even just having a mental straw to cling to.

But in less desperate situations, having to give a drug for this long a period is hugely problematic. There are all the technical issues about veins blocking up during the infusion, or the pump failing or the tubing becoming disconnected or infected. However, the biggest drawback is that it effectively confines the patient to the hospital for a whole week. This ties up beds and also increases expenses substantially, compared to managing things on an outpatient basis.

It is also a major problem for patients who aren't yet terminal. They understandably don't want to spend a significant proportion of their limited remaining time being hospitalised. If it were going to guarantee them a cure of their disease, then they would all be queuing around the block to get into the hospital. But when a treatment is offering a small chance of a much more limited respite, these considerations assume a greater importance. If you're one of the people in whom a new drug turns out not to be doing anything, you've just wasted an awful lot of non-refundable time staring at the ceiling.

Wherever possible therefore, chemotherapy is given on an outpatient basis. This is helped by the increasing number of oral cancer drugs. Many injectable ones can also be managed in this way. There are even some which can be given as very prolonged infusions, over a number of days, without the need for the patient to be in hospital.

151

One is a drug called 5-FU (*5-fluorouracil*), which is widely used in breast and colon cancer, amongst many others. However, 5-FU is very highly concentrated and so large doses can be squeezed into a limited volume. This allows it to be given via a very small mechanical pump, about the size of an old-style Walkman, worn conveniently around the waist.

In contrast, AS1411 had to be given in large volumes of fluid, which needed to be changed frequently. This could only be practically managed with the patient in hospital. Otherwise, they'd have to wander around with enormous tanks strapped to their back, like some kind of terrestrial scuba diver. We could probably have improved this over time. It might eventually be possible to get things to a stage where the drug could be managed on an outpatient basis. However this was far from guaranteed and represented yet another development burden to add to the burgeoning total.

That was in addition to all the others already attached to AS1411. The difficulties it threw up at every twist and turn were enough to write a textbook around. Pretty much all the chapters of what could complicate drug development would be covered by it.

Looking at things dispassionately, we had a drug with any number of complexities. These included understanding how it might work, whether it did work, whether we had the right dose, whether we needed to look at higher doses and the need for it to be given for inconveniently prolonged periods of time.

And that was before we began to even consider the problem of which type of cancer to develop it in.

The Phase I study from Louisville had shown a signal of possible activity in advanced kidney cancer. At any other time, that would have been exciting. But right now, AS1411 seemed to be in the wrong place at the wrong time. It was a graphic example of just how complicated and unpredictable developing any new drug could be.

XIII

Kidney cancer accounts for about three per cent of adult cancers and is responsible for twelve thousand deaths each year in the US alone. Up until recently, there had been no significant advances in the treatment of the disease for about two decades. This particular type of cancer was very resistant to conventional chemotherapy.

Because of this, treatment approaches had largely been limited to the use of immunologically active agents, such as *interleukin-2* and *interferon*. These are both constituents of the normal immune system, belonging to a class of signalling chemicals known as *cytokines*. They act by amplifying and directing the attack of killer immune cells against threatening enemies, such as bacteria and viruses and sometimes tumor tissue too.

These were exceptionally toxic agents though. With the exception of a few patients who did very well, they weren't particularly helpful in keeping the disease under control. Historically, advanced kidney cancer had a particularly bleak outlook with very limited treatment options. Those that were available mainly succeeded only in burdening unfortunate patients with a whole raft of toxic side effects, for little if any discernible benefit.

But all that changed overnight in December 2005, when FDA approved *sorafenib* (Nexavar). This was a new drug for kidney cancer from Bayer and its partner Onyx. A couple of months later, in February, this was followed by the approval of Pfizer's *sunitinib* (Sutent) as well.

Both these drugs were examples of a new wave of specific directed therapies. They shared the same molecular target, an enzyme called *tyrosine kinase*.[15] This was a key regulator of many vital processes necessary to keep cells alive. It was broadly the same kinase target as Gleevec, which was revolutionising the treatment of chronic myelogenous leukaemia (CML) following its approval five years earlier.

The efficacy of Sutent and Nexavar in advanced kidney cancer was however much more modest than that of Gleevec in CML. Neither produced much tumor shrinkage and there were virtually no radiological responses at all with Nexavar. But they were undoubtedly altering the biology of the cancer, as both drugs prolonged progression free survival by a significant amount. It increased from six weeks with no treatment, to six months when the new agents were used. They were toxic however, with a lot of nasty blood pressure and skin problems, along with quite a bit of diarrhoea.

Despite these limitations, both drugs were received with open arms by oncologists treating kidney cancer. Until now they had been starved, in some cases for their entire career, of anything new to offer their patients.

And there was more to come. Over the next few years FDA would approve another four drugs, all for kidney cancer. Avastin (combined with interferon) was approved towards the end of the same year as Nexavar. Then there were two drugs of a new class called *mTor inhibitors*.[16] These acted on another important pathway of cellular control, which was particularly implicated in many types of kidney cancer. Wyeth's temsirolimus (Torisel) was approved in 2007 and Novartis's everolimus (Afinitor) in 2009. Also towards the end of 2009 along came GSK's pazopanib (Votrient), another tyrosine kinase inhibitor.

All this activity was obviously great news for patients with kidney cancer and the clinicians treating them. It wasn't such good news for AS1411 though. The problems created by this feast of plenty became very clear, when we arranged a meeting in June 2006 with half a dozen top US kidney cancer clinicians.

It was quite common to have this sort of get together, when you weren't quite sure where to go next with a drug development project in a particular malignancy. We wanted to know what they thought we should do. It was a bit of brainstorming, with some pretty big brains.

These events often resembled a musical jamming session. You'd all sit around, whilst one or two people threw out a few chords to see whether the ensemble as a whole could then get a rhythm going. It was a bit touch and go, with a lot of opening gambits failing to come together. But every now and then everyone found themselves playing in tune and suddenly you were making music.

We had chosen to get together at the Ritz Carlton Hotel, in Marina del Rey in northern Los Angeles, right on the Pacific Ocean and just south of Venice Beach. It was a hot summer's day outside but it quickly grew a lot hotter inside. Gathered in The Rose Garden Meeting Room, we went round and round and round, edging slowly towards a realisation that there was no immediately obvious place to take AS1411 in kidney cancer. Which was surprising, given that we were, after all, talking about a disease which was still completely incurable, at least in its advanced stages.

There were already those two new drugs available to use for front line treatment of kidney cancer. Furthermore, both Sutent and Nexavar were given as tablets. It was difficult to see why many patients would be motivated to enter a clinical trial with an unproven therapy like AS1411, which would require them to spend a whole week in hospital. Instead they could receive an approved treatment, which clearly had efficacy and which simply needed to be taken with a glass of water each day.

There were of course patients who couldn't tolerate either Sutent or Nexavar, because of side effects. There were also large numbers in the US who had been receiving these drugs for some time, as part of clinical trials they had been in. Many of this group were now no longer responding to treatment. Experience was showing these agents could only hold back the cancer for so long. So maybe one possible direction for AS1411 could be those patients who were intolerant of, or failing on, one of these newer agents?

That sounded promising but the difficulty here was that clinicians were already beginning to deal with this problem by themselves. They were taking these patients and if they had been on Sutent when they ran into trouble, switching them to Nexavar instead, and vice versa. It seemed to be working as well. Many patients who couldn't get on with one drug managed to tolerate the other, even though they had quite overlapping toxicities. Also, those patients whose disease was now beginning to progress with whichever of the two they had been receiving first, found that things came back under control, for a while at least, when they switched to the alternative one.[17]

On top of this pick and mix approach, Novartis's Afinitor was being developed for *just* this patient population – those who had already failed on a tyrosine kinase inhibitor. It was way ahead of us, already in large Phase III clinical trials. Also it had the added advantage of being another tablet, rather than a troublesome infusion.

Wyeth's Torisel was being targeted a bit differently at patients whose disease characteristics suggested from the outset that they had a *particularly* grave prognosis. Which was saying something, given the dismal outlook for any sort of kidney cancer.

It seemed to be doing quite well in that uniquely blighted group though, again making it a less promising avenue for AS1411. There would be a lot less room for two drugs, with Torisel already well ahead of us. It was therefore another door closing in our face. Exactly where Avastin and Votrient were going to end up was a bit unclear. But just them being on the scene wasn't exactly going to help us any.

Maybe we could try for the third line treatment slot, after patients had failed tyrosine kinase inhibitors and something else too. It wasn't that far away from where we were now with the Louisville study after all. That space would almost certainly be available to us, if for no reason other than no one else would really want to be there. The chances of convincingly showing that any drug worked in disease that far gone and that heavily pre-treated were fairly low. The market size was also small. There were a limited number of patients who had the physical and mental fortitude to endure that much preceding chemotherapy and actually survive to be available for even more.

Perhaps alternatively, we could try to crack the problem by *combining* AS1411 with something else. The tyrosine kinase inhibitors were good drugs, in the sense that they were infinitely better than anything that had come along before. But they could still be improved on, by using them along with another agent. Sooner or later, pretty much everyone's cancer started to develop resistance to these drugs and the disease began to progress again. The apparent lack of toxicity seen with AS1411 so far would help when adding it with something else. It shouldn't make the overall safety too much worse than it already was with another drug by itself.

But the problem was how to combine our drug with anything else, when we didn't understand how AS1411 worked. For all we knew, it might be doing something that antagonised the useful effects of the other compound.

There were plenty of instances of that happening in the past, even when you *did* understand how different drugs worked. The two antibodies Avastin and Erbitux,[18] each with separate molecular targets, had recently been tried

155

in colon cancer, for example. In theory, they should complement each other perfectly. One targeted the tumor vasculature, the other blocked a key growth signalling receptor on the cancer cell itself.

To everyone's surprise however, the two used together turned out to be *worse* than either alone. Adding Erbitux on top of Avastin and chemotherapy resulted in a significant shortening of progression free survival, compared to using Avastin and chemotherapy alone.[19] Once again, it showed that in cancer medicine there was very little you could take for granted.

Everywhere we looked seemed to have obstacles blocking the path ahead. We were also stuck in a vicious circle. Until we had more convincing evidence that AS1411 did actually work, it was hard to persuade people of its merits. We needed to put something on the table to counter the drawback of a week in hospital receiving a drug that could be doing as much harm as good.

But unless we could somehow complete a clinical trial or two, we would never manage to get the kind of information we needed to justify starting them in the first place. Basically, patients with kidney cancer, and their clinicians, weren't as desperate as they had been in the past. They could almost afford to pick and choose drugs at the moment. And we were well towards the bottom of their Christmas list.

The discussion around the table ebbed and flowed, like the waves lapping up against the boats in the marina outside the window of our meeting room. But the more we talked, the clearer it became that there was no obvious place for AS1411 to fit into right now. By the end of the meeting, the most widely accepted proposal was to try it out as second line treatment in patients who'd failed at least one, and more likely two, tyrosine kinase inhibitors. But by that stage, any agreement was probably as much the result of collective mental exhaustion as any rational reasoning.

But at least it was a plan of some sort. Sometimes in drug development, you had to define a starting point. You needed a point of reference. It allowed you to subsequently see if you were moving away from it, in the direction you'd intended. Or whether you were going off at a tangent, or even just moving in circles. Unless you started *somewhere* though, you'd never end up *anywhere* else.

XV

Later that day, after we finished our deliberations, I had another meeting to go to. It was at the Ronald Reagan Medical Centre, on the enormous UCLA medical campus in Westwood. Strolling back, in the late afternoon sun, I wandered into the Westwood Village Memorial Park. It's just off the intersection of Wilshire Boulevard and Westwood Boulevard.

The final home of such celebrities as Marilyn Monroe, Walter Matthau, Billy Wilder, Roy Orbison and countless others, it is a small almost nondescript plot. The perimeter walls contain thousands of little crypts, each with a memorial tablet recording whose remains lie there. That afternoon, it seemed a perfect metaphor for much of drug development. Thousands of starring ideas, which had briefly sparkled and shone, only to end up as piles of ash. All ultimately consigned to anonymity in a park wedged between a school and a superstore. It was a sobering thought.

But we weren't ready to bury AS1411 just yet. We needed give it a new lease of life somehow. So if kidney cancer was a dead end, what might be a better pathway to go down?

XVI

Trying out AS1411 in acute myeloid leukaemia had been an early idea from the Louisville group. Although no one now could quite remember why. It did have some merit though. Patients undergoing standard induction chemotherapy, to get their disease into remission, usually received combination therapy. That normally involved seven days of the anti-leukaemia drug cytarabine. This was often used along with another drug called doxorubicin, given for three days (*known as the 7+3 regimen*).

Cytarabine was given as a continual infusion, like AS1411 and so the two would go well together. Because these patients were very sick, and the complications of the treatment could be severe, it was normal to hospitalise them. So here was one situation where the infusion difficulties of AS1411 would be easily manageable.

In addition, there was some evidence from both Louisville and our own labs that AS1411 and cytarabine worked better together to destroy leukaemia cells than they did alone. When the two drugs were mixed in a test tube with cells collected from patients, the combination worked *synergistically.*

The effect of the two drugs *combined* was greater than the sum of the effect of either of them when used *individually.* (So if each killed say twenty per cent of leukaemia cells alone, then rather than forty per cent, they might kill sixty per cent when used together. Each was helping the other achieve more than it could by itself).

Around about this time, Nigel Courtenay Luck had also brought back some photographs from the Haematology Department of the Medical University of South Carolina. While he was there, Nigel had also managed to fix himself up with a Visiting Professorship, which wasn't bad going for an afternoon's work.

Nigel's images were of AML blast cells, taken from the bone marrow of dying patients. They appeared to be coated with nucleolin, when examined with the right sort of imaging agents. This strongly suggested AML might

157

be a suitable target for a drug like AS1411, acting as it did through nucleolin.

Collecting all this information together, on the face of it AML seemed worth looking at in a bit more detail.

And so a month or so after the meeting in Marina del Rey, we were gathered together again, this time at the Washington Duke Inn and Golf Club. It was a three hundred acre *"Old English Country Inn Style"* hotel on the campus of Duke University, about twenty minutes from Research Triangle Park near Durham, North Carolina.

The hotel was named after Washington Duke, a penniless Confederate soldier returning from the American Civil War. He subsequently went on to build the American Tobacco Company.

Getting together that morning, in the Holloway Boardroom of the hotel, we were hoping to build something too around AS1411. We needed a pathway forwards for a drug that was at risk of provoking civil war of its own within the company, if we didn't soon find a direction and definition for it.

A number of people were beginning to think that AS1411 and the whole aptamer approach were becoming too expensive, protracted and complicated. There seemed to be no end of development challenges associated with it. One or two would have been OK, but not all of them together. We'd been so busy trying to sort out all the problems with AS1411, that we hadn't even got around to something as simple as finding a name for it yet.

Maybe if we kept on forever we could have made some headway. Sometimes though, you have to cut your losses and move on. That however was always a difficult decision to reach. Little was ever clear cut. There were *always* ambiguities with data from a novel compound.

If the results were disappointingly negative, there was usually an alternative explanation, apart from the one that the drug didn't work. You hadn't done the experiment as well as you could have. Maybe if the clinical trial had been designed slightly differently, the results would have been better. You should have used a higher dose of drug. Or a lower dose. Or the same dose but given for longer. Or more frequently. If you looked hard enough, there was always a reason why the next trial would be different.

AS1411 was fortunate however in benefiting from the support and loyalty of a small but influential minority within Antisoma, who were clearly in the *glass is half full* camp. It was a drug with friends in high places. Furthermore, it might be difficult to unceremoniously dump it, with the Mayor of Louisville looking over your shoulder.

Faced with such a well connected drug, we had no choice but to show it due deference.

Which is why we found ourselves in the Holloway Boardroom, themed in an old English country inn style by someone who'd clearly never left

North Carolina in their whole life. They'd certainly never been to England, or visited an old country inn.

We had four leading US leukaemia specialists there, including Professor Rob Stuart from the Medical University of South Carolina (MUSC) in Charleston. He, along with his colleague Professor Dan Fernandes, had a long standing interest in the potential role of nucleolin in leukaemia. Their lab had done a lot of the experiments which appeared to support taking AS1411 in this direction.

Rob, who looked like a more distinguished John Denver, had spent ten years at MUSC, playing a key role in the founding of the Hollings Cancer Centre there. He'd left in 1997, to become Chairman of the Department of Oncology at the King Faisal Specialist Hospital and Research Centre in Riyadh, Saudi Arabia.

However, this was cut short in 2001, when he returned to MUSC as his wife, Charlene had actually developed AML herself, whilst out in the Middle East. He successfully treated her, including getting through two bone marrow transplants. It was an extraordinary juxtaposition of husband and healer. But between the two of them, they'd somehow managed to pull it off. This personal experience had given him an even greater motivation to find better treatments for such a devastating disease.

When we sat down to consider the possibilities for AS1411 in AML, the discussion in some ways was easier than it had been for kidney cancer. Sadly there was no glut of promising new drugs to confuse everything. Nothing seemed promising in AML in fact. But on the other hand, it was a more complicated disease than kidney cancer. And it was also a lot less common. Which meant there were fewer patients to go around for clinical trials.

Unlike kidney cancer, AML was a more diverse disease. There were four or five different types of malignancy which could affect the kidney but the vast majority were all one type. AML however was classified into a bewildering number of different sub groups, defined by particular chromosomal or genetic abnormalities in the leukaemic cells themselves.

It was then further subdivided, according to a whole host of other prognostic factors, the most important of which was the age of the patient. The older the patient, the worse they did. Not that the young exactly fared that well either.

Trying to organise all the different potential variants of AML was like playing a particularly demanding game of *Tetris*.

Another complexity of AML was the variable and sequential way the disease was treated. There was initial chemotherapy, then more intensive chemotherapy, or a bone marrow transplant, or maybe both, and then after that perhaps some more chemotherapy still.

And unhelpfully, there was no uniform agreement over which combination of chemotherapy agents to use. 7+3, MEC, ICE, HiDAC,

IDAC, CLAG, FLAG-Ida, MTC, S-HAM, FS-HAI, S-HAI, CAT, the acronymic list of treatment options was a long and daunting one. Each permutation was testament to the ingenuity of the clinicians who'd invented it. The sheer diversity on display was however evidence of the overall dissatisfaction with what each had to offer individually.

There was a similar degree of variability about bone marrow transplantation. Did you use bone marrow or stem cells. Or even umbilical cord blood. How closely matched did the donor and the recipient need to be. How many cells from the donor did you transfer to the patient. After the transplant did you give drugs to prevent any immune reaction and if so which ones and for how long. Did you use donor lymphocyte infusions to accelerate immune reconstitution or not. The possibilities were endless.

AML was the Wild West of cancer, with no rules and no regulation. It was a disease where medicine, magic and mumbo jumbo all seemed to play similar roles. This variability made clinical trials in AML a nightmare. Clinical studies are completely antipathetic to such a lack of consistency. The ultimate objective of all clinical trials is to ensure standardisation of as much as conceivably possible, so that the only variable left is the presence or absence of the experimental drug. AML just didn't lend itself to that approach.

In addition to the complexity of the disease and the confusion of the treatment, there was also the challenge of the competition for the patients. Apart from the minority who were likely to do well (younger patients with the most favourable disease characteristics) the choices for most were so dismal that pretty much all patients ended up in clinical trials sooner or later. This was usually on the assumption that an experimental approach couldn't possibly be any worse than the established ones.

That created huge problems for companies trying to undertake clinical trials in such an extensively researched disease as this. Particularly as there weren't that many patients with AML in the first place. In this combative environment, almost every patient was fought over for competing studies. This was irrespective of whether they originated with pharmaceutical companies, collaborative groups, other academic organisations, or as a consequence of a clinician's own initiative. It was the modern day equivalent of body snatching.

We'd considered all of these obstacles and their various implications back in London. Before going to the meeting, we'd come down in favour of a trial of AS1411 as mono-therapy, for the first line treatment of elderly AML patients. This was the largest overall group with the disease and moreover the most underserved by existing treatments. It was also one of the easier AML groups (or rather one of the less difficult) in which to examine a new drug. The relative frailty of this particular population also made it an attractive one for a drug like AS1411, given its apparent lack of toxicity.

160

To our surprise, we found ourselves leaving the meeting, some hours later, with a trial combining AS1411 and a very high dose of the conventional drug cytarabine, in relapsed or refractory patients. These were ones who'd failed on existing therapies and now had no obvious therapeutic avenue available to them. This was traditionally the graveyard of new anti-leukaemia drugs.

It was exceptionally difficult to detect activity in patients with disease as advanced and as intractable as this. These were the sorts of patients you intercepted getting on the bus to Lourdes. There was a whole litany of drugs that had failed here and never seen the light of day again.

If leukaemia had been an enemy we were fighting, we'd just decided to take on a crack troop of special forces, rather than our original plan of tackling a dad's army of reservists.

But the graveyard was the only place that seemed to have room for us. Elderly patients with AML, who were candidates for first line therapy, were even more in demand than normal. In part, this was due to a very large trial being run by J&J, with a novel leukaemia drug called tipifarnib. It was one of the new targeted therapies and there was a lot of excitement around it. They were hoovering up all the elderly patients. Which showed just how competitive it was out there. One large trial could corner the whole market.

On the other hand, the majority of patients who actually underwent first line therapy eventually ended up in the relapsed or refractory category. Either their disease never responded in the first place or it rapidly returned, reinvigorated for a fresh fight. This meant they were in more abundant supply, although still not exactly falling off trees.

The experts in our group were very clear though that if we wanted to get a trial done anytime soon, particularly in the US, then this was the only way to go. Which didn't really leave us with much choice. We could hang around forever and a day, waiting for a seat to become free on the elderly bus, or we could take the relapsed and refractory death ride right now.

As we left the meeting, it was pretty much a foregone conclusion which one we would be buying tickets for. You have to keep momentum when developing a new drug. You can't always hang around waiting for a door to open. Particularly when it looks like remaining firmly closed for quite some time to come. Which frequently means making pragmatic decisions, rather than perfect ones.

It was time for us to start planning for a plot in the cemetery.

XVII

The future of AS1411 was looking fraught therefore. In AML, we faced the prospect of a clinical trial arguably based more on the do-able than the desirable. In kidney cancer, there wasn't any obvious direction at all.

But that was exactly the sort of dilemma you often faced in early stage drug development. It was like being on a particularly arduous hike and suddenly realising you'd lost your map and compass. You couldn't stay where you were but there was also nothing to help guide you forwards. All you knew was that you had to keep moving.

So in the end, we decided to do both. Double or quits, we thought. That's how we liked to roll. If anyone was going to give the nucleolin theory of cancer a proper run for its money, then it was going to be us. We had no room for the modesty and moderation of more lacklustre companies.

With AML, we might have a dance partner we wouldn't otherwise have chosen but it did mean we were still at the Ball. Also, the fact that kidney cancer was a field more crowded that a Tokyo subway train wasn't going to put us off either.

And so a month later, we found ourselves standing outside the UCSF Mount Zion Cancer Centre, on Divisadero Street in San Francisco. Divisadero ran north south from the Marina to Castro Street and was reputedly the dividing line between foggy San Francisco and sunny San Francisco. We must have been on the foggy side that day.

We were there to meet with Professor Jonathan Rosenberg, for another discussion about AS1411 in kidney cancer. Physically, Jonathan was a very big man and must have looked even bigger still to his patients, whose cancers were wasting them away in front of him. He had a cherubic face, possibly apart from the bright orange beard and almost looked too young to be the highly experienced kidney cancer specialist he was.

He'd been at the meeting a couple of months earlier at Marina del Rey. We'd known him for a while before then though, as he had a general interest in nucleolin in malignancy.

At Marina del Rey, the mood of the meeting had been that if we were to do anything in kidney cancer, the best thing would be second line treatment, in those who had failed a tyrosine kinase inhibitor as a first line approach. The big problem then had been that Novartis were already there, with their Phase III trial of *everolimus* (later to become known as Afinitor) in exactly *that* patient group. It crowded out AS1411, more than a little. And that had put us off.

But Jonathan had been keeping a careful eye on the Novartis trial, which was known as the RECORD-1 study. This was now reaching a point where initial results would shortly be available. There was a general impression that they weren't going to be outstanding.[20] That was the story on the street. Maybe there would be some room for AS1411 after all.

Also, now that the everolimus trial was ending, there would be a window of opportunity to recruit into an AS1411 study. We could grab patients who might otherwise all have gone into the RECORD-1 trial.

"But everolimus is a tablet Jonathan. If we have to give AS1411 as a seven day infusion isn't it going to have to do something really dramatic to compensate, like grow back a kidney for the patients or something?"

However for some reason, Jonathan seemed more optimistic now about the prospects for AS1411, than he had been in Los Angeles. And so we emerged from Mount Zion a couple of hours later with a plan for a large randomised Phase II trial. It had only taken Jonathan's change of heart to tip the balance. The confusion of our previous deliberations seemed to slip away, like the fog rolling back from the Bay.

The proposed study would compare AS1411 to placebo, in patients who'd failed on Nexavar, Sutent or both. There had been a lot of debate about including a placebo arm. Clinical trials with a placebo were exceptionally helpful, as they gave the clearest and cleanest comparison when assessing the safety and efficacy of a new agent. They were much easier to interpret than using another active drug as the comparator.

It was a complicated issue for cancer studies though. There was an argument that anything must be better than nothing and so it would be unethical to allocate patients to placebo alone in any context. With many cancers, especially in the early stages, there are obviously effective *established* treatments. It would be impossible to deny these to patients and so a pure placebo arm would be untenable.

On the other hand, the majority of *experimental* drugs still carry the risk they may be doing more harm than good. Furthermore, in patients with more advanced cancer, there often aren't alternative therapies. This makes the use of a placebo more justifiable. Whilst patients allocated to one couldn't be expected to derive any benefit, they wouldn't be missing out on any other clearly worthwhile treatment options either. They would also avoid the risk of toxicity with a new experimental drug, which could well turn out to lack anti-cancer activity anyway.

Overall, they might therefore be no better or worse off with a placebo than whatever the alternative might have been. That's how the argument in favour of placebos went. Despite this, there are no hard and fast rules.

The number of cancer trials employing a placebo is probably diminishing. It goes hand in hand with the pace of therapeutic progress. Most of the time, there are too many active alternatives around. Only a minority now use one. The fact that it is still possible though, is an indication of how many advanced cancers remain without genuine treatment choices. And that seemed to include the patients we now had in mind for AS1411.

When we subsequently phoned around the others, who'd been at Marina del Rey, they were happy to fall in line behind Jonathan, now that he had changed his mind and provided the leadership. That was the strange thing about oncology drug development. *Nothing* seemed to be really tangibly objective. Opinions on what could or couldn't, should or shouldn't be done might change overnight. It depended on who you talked to and when and what they knew at the time.

It was a game, where the rules kept altering as you played and no one was quite sure how you were supposed to win or lose. But that's what made it so interesting to us. It was the utter unpredictability of it all.

And so we flew back from San Francisco to start mobilising the small army required to support Phase II trials in both kidney cancer and AML.

There was drug to be manufactured, put into vials and labelled up. Protocols needed to be written for each study, describing exactly how everything would be done, in minute detail. This was in the hope that the more accurately you described something, the greater the chance of successfully standardising it across all the centres in the trial. Each protocol rapidly became an unwieldy document running to about three hundred pages.

Summaries of all the pre-clinical and clinical information on AS1411 needed to be compiled. Explanations of the trials in layman's terms had to be written for patients, who would most likely never read them. Documentation for the clinicians needed to be developed, to capture all the clinical trial data in a way that could subsequently be entered into a database for analysis of the results. Exhaustive information needed to be pulled together and submitted to the US and other regulatory authorities. They would need to give their approval before the trials could start.

Information packs needed to be prepared and submitted to hospital ethics committees for their approval too. Nurses, pharmacists, and other support staff needed to be trained up. There was the laborious process of needing to negotiate contracts with each hospital, to be able to use their facilities. Additionally, there was the need to sort out contracts with a whole host of companies providing services ranging from clinical quality assurance to couriering.

Overall, there were many needs having to be met. Those with reservations about AS1411 may have thought we were doing too much too soon but the programme now had an almost unstoppable momentum. Like an enormous advancing army, it couldn't be halted and turned around without a huge amount of forethought and planning. With all of this going on, the company was humming with coordinated frenetic activity, just like some mobilising military machine.

XVIII

There were still a few loose ends to tie up though. At least they appeared to be nothing more than that. A few final boxes to be checked for the regulator's roster.

The original Louisville clinical study hadn't detected any significant side effects with AS1411. This however was both good and bad news. There are two main reasons for the absence of side effects with a new drug, when it is given to patients. The first is that it's not actually causing any real toxicity and so there is nothing to see. That is very unusual with a cancer drug. The second is that side effects are there but you just haven't picked them up, due to not looking carefully enough. Pharmaceutical companies prefer the former interpretation whilst regulators veer towards the latter.

To help sort this out, it is useful to have some information from studies in animals. You want to know what sorts of damage the drug does and whereabouts it occurs, when you give enough of it to eventually elicit toxicity.

For example, if studies in animals showed an effect of the drug, even if only at incredibly high doses, on the eye then you would want to incorporate detailed ocular examinations in your clinical trials. Just to make sure you weren't missing anything. Or if a drug caused damage to the heart in animals, you might need to undertake specialised clinical evaluations of this in patients.

Ordinarily though, you wouldn't do this level of testing, because it is expensive and time consuming and would rarely pick anything up. The toxicity findings in animals therefore guide you where to probe most deeply in patients. If something clinically undesirable is going on, hopefully you can pick it up before too much damage has been done.

Regulators call these sorts of toxicological findings *target organ toxicities* and they really don't like it if you can't demonstrate any. With patients in clinical trials, it's not possible to perform every single medical test under the sun, just to be sure you're not missing anything untoward with a new drug. You normally conduct some basic routine testing and only add in anything more specific, if there is something you are particularly concerned about from animal testing.

Without the animal pointers of target organ toxicity to guide you, there is always the worry that you might be overlooking drug toxicity in the clinic. It's amazing how much damage a drug can do, if you carry on giving it, before it reaches a point where it would be picked up with routine testing. You don't want to wait for someone to go blind months later, before realising your drug has been causing eye damage from the outset.

And so we needed to find some toxicity with AS1411 in animal testing, to satisfy FDA and others. We had to be able to demonstrate we had checked everything we needed to in the clinic. To get this done as expeditiously as possible, we decided it would be best to use as much drug as we could get into the animals. We would give them enormous multiples of the highest clinical dose we could anticipate using. We'd also give it massively more frequently than could possibly be the case in real life.

That's basically what toxicology testing was all about. To dramatically exaggerate in animals what you would be doing in the clinic with people.

It was an example of the delicate balancing act required when designing toxicology studies. You wanted to give enough drug to be certain of exaggerating any clinical side effects it may have. But you also needed to stop short of overtly poisoning the animals in some kind of non-specific way. Sometimes though, if you weren't careful, you could lose your balance and fell over. It was a fairly regular occurrence in drug development.

Things rarely go according to plan however, when trying to marry together complicated non-clinical and clinical studies into a seamless continuum. Especially when you most need them to. And now was no exception. To our dismay, we found that completing this animal work ended up taking much more time than we had originally envisaged.

It often turned out that way, when you were trying to secure slots for this kind of specialist undertaking, in the very limited number of commercial laboratories which were capable of doing it. Sometimes you also found that one study would complete, only to raise as many questions as it answered. This then created the need for a second one, as a follow on. It all took time.

This meant that the AML trial suddenly overtook the kidney one and reached pole position first. In AML, we were only giving a single seven day cycle of AS1411. We were pretty sure we could press ahead with this, without waiting for the toxicology to complete. The kidney trial envisaged a more complicated dosing regimen and we couldn't start that until we had the results of the animal testing.

Nothing was predictable in drug development and so we had to suddenly shuffle things around and put AML at the forefront of our clinical activities and corporate consciousness.

But at least we were now in a position to finally give AS1411 a chance to show us what it was capable of. We had at long last reached that magic moment of *initiating* a clinical trial.

XIX

It was therefore with some sense of relief that we arrived one Friday in August 2007 at the St Regis Hotel. It's just off 5th Avenue, near Central Park in New York. We were there for an inaugural meeting with all the leukaemia clinicians who were going to be involved in the upcoming AS1411 trial.

Our intention was to recruit sixty patients with relapsed or refractory AML. They would be randomised to receive either a standard treatment of high dose cytarabine alone, or high dose cytarabine combined with one of two dose levels of AS1411. It was a reasonable sized study, which should give AS1411 a chance to show what it could do.

Cytarabine had been around for about thirty years. Despite its longevity, it remained the linchpin of most AML treatment strategies. It was a useful drug for the disease but was limited by modest efficacy in many patients and profound toxicity in most. We figured therefore that plenty of room remained for demonstrating an improvement by adding in AS1411. The new kid should be able to show the old-timer a trick or two. So we thought.

We had seven big cancer centres from the US involved (although we were to subsequently add a few more from Australia) and they all came along to New York.

The meeting went very well. The St Regis was exceptionally smart. My room even came with its own personal butler. On Saturday morning I ended up searching high and low all over the hotel for a jacket, which I was convinced I must have lost somewhere. I eventually discovered that the butler had hung it up in the wardrobe. Which was the last place I would have thought of looking.

It wasn't the only thing that was misplaced that weekend though. There was a sense of optimism about the meeting which subsequently turned out to be equally out of place.

"AS1411 has shown real promise against AML in pre-clinical testing," said Rob Stuart in a quote we had written for him. It was part of a press release announcing the start of the trial.[21] "There is a strong biological rationale for evaluating the drug in this disease and so we are pleased to be testing AS1411 in our leukaemia patients."

"Our robust randomised trials should provide clear evidence of any benefit with AS1411," Glyn added. "And therefore have the potential to add significantly to its value over the next couple of years."

However, nothing was to turn out to be so straightforward. The trial took longer to complete than we had anticipated and didn't finish until a year and a half later, at the beginning of 2009. Patients, who had seemingly been in abundance before the study started, appeared to disappear overnight, once it had actually commenced. Which inevitably slowed things down.

It didn't help that one centre, Stanford University in Palo Alto, California, were unable to enter any patients at all. It took the entire eighteen months that the trial was running to negotiate an agreement with their contracts office. It only seemed to be open for half an hour, every other Wednesday. As far as anyone could work out, it was also manned by one blind and deaf person, who lacked a phone or computer. The study had actually finished, before they were in a position to start.

With the loss of Stanford, about half way through the trial we were becoming concerned about the leisurely rate of recruitment. To do something about it, we eventually decided to expand the study to Australia.

It's a country where it is relatively quick and straightforward to get clinical trials up and running. The process is less protracted than applying for a parking permit in Palo Alto. This helped get us back on track but added to the cost and complexity of the whole thing. However we did at least manage to get it finished eventually.

One day early in 2009, Albert was ready with the preliminary results. Albert Chau was our Head of Biometrics, in charge of all the statisticians and computer programmers and database operators. These were the people who churned all the data, turning it into something comprehensible.

Originally from Hong Kong, he'd worked in the UK all his professional life. Apart from being a highly skilled statistician he was also a gourmet, running the acclaimed *Chau on Chow* blog. On top of that, he was an accomplished wildlife photographer, particularly of penguins in remote Arctic tundral parts of the world. He and his partner Russell, also had a disturbingly large collection of Wallace and Gromit memorabilia, distributed throughout their West London house.

But we were a broad church and we could put up with the penguins and the puppets, given how good he was at what he did.

However, when we sat down to have a look at the AML results, we found we couldn't work out what was going on at all.

"It's all Chinese to me Albert," I said, repeating the tired old joke we'd used so many times before, when trying to decipher the complexities of clinical data. He gave me back the same tired old look as always.

As we'd seen in the original Louisville study, AS1411 didn't seem to be causing any extra toxicity in this trial, beyond that which was clearly due to cytarabine. So that was a bonus. But unfortunately, it was also unclear whether it was contributing any extra efficacy either.

The optimal treatment for patients with the sort of relapsed or refractory AML we were studying was controversial. It wasn't helped by the hugely heterogeneous nature of AML patients and how likely they were to respond to therapy of any sort.

Some experts preferred high doses of the single drug cytarabine, whilst others tended to opt for a cocktail of different drugs. There wasn't much evidence that one approach was better than the other. There also wasn't that much information about the best dose of cytarabine to choose. This resulted in a range of differing doses being used, usually with little rhyme or reason. This was AML after all.

This variability made it difficult to estimate the benchmark response rate we should expect in our study, for those patients who'd received cytarabine alone. The results from other trials in the medical literature suggested anywhere between twelve and thirty per cent.[22]

It came as a bit of surprise therefore, when we saw only five per cent of patients had responded in the cytarabine arm in our study. We weren't expecting that. On the other hand, about twenty per cent of patients appeared to have responded in both the lower and the higher dose AS1411 groups.[23]

So on the face of it, AS1411 had a four times higher success rate than cytarabine. We should have been jumping for joy.

But the difficulty was that the patients hadn't received AS1411 alone, they had received AS1411 *and* cytarabine. It was entirely possible that the effect we were seeing in all three treatment groups could just be down to the cytarabine component alone.

The twenty per cent response rate with AS1411 plus cytarabine fitted within the range of twelve to thirty per cent reported in the past for cytarabine by itself. So maybe everything we were seeing was due to the cytarabine. The lower response rate in the cytarabine alone group and the higher response rates with AS1411, could all be nothing more than chance findings. There were only about twenty patients in each of the groups and so it was quite possible that we might see an odd random variation between them, just because of the small numbers involved. You often find that sort of thing happening in clinical trials.

If you took this view of things, AS1411 wasn't contributing anything extra. It was nothing more than a hanger on.

However, if you were a fan of AS1411, the other way of looking at it was that the five per cent response rate represented exactly what cytarabine was doing in this study, low though it was for some reason. The better result of twenty per cent in the AS1411 plus cytarabine groups must be due to the addition of AS1411.

The drawback with this interpretation of events however, was explaining why cytarabine should be doing so much worse this time, compared to other studies in the past. There didn't seem to be any obvious reason. We just couldn't fathom it out.

Once again, AS1411 had thrown us a curved ball. As with many early stage clinical trials, it was difficult to discern just how strong a signal of drug effect we were seeing. It was like walking through a hall of mirrors in the fairground. Whichever way you turned your head, there were different images of the same thing. And some of them were very distorted.

When we looked at the individual patients in the study, it was obvious that they were by and large a very ill group, even by the standards of AML. They all had advanced disease, with many of them having received extensive previous therapy.

Maybe that would explain why the cytarabine effect was so small. Perhaps we had ended up with a group in a worse condition than in other studies in the past. Just by chance. As a consequence, they were less amenable to treatment now. There's only so much response any one drug can drag out of a disease. And so maybe AS1411 really was adding something on top. It was helping the flagging cytarabine go that extra distance.

We just didn't know. This one study seemed to have raised as many questions as we'd hoped it would answer. That was often the case with drug development though. It was the nature of experimentation. One step forwards and two back. As in the earlier Louisville study with kidney cancer, the AML trial was showing a signal of some sort. You couldn't ignore it. But then again you didn't know how real it was either.

Arguably, we weren't that much further forward at the end of the trial than we had been at the beginning, twelve months and several million dollars earlier on.

But in the meantime, whilst AML seemed to remain a firmly closed door, another one was starting to creek open again.

XX

"AS1411 showed an excellent safety profile and promising signs of activity in renal carcinoma patients in Phase I testing," said Dr Jonathan Rosenberg, now at the Dana-Farber Cancer Centre in Boston.[24] He was announcing the start of the AS1411 Phase II kidney cancer study. It was another of our press releases. These were words we had been waiting to hear.

"And so we are delighted to further evaluate its potential in this setting. While a number of new therapies are now available, advanced kidney cancer remains an incurable illness in the large majority and there is still a clear unmet need to improve treatments available to these patients."

Whilst the AML trial had been ticking along, we had managed to catch up on the kidney cancer programme.

We had completed the animal testing and along the way, we had also taken the opportunity to think again about the design of the clinical trial. Taking a fresh look at it, the study now seemed too complicated for an initial assessment in kidney cancer. For various reasons therefore, we now wanted to conduct a more limited trial but still hopefully answer most of the issues the original more elaborate design had been intended to address. In other words, we wanted to have our clinical cake and eat it too. We were looking for a faster and simpler study, which would deliver the same bounty as the slower and more sophisticated one we had originally come up with.

There were innumerable internal discussions about how to achieve this. When dealing with something as open ended as clinical strategy, there are an infinite number of differing positions any one person could choose to adopt. Which is what we subsequently all did. The ensuing debates frequently seemed to involve the conceptual contortions and mental sophistry of mediaeval monks, engaged in intense theological debate.

There is though nothing more awesome than the sight of a group of highly intelligent individuals engaged in the intellectual equivalent of tag team wrestling. Although obviously without the Lycra leotards.

The compromise ended up as a thirty patient study, utilising one dose level of AS1411, for just two cycles of treatment. This was a somewhat attenuated study, compared to the one we had put together the previous year at Mount Zion. That had ambitiously envisaged larger numbers of patients, more dose levels of AS1411, multiple cycles of treatment and a randomised design, with a placebo control group.

At least it still had the same patient population, those who'd failed treatment with a tyrosine kinase inhibitor.

Still, needs must. This was the best we felt we could do under the circumstances. Often in cancer medicine you had to cut your coat according to the cloth you had. Even if that meant wandering around in some very bizarrely shaped garments.

There were five US hospitals taking part in the trial, including Jonathan in Boston and also Damien Laber from Louisville, who'd undertaken the original Phase I study. Showing what a small world it was, we even had Lucky Lara in the study, wearing his other hat as a genitourinary oncologist. That was when he wasn't being a lung cancer expert. He was equally adept at both.

The fact that clinicians were prepared to take part at all showed that some of the shine was coming off the newer agents, which had emerged over the last few years. Many drugs failed to maintain their initial promise, once greater experience was obtained in more widespread clinical practice. This appeared to be what was happening with the kinase inhibitors.

Even so, we knew it would be a struggle to define a therapeutic niche for AS1411, relative to the other available drugs. And so we had gone for broke in a sense. We had decided this study would need to show at least three Louisville miracles, to justify carrying on with AS1411 in kidney cancer.

We would be looking for three complete responses out of the thirty patients in the study. That was a similar frequency to the one out of twelve seen in the earlier Phase I trial. It would almost certainly require divine intervention to achieve this, because complete responses were few and far between in these sorts of patients. The drug interleukin-2 (IL-2) was known to be able to do this, in a very small proportion of patients. However it was so toxic that it put most of them into intensive care along the way.

But crucially, years of experience with IL-2 had taught clinicians how to select the five per cent or so of patients who were the best candidates, with the greatest chance of success. With AS1411, we didn't have this advantage and so were shooting in the dark.

Because we were looking for Louisville miracles, there was disagreement about whether to actually include Louisville in the study again. As with early stage oncology trials with any new drug, there was an argument that the results of a subsequent study would have more credibility if they were reproduced in different centres from the original one. It was the *lightening doesn't strike twice* line of reasoning.

The counter was that Louisville had recorded the miracle in the first place. If you had a proven goal scorer already, why keep him on the subs bench, when you were playing such a crucial game.

171

In the end, we included them, largely because we feared this would be a difficult trial to recruit and they would be likely to put in more patients more quickly than most other places, due to their unbridled enthusiasm for the drug. And the fact that a week or two in hospital would be a highlight of the Louisville social season.

Eventually, the study got going towards the end of 2008 and actually took just over a year to find thirty patients. That was much quicker than any of us were expecting. Which showed how rapidly things could change in cancer medicine. Eighteen months earlier, it would have been all but impossible to find patients for a study like this. Now, it appeared to be no problem at all.

With the trial completed, one frosty Thursday morning in November 2009, Albert came to see me with the results. We sat down to look at them. "It's all Chinese to me Albert," I started. He gave me back his withering look.

But the results really were far from clear this time around too. They might as well have been in Cantonese.

Well, some of the outcomes were fairly straightforward at least. There weren't any complete responses. The best we could come up with was one partial response. There had been no miracles. That was very obvious. So our Lourdes-like luck seemed to have run out. Thursday didn't seem to be one of the lucky days in the Chinese calendar. Along with the lack of responses, there was again a lack of any real toxicity with AS1411, just as we'd seen in previous studies.

The complexity came when we looked at the progression free survival data we had also collected in the study. It was a measure of how long the drug kept the disease at bay and stopped it spreading and advancing. This now became all the more important, given that we hadn't seen any effect on tumor shrinkage or response rate. It would be our only clue as to whether the drug was actually doing anything.

In the study, the clinicians themselves had read the MRI scans, to work out when an individual patient's disease had started to progress. But we also had the same scans interpreted independently by a radiologist who hadn't been involved in the study. And so we had both an *investigator* assessment and an *independent* assessment.

That's a normal thing to do in cancer trials, especially ones where the clinicians are aware of which drugs the patients are receiving. When reading scans and making measurements, physicians are often overly generous in their assessment of responses. They can't help giving a new drug the benefit of the doubt. And so normally you'd have the results checked independently, by someone with a more dispassionate view of things.

When you do that, the effect of a drug usually turns out to be less, typically by about ten or fifteen per cent, compared to what the clinicians involved in the study thought. But in this case it was the *other* way round. The progression free survival (PFS) was 3.9 months, according to the independent assessment and 1.9 months according to the investigator one.[25] That was an unusually large difference between the two different interpretations, as well as being in the wrong direction.

This created a problem for us, as things weren't happening the way they usually did. Which meant we didn't really know how to interpret what we were seeing. It became even worse, when we compared the results to those of the Novartis RECORD-1 trial with everolimus.

That had been a study in the *same* sorts of kidney cancer patients and had also included a placebo group. So in many ways, it was a good trial to use as a yardstick. The everolimus PFS had been 4.9 months and the placebo PFS 1.9 months.[20] And this pattern of results had been essentially the same, whether you used the independent or the investigator view of things.

So, in terms of working out what was happening with AS1411, if we believed the *independent* PFS of 3.9 months, then this was very similar to the everolimus PFS. That suggested AS1411 was actually doing something. However, if we thought the *investigator* PFS of 1.9 months was more accurate, this would make AS1411 no better than placebo, indicating it was doing nothing.

We couldn't work out which one was more relevant, the investigator PFS or the independent one. We couldn't find a reason why the two were so different. Which made it difficult to decide which to put more reliance on. It was yet another example of the elusiveness of AS1411. It seemed to evade all attempts to characterise it, in a way which didn't turn out confusing and contradictory. Again we found ourselves not really having any clear idea of whether this drug was doing anything.

But in a way, it didn't matter. Even if AS1411 had been exerting some sort of beneficial effect on PFS, the drug was probably still dead. At least as far as a future in kidney cancer was concerned.

All it would have meant was that, at best, AS1411 was not quite as good as everolimus. Which was further advanced, better established and infinitely easier to administer. We'd decided in advance that we required a dramatic effect on complete response rates. We needed the hand of God to touch this study but He seemed to be looking the other way at the time.

In the light of this intransigence from the Almighty, we all agreed it was finally time to throw in the towel. It was a rare moment of unanimity, as far as AS1411 was concerned. We slipped out an announcement, just before Christmas, saying that we wouldn't be pursuing it any further in kidney cancer.[26]

Although the drug now seemed to have one foot firmly planted in the grave, AS1411 wasn't about to give up that easily. We still needed another AML trial, to see if we could unlock the puzzle left by the previous study.

Whatever the cost, Glyn and the Board seemed willing to give up an arm and a leg for it.

We admired his conviction and his courage. It was a real example of leadership in the face of adversity and setback. Glyn was at his best when our backs were up against a wall. The bigger the problem and the more insoluble the solution, the more dismissive he would become of the difficulties. It encouraged the rest of us to dig more deeply within ourselves and find that little extra bit we didn't even realise was there.

XXI

It wouldn't have surprised me therefore, as I turned around at the increasingly urgent sound of the stump tapping on the window of my car, to see that it was actually Glyn. Maybe he'd made the ultimate sacrifice and given up a limb, to keep the legs on AS1411, as it were.

But it couldn't really have been him. It was January 2010 and it wasn't London. Instead, I was stuck in one of the interminable traffic jams which seem to plague Mumbai. I silently urged the driver to somehow carve a way through the sea of motorised rickshaws, battered buses and over laden lorries, all competing for the same tiny stretch of road in front of us.

I looked out of the window, at the rest of the indigent beggar attached to the stump. He couldn't have been more than about twenty. Dirty and dishevelled, he had a face covered in grime. But his eyes burned with a fierce glow born of desperation and destitution. Or drugs. The remaining stump of his left leg kept tapping away and the rhythm was augmented when his fingerless right hand started drumming incessantly on the roof.

The windows and doors of the car were locked. I'd been forewarned never to give in to this sort of emotional blackmail and actually hand over money. God's knows why not though. I felt all the more uncomfortable to be sitting in the back of a leather clad, air-conditioned BMW. Which was being driven by a white uniformed chauffeur complete with cap. It was hard to get used to the brutal collision of searing poverty and suffocating opulence which had characterised my twelve hours in India so far.

The Mumbai Oberoi Hotel on Nariman Point, overlooking the Arabian Ocean, had been surreal enough. I'd arrived there from the airport in the middle of the previous night. The Oberoi, protected by its own machine gun nests at the entrance, was undoubtedly well towards the top of the very long list of luxurious hotels I had stayed in around the world. My suite was bigger than my house back in England. In fact the walk in wardrobe was bigger than what I called home.

But opposite the heavily fortified gates to the hotel, there was a whole family living in a bush, which sprouted out of a bit of grass in the middle of a mini roundabout. *A bush*. A bit further down the road another group appeared to have set up home in a large concrete circle, which looked part of a mains drainage project.

It was hard not to feel guilty, almost ashamed, when comparing your hand of cards to those these people had been dealt. On the bright side, at least they didn't face the difficult dilemma of which of the hotel's three swimming pools to choose from though.

I was making my way now, in the hotel car, across gridlocked Mumbai to the Tata Memorial Hospital, in the Parel region of the city. Founded in 1941, it had evolved over the years into India's Comprehensive Cancer Centre, treating over forty five thousand patients annually. It dealt with every type of malignancy, having facilities for medical oncology, surgery, radiotherapy and rehabilitation.

I was on the quest for centres around the world to participate in our second AS1411 AML study. The first trial had been undertaken in the US and Australia only but had taken a long time to finish. In an attempt to speed things up, this time around we were also going to use hospitals in India, Taiwan and Korea. South Korea that is. We weren't yet desperate enough to consider the Pyongyang Polyclinic, or whatever they had up there in the People's Paradise.

We'd modified the study design too, in an attempt to get a stronger signal of efficacy. This time we meant business. There were still three groups. One receiving cytarabine alone and the other two a combination of cytarabine and AS1411. But we'd increased the dose of cytarabine by a third from twelve gm/m^2 (*of body surface area*) to sixteen gm/m^2. This was an heroic level of chemotherapy.

We'd also raised the higher dose of AS1411 to eighty mg/kg (of body weight). This was a dose twice as high as anything we'd looked at before in the clinic. The lower dose of AS1411 we kept at forty mg/kg. We also increased the number of patients from twenty to thirty per group.

Probably most importantly of all, we had refined the types of patients we were looking for. We still wanted relapsed or refractory ones. But this time, we would only accept those who'd received much less treatment in the past and whose disease was at an earlier stage than in the previous study. By doing this, we hoped to pick a more *responsive* group of patients, in whom it would be easier to detect a drug effect.

The process of developing a drug involves taking one study design, which may not have given you the answer you were hoping for and considering altering it in as many ways as you can think of. You do this to maximise your chances of getting the result you want in the next trial. Learning from your mistakes, if you like. But the skill is in actually trying to *minimise* the changes, so that you can dissect out which ones were really responsible for producing a better result second time around.

Change too much and you can never work out which alteration really made the difference. Change too little and you'll just get the same as last time. The eventual design is a compromise between these two opposing tendencies. And it was probably about right with that second AML trial. It was sufficiently different from the first study to give AS1411 a better chance. But there was still substantial overlap between the two, so that we weren't effectively starting all over again.

However, there were still one or two big differences between the studies. One of those was definitely the inclusion of the Tata Memorial Hospital.

XXII

India's leading cancer institute was situated down a crowded street, lined by ramshackle rows of tiny shops, food outlets, tobacconists, light industrial units, coffin makers, rickshaw repairers and electrical engineers, all crowded together in a cacophony of confusion. The hospital was slightly set back from the road and looked like any one of the innumerable nondescript sprawl of government buildings, which proliferated throughout Mumbai.

Built in the early 1950s, the hospital hadn't changed since. There was a large central entrance area, with all the anonymity of a railway station concourse, and two long narrow corridors radiating out from either side. These contained the different outpatient clinics. Turning into one corridor, the scene was like news footage from a refugee camp, after a particularly devastating natural disaster. Going in the other direction wasn't any better.

The corridor was a couple of hundred yards long with doors leading off it on either side, each bearing the name of a particular type of cancer, written on a faded wooden sign. *Breast Cancer, Colon Cancer, Lung Cancer, Prostate Cancer, Stomach Cancer.* It was like the index of a textbook. They were little wooden signs, eventually heralding little wooden crosses.

There were people everywhere. People sitting on benches. People lying on benches. People lying underneath benches. People lying on the floor. People on top of one another, like an emaciated circus troupe. People milled around anywhere there was any space, which was nowhere. It was almost impossible to move. They were all patients and their relatives. Some appeared really unwell. All had that look of resigned inevitability, which seemed to characterise trying to get anything done in India.

There were patients with pretty much every type of malignancy, all clustered in little anatomical groups. Breast cancer here, prostate three doors down that way, lung cancer over there, by the toilets. There were no concessions to confidentiality here. You wore your cancer classification on your sleeve. If you could afford clothes that is. They all waited their turn, whenever that might come, to be taken through the door marked with their particular disease and into the clinic beyond to meet their particular destiny.

I struggled through the crowd to eventually find the door with *Haematology* marked above it. On the assumption that I obviously didn't look like a patient and that it was therefore acceptable to barge in ahead of all the others and their patiently accumulated hours of waiting, I shoved my way through the door. On the other side was another narrower corridor, leading off to a labyrinth of other rooms.

It was much quieter here though, unlike the mass of pulsating patients outside. In fact, there weren't any patients in sight. You'd have thought a few would have inadvertently trickled in, carried there by Brownian motion if nothing else. But it was completely free of cancer clutter. There was a small station with a metal desk and some office furniture, all looking like original fittings from way back when the hospital's doors had first opened. It was staffed by three or four people, who appeared to collectively be doing the job of just one.

I was there to see Dr Hari Menon, a leading Indian leukaemia specialist, who was going to take part in the AS1411 study. Asking for him provoked a flurry of activity behind the desk. There seemed to be lots of different documents needing to be consulted to confirm his existence, despite the fact that I could clearly see his name on a door a bit further down the corridor.

A number of frantic phone calls ensued in urgently guttural Gujarati, each increasingly more vehement. This was inevitably followed by the furious stamping of various bits of paper. This appeared to be the Indian equivalent of "the doctor will see you in a moment."

Eventually, being led into the small room which bore Dr Menon's name, he rose to greet me from behind a desk just as battered and outdated as the one outside. He was much younger than I'd anticipated, looking only about twenty five or so.

"You have a very busy clinic," I said, gesturing through the walls to the milling masses somewhere on the other side.

"The doctors are very busy," he agreed.

"We are very excited at Antisoma about working with you on this trial and your support for our nucleolin hypothesis of AML," I continued.

He gave one of those head rolling gyrations Indians seemed to do, when they are confronted by something perplexing or puzzling but said nothing.

"So how many beds do you have in the hospital then?" I asked, after the silence had gone on for a while.

"About seven hundred and fifty," he finally volunteered, after a period of intense introspection.

"Are you involved in many other clinical trials at the moment?"

He paused and looked me up and down for a long moment. "I'm not Dr Menon," he eventually helpfully explained. "He isn't here. He is in some other place. I will go to that place and bring him to this one."

With that, he disappeared through the door and I never saw him again. I waited a while, hoping the process of getting Dr Menon from one part of the hospital to another wouldn't involve too much form filling and paper stamping along the way. But judging from my recent experiences I was mentally preparing myself for a long wait. Maybe I should send the driver back to the Oberoi for an overnight bag.

XXIII

Hari Menon, when he eventually arrived, was charming, articulate and spoke wonderfully fluent English, having trained at MD Anderson in the US earlier in his career. He also looked a bit older than twenty five and a lot more experienced.

Hari explained that the hospital divided patients into three groups. The majority, unsurprisingly, were more or less completely indigent and didn't have the funds to pay for any sort of medical care themselves. Their costs were covered fully by government funding. Another group were private patients with medical insurance, who tended to get the best treatment. The third was a group somewhere in between, who didn't have private insurance but were deemed able to contribute something to their health care.

It sounded like a process requiring an awful lot of form filling along the way.

We were, he explained to my amazement, in the private end of the hospital right now. God alone knew what the rest of it was like then.

These sorts of chaotic clinics weren't as bad as they looked, he explained. Once you got used to them, you could get through the patients with surprising efficiency. I found this hard to believe, coming from Europe but he looked so confident and relaxed about it all.

According to Hari, they were able to treat most patients with AML to broadly similar standards as in Europe or the US, routinely using the same treatment approaches. One of the few things AML had going for it as a disease was that the drugs used were so old they tended to be cheap enough even for hospitals with the most limited funding.

The big problem in India though was patients who needed a bone marrow or stem cell transplant. Which was usually the majority. These were only available to those fortunate enough to be able to fund the full cost themselves. There was no money from public sources at all. The concept of bone marrow donation was also far from well established in India. That resulted in a big shortage of tissue, even if people had been able to pay for it. Which inevitably meant there weren't that many transplants done in India and therefore few patients received a potentially curative treatment.

That was bad if you happened to have AML but ironically helped our AS1411 trial no end. The lack of this treatment approach resulted in many more relapsed patients knocking around, who might otherwise have avoided falling into that unfortunate condition, if only transplantation had been more widely available. It was a macabre case of swings and roundabouts.

We walked through the hospital to visit Hari's leukaemia wards, which were located on one of the upper floors. As we left the outpatient clinic, I could feel the collective quizzical stare of the amassed patient throng. They were all doing the frantic mental arithmetic of recalculating how much longer Hari's departure meant they would now have to wait. Days, by the look of it.

Everywhere there were jostling crowds of people queuing for one thing or another, whether to pay bills at the cashiers, collect something from the pharmacy, wait for a blood test or an X-ray or simply to find out which part of the hospital they were supposed to be in next. Whatever it was, wherever it was, there were people queuing for it. And everyone was clutching sheaths of paperwork of one sort or another, which were indispensable to getting anything done.

Little men wandered around with large kettles swinging from metal chains, selling tea. Rusty and tarnished, the cups looked as though they harboured more diseases than all the patients put together. It was however the only activity in sight, which didn't seem to have a substantial administrative burden attached to it.

The air was hot and humid, with a people smell so strong that you became physically aware of sucking it in and out. It was like trying to breathe through a hood over your head. I wondered what my personally allocated *Manager of Luxury* back at the Oberoi would have made of all this.

Hari led me down a side corridor which became narrower and narrower, forcing us to walk in single file. We came to an abrupt end opposite what appeared to be a broom cupboard. It turned out to be the world's slowest and smallest lift. Crammed into a cage about the size of an average chest of drawers, we ascended two floors at a pace so slow there was almost no discernible sense of movement.

Emerging on to the Leukaemia Floor and stretching forcibly, in an attempt to regain an upright posture, I stooped into the nearest ward like some simian forebear. Entering was like going around one of those exhibitions on the history of medicine at the Science Museum in London. Nothing could have changed here from the early 1950s.

There were rows of patients, crammed together and lying listlessly on what weren't even proper beds, just tables really. Like the sort of thing you could remember your dad using to put paste on to wallpaper, when you were a kid helping him do the decorating at home.

There wasn't anything else at all. No curtains, no bedside cabinets, no TV, no blankets, no bowls of fruit or uneaten boxes of Terry's Chocolates.

No hope, no privacy. Nothing to help personalise and fight off the anonymous institutionalisation that terminal illness and repetitive hospitalisation rapidly came to represent.

We moved on to the isolation ward for patients who were at high risk of serious infections, because their body's defences had been so badly damaged by chemotherapy. In the US they would be in rooms of their own. There would be strict controls to minimise being inadvertently exposed to bacteria or other sources of infections, from staff or visitors or even their own food.

But here, there were patients arranged together in serried rows along the edges of a large open room. Some had drips in their arm, some didn't. Some looked well, some definitely didn't. I wasn't sure if one wasn't dead.

It seemed identical to the other ward, except that we had to put plastic covers over our shoes before coming in. That seemed a token gesture at best. In an environment like this, a packet of medicated *Wet Ones* would represent a substantial technical advance. From a western perspective, it was surprising if not shocking. It wasn't clear how you could manage something as complicated and dangerous as leukaemia, in conditions of such seeming deprivation.

And yet all this appeared irrelevant to Hari and the rest of the staff. They knew what job they needed to do and how to get it done. They didn't need, although doubtlessly would have liked, the sophistication of a better equipped western hospital, with its endless facilities and finesse. There was a quiet determination and air of control, in the midst of complete chaos, that was both impressive and reassuring. Whilst the physicians at MD Anderson, or any other ultra-advanced medical facility, might be better *technicians*, I had no doubt that Hari Menon was the better *clinician*.

The US doctors might have more technology at their disposal but people like Hari hadn't forgotten the art of sitting down at the bedside and working out what was wrong and what to do about it, improvising if necessary to make the means meet the end.

We had done some research before deciding to use India in the trial. There wasn't a huge amount of information in the medical literature about Indian centres. What did exist suggested that they could achieve comparable short term results to most of the western world. They could get patients into that all important initial remission. After that though, survival tended to be much better in more sophisticated medical environments, as you'd expect.

But for our trial, what we were most interested in was seeing whether AS1411 could improve remission rates. That was the key. The rest, such as longer term survival, was secondary. Indian centres should therefore serve our purposes. Going to India was like buying a car without a warranty. It might cause us problems later on but at the moment all we were interested in was driving it off the garage forecourt and round the block. As long as it was reliable enough for that short journey, we were happy enough.

I left the hospital with huge admiration for Hari Menon and others like him. They took in their stride every day a workload that most US or UK clinicians would struggle with over a whole week. And they did so more despite the facilities at their disposal, rather than because of them. And yet they still achieved acceptable results most of the time. It really seemed possible they could meet the exacting demands of the AS1411 study, to just the same standard as all the other participating hospitals scattered over four different continents.

How they would overcome the lack of expensive anti-infective drugs, intensive care units and things like that was a little unclear. But surely they must have figured out ways around that. They seemed to be very adept at taking the little they had and making it go a long way.

Little did we know how wrong we'd eventually turn out to be.

XXIV

Driving back through the madness of Mumbai, it was a reminder once again of the unavoidable geographical diversity of modern oncology trials.

Cancer might be the second commonest cause of death worldwide, it might affect three out of four people in the West at some point in their lives, we might all know someone who had it but *still* only five per cent of patients with cancer ever made it to a clinical study. The vast majority were inaccessible to the testing of new drugs.

The only way to cope with the never-ending demand for a limited supply of patients, was to expand to ever more distant geographical territories. What would happen after our inexorable march eastwards ultimately ended up at the Kabul Comprehensive Cancer Centre was unclear. We would have to worry about that at the time.

For now at least, the arrangement of far flung clinical trials seemed to work well for all involved. Companies gained greater access to patients, which offered the possibility of clinical trials being completed more rapidly. For the clinicians and patients, it represented a chance to receive not only new experimental drugs but often also established ones as well. These might otherwise have been beyond their financial reach, were they not provided for free as part of a trial. And for the hospitals it meant some funding, in return for the use of their facilities, which they otherwise wouldn't have received.

Whilst everyone gained from this multinationalism, it did have a cost attached. There was a substantial complexity to managing any number of diverse and disparate countries and cultures, seemingly having in common only the enormity of the distances separating them. Cancer trials weren't the kind of undertakings you could simply set up and then sit back, waiting for them to run according to plan. That would never work. They needed constant attention and nurturing, if they weren't to unravel into a complexity of confusion and miscommunication.

You had to go and meet all the people involved, on a regular basis. Sometimes there were problems specific to a particular hospital which needed a visit to sort out. But often just making the journey had a value all by itself. Being prepared to travel half way round the world, for an hour's meeting, definitely showed how much you valued someone and their involvement in your study.

In return, clinicians often seemed to feel obliged to make an extra effort. Quite often, a centre which hadn't recruited for ages would come up with a couple more patients out of thin air, shortly after going to see them. It nearly always did the trick.

It did however require a lot of travelling.

At Antisoma, we had perfected the art of the day trip. Even to Australia. There was a British Airways flight leaving London at ten in the evening and getting to Singapore about twelve hours later. After a brief interlude, blinking your way around the garishly floodlit shopping concourses of Changi International Airport, it was another ten hours to Melbourne. The plane arrived about six in the morning and then there was an evening flight leaving at six pm, going back to London via Bangkok.

That left plenty of time to get to a hospital and meet people. It did though mean going through two sunrises and two sunsets to get there and then a day of wandering around vaguely comatose. The key to coping with this was to clean your teeth and change your underpants on a regular basis, every six hours or so. It somehow broke the monotony down into psychologically manageable chunks. And kept the cabin crew guessing what you were doing in the toilets for so long and so frequently.

The big advantage was that you could leave London on a Monday evening and get back on a Thursday morning. It wasn't long enough to start adapting to the time difference and at worst felt like a couple of nights bad sleep. It did however require an ability to slumber through the duty free trolley crashing down the airplane aisle, trying to sell you a four foot Toblerone at three in the morning. That and being able to survive the British Airways fish pie, if it was on the menu. This was undoubtedly a much greater danger to the travelling public than deep vein thrombosis, terrorist hijacking, engine failure or any other potentially life threatening hazard of modern aviation.

Taking stock at the end of April, in the weeks after the ASA404 failure, it was too soon to know how useful an asset AS1411 might become. The history of the drug hadn't exactly been promising though and it was now in a final clinical trial in one of the toughest and most resistant cancers on the planet. There couldn't be that much hope it would come through and deliver an unexpectedly promising result.

Along with amonafide however, it was the only hand we had left to play. We were down to our last few chips and there was a real danger we would be asked to leave the casino soon, if our luck didn't change.

So we had to make sure nothing happened to threaten either programme during the rest of the year. We would need to nurse them both along, until we could get some initial results at the beginning of 2011. That and hope for the arrival of a white knight out of somewhere, to revive and rescue our fortunes. It didn't even have to be a white knight. A bitter and twisted black one would do, if all else failed.

In the absence of that, our fate revolved around two drugs for a condition where there had been no significant progress in the last fifty years. Was there, we idly wondered, anything in the history of that last half century of cancer drug development, which might have relevance to us in our current predicament.

Could the lessons of the past teach us something useful for the present and help us avoid potential disasters for the future?

FIVE

YESTERDAY'S PAPERS

Why is it taking so long to get the upper hand with this disease? The history of cancer medicine, from a rabbit with syphilis to a man on the moon. Can Antisoma learn from the lessons of the past?

I

Around the time of the ASA404 collapse, in the spring of 2010, the prestigious journal *Science* announced the creation of the world's first *synthetic* organism.[1] A group of scientists from the J. Craig Venter Institute in Maryland, had managed to chemically synthesise all the genes of a bacterium (called *Mycoplasma mycoides*) using just a computer record as a guide. They then transferred these artificial genes back into a different type of bacterium (called *Mycoplasma capricolum*) from which all the normal genes had been removed.

Amazingly, the bacterium was then able to function and replicate entirely normally but this time as *mycoides* not *capricolum,* in accordance with the artificial genes it had been given. It marked the end of a fifteen year and forty million dollar research program. In the words of Craig Venter, himself the originator of the Human Genome Project, it was "the first species...to have its parents be a computer."[2] His genomics was much better than his grammar.

In a tentative fashion, this amounted to the bypassing of Nature. It opened the way for the generation of life in the laboratory. According to Arthur Caplan, Professor of Bioethics at the University of Pennsylvania, it was "one of the most important scientific achievements in the history of mankind."[3] It may not have been quite *that* significant. At least not yet. But the potential was there and it raised many issues about the future dangers posed by such advances.

However, there was an even bigger question.

This kind of science provided the power to take over and replace the very essence of a cell and have it do a different bidding. Biology didn't get more fundamental than that. If you could take control of an entire organism, then why was it proving so difficult to rein in a malignant cell, which was running amok and out of control? With techniques like this at our disposal, surely we should be able to get the upper hand with cancer?

The answer is that cancer has hijacked the most powerful of all biological forces. It has subverted Nature itself for its own ghastly purposes, using it to foil our attempts to defeat the disease. Venter and his scientists needed advanced computing to manipulate genes and take control. Cancer does the same thing by instinct alone.

II

Millions of years of evolution have resulted in exquisitely complicated and interrelated systems, which act to keep the normal cell tightly under control. And it needs to be. We all start off as a single cell, formed by the fusion of a sperm and an egg. From that, a process of division and differentiation leads ultimately to the seventy five *trillion* or so cells which comprise a normal human being. That's about fifteen thousand times more cells than there are people on the whole planet. Put another way, there are more cells in someone's little finger than all the people in China.

Unless they are kept in check, only dividing when they need to, all hell would break loose. Cells would be proliferating out of control all over the place. To prevent this, nature has developed an elaborate system of checks and balances regulating the whole process. There are multiple pathways which *promote* cell division and each tends to go hand in hand with an opposing pathway which in turn *prevents* cells dividing.

These individual pairs of stimulatory and inhibitory pathways exist in a state of dynamic tension. One or the other prevails at any given time, depending on how strongly they are each being driven by signals from outside the cell. It's a kind of *yin-yang* thing, hopefully producing perfect harmony.

If a human cell were a car engine, you would be able to rev it right up to the limit without detecting the slightest vibration or sign of internal movement. So perfectly balanced would it be. This allows the state of a cell to be controlled with an extraordinary degree of precision.

Every complicated aspect of cell survival and cell division is regulated by its own set of positive and negative pathways, each consisting of a series of chemical messengers transmitting signals like a baton passed on in a relay race. Positive and negative signals pulse back and forth in a complex interrelated flux. It's like the autopilot on an aircraft, making continual tiny adjustments to keep the plane at a constant altitude by preventing it falling or rising. And like on a plane, there is always a backup. If one system goes down there are two or three others which could take over.

It has taken Nature since the dawn of evolution come up with a system this complicated and to learn how to keep control of it. If you drew out all the cell control pathways, or at least the ones we already know about, it would rapidly resemble a map of the Tokyo subway system. And nothing on Earth is more complicated than that. Which is why cancer is such a formidable opponent. It takes all that elaborate machinery, so carefully constructed since the very origins of life on Earth, and uses it for its own evil purpose. It's like stealing the enemy's secret weapon and turning it back on them.

Cancer cells exist simply to divide and spread. That's all they are interested in. They often don't even have time to mature properly. Which is why some cancers are so primitive looking it is almost impossible to work out which part of the body they originate from.

With an aggressive cancer type, such as advanced melanoma, a tumor can double in size every sixty days or so. In some cases, it can be as fast as a week. Given that there are about a billion cancer cells in every cubic centimetre of tumor, it needs a lot of cells to be dividing very rapidly to achieve that sort of growth rate. In fact, cancer cells divide so fast that eventually the tumor can't keep up and growth then has to slow down, due to an inadequate blood supply.

Malignant cells are able to achieve these prodigious rates of proliferation, at least early on, because they have the ability to turn all the normal cellular control mechanisms on their heads. They can switch off the inhibitory control pathways, which normally dampen down growth and proliferation. And they can turn the stimulatory ones up to full volume. Because evolution has produced such a sophisticated system of *regulation*, the converse is that the malignant process can now turn this into an equally sophisticated system of *dysregulation*. By subverting so many of the pathways so thoughtfully provided by Nature, the malignant transformation of a cell can propagate itself by generating self-sustaining growth signals on multiple levels, all at the same time.

And that's why it is so difficult to make big steps in treating any particular malignancy. You can use a drug to attack the cancer on one level, maybe blocking one or two pathways which were stimulating uncontrolled growth. But sooner or later, the cancer can regroup and divert its resources down one of the remaining intact growth signalling systems.

You then need to strike again and take that one out, to have any hope of gaining another temporary respite. It's jungle warfare. You make a small advance against the enemy but then it melts away, to keep coming back at you from a different direction, time, after time, after time.

So effectively cancer is taking advantage of four billion years of biological evolution to thwart our attempts to attack it. It's not surprising that so many drugs fail in the face of such an unfair contest. Taking on cancer was always going to be an uphill struggle, given that we have only been fighting back for the last hundred years or so.

Since 1908 in fact, when it all started with a rabbit suffering from syphilis.

III

Until his death in 1915 at the age of sixty one, Paul Ehrlich was a prolific German medical researcher and eventual Nobel Prize winner. In the early years of the twentieth century, whilst at the *Institut für Experimentelle Therapie* in Frankfurt, he became the first person to demonstrate the value of animal models of disease, in screening chemical compounds for potential therapeutic activity in man.

Results of experiments with his rabbit model of syphilis were to lead by 1910 directly to the drug Salvarsan 606 (so called because it was the 606th in the series of compounds tested). This was to become for a while, the world's most widely prescribed medicine. It went on to remain the standard treatment for syphilis until the advent of penicillin in the late 1940s.

In achieving this advance against syphilis, he was also indirectly making the first major contribution to cancer drug development. He just didn't realise it at the time. Ehrlich had managed to validate the general concept of animal *models* of disease. This would turn out to be the essential first step towards discovering effective cancer chemotherapy.

Ehrlich couldn't claim the credit for the development of animal models *specifically* for cancer though. That was to come from the foresight of a historical contemporary of his, a Buffalo surgeon called Roswell Park. Park was becoming increasingly frustrated with the almost non-existent treatment options for patients with cancer.

In 1898, along with Edward Butler, publisher of the *Buffalo Evening News*, he founded the eponymous Roswell Park Cancer Institute, the world's first medical centre dedicated to the research and treatment of cancer. Starting as just three rooms in the University of Buffalo School of Medicine, it has grown to now occupy an entire campus of twenty five acres in downtown Buffalo, New York State.

Park was one of the first to recognise the enormity of the health burden cancer would come to represent. He also deplored the inadequacy of the then prevailing lack of organised efforts to investigate it. There was no systematic attempt to understand cancer. Historically, everything had been based on chance clinical findings and observations.

A typical example of this lucky dip approach was the use of *Fowler's solution,* to treat chronic leukaemia. Named after a Staffordshire physician Thomas Fowler, his solution, which consisted of a mixture of arsenic trioxide and potassium bicarbonate, was originally introduced in 1786 as a general tonic. It was the *Red Bull* of its day.

Almost a century later, in 1865, the German physician Heinrich Lissauer reported the use of Fowler's solution to treat a seemingly moribund thirty two year old female patient with chronic leukaemia, apparently with beneficial effect.[4] After five more months in hospital, she was well enough to be discharged. It was a miraculous turnaround. Following this observation, arsenic containing compounds were to remain in use for the treatment of various leukaemias until the 1930s, when they fell out of favour with the advent of radiation therapy.

Arsenic is a case of medicine coming full circle. It's the oldest recorded anti-cancer treatment, having been mentioned as far back as 1500 BC, when it was used by ancient Egyptians to treat malignant ulcers.[5] Three and a half thousand years later, arsenic (trioxide) was approved in the US in 2001, for use in a particular type of leukaemia, known as acute promyelocytic leukaemia (APL). This is a disease where it has proven to be particularly effective, even by current standards.

Modern biology has now revealed that arsenic reverses the particular genetic abnormality (the *PML-RAR* mutation) which characterises APL.[6] By acting to block a specific gene defect, arsenic trioxide has travelled all the way from pre-history to become one of the molecular medicines at the very forefront of the biotechnology revolution.

Obviously, Lissauer couldn't have known any of that though. His use of arsenic was based on nothing more than the observation that horses looked healthier and enjoyed glossier coats after being given a dose or two. Why this led him to conclude that it might be of value in treating leukaemia is sadly lost to history.

It was however the entire scientific basis for what was the earliest documented successful therapeutic intervention against a malignant disease. In reality, it was nothing more than a serendipitous event based on chance observation. It certainly lacked any experimental basis or rational justification.

Park recognised that this historically haphazard approach could never meet the challenge of finding effective cancer therapies. His opinion was that:

"Only with a deliberate, well planned, combined attack from various directions by means fitted for such work could real advances be made, and the relationship of laboratory work, clinical study and education must be closely associated."[7]

For the time, this was a revolutionary view and anticipated, by at least a generation, the emergence of the integrated approach which characterises all modern biomedical research today.

IV

Excited by Park's vision, in 1901 a young English chemist called George Clowes emigrated from Ipswich to Buffalo, to join the New York State Institute for the Study of Malignant Disease, as Roswell Park was then known. This was despite having briefly worked in the labs of Paul Ehrlich in Germany and being advised there by the great man that a career in cancer research would most likely lead only to despair and despondency. Despite the enormity of his achievements, it appeared that Ehrlich wasn't one of life's natural optimists.

It can't have helped when he found out that his first work in Buffalo was on the relationship of freezing point depression and specific gravity of urine. It didn't exactly sound like ground breaking research. Furthermore, the facilities at Clowes' disposal, in those early days, were rudimentary at best, as recorded by one of his contemporaries, Ernest Tyzzer, who would go on to become one of the leading American parasitologists of his day:

"With my present facilities I find too large a portion of my time is taken up in routine work – cleaning slides, cover glasses and other glassware, imbedding of tissues in paraffin and technical work of such a nature that anyone of moderate intelligence could learn in a short time to perform it satisfactorily. Some operations, such as the inoculation of mice necessitate a helper and up to the present I have been obliged to depend on the transient aid of friends.

I feel that a girl, such as may be hired for $40.00 a month, to do such work as cleaning glassware, imbedding tissue, cutting sections would add not only to the amount but the character of the work."[8]

It wasn't a lot of resource with which to start tackling the greatest therapeutic challenge of all time.

Despite these limitations, by 1903 Clowes was well in his stride though, producing a paper entitled *"A Theoretical Note on the Vital and Toxic Theories of Cancer and their Bearing on the Parasite Theory."*[9] This referred to a belief, popular at the time, that cancer was an infectious disease caused by some kind of intracellular parasite, which somehow stimulated the host cells to start proliferating uncontrollably.

It would also have not been lost on Clowes that Ehrlich's great success had been to use an animal model of another infectious disease, syphilis, to develop one of the most widely used drugs of the time with which to treat it. Maybe that was the way forwards for cancer therapy too, he hypothesised.

These considerations helped eventually guide Clowes towards his really important contribution to cancer medicine. This came, somewhat improbably, following a successful transatlantic journey from Denmark made by two white mice.

A year earlier, Clowes' colleague Dr Harvey Gaylord had returned from a trip to the laboratories of the Scandinavian researcher Professor Carl Olaf Jensen, who was Director of the Danish Veterinary and Agricultural College.

Jensen had been working on trying to "infect" mice with cancer and Gaylord brought back two white mice with actively growing tumors. Unfortunately, the mice survived the transatlantic trip, only to die on the train from New York to Buffalo.

However in the laboratory, Clowes took tumor tissue from the two dead mice and injected it into other mice. He wanted to see if he could "inoculate" the malignancy.

But it wasn't that straightforward. The tumor tissue from one of the dead mice failed to take at all and didn't grow in any of the animals it was injected into. With the other dead mouse though, something quite different happened. The injected tumor from this second animal started multiplying in the majority of mice and in some it continued to *grow with great virulence, showing no tendency to regression.*[10] But in other mice the tumor grew for a while, then appeared to spontaneously shrink and disappear again.

Furthermore, Clowes found that if he took blood samples from the mice where the tumor was shrinking and injected the blood into mice whose tumors were still growing, they too then started to regress all by themselves. He seemed to have stumbled upon some sort of "anti-tumor agent" in the blood of these animals.

Additionally, he found that when looking down the microscope, the appearance of tumors shrinking by themselves in mice was similar to shrinkage produced with X-ray treatment in humans. This suggested to Clowes that the mice findings might represent a real therapeutic possibility for man. However Dr Park was somewhat premature when he conjectured, in a rush of enthusiasm, that *the cure of cancer is just around the corner.*[11]

As it was to turn out, all that was around the corner was another dead end.

What Clowes and his group were really doing in fact was *transplanting* tumor tissue from one mouse to another. What they were seeing, although they couldn't have known it at the time, was the phenomenon of *rejection*, with which we are very familiar today. If a patient is given a liver or kidney transplant from someone else, their body will reject it, unless they also receive powerful drugs to suppress their immune system. The recipient's immune defences detect the donated organ as foreign and attempt to attack and destroy it, unless prevented from doing so.

And it was the same phenomenon at play with the mice in Clowes' laboratory. They were detecting the injected tumor as foreign and attacking it accordingly. The blood transferred from one mouse to another would have contained activated cells of the immune system, which then went on to attack the tumor of the mouse they were injected into.

What was less clear though was why some mice could mount an immune attack and cause the injected tumor to regress whereas other mice presumably couldn't, as the tumor continued to grow unabated in them. A century later, it is impossible to answer this question. Today when mice are used in cancer experiments they are specifically bred for the purpose and their genetic composition is well characterised.

Back when Clowes was running his laboratory work, they got hold of mice from wherever they could and the origins were usually unknown. It is possible that the strain of mice in which the tumors grew unchecked were sufficiently similar to the original mice from Denmark for the transplanted tumors to go unrecognised. They weren't foreign enough and hence were unable to provoke an immune response.

Clowes and his colleagues could easily have been side tracked into pursuing the possibility of an immunological cure for cancer, something still being sought today. However, the real importance of their experiments lay elsewhere. They had established, in certain strains of mice, a means of growing tumors in live animals. An animal model of malignancy now existed for the first time. In more sophisticated variants, this has been the bedrock of anti-cancer drug testing ever since.

It is difficult to overstate the importance of this achievement. Even back in 1910, chemical companies were producing thousands of dyes and other chemicals with possible therapeutic properties. The number has since exploded into very many millions. Without animal models of cancer, it would be impossible to screen this prodigious output and narrow it down to that hopeful handful which eventually look promising enough to test in man.

But why were models needed anyway? After all, apart from the earthworm, which appears to be immune for some unknown reason, pretty much all animals get cancer spontaneously. So why not just use mice, once they have developed malignancy of their own accord?

One reason is that mice live for about two years. You don't really want to sit around that long, waiting to see if cancer is going to show up. Even then, the first you might know about it is when the mouse dies of the disease. After which it is obviously no use to you.

And if it did get cancer, it might turn out to be a tumor in the colon whereas you really wanted to know what effect a new drug might have on kidney cancer for example. And how would you measure whether a tumor was getting bigger or smaller if you couldn't see it? You couldn't keep putting mice through a CT or MRI scanner. Especially if they hadn't been invented yet.

And so the mouse model was essential. It allowed you to grow particular types of cancer in a predictable way. Also you could get the tumor to grow under the skin or some other place, where it was easy to measure it. Without that early work, much modern cancer research would never have taken place.

Although it was a huge step forwards, Clowes mouse model had the disadvantage that it could only grow *mouse* tumors. Which was much better than nothing but not as good as an animal model of *human*

191

tumors. This evolution had to wait until the development of the *nude mouse* at the US National Institutes of Health (NIH) in the late 1930s.

The nude mouse has a specific genetic mutation, which means that its *thymus gland* doesn't work properly. The thymus is important in the maturation of key components of the immune system, called T cells. Without these, the body struggles to attack and reject foreign tissue.

The nude mouse (so called because for some reason, the genetic defect also means it doesn't develop body fur) can therefore theoretically be transplanted with human tumor tissue. This should then grow and proliferate unimpeded, because the mouse can't mount an effective immune response.

This ability to create *xenograft* models (*transplanting tissue from one species to another*) was a significant step forwards in the search for new cancer drugs. However, it took another three decades to perfect the technique.

There was a certain historical symmetry too, as xenotransplantation was first achieved in the late 1970s by Carl Povlsen of the University Institute of Pathological Anatomy in Copenhagen, the city where Clowes first mice originated from sixty years earlier.

Povlsen's work was to establish a quantum leap, in terms of the experimental systems available for cancer drug evaluation.

The xenograft model has over time become more elaborate, with evolutions such as the SCID (*severe combined immunodeficiency*) mouse, which lacks both T cells (as in the nude mouse) and also B cells, which are the other main component of the immune system.

However, the basic principle is the same, in that it allows you to study the effects of a new drug on living growing human tumor tissue in mice, in the laboratory, before going ahead and actually giving it to patients.

Use of these models is so widespread and routine that you can now order the mouse of your specification over the internet. Taconic, based in Hudson, New York are one of the world's largest suppliers of animals for biomedical research. They will provide a pre-specified female nude mouse with six pups for just over five hundred dollars, for example.

And the quality of these animals, compared to those in Clowes' time, is shown by the fact that a Taconic mouse can trace its pedigree from the US NIH in 1937, on to the US Naval Medical Research Institute and then to the Zentralinstitut für Versuchstiersucht in Hannover and finally in 1961, on to Taconic in Europe. Not many rodents can track their ancestry back that far.

Even though Clowes' early animal models suffered serious limitations, compared to their modern descendants, they still served to usher in an era of intense sifting and screening of vast numbers of chemicals. A massive search was starting for agents showing any possibility of anti-cancer activity.

There was a pressing need for this type of initiative to uncover new compounds. Because at the time, in the period immediately after the First World War, there was a drastic shortage of promising approaches to cancer.

A typical example of the paucity of effective treatments was the hope pinned to passing fads and fantasies, such as *lead* as a potential chemotherapy for malignancy.

V

The idea of using lead was based on the work of William Blair Bell, who wasn't an oncologist at all. He was actually Professor of Obstetrics and Gynaecology at Liverpool Royal Infirmary. It seemed a bizarre idea, even at the time but if arsenic appeared to work, then who knew what lead might do.

As far back as 1909, he had developed an hypothesis that the tissues of the placenta behaved in many ways like a malignancy. They displayed a similar ability to invade into surrounding structures. Which is how the placenta normally establishes itself in the womb during pregnancy.

Blair Bell observed that lead was widely used as a powerful abortifacient. It exerted toxic effects on cells rich in chemicals called *phosphatides* (which are important lipid components of cell membranes). This included tissues of the placenta and the embryo but also many malignant cells too. It was therefore a logical step to conclude that lead might also exert beneficial effects on cancerous growths.

In 1920, Blair Bell was ready to test his idea. He treated a woman with inoperable breast cancer, using an injection of lead iodide. In those days it was possible to do things like that, almost on a whim. Within a month her tumor had virtually shrunk away and enlarged glands nearby had started getting smaller too.[12]

Based on this promising single result, further experiments were undertaken by Blair Bell. A Cancer Research Committee was even set up by Liverpool University to support him in his endeavours. By 1930, he had published more than sixty papers on the subject of lead and cancer. He'd treated more than five hundred and fifty cases, claiming to have cured or arrested sixty three of them. For the time, this was a simply unprecedented outcome. Even by today's standards it wouldn't be bad.

However, despite this promise, other clinicians had less than dramatic experiences with lead themselves. Many began to question the true nature of the responses Blair Bell had reported. Concerns were raised over the diagnoses of many of these patients, which were being made by an obstetrician rather than an oncologist. There were also serious reservations over the criteria used to assess responses to treatment, anticipating a debate which still rages to this day.

An anonymous review was published in the 1930 *Archives of Internal Medicine* of an enormous five and a half thousand page book of Blair Bell's collected papers on lead therapy for cancer. Its conclusion was damning.[13]

"This brief analysis of the statistical evidence of the therapeutic value of lead shows clearly...that so far at least, the evidence presented amounts to practically zero. In as important and difficult a field as the evaluation of any form of therapy for cancer, the presentation of such slip shod incomplete evidence in which a large number of cured cases, cancer has not been proved and in a still greater number of which all the other weapons in the armamentarium of the profession has been applied, cannot be too strongly condemned."

The generously minded reviewer continued that "lead therapy for cancer has received but little consideration after attempts at its use in other clinics, one cannot but help wonder what the reason was for the publication of all this enormous mass of material at such great expense."

Few, if any, publications on lead therapy appeared after this indictment and it died a rapid death thereafter. More than anything, the temporary enthusiasm for aberrations such as this emphasised the desperate need for effective chemotherapeutic agents. Much hope was therefore invested in the 1930s in the screening programmes now underway, following on from the original work of Clowes.

Despite the eventual enormity of this screening endeavour, the ultimate outcome would unfortunately turn out to be surprisingly futile. This was graphically demonstrated by the exceptionally limited success of one of the most prolific screening programmes of all time.

VI

This ambitious endeavour started off in the mid-1930s and was run by a researcher called Murray Shear.

Shear was a biochemist, originally from New York, who'd worked at Harvard Medical School before joining the National Institutes of Health[14] in 1939. He would go on to become known as the "Father of Chemotherapy," serving for fifteen years after the Second World War as Chief of Chemical Pharmacology at the National Cancer Institute (NCI).

Up until this point, the amount of organised cancer research in the US had been extremely small. It was certainly far too modest to support the ambitions of Shear and others like him. If he'd started off even just a few years earlier, Shear's dreams would have been doomed from the outset. However, all that was about to change.

A series of phenomena seemed to coincide in the Thirties to accelerate the pace of cancer exploration. A number of private foundations began to emerge, dedicated to supporting such activities. These included the Anne Fuller Fund in 1931, the Donner Foundation in 1932 and the somewhat unfortunately named Jane Coffin Childs Fund in 1937.

Although the amount of money they provided to researchers was limited, it was the fact that they even existed which was the significant development. Alongside these private initiatives, it was also a time of greater public awareness of cancer in general. Cancer research was increasingly becoming a subject for hearings held by Congressional Committees and was beginning to receive more attention in Washington.

This public momentum, along with increasing governmental interest, eventually resulted in 1937 in the founding of the National Cancer Institute. Based in Bethesda Maryland, the job of the NCI was to coordinate the US national cancer programme. It was also tasked with conducting and supporting "research, training, health information dissemination and other programs with respect to the cause, diagnosis, prevention and treatment of cancer, rehabilitation from cancer and the continuing care of cancer patients and the families of cancer patients."[15] That was a lot of commitment.

Today, the NCI has an annual budget of five billion dollars. Back in 1937, it was four hundred thousand. But that was enough to fund the screening programme put into place by Murray Shear.

For Shear, finding a cure for cancer was more than a job. It was an obsession. It even led him to trawl through annals of superstition and folk lore. His justification was that "Every nation colour creed and culture suffers from cancer. The ancient Chinese, the Greeks and Romans, the Egyptians of the Pyramid era and the Assyrians had it. I hope some old home remedy might provide a clue to curing cancer."[16]

If he was prepared to go to those lengths, who knows, he might even have taken a shine to AS1411. With that degree of devotion, he was however ideally suited for the grindingly arduous task ahead. He would eventually screen over three thousand chemical compounds for potential anti-cancer activity. It would take him until the early nineteen fifties, when the program was eventually closed down.

Shear used an animal model of cancer called the *murine S37* model. This involved mice with an exceptionally aggressive cancer called a *sarcoma*, which originates in a particular type of tissue distributed around muscles and under the skin.

For each compound he examined, there was a huge amount of work involved. Firstly, there was a need to transplant sarcoma tumor tissue into normal mice in sufficient numbers to be sure of getting five to ten animals in whom the tumor would start to grow. He then needed to wait a couple of weeks for the tumor to reach a measurable size in these mice and after that, start treating them with whatever particular chemical he was looking at.

But he wouldn't know how much of the chemical to give, or for how long and so would have to experiment with a number of dose levels, each in different groups of mice. And then he would need to wait and see whether the tumor started to shrink or not and if so, whether it happened in just one of the mice, or all of them, or somewhere in between. It was painstakingly slow work with little reward. It needed a certain sort of phlegmatic patience to cope with this kind of relentless routine.

Despite screening a wide range of different substances, including both natural products as well as chemical molecules, only *two* of the *three thousand* or so compounds examined by Shear ever made it to the clinic. And they both turned out to be too toxic for use in humans.[17] Perhaps unsurprisingly therefore, they eventually threw in the towel and the whole programme was finally shut down in 1953.

Historically, this slow rate of progress would come to be seen as nothing more than an initial setback for an approach which would ultimately prove its value. However, given such a miserable failure rate, an understandable disillusionment with chemical screening began to develop at the time.

This was exacerbated by the fact that the only piece of good news, in those nihilistic pre-war years, came out of findings involving the use of *hormones* rather than *chemicals* to treat cancer.

VII

The promise of hormonal manipulation in cancer had been known about anecdotally for some time. In 1896, Colonel Sir George Thomas Beatson, Professor of Surgery at Glasgow's Western Infirmary, published a medical paper describing three cases of women with advanced breast cancer who all experienced tumor shrinkage after having both ovaries removed.[18] This operation was to go on and become the standard treatment of this condition for many years after this.

It is now known that the majority of breast cancers have receptors for the female sex hormone *oestrogen* and that this can stimulate growth of these tumors. Tamoxifen and other agents like it, which block the binding of oestrogen to the tumor, are today some of the most widely used drugs in the treatment of this type of malignancy.

Beatson's approach of removing the ovaries, which are the main source of oestrogen production, would have produced the same effect. But Beatson didn't know that at the time. His work was based on observations in sheep and cows and the effects of pregnancy on their milk production. From this, he concluded that the ovaries exerted some kind of effect on the breast and by inference may have some role to play in breast cancer.

It was a wonderful demonstration of the art of clinical observation and deduction. Beatson's abilities in drawing major conclusions from minor observations easily equalled the skills of the contemporaneous, albeit fictional, Sherlock Holmes.

But the hormonal contribution to cancer medicine would never progress at the rate it needed to, were it to continue relying on clinical detective work and serendipity. It required a more *rational* approach, which was eventually to be supplied through the work of one Charles Huggins, in the 1930s.

Huggins was a Chicago physician, who would go on to receive the 1966 Nobel Prize for his pioneering insights into the role hormones played in cancer.

On a wall above his office desk, a plaque bore his motto: "Discovery is our business."[19] And what Huggins went on to discover, through his experiments in the lab, was that male sex hormones, such as *testosterone*, were important for the functioning of the normal prostate gland. From this, he reasoned that interfering with the effects of these hormones might also influence the course of prostate disease. In particular, he concluded that it could be a way of making prostate tumors regress.

This could be achieved by removing the testicles, which were the main source of these hormones. The same effect also occurred after giving the female hormone oestrogen, which then counteracted the effects of the endogenous male hormones.

When he tried out this therapeutic castration, some of the clinical responses Huggins described were dramatic. Tumor shrinkage and relief of pain started within days, and sometimes even hours, of treatment. Four of his original group of twenty one hormone treated patients went on to live for over twelve years. For the time, that was a remarkable achievement.

To this day, hormonal manipulation, in one variant or another, has remained the mainstay of initial treatment for prostate cancer. Huggins himself anticipated this almost from the outset. He recorded the moment when he first realised he may have found an effective treatment for a previously incurable disease:

"That night I walked home – one mile – and I had to sit down two or three times, my heart was pounding so. I thought, this will benefit man forever...a thousand years from now people will be taking this treatment of mine."[20]

Maybe a thousand years will turn out to be a bit optimistic but a century later, the Huggins approach is still going strong.

The importance of Huggins' findings transcended their clinical relevance to prostate cancer, substantial though that was. They showed for the first time that it was possible to develop a *rational* approach to the treatment of a malignancy and to arrest its growth. Rather than *the try it and see* haphazardness of previous therapeutic attempts, there was now evidence to justify interventions built around initial experimental observation. It was a significant advance over Beatson stumbling around in cow fields.

Prior to this point, an almost universal belief had developed that proliferating cancer cells were essentially autonomous and impervious to external intervention. Planned experimentation and hypothesis testing had now shown this was not the case.

It was therefore a conceptually transformational development, countering forever the prevailing preconceptions, if not prejudices of the day. His results, published in a landmark paper in 1941, are still regarded as one of the most significant milestones on the cancer highway.[21] They introduced a ray of hope at the end of what had otherwise been four decades of disappointment for cancer research.

This new found optimism was to be all too short lived however. Soon afterwards the world would be plunged into the chaos of an all engulfing war. But paradoxically, it was out of the destruction and devastation of those subsequent five years that the next major step forward in cancer medicine was to come.

VIII

The port of Bari, on the Adriatic, is five hundred km southeast of Rome. On the night of December 2nd 1943 it contained about thirty ships of American, British, Polish, Norwegian and Dutch origin. They were all busy discharging supplies to support the Allied forces, engaged in the battle for Rome. And so it was brightly lit that night, to help speed up the unloading process.

It was also very poorly defended. There were few ground defences and no nearby RAF squadron. But then nobody was expecting an air raid on Bari. That very afternoon during a press conference, the commander of RAF First Tactical Air Force, Arthur Coningham, had pronounced the Luftwaffe a spent force. He declared it would be "a personal affront if they should attempt any significant activity in this area."[22] This must have come as something of a surprise to the German command of Luftflotte 2, who had successfully mounted air raids on the port at nearby Naples four times in the last month.

Apparently unaware of Air Marshal Coningham's pronouncement earlier in the day, that night 105 German *Junkers Ju* 88 bombers set out for Bari. They left from airfields in Italy and Yugoslavia and arrived over the port at about seven thirty in the evening. All hell broke loose then.

Two ammunition ships were hit early on, causing detonations which shattered windows ten kilometres away. A petrol pipeline was fractured and then ignited, spewing out a burning sheet of fuel which rapidly engulfed the harbour. Thirty four thousand tons of cargo and seventeen ships were destroyed.

One of these was the US Liberty ship the *John Harvey,* which also had a mysterious undisclosed cargo on board. This subsequently turned out to consist of two thousand M47A1 World War One mustard gas bombs, each containing about thirty kg of sulphur mustard. It wasn't exactly something you'd want to go up in flames.

These had been sent in great secrecy to Europe. They were intended as retaliation, should Germany at some point resort to chemical warfare. It did after all have a track record there.

The Germans had first used nitrogen mustard in World War One at Ypres, in the spring of 1915. Five hundred deaths and over fourteen thousand casualties had resulted from this initial exposure alone. Ever since, the prospect of chemical weapons had filled all sides with fear and trepidation.

That night in December, the destruction of the *John Harvey* resulted in the liquid sulphur mustard from the bombs spilling over into the waters of the harbour, which were already coated in oil from other damaged vessels. Hundreds of sailors, who'd jumped from their ships, were coated in this oily mixture, which became a perfect solvent for the sulphur mustard. Outside of the Nazi concentration camps, this was to become the only incidence of chemical agents being released in Europe during the entire Second World War.

Within days, the first symptoms of mustard poisoning, which included chemical burns and blindness, began to manifest themselves in the six hundred and twenty eight survivors and staff at the surrounding medical facilities.

The scene was captured by an eye witness account of a nurse at the time.

"Only a few hours after dawn following the raid, we began to realize that most of our patients had been contaminated by something beyond our imagination. They were complaining of intense heat and began stripping their clothes off. Patients confined to bed were trying desperately to rip their dressings and bandages off. With what little knowledge we had, our first thought was that these boys were suffering from mustard gas burns. There were blisters as big as balloons and heavy with fluid on these young bodies."[23]

In the absence of knowing the real facts, it was a puzzling picture. The confusion was compounded further by the arrival of hundreds of local Italian victims, coughing and spluttering and covered with burns and blisters. They were seeking treatment after exposure to the cloud of sulphur mustard which had been blown into Bari by the initial explosions. Things weren't exactly helped by the fact that as time went on, no one actually became aware of the existence of the mustard bombs. Nearly all the crew of the *John Harvey* had been killed when the ship went down.

And apparently others in the know weren't letting on either. Everyone though had started to wonder what was causing the strange pervading garlic like smell, all around the port. At first Allied High Command tried to conceal the existence of the mustard bombs, terrified that knowledge of them might provoke the Germans into a pre-emptive use themselves.

Cynically depriving the local medical staff of this vital information could only have exacerbated further the dreadful suffering of the unfortunate victims. It was ultimately futile too. There were too many witnesses to keep the truth a secret for long.

Eventually, in February the following year, the US Chiefs of Staff were forced to issue a statement confirming the nature of the accident. It was wishful thinking to believe they could keep the lid on a disaster that dramatic and destructive.

Knowledge at last of the existence of the sulphur mustard helped explain something which was perplexing doctors caring for the survivors. In many of the victims, their lymphoid system had atrophied away to virtually nothing after the bombing incident. No one could work out why this should have happened. It was an unusual finding, to say the least and it just didn't make any sense.

Military intelligence was nothing if not extensive and these observations eventually worked their way up the tortuous chain of army communication. They finally came to the attention of Milton Winternitz, who was Professor of Pathology and subsequently Dean, at Yale School of Medicine in New Haven Connecticut. He was also in charge of the *US Army Medical Division of Chemical Warfare Service* and the *Army Laboratory School*, both also located at Yale.

Winternitz had been working with the US Army to research the effects of the poison gases used in World War One. He'd already noted in animal experiments that nitrogen mustard was particularly lethal to the bone marrow and the tissues of the lymphoid system such as the lymph nodes.[24] The disaster at Bari confirmed that similar effects could be reproduced in man. This led him to wonder whether these sorts of chemicals might have any utility against cancers of the lymphoid tissues.

Armed with the information from Italy, Winternitz approached a couple of Yale pharmacologists, Alfred Gilman and Louis Goodman, with a view to exploring the idea further. Goodman and Gilman are names familiar to medical students throughout the world. Their textbook, *The Pharmacological Basis of Therapeutics*, although first published in 1941, is still essential reading to this day. Gilman's son, also called Alfred Gilman, would himself become a pharmacologist and go on to win the Nobel Prize in 1994. Having his dad's book around the house during his formative years clearly had an influence on him.

Goodman and Gilman readily accepted the challenge from Winternitz and their first step was to establish a mouse model using a transplanted lymphoid tumor.

The lymphoid system in the body is a complex series of interconnected channels which drain a clear fluid called *lymph* and then return it to the blood. Lymph is formed of water and proteins which have been squeezed out of the blood, as it passes around the circulation. Unless these were returned back to the blood, it would eventually dry up.

The lymphatic system comprises the lymph channels and also the lymph nodes, the spleen, the thymus and the tonsils. Lymphatics occur in every part of the body, except the brain and spinal cord.

In addition to this drainage function, the lymphatics play an important role in channelling and processing specialised white blood cells, called *lymphocytes*, which are an integral part of the immune defence mechanism.

Lymphoid tumors (or lymphomas) occur when the lymphocytes they contain become malignant. These then proliferate out of control and start accumulating in the tissues of the lymphoid system, such as the lymph nodes or the spleen. There is extensive overlap between lymphomas and some leukaemias, which are caused by malignant lymphocytes accumulating in the bone marrow rather than the lymphoid tissue.

Broadly, lymphomas are divided into *Hodgkin's* lymphoma and *non-Hodgkin's* lymphoma, the main difference between the two being the precise type of malignant cell involved.

Hodgkin's lymphoma (or Hodgkin's disease, named after Thomas Hodgkin who first described it in 1832) is today one of the most curable cancers. The origins of this modern success lie with those initial experiments of Goodman and Gilman back in the later stages of World War Two.

In those original experiments they found, along with a collaborator of theirs, an anatomist named Thomas Dougherty, that treating their transplanted mice with nitrogen mustard induced a marked shrinkage of lymphoid tumor tissue. In a mouse with an advanced tumor, regression was noticed after two doses and eventually the disease became impalpable. The tumor subsequently recurred but could be successfully treated again, although this time with less regression. Normally, animals with this type of tumor would live for a couple of weeks but the treated animals were surviving almost three months.

Armed with this animal information they turned to a colleague of theirs, Gustaf Lindskog, a thoracic surgeon who would go on to become Professor of Surgery at Yale. He just happened to have a patient suffering with a lymphoma who had severe airways obstruction, due to a large mass of tumor pressing on his windpipe.

The pressure of the tumor had also blocked surrounding blood vessels, causing his face to distend markedly. Chewing and swallowing had become almost impossible. On top of that, the poor man could no longer bring his arms down by his side, due to enormous masses of tumor swelling the lymph glands in his armpits.

The patient was a forty eight year old silversmith who had stopped responding to the only other available treatment at the time, radiation therapy, which he had been receiving on and off for the last few years.

With disease this advanced the patient probably had little to lose. Lindskog was persuaded, in an event which would become a landmark milestone in the history of cancer medicine, to try out nitrogen mustard on him. It's unclear though whether the patient had much say in the matter. The battlefield poison was subsequently injected, in May 1942, in ten consecutive daily doses of increasing strength, as no one had any real idea of how much you needed to give.

History doesn't record what they expected to see but it's reasonable to assume everyone would have been pleasantly surprised when, within two days, the tumor started to soften and then shrink. By the end of the treatment period virtually all signs of his disease had disappeared. It was exactly what the animal experiment had predicted would happen.

Unfortunately the lymphoma came back just four weeks later and although the patient received two subsequent courses of treatment he eventually stopped responding. He also developed marked bone marrow suppression, which was to become one of the limitations to the use of the drug. Although he died shortly thereafter, he had survived long enough to earn himself a place in the annals of medical history.

The effect may only have lasted a month but nitrogen mustard (or *methyl-Bis (Beta-Chloroethyl)amine Hydrochloride*, to give its full name) had just become the first ever successfully administered cancer chemotherapeutic agent to arise from a programme of research. Although no one except Goodman and Gilman actually knew its real identity at the time. Still engulfed in the war and shrouded in military secrecy, the nitrogen mustard used was labelled only as "Compound X."

But despite its anonymity, nitrogen mustard was the fruition of the vision, half a century earlier, of pioneers such as Roswell Park. The experimentation of Goodman and Gilman had finally replaced the empiricism of Lissauer and Blair Bell, ushering in a whole new era of rational chemotherapy for cancer.

IX

The excitement and enthusiasm this initial success engendered in the Yale group led to a rapid expansion of clinical experimentation with nitrogen mustard in a variety of terminal patients with differing malignancies. They expanded the programme to include hospitals in Salt Lake City, Boston and

Portland, Oregon in an early forerunner of what would later become the multicentre clinical trial.

In all, sixty seven patients were studied and the results were reported in the *Journal of the American Medical Association* in September 1946.[25] They included patients as young as three and as old as seventy six, with the majority having Hodgkin's disease and the rest a mixture of other lymphomas and leukaemias.

The statistical complexity which bedevils current clinical trials was absent then, with most of the study results consisting of anecdotal reports on individual patients. Phrases such as "satisfactory remission," "good result," "dramatic response," "no appreciable value," "not particularly encouraging," and, wonderfully, "the ingravescent course and ultimately fatal outcome were not altered," were employed with a simple charm which contrasts sharply to today's frenzied quest for unequivocal precision in efficacy outcomes.

Although they may have been deprived of the elaborate clinical trial methodology currently employed, it wasn't difficult for the experimenters to conclude that nitrogen mustard was not going to be a cure for cancer. Whilst it could induce remissions, sometimes for a number of months and particularly in patients with Hodgkin's disease who'd ceased responding to irradiation, *everyone* eventually relapsed. They were also surprised by the unpredictability of some patients, who didn't show any sort of response at all and others who did dramatically well.

The use of nitrogen mustard was further complicated by its toxicity, which was hardly surprising, given its origins as an agent intended for chemical warfare. Severe bone marrow suppression occurred at doses not much higher than those required for efficacy. Patients also experienced nausea and vomiting so severe that most were anaesthetised with barbiturates, prior to receiving the nitrogen mustard injection. Also, great care had to be exercised not to spill any of the solution on to the skin of patients or physicians, otherwise severe chemical burns would rapidly ensue.

In the opinion of Goodman, Gilman and the others involved, "the use of these agents would seem to represent a definite but limited advance in the management of lymphomas and leukaemias, though perhaps the clinical implications are less impressive than the heuristic."

But they also anticipated the true significance of their work, which was perhaps not so much the clinical results *per se* but the collaborative process by which they had been obtained:

"Chemicals discovered to be therapeutically active in neoplastic disease deserve close study by clinicians, experimental pathologists, enzymologists and others interested in cancer and cellular biology. From this point of view, the heuristic aspects of the actions of the beta chloroethylamines reported here may eventually prove of greater importance than the clinical results obtained to date."

Despite the limitations of their clinical findings, the results published by the Yale Group sparked off a wave of enthusiasm for nitrogen mustard. Its use in lymphomas spread rapidly throughout the United States in the following years. In England, two doctors, John Wilkinson and Frank Fletcher at Manchester Royal Infirmary, had also started working with nitrogen mustard, although they were using lower doses than the Yale group.

Like Goodman and Gilman, they too had been labouring under military limitations. The results were published in the *Lancet* in 1947 although as they pointed out, "the whole of the original work was done during the war, when the substances were subject to severe restrictions of secrecy. It is only now that we can report briefly our results."[26]

Unfortunately the wait didn't seem that worthwhile, as they found only short lived benefits in chronic myelogenous leukaemia and Hodgkin's disease, with these outcomes frequently being deemed "*sub-judice.*"

At Memorial Hospital in New York two more physicians Frank Adair and Halsey Bagg, had already tried applying nitrogen mustard directly on to tumors that were easily accessible, such as malignant melanomas of the skin. This was based on empirical observations of its ability to induce battlefield burns. Unsurprisingly, they were able to document a "violent therapeutic reaction" in twelve patients who received this therapy, including two unfortunate individuals with carcinoma of the penis.[27] All the patients showed regression of their tumors for some months. Topical use of nitrogen mustard eventually found a routine place in clinical usage in the mid-1950s, as a treatment for *mycosis fungoides*, which is a rare form of lymphoma particularly affecting the skin.

The widespread use of nitrogen mustard following the Yale experience also coincided with the emergence, for the first time in the US, of effective antibiotic therapy to combat severe bacterial infections. The advent of penicillin heralded a whole new era of anti-infective chemotherapy. It was difficult to resist the encouraging inference that similar progress was just around the corner for cancer chemotherapy too.

This optimism helped fuel an initial belief that the shortcomings of nitrogen mustard would soon be overcome. William Dameshek from Boston, one of the original group of Yale experimenters, wrote in 1949:[28]

"It is realised that the use of HN_2 (nitrogen mustard) leaves much to be desired since it destroys abnormal cells leaving others which continue to maintain neoplastic potentialities. These ultimately proliferate, leading to relapse. However it is hoped that further research will result in the development of even more potent chemotherapeutic agents for the ultimate control of the disease."

In those bleak post-war years, it appeared that the battle against cancer might be on the verge of scoring some victories.

Nitrogen mustard, or mechlorethamine as it became known, is one of a class of cancer compounds now known as *alkylating agents*. They work by altering the structure of DNA, through the addition of a small chemical cluster called an *alkyl* group. That minor modification disrupts the DNA sufficiently to prevent the cell from functioning normally, leading to self-destruction and death.

Following on from the early success of mechlorethamine, in the mid-1950s, a number of other alkylating agents were discovered, just as Dameshek had foreseen. Many are still in widespread clinical use today, including chlorambucil, melphalan, busulphan and cyclophosphamide.

For once, a significant contribution to their discovery came from outside the US, with the first three compounds originating at the Chester Beatty Research Institute in London, whilst cyclophosphamide was discovered by chemists working in Germany.

However, whilst these subsequent agents had generally more favourable toxicity profiles, their pattern of efficacy when used alone was not that different from the original report with mechlorethamine. They didn't exactly represent a significant step forwards.

The limitations of these drugs as mono-therapy means their use today is mainly as one component of a *combination* of cancer drugs used to treat a malignancy. Experience has shown that single agents, employed alone, are unlikely to be effective enough against most cancer types. But back then, the importance of combination chemotherapy was unknown and unappreciated. Which probably wasn't surprising, given that clinicians were lucky to have a single drug to try out, let alone more than that.

If there was a shortage of encouraging agents though, it wasn't for want of trying. The decade after the end of World War Two saw intense screening activity in a number of countries worldwide. In the US, in addition to Murray Shear at the NCI, there was a large project at Memorial Sloan-Kettering Hospital in New York, run by Cornelius "Dusty" Rhoads. Another was established at the Children's Cancer Research Foundation in Boston supervised by Sidney Farber. A third originated at the Southern Research Institute in Birmingham Alabama under Howard Skipper. These were three people destined to make big contributions in decades to come.

The enthusiasm for screening also spread outside of the US. In London, a programme sprung up at the Chester Beatty Research Foundation run by Alexander Haddow. Further afield, similar initiatives were started at The Cancer Institute in Moscow under Professor L.F. Larionov and also at the University of Tokyo, run by Tomizo Yoshida.

However, as the 1950s progressed, a lack of understanding of the unavoidable limitations of single agent therapy was compounded by unrealistic expectations engendered by the initial results with nitrogen mustard. These vain hopes were exacerbated further by comparisons with the early and sustained success of anti-infective drugs.

The result was a growing disillusionment and disappointment with chemotherapy in general, as the limitations of mechlorethamine in particular became ever more apparent. Early and enthusiastic proponents, such as Dameshek, who was to become America's pre-eminent haematologist in the 1950s and 1960s, became convinced that chemotherapy alone could never cure cancer.

Increasingly, drug screening programmes were also seen as an inappropriate waste of resources. In hindsight, the animal models used were too limited and too laborious to ever produce the efficiency of throughput needed for success. Despite the heroic endeavours of these chemical crusaders, they just couldn't churn through enough compounds to have any hope of producing promising leads in sufficient numbers. It was a Herculean task ultimately doomed to hopelessness.

Unsurprisingly therefore, the next significant step forwards actually had nothing to do with any of the frenzied screening activities. What was to become the first effective drug against leukaemia came from a completely different direction. Although it enjoyed a firm conceptual overlap between anti-infective and anti-cancer chemotherapy approaches, its discovery turned out to be more haphazard and erratic than anyone might have expected.

X

The first effective anti-infective agents against bacteria were a class of drugs called *sulphonamides*. These were originally derived from coal tar dyes in the 1930s. They would go on to pave the way for the subsequent antibiotic revolution. For a long time though, it was unclear how they actually worked. However, in 1940 evidence emerged from a biochemist called Donald Woods, based at Oxford University, suggesting that sulphonamides inhibited bacterial growth by blocking a pathway responsible for producing a chemical called *folic acid*.[29]

Folic acid, also known as Vitamin B9, is a naturally occurring vitamin found particularly in leafy vegetables, such as spinach or asparagus and also in eggs, liver and kidney. Its natural origins account for it being named after *folium*, the Latin for leaf. It is now known that dietary folic acid is an important growth factor, essential to many aspects of cell activity and cell division.

In contrast to the dietary supply in humans, bacteria manufacture their own folic acid. When prevented from doing this, they can't survive, thus explaining the efficacy of sulphonamide drugs.

Wood's findings *eventually* provided a rational basis for trying to block folic acid in cancers. Doing so might produce similar effects to antimicrobial agents and deprive the cancer of essential growth factors. Tumor growth would be inhibited as a consequence. That seemed an eminently logical proposition on paper. But in practice, the story of folic acid and cancer was an example of how easily those early pioneering clinicians could take a misleading turn. It was as though they were orienteering without a map.

Things started diverging in an unexpected direction with the work of Richard Lewisohn, an unusually gifted surgeon working at Mount Sinai Hospital in New York, in the early 1940s. He already had a distinguished research career, having devised, in 1913, a technique which prevented blood clotting outside the body.[30] This was a hugely significant achievement, which became the basis of all modern blood transfusions.

More recently he had turned to cancer research and had been performing extensive laboratory work, looking at regression of breast tumors in mice being treated with yeast extracts. These were a cheap and convenient source of B group vitamins. In fact so prolific was his work, that he was getting through nearly four thousand mice each year. Furthermore, he was achieving extraordinary results, with almost one third of tumors showing some degree of regression.

With the entry of the US into World War Two at the end of 1941, it became impossible for him to continue obtaining the German brewers' yeast he had been using to make his extracts. Seeking alternative sources, Lewisohn turned to barley extracts and enjoyed similarly dramatic results.

Unaware of the work of Woods back in Oxford, at the beginning of 1944 Lewisohn hypothesised that the common active anti-cancer element in his yeast and barley extracts might be folic acid itself.[31] Both contained copious quantities of it. To confirm his idea though, he first needed to get his hands on some of the compound.

Folic acid however, had only been chemically identified a few years earlier and was proving incredibly difficult to synthesise. It was therefore in very short supply. Never one to be deterred though, Lewisohn turned to Lederle Laboratories for support.

This was a division of the American Cyanamid Pharmaceutical Company and was located conveniently near to him in Pearl River, New York, just twenty five miles north of Manhattan. Scientists there had been attempting to derive folic acid from the fermentation products of a bacterium called *Lactobacillus casei*. This was however an exceptionally complicated process, which involved trying to crystallise out the folic acid from a broth of other substances also made by the bacteria. Nevertheless, they did have a small amount they were willing to share with Lewisohn.

Initial studies on seven mice with the product supplied by Lederle showed the greatest degree of tumor suppression Lewisohn had ever seen. Subsequent experiments in larger numbers of animals confirmed these initial findings. It looked like folic acid might turn out to be a powerful anti-cancer agent. This was despite the fact that Lederle scientists were subsequently to discover that the material they had supplied to Lewisohn *wasn't* actually folic acid. They had given him the closely related *pteroyl triglutamic acid* rather than folic acid itself, which is *pteroyl monoglutamic acid.*

It was a small molecular difference but one with big implications. Given the chemical complexity of what they were trying to achieve it was perhaps inevitable that the odd mistake might happen here and there.

However, when the Lederle derived pteroyl monoglutamic acid (the *real* folic acid) itself was eventually tested in mice with breast cancer, it failed to do anything at all. Despite the previous findings of Lewisohn, folic acid appeared to be ineffective as an anti-cancer agent. Suddenly, Lewisohn's work didn't seem to be adding up the way it should have done.

Furthermore, in view of the amazing nature of his earlier results with barley and yeast extracts, the International Cancer Research Foundation,[32] which was sponsoring Lewisohn's research, had felt the need to arrange an independent inspection. What they were seeing seemed too good to be true.

A cancer researcher from a different New York institution, Memorial Hospital, had been sent to investigate and attempt to repeat the findings. When these independent results finally became available, it proved impossible to achieve anything like the same efficacy rates in mice. This created significant doubts over Lewisohn's earlier success, along with his folic acid hypothesis. This lack of consistency, when attempting to replicate experimental findings, showed just how complex an art some of these experimental systems had become.

However, by the time these fundamental reservations eventually became apparent, the story of folic acid and cancer had already moved on apace.

This was thanks to the actions of two men, called Yellapragada Subbarao and Sidney Farber.

XI

Born in Bhimavaram, India, Subbarao spent his working life as a gifted chemist in the US. Following a period at Harvard Medical School, where he made a number of important contributions to the understanding of human biochemistry, he joined Lederle Laboratories. This was after having been overlooked for a permanent position at Harvard.

Between 1945 and 1946, Subbarao and his group managed to pull off the tricky task of synthesising folic acid, thus providing a more reliable supply for future research. Although far from straightforward, it was easier to chemically manufacture the substance from scratch rather than to try extracting it from a bacterial soup.

Before his untimely death in 1948, he also managed to discover the widely used anti-parasite drug diethylcarbamazine (Hetrazan) and head up the group responsible for Aureomycin, the first of what would become the widely used tetracycline group of antibiotics.

Yellapragada Subbarao isn't a name which has lived on in the annals of medical history. His scientific achievements were wide ranging but his recognition remains strangely limited. To some extent this was due to his self-effacing character, never giving interviews, never lecturing, not even patenting any of his many and varied discoveries. In part, there was also a degree of discrimination against him at the time, due to his non-American origins. The immediate aftermath of the war was often a fiercely patriotic and parochial period.

However, on his death the New York *Herald Tribune* went so far as to describe him as "one of the most eminent medical minds of the century."[33] American Cyanamid designated a new species of fungus, discovered in their labs, in honour of him. It was named *Subbaromyces splendens.*

This was a fitting tribute, given that his discovery of Aureomycin had been the result of a huge collaborative fungus collecting exercise at the end of World War Two. Returning US soldiers from all over the world had been instructed to bring back soil samples with them. Lederle Laboratories would then screen them for possible anti-microbial agents arising from natural soil fungi. Aureomycin was one of those discovered in this way.

In contrast to Subbarao and his fungus, the name Sidney Farber is still familiar to anyone with even the most passing involvement in cancer medicine. One of the world's most prestigious medical institutions, the Dana-Farber Cancer Centre at Harvard is named after him. There aren't many honours greater than that. It's on a par with Kennedy Airport or the Rockefeller Plaza.

Sidney Farber was one of fourteen children, born in Buffalo in 1903, shortly after George Clownes had arrived there from England. Two of his brothers would also enter medicine, whilst a third became a professor of philosophy. They were a gifted family.

After attending Buffalo University, Farber went on to Harvard Medical School, eventually becoming a pathologist at the Children's Hospital there in the late 1920s.

He was to remain here for the rest of his life, until suffering from a fatal heart attack at work at the age of seventy three. He died, just as he hoped he would, at his desk in the institution he had devoted himself to for over fifty years. The Children's Hospital was the best place to spend his career. As a child himself, he recalled being "deeply disturbed by the little white caskets leaving homes with tiny victims of diphtheria and scarlet fever. Working with children and wanting to help them was natural for me."[34]

Farber was from the outset an imposing figure at the hospital, standing over six feet tall and always immaculately dressed. He was a dignified and formal man but at the same time could strike an immediate rapport with any child.

During his professional life he achieved that much coveted but rarely attained distinction of having an actual disease named after him. *Farber's Disease*, or disseminated lipogranulomatosis, as he described it in 1952,[35] is a rare condition arising from an inherited deficiency of the enzyme *ceramidase*. This is required for the normal processing of fatty materials in the body. Lack of it results in serious damage to most of the major organs, with affected children usually dying by the age of two. There is no known treatment.

Unlike two related eponymous conditions, *Niemman Pick Disease* and *Hand Schüller Christian Disease*, Farber enjoyed the additional accolade of not having to share the name of his syndrome with anyone else. He'd discovered it all by himself.

It was testament to the tireless devotion to research he displayed throughout his career. It was this commitment to understanding the fundamental elements of disease processes which would eventually bring him into contact with Yellapragada Subbarao.

Early on after arriving at the Children's Hospital, Farber had developed a passionate personal commitment to the challenge of treating cancer. He was convinced that overcoming it was just a matter of sufficient endeavour and experimentation. It was nothing that hard work couldn't sort out. As he was shortly to demonstrate.

From the outset, one of the worst malignant diseases confronting Farber was childhood leukaemia. Although today the majority of children survive the disease, back in the 1940s it was a death sentence within months of diagnosis. The outlook hadn't really changed since leukaemia was first described back in 1845.[36]

In the early 1950s both childhood acute lymphoblastic leukaemia (ALL), which accounted for about ninety per cent of cases and acute myeloid leukaemia (AML) were lumped together as "acute leukaemia." They had an average survival of about three and a half months. In between 1926 and 1947 only three out of one hundred and fifty patients with acute leukaemia at New York's Memorial Hospital survived a year. Diseases didn't come more deadly than that.

Farber saw children with leukaemia dying in front of him, from infections or haemorrhages. The only drug available to physicians was the steroid cortisone, which bought only the briefest of respites, if that. Not surprisingly childhood leukaemia was regarded at the time as a hopeless disease. It was the worst possible hand fate could have dealt these tiny tragic victims.

The prevailing wisdom was to leave these patients to die as peacefully as possible, rather than risk prolonging their suffering with experimental approaches almost certainly doomed to failure. There was, if anything, an active resistance to intervention of any sort.

But Farber was different. Unlike his colleagues, he was ready to rise to the challenge of leukaemia. The daunting nature of the disease didn't deter him in the slightest. Farber was willing to embrace anything new, rather than accept the existing dogma that doing nothing was best. And what's more, he'd managed to get hold of some folic acid from Yellapragada Subbarao.

XII

Farber and his colleague Louis Diamond, a haematologist and paediatrician at Harvard Medical School, were aware of the earlier experiments from Mount Sinai which appeared to show an anti-tumor effect for folic acid in breast cancer. They didn't yet have access to the subsequent findings which would discredit this approach. Based on what they did know, the pair embarked in 1946 on a clinical trial of their own, in which they administered folic acid to ninety patients with late stage cancers, including eleven children with acute leukaemia.

As it turned out, none of the patients showed any benefit from folic acid, whilst the children with leukaemia actually got *worse*. They died even more rapidly than would have been expected otherwise. Furthermore, Farber discovered that the amount of leukaemic disease in their bone marrow was much *greater* after receiving folic acid "to a degree not encountered in (my) experience with some 200 post-mortem examinations on children with acute leukaemia not so treated."[37]

This was something he described as an *acceleration phenomenon*. Knowing, as we now do, of its potency as a growth factor, the discovery that folic acid actually appeared to exacerbate cancer is more understandable. In fact, the debate over whether folic acid supplementation contributes to the development of some types of malignant disease, such as colon and prostate cancer, is one which is still ongoing today.[38] However at the time, the properties of folic acid were less widely appreciated. The clinical findings were both unexpected and unexplained.

A lesser mind might have been deterred from carrying on at this point. Farber though reasoned that if giving folic acid made leukaemia worse, then maybe instead it would be better to give something which *antagonised* the effects of folic acid. Perhaps that would improve things. Although it seems obvious in retrospect, it was a brilliant insight at the time. Farber was independently reaching the same conceptual conclusion in cancer as Woods had experimentally with anti-microbial chemotherapy.

The only problem was that Farber didn't know of anything which could block folate in humans. Sulphonamides only worked in bacteria. But he did know someone who might know. At Farber's insistence, Subbarao and his team at Lederle developed a series of anti-folate drugs, known as folic acid *antagonists*. They found that these could disrupt the metabolism of leukaemic cells grown in chicken and mice and that this effect could then be reversed by giving folic acid again.

Spurred on by these encouraging results, Farber began a trial of the anti-folate drug *aminopterin,* which was one of the most powerful of those coming from the Lederle laboratory. On December 16th 1947 he began daily administration of aminopterin for six days to a critically ill eight year old boy, W.G., dying of leukaemia. Two weeks later the number of leukaemic cells in his blood had fallen by two thirds, from sixty thousand to nineteen thousand. His appetite and general wellbeing were improving too.

Over the next four months he received two more courses of aminopterin. Whilst bone marrow examinations showed that he was far from cured, he was, against all expectations, still alive and moreover in "excellent physical condition."[39] In all, Farber and his group examined aminopterin in sixteen children with acute leukaemia. Ten showed responses which were, by the standards of the day, dramatic whilst the other six failed to demonstrate any benefit, four of them dying quite rapidly after the start of treatment.

However, in patients who did respond, these improvements were only temporary in nature. As was to be the general case with future chemotherapy, Farber also found that the use of aminopterin was complicated by the emergence of serious side effects. These included severe ulceration of the lining of the mouth (stomatitis), internal haemorrhage and marked bone marrow damage.

Attempts to attenuate these toxicities through the use of crude liver extracts (a rich source of folic acid) were only partially successful. Even so, with roughly sixty five per cent of patients showing some sort of benefit, these were unequivocally impressive results. Particularly compared to the alternative without any treatment, which was rapid and certain death.

Farber published his results in the *New England Journal of Medicine* in June 1948.[39] He was cautious in his assessment of the significance of his findings. On the positive side, he was able to point out that:

"The observations on these patients show that aminopterin has a marked effect upon the leukaemic bone marrow and upon the immature cells in the peripheral blood, and judging from the disappearance of enlargement of the spleen, liver and lymph nodes, when these organs were enlarged, very probably on leukaemic deposits in the viscera as well."

However, he also felt that "the toxic effects (*of aminopterin*) may make continued use of the drug impossible." Farber was realistic in his judgement, realising that "no evidence has been mentioned in this report that would justify the suggestion of the term "cure" of acute leukaemia in children." His conclusion was upbeat though. "A promising direction for further research concerning the nature and treatment of acute leukaemia in children appears to have been established by the observations reported."

Despite Farber's reservations, two of his treated patients, including little W.G., were to remain alive nearly two years after the onset of their disease, which was almost unbelievable by the prevailing expectations of the time. In fact so outstanding were his initial experiences with chemotherapy for this most intractable of diseases, that Farber's early results were greeted with profound scepticism within the medical community. His findings seemed too good to be true.

Partly Farber was up against a powerfully held cultural preconception at the time, that leukaemia was simply a disease which could not be treated successfully. After all, nothing had worked against it in the entire history of medicine, ever since cancer was first identified by the ancient Greeks. Many were convinced that things could never change for the better. Their minds weren't going to be altered, despite the evidence Farber was waving in front of them.

The negative response he received was due to more than just entrenched pessimism though. Within the heady halls of Harvard, there was also an intellectual antipathy to accepting that a young researcher, working in a basement laboratory without staff or funding, could have come up with such a momentous achievement.

But despite the disdain on his doorstep, Farber did achieve recognition elsewhere. He began receiving requests from other physicians, at first in New England but subsequently from further afield too. They wanted more information, once his initial findings became more widely known. Others were quick to try aminopterin for themselves. The results however were generally more varied.

Farber himself was later to acknowledge the difficulty of obtaining reproducible results in a condition as complicated and heterogeneous as acute leukaemia. He'd identified a problem persisting to this very day and which still bedevils drug development in this condition.

"It is obvious that no two children with acute leukaemia present strictly comparable problems," he wrote, some years after his initial experiences with aminopterin. "It should not therefore be surprising if one research group reports five consecutive remissions (*using aminopterin*) or that another group observes a fatal outcome in ten consecutive patients before one remission is observed."[40]

He also anticipated one of the greatest and unresolved debates in cancer medicine, over how to measure the efficacy of a new drug:

"It should be expected therefore that considerable variation in the results of different investigators will be reported, until a sufficiently large experience

213

has been obtained, or until a long enough period has elapsed, to permit the use of the period of survival alone as the simplest criterion of therapeutic effect."

The use of survival as an endpoint in cancer trials is still the most controversial subject in modern drug development. The intervening half century has introduced little more clarity than when Farber wrote those prophetic words.

One of the biggest problems Farber had found with aminopterin was the toxicity of the drug. "Too rapid a drop in white count, diarrhoea of unknown origin, the presence of stomatitis, a sore tongue or ulceration of the mucus membranes of the mouth should serve as reasons for the cessation of therapy until the exact cause of these disturbances has been determined," he had concluded.

There was therefore a need for follow on drugs to improve on aminopterin. Sadly Subbarao had died in August 1948, barely living long enough to see the earliest clinical validation of his laboratory endeavours. But his group at Lederle survived and were able to provide Farber with two other anti-folate compounds which were closely related to aminopterin. These were named amethopterin and aminoanfol.

Amethopterin subsequently became known as *methotrexate* and proved to be as effective as aminopterin but with less toxicity at clinical doses. Methotrexate remains one of the most widely used anti-cancer drugs today, with efficacy in acute lymphoblastic leukaemia as well as many other adult tumors, such as breast cancer, bone cancer, lung cancer, head and neck cancer and lymphomas.

Methotrexate's ongoing utility is an enduring testament to the ingenuity of Yellapragada Subbarao and Sidney Farber. Its widespread adult usage, arising from its paediatric origins, fulfilled the latter's maxim that "*in cancer, the child was the father to the man.*"[41]

Farber's contribution to cancer chemotherapy extended way beyond methotrexate itself. His pioneering achievement, in showing that it was in fact possible to strike a blow against a condition as hopeless and emotive as childhood leukaemia, went a long way towards reversing the negativity of the early 1950s. This was a period which had been characterised by a sense of despondency amongst the clinical cancer community over the limited potential of chemotherapy approaches.

Disillusioned doubters, such as William Dameshek, were brought back into the fold. His team at Tufts University New England Medical Centre tried out the new anti-folates and found that ten out of thirty two patients with acute leukaemia responded, including one adult. Again, as Farber had found, these responses were temporary and far from a cure. But they were *something* and led to a reappraisal by Dameshek of the potential promise of chemotherapy.[42]

He was to conclude optimistically that "the results of therapy may be said to represent the beginning of a new era in the therapy of this dread disease." He was even as bold as to state that chemotherapy may just hold "the fate of the ultimate control of cancer and related diseases." It would turn out to be a very long time into the future before chemotherapy could claim to have any semblance of control of cancer. At long last though, Dameshek and others were witnessing the first tentative steps on that pathway.

XIII

The work of Farber was also significant in influencing not just his professional colleagues but also the public at large, in a way which hadn't happened before.

Soon after his work started attracting attention, Farber was approached by the New England Chapter of The Variety Club,[43] a charitable organisation founded by members of the entertainment industry. In the late 1940s, there was a lot of money in the movie business, film making having been one of the few immensely profitable activities during the war years. The people in it were now looking for worthy endeavours to espouse. Diverting some of that money to good causes could only help the reputation of the industry in the immediate post-war period.

As a result, on May 22nd 1948, the then popular weekly radio quiz show *Truth and Consequences* featured one of Farber's patients, a twelve year old boy called only "Jimmy." Farber used to refer to all his patients as *Jimmy* or *Jane* in public, to protect their identities.

The boy's real name was Einar Gustafson and he was suffering from blood cancer. When they first met, Gustafson had told Farber of his secret desire for a TV set to watch his favourite baseball team, the Boston Braves. This caught the attention of the programme's researchers and led to his selection for the show.

On the radio that night, Gustafson was interviewed from his room at the Children's Hospital by the programme's host Ralph Edwards, all the way from a studio in Hollywood.

Half way through the broadcast, the Braves players suddenly trooped unannounced into Jimmy's room in Boston. They were singing *Take Me Out To The Ballgame*, the anthem of baseball for the last half century. It was a scene which captured the hearts of the listening nation. Many people who heard the programme were learning for the first time that children actually suffered from leukaemia and that through Farber's work, their lives could now be extended.

The show ended with an appeal for donations to help Jimmy buy his TV set. The response was both immediate and electric. People who had been listening on car radios drove to the hospital there and then, leaving donations at the front desk. Money was posted from all over the US, often just addressed to *Jimmy in Boston*.

Fund raising events and collections were held across the nation. Seemingly everybody wanted to help. Over the next three years the Variety Club of New England Children's Cancer Research Foundation or Jimmy Fund, as it quickly became known, was to raise over a million dollars in public donations.

Jimmy, or Einar, lived to get his television in the end. In fact Einar wasn't suffering with the death sentence of leukaemia. He had an even rarer cancer, which fortunately carried a better prognosis. Today this would be classified as a blood malignancy called Burkitt's lymphoma, which was only described for the first time in 1956, in equatorial Africa. It would have been an unrecognised disease at the time of Einar's diagnosis. He was therefore lumped in with all the other leukaemias and lymphomas.

Young Einar actually survived his disease, although he disappeared off everybody's radar shortly after the radio broadcast. For the next fifty years, he lived in obscurity as a truck driver in North Maine. Everyone assumed he had died of his illness in childhood.

However, on the fiftieth anniversary of the Truth and Consequences show in 1998, Einar decided to re-emerge into the spotlight. The passage of half a century had done little to diminish his appeal. He was accorded the honour of throwing out the first pitch at a Boston Red Sox–New York Yankee game at Fenway Park, something normally reserved for much greater celebrities.

He subsequently worked tirelessly as a fund raiser for the Dana-Farber Institute until his death from a stroke in 2001. When he died, he still had the little Boston Braves outfit he'd been given back in 1948.

Perhaps more importantly than purchasing Einar's TV, the Jimmy Fund also enabled the construction, at the Children's Hospital in Boston, of the Jimmy Fund Building to support further research into childhood cancer.

A four story structure in Binney Street, it cost one and a half million dollars and housed state of the art research laboratories. In 1973, after Farber's death, this was renamed the Sidney Farber Cancer Institute. In 1981, it was renamed again as the Dana-Farber Cancer Institute, following a thirty three million dollar donation from the Dana Foundation, a private philanthropic organisation.[44] That was obviously an enormous sum of money.

In contrast though, Farber's contribution was probably priceless. Since its inception, the Jimmy Fund has raised something like four hundred million dollars for cancer research. Although the Dana-Farber Cancer Institute now encompasses adult cancer too, it has been responsible for research helping childhood cancer cure rates jump from ten per cent to nearly eighty per cent. Without Sidney Farber, much of that may never have happened.

Farber's initial brush with the entertainment industry and the New England Variety Club seemed to bring out something of the showman in him too. Somewhat improbably for a slightly ponderous pathologist, from the 1950s onwards he became a frequent performer at Congressional and other hearings on cancer appropriation.

He found that he was a compelling speaker, with a flair for the dramatic and of course, an endless source of emotively tragic material upon which to draw. Along with health activist Mary Woodard Lasker, Congressman John Fogarty and Senator Lister Hill, Farber was responsible for initiating a massive expansion of federally funded cancer research. This resulted in the National Cancer Institute's annual budget trebling to two hundred million dollars by the time of the first moon landing in 1969.

These efforts of Farber and others changed the course of cancer research forever. Although there was no evidence that drugs could cure cancer, or even help most patients that much, there was now a feeling that cancer chemotherapy might not be a complete waste of time. It would be wrong to underestimate the still prevailing pessimism that surrounded the disease in the 1950s. However, clinicians were increasingly prepared to concede that chemotherapy had a potential role to play, although it was one which remained very much to be proven.

XIV

To help exploit this apparent promise, US federal funding was provided in 1955 for an organisation called the *Cancer Chemotherapy National Service Center* (CCNSC), which was part of the NCI. The CCNSC was to go on and establish the most extensive cancer drug research programme the world had ever seen. At last cancer was getting the sort of serious *coordinated* attention envisaged over half a century ago by Roswell Park, up in Buffalo.

The CCNSC promoted differing areas of research and development, collaborating in the process with academic groups and an, at the time, relatively disinterested pharmaceutical industry.

It established extensive organic chemistry initiatives to synthesise potential new drug compounds. Despite earlier disappointment and disillusionment with the approach, it also set up screening programmes to evaluate these new chemical sources. There wasn't any other obvious way of dealing with the anticipated prodigious quantity of compounds which would be queuing up for evaluation.

The CCNSC eventually took over other existing centres, such as the one at Memorial Sloan-Kettering, which had become the largest post war cancer drug screening and development facility.

At its height, the programme would annually produce over three million mice with transplanted tumors, using them to screen over fifty thousand

217

chemicals a year. Compounds successfully passing these screens would undergo more detailed biochemical and pharmacological evaluation in CCNSC sponsored programmes.

A final few would survive to reach the fourth stage of clinical testing. The CCNSC was instrumental in pioneering clinical trial facilities and standardising approaches, through the use of protocols and guidelines. The current US collaborative clinical cancer organisations all had their origins here.

An early example, initiated in 1955, was the Eastern Solid Tumor Group, which would go on to become the clinical trial powerhouse that is now the Eastern Cooperative Oncology Group (ECOG).[45]

ECOG along with *SWOG* (South West Oncology Group), *CALGB* (Cancer and Leukaemia Group B), *NCCTG* (North Central Cancer Treatment Group), *NSABP* (National Surgical Adjuvant Breast And Bowel Project), *RTOG* (Radiation Therapy Oncology Group) and *GOG* (Gynaecology Oncology Group) are all modern day cooperative alliances, sponsored by the US National Cancer Institute.

They consist of networks of cancer specialists who work together to run clinical trials with new cancer drugs, either in partnership with, or more usually independently of, pharmaceutical companies. They comprise member institutions drawn throughout the country, despite the regional affiliations suggested by the names of ECOG and SWOG. The only exception is NCCTG, which is a truly regional group, centred on the Mayo Clinic in Rochester, Minnesota.

These collaborative groups are very fertile sources of research with new cancer agents. They pay for and run the studies themselves. They can also usually set up trials more quickly than whichever pharmaceutical company a particular drug belongs to. They tend to be more nimble and less cumbersome.

Previously, there were only a handful of institutions with units dedicated to clinical drug testing in cancer patients. There had been Memorial Sloan-Kettering Hospital and Delafield Hospital, both in New York, the Children's Hospital in Boston and the Chester Beatty Research Institute in London. And that was about it. It wasn't much compared to today, where pretty much every major hospital would be able to undertake those kinds of activities.

The CCNSC provided a unique centralised resource to research and progress the development of potential new anti-cancer agents. Activity on this scale hadn't been possible previously, at academic centres, working on university funded cancer programmes. It essentially established all the elements of the drug development process, from chemistry to the clinic.

Ultimately, these would be taken over by the pharmaceutical industry, once they began to perceive commercial value in cancer chemotherapy.

But for some, this progress came at a cost. At the time of Goodman, Gilman and Farber, cancer research was largely an informal part time activity. It involved a small number of people, who were primarily employed to teach or run clinics or provide laboratory services. Working on new therapeutic approaches was almost an afterthought. But cancer research had now become a full time professional activity.

The new reality was summed up by Murray Shear, of the NCI, in his Presidential Address to the 1969 annual meeting of the American Association for Cancer Research.[46]

"In return for the abundant financial aid now available from government agencies and private foundations, the scientist must give ever more freely of his time to serve on innumerable advisory committees and panels for judging the relative merits of applications for research grants and fellowships – undergraduate, graduate, post-doctoral and even more senior."

And furthermore, "the drawback of this fair but elaborate system lies in its demand upon the academic scientist for an ever increasing proportion of his one priceless and most strictly limited commodity, his time."

It was certainly true, as with any government initiative, that the unwieldy machinery of administration was full of inefficiencies and inconsistencies. There were so many publically and privately funded organisations contributing to this cancer drive that differences of opinion inevitably developed, over how best to direct these research efforts.

As Shear sarcastically wrote, "Should there be a crash program on the cure of cancer with hypnotism? Or the paleobotony of cancer? Should financial support be upped an order of magnitude for studies on the geology of cancer? Or are we missing the bus by overlooking cancer of the giraffe or in the barracuda?"

With so many new toys to play with, the odd tantrum from him and others of an earlier era, was probably inevitable however.

Those of a more cynical disposition argued that there were now as many people living *off* cancer as were actually dying from it. But cancer research was now too big to be contained and it needed administration and coordination to keep it all together. Many though saw it as a painful contrast with the preceding earlier and simpler era. That was a period depicted by the English scientist and author CP Snow, when scientific culture had a "touch of the frontier quality," about it and those engaged in its pursuit were "impatient, intolerant, creative rather than critical, good-natured and brash."[47]

But the future had no room for nostalgia. It was less about the individual and more to do with the institution. It was a reality eventually acknowledged even by Shear too, a man who spent virtually his entire career in the NCI, at the very heart of the federal bureaucratic spider web.

"We can continue to pretend that we are working undisturbed in a scientific sanctuary," he wrote. "Or we can face up to the reality that cancer research is no longer conducted in an ivory tower. It has acquired an importance from many points of view – sociologic, financial and political."[46]

Despite these bureaucratic burdens and the antipathy displayed towards them by many pioneers of a previous era, by the time the CCNSC was absorbed into the NCI's Developmental Therapeutics Programme in 1976, it had generated an unstoppable momentum in cancer drug research. Furthermore, it has created the basis, through collaborative arrangements with individual companies, for what would become the multi-billion dollar cancer pharmaceutical industry.

Without it, many modern drugs would never have seen the light of day.

Just one example is *paclitaxel*, now one of the world's bestselling cancer drugs. It's used in an extensive range of malignancies, including ovarian, lung, head and neck and breast cancer. However, without the existence of CCNSC, paclitaxel probably wouldn't have been discovered. It would, to this day, remain overlooked, deep in a dark dank wood, in a remote region of North West America.

XV

On August 21st 1962 a botanist, Arthur S Barclay, decided to collect some bark from a single Pacific yew tree, known as *Taxus brevifolia.* He'd discovered it growing in a forest just north of the town of Packwood, in Washington State. This was part of a four month trip Barclay had been undertaking, to collect material from some two hundred different species.

In 1960, CCNSC had commissioned United States Department of Agriculture botanists to collect samples from about one thousand plant species per year. It was hoped this would provide material for cancer drug screening programmes.

Barclay's hoard was eventually processed by CCNSC some four years later. In May 1964, material from this particular tree sample was found to have cell killing properties. It was *cytotoxic* when examined in the laboratory. In view of this, early the next year work was started by Dr Monroe Wall in Research Triangle Park, North Carolina to try to isolate the active ingredient. Eighteen months later they'd worked out what it was and named the compound *taxol* (later to become *paclitaxel* with the trade name Taxol).

Encouraged by this early promise, CCNSC went ahead and commissioned work to collect some more Taxus bark. This would be needed in order to isolate a little more taxol. By 1969 they had isolated twenty eight kg of crude extract, from almost twelve hundred kg of bark, although this would only go on to yield an incredibly small *ten* grams of pure material.

But then taxol got "lost" somewhere in the bureaucracy of CCNSC. That happened surprisingly frequently in a large government organisation dealing with so many substances. It wasn't picked up again until 1975, when the ten grams of the compound were shown to have activity in another laboratory testing system. Having passed these basic assessments, taxol was now ready for evaluation in one of the mouse tumor screening models. However this would require another six hundred grams of material, which meant getting hold of another seven thousand pounds of tree bark.

With time, this exercise was becoming increasingly difficult, as collecting the tree bark unfortunately also destroyed the tree in the process. But it was eventually accomplished and by the end of 1978 taxol was proving to be effective in animal models against a number of different tumor types.

These encouraging findings emerged at the same time as work by Susan Horwitz, a molecular biologist at Albert Einstein College of Medicine in New York. She showed that taxol had a unique mechanism of action, destroying the internal scaffolding of the cancer cell nucleus.[48]

This information represented sufficient justification to start a small clinical trial with taxol. It was however an undertaking which would require an extra twenty thousand pounds of bark, which someone would have to go and collect. Initial clinical results in 1985, from the MD Anderson Centre in Houston, appeared to make these efforts worthwhile though. There were encouraging signs of activity in a range of solid tumors.[49] In turn, this meant that yet another twelve thousand pounds of bark would now be needed, to allow treatment of a slightly larger number of patients.

By this stage CCNSC had contracted Hauser Chemical Research, of Boulder Colorado, to handle the collection of bark on the semi-industrial scale now required. With a secure supply of material, further clinical trials were conducted and by the middle of 1988, taxol was demonstrating definite promise in both malignant melanoma and also in patients with advanced ovarian cancer.[50]

At this point however, the scientists at CCNSC calculated that treating patients in the US *alone* with melanoma and ovarian cancer, would involve the destruction of well over three hundred and sixty thousand yew trees annually. That was almost one tree per patient. This unprecedentedly large requirement was raising serious ecological issues over the impact on yew tree populations. It also engendered substantial unease amongst local politicians and foresters in the Washington State area.

Faced with these practical and financial implications, CCNSC realised it was time to bring in a commercial partner. They needed someone from the pharmaceutical industry, who would be willing to fund the rest of the programme and sort out the taxol supply problem.

Four companies showed an interest and eventually Bristol Myers Squibb were selected in December 1989. The terms of the deal were the subject of much controversy at the time. The US General Accounting Office eventually concluded that the CCNSC/NCI team had failed to obtain sufficiently favourable terms, considering how much federal funding had been invested in this project to date.

BMS also received an exclusive first right of refusal on all federal supplies of *Taxus brevifolia*, giving it a virtual monopoly over supply of the compound.

This level of commercial naivety was perhaps to be expected, given the lack of experience of CCNSC with this type of negotiation. It would be a very different situation today.

However, one commitment which they did manage to secure from BMS was to develop a means of supplying taxol (or paclitaxel as the drug was now known) which wouldn't be so dependent on the yew tree. This would subsequently involve a huge investment to explore innovative technological alternatives.

It wasn't until 1994, after twelve years of effort, that an initial solution was found. Robert Holton from Florida State University managed to develop the total chemical synthesis of paclitaxel, from readily available petrochemical starting materials. But although chemically very elegant, this was far too complicated to be commercially viable.

And so Holton went on to come up with a *semi-synthetic* means of manufacture. This involved chemically manipulating a starting material which was itself derived from the European Yew tree *Taxus baccata*. For some years BMS made paclitaxel by this means from a plant in Ireland, thus taking the pressure off the dwindling supplies of Pacific Yew in the US. But this source of supply still relied on yew trees of one sort or another. It wasn't therefore a long term solution.

Today, paclitaxel is made by a revolutionary technique called *plant cell fermentation*.[51] This involves incubating isolated yew cells in huge vats as big as seventy five thousand litres. The cells then produce paclitaxel directly, without any need to use actual trees or chemical synthesis. Although it sounds simple in principle, this technique actually required over two hundred man years of research to turn it into a commercial reality.

In return for this enormous future investment in finding an acceptable means of manufacturing paclitaxel, BMS acquired from CCNSC a drug which was approved by FDA two years later, at the end of 1992. Since then it has since reached annual sales of over one and a half billion dollars.

The development of taxol/paclitaxel is an example of a true collaborative process between government and industry. Without the huge federal reach of CCNSC, the chemical would never have been discovered and evaluated. No pharmaceutical company could undertake an activity as extensive, demanding and open ended as the process which ultimately delivered paclitaxel. And without the specialist skills and longer term financial resources of a pharmaceutical company like BMS, paclitaxel could never have been turned into a commercially viable drug.

This kind of arrangement helped generate the momentum to create a self-sustaining pharmaceutical industry, committed to cancer drug development. It was all in sharp distinction to the *ad hoc* haphazard relationship between Sidney Farber and Lederle Laboratories forty years earlier.

The contrast between the two emphasised the extent to which cancer drug development had progressed since the initiatives sparked by Farber's experiences with methotrexate in childhood leukaemia.

However, the historical contribution of methotrexate wasn't quite over yet. This drug had a further significant role to play. The best was still to come.

XVI

Chiang Kai Shek and Mao Zedong seem unlikely contributors to the war on cancer. And yet the Chinese Revolution of 1949 played an unexpected role in the further exploitation of methotrexate as a weapon. In fact, it helped secure the first significant victory against the disease. The credit lay with one of their countrymen.

Min Chiu Li trained as a doctor in China and then came to the US in 1947, to study at the Post Graduate Medical School of the University of Southern California. Prevented from returning to his homeland by the revolution which had erupted there, he ended up marooned in the US. The history of cancer medicine might have been quite different, had he been able to go back home.

Li eventually migrated to Memorial Sloan-Kettering Hospital in New York. Whilst there, he received a draft card for the US army in August 1955. As an alternative to military service, he was offered a position with Dr Roy Hertz at the National Cancer Institute. Hertz was Chief of the Endocrinology Branch there. Given the choice, Li opted for Maryland rather than the Marines.

It was whilst at the NCI that he was to make one of the most important advances so far in the treatment of malignancy. It began when he started studying laboratory markers of tumors and in the process became the first person ever to actually *cure* a cancer.

It had been known for some time that certain types of cancer produced specific chemicals which spilled out from the tumor and could then be measured in the blood. These were called *tumor markers* and their levels in the blood tended to correlate with how widespread the cancer had become. Prostate cancer produced a marker called PSA (*prostate specific antigen*) and colon cancer a marker known as CEA (*carcinoembryonic antigen*). Some malignancies, mainly gynaecological ones, were associated with the marker HCG (*human chorionic gonadotropin*). This is also produced normally by the placenta during pregnancy and forms the basis of most pregnancy testing kits.

Li was interested in trying to further understand the significance of HCG levels in cancer. Before leaving New York for the NCI, he had treated a patient with metastatic melanoma with methotrexate. At the time, this drug was increasingly being tried out in cancers other than leukaemia. These exploratory endeavours followed on from Sidney Farber's original observation in *solid* tumors of "temporary, definite but inconstant carcinolytic action (*following administration of methotrexate*)."[40]

Melanoma is a cancer which only rarely produces HCG as a tumor marker but this particular patient happened to be one of those. Li found that methotrexate unfortunately had no effect on his patient's tumor. However, it markedly reduced the levels of HCG, leading him to conclude that it might work on other HCG producing cancers. It was at least worth a try.

Meanwhile, Hertz had been undertaking work showing that the female womb needed high levels of folic acid to work properly during pregnancy. Furthermore, folate blocking drugs could prevent oestrogen induced cellular proliferation and thickening of the womb lining.

Putting all this together, Li hypothesised that a folate blocking drug, like methotrexate, might work in cancer of the womb, to prevent the hyperproliferation which characterised the disease. It should also reduce the levels of HCG detectable in the patient's blood or urine.

By early 1956, with this rationale under his belt, Li felt justified in trying out his ideas in patients. He first used methotrexate as an emergency treatment for a critically ill twenty four year old woman. She was suffering with widespread choriocarcinoma, which was a particular type of womb cancer. Following his intervention, the patient subsequently showed a dramatic clinical and radiological improvement.

However, Li observed that although the tumor disappeared rapidly, the levels of HCG remained elevated. He hypothesised that this might indicate the presence of remaining residual cancer disease. His great insight at this point was to realise the need to carry on treating the patient, even though she appeared clinically to be in remission.

This was the beginnings of one of the most important concepts in cancer chemotherapy, that of treating the patient even after the disappearance of all their *detectable* disease. Otherwise the persistence of *invisible* (micrometastatic) malignancy would inevitably lead to relapse and cancer recurrence.

Having gone into hospital almost moribund, Li's patient returned home four months later fully recovered from her disease. She had just become the world's first ever patient to be cured of a solid tumor using chemotherapy.[52]

Choriocarcinoma is a relatively rare and also complicated type of tumor. It arises from the membrane lining the embryo during the very earliest stages of pregnancy. Normally, these cells help the embryo infiltrate into the lining of the womb to create the placenta, as the pregnancy becomes established. Very occasionally however, they can become malignant and develop into a cancer called a choriocarcinoma.

Once this has happened, the tumor starts to invade surrounding tissues in an uncontrollable manner. It also has a tendency to rapidly spread to the lungs. It is fatal in about half of patients with disease which hasn't spread and in well over ninety per cent of those in whom it has. Given this dire prognosis, Li's result with his single patient was outstanding. Unsurprisingly, he pressed ahead with treating two more women that year and a further twenty seven after that.

Hertz would subsequently find ways of administering more intensive methotrexate, without necessarily incurring the serious and irreversible toxicities which had so limited its use up until then.[53] With advances like this, by 1962 the cure rate for choriocarcinoma, previously almost inevitably fatal, had reached nearly eighty per cent.

The work of Li and Hertz was a major milestone. Using just a single anti-cancer drug it was now possible to cure patients with widespread malignant disease who otherwise would undoubtedly have died. This would later come to be seen as one of the greatest achievements to date in the history of the war on cancer.

Li and Hertz would both eventually be accorded their rightful place in the roll call of historical honour. But as a sign of the prevailing mood of the time, Li's initial results were treated with a doubt that almost bordered on derision.

When he presented the results of his first two cases of choriocarcinoma, his colleagues at the NCI refused to believe that the remissions hadn't occurred spontaneously. Li must somehow be provoking an immunological response in these women, which was then causing the tumors to shrink. It was certainly nothing to do with the chemotherapeutic effects of methotrexate. They just wouldn't consider that as a possible explanation.

So entrenched was the view that a cure for malignant disease was simply unattainable, even amongst this group of dedicated cancer researchers at the National Cancer Institute, that Li was actually told to either desist from using this controversial treatment or leave the NCI altogether. In addition to scientific scepticism, one can only begin to imagine the politics and petty jealousies at play in such an internecine institution. If anyone was going to claim to have cured a cancer, it wasn't going to be an itinerant Chinaman stranded five thousand miles from home.

But then NCI weren't alone in demonstrating a seemingly implacable lingering opposition to chemotherapy, despite the facts now staring them in

225

the face. There were other institutions too where disillusionment with the apparent intractability of cancer and the perceived futility of drug treatment, engendered a sense of almost irrational hostility.

This was compounded by the fact that medical oncology didn't come into existence as a recognised speciality until the 1970s. Until then, those involved with chemotherapy were widely regarded as inferior to their other medical colleagues. Cancer drugs were considered to be little more than toxic poisons which more or less betrayed the physician's Hippocratic promise to do his patient no harm.

At Yale, in many ways the eventual home of the chemotherapeutic era, the distinguished physician Paul Calabresi was forced to leave. He was regarded as having become too involved in the unpopular exercise of early cancer drug testing. It didn't hold him back though. He departed for Brown University, Rhode Island, founding the Brown University Cancer Centre there in 1968. He went on to become an internationally recognised medical oncologist and expert on the pharmacology of anti-cancer drugs.

Not too far from Rhode Island, the Delafield Hospital in New York was one of the first examples of a university based cancer centre. It was even associated with the prestigious Columbia University College of Physicians and Surgeons. However two successive chairmen of medicine at Columbia, Robert Loeb and Stanley Bradley, both prevented junior doctors working at Delafield.

They felt cancer chemotherapy was an inappropriate use of medical resources. Loeb once even described the distinguished Delafield oncologist Alfred Gellhorn as belonging to "the lunatic fringe."[54] Perhaps unsurprisingly, the Delafield program closed down in 1971.

But the prejudices and preconceptions were worst at the NCI itself. The renowned haematologist George Brecher used to refer to his own leukaemia service there as the "butcher shop."[54] God alone knows how he viewed the other cancer departments. The prevailing view was well summarised by Murray Shear in his 1969 lecture.[46]

"No one knows which part of the enemy's citadel is beginning to crumble," he wrote. "The walls of Jericho are still standing despite the blaring of "breakthrough" on the trumpets of propagandising Joshuas."

Nice words of encouragement from a colleague in the field. But perhaps understandably, twenty years of unproductively slaving away at mouse screening models might have allowed a degree of cynicism to seep in to Shear's view of the world.

The early oncologists involved in initial chemotherapy successes were outlaws and pioneering settlers, fighting for their territory even as they were discovering it. They were an isolated group disdained by outsiders and mutually mistrustful, fearful of one stealing a march on the other.

Maybe it wasn't surprising therefore that Li chose to leave the NCI. He returned in 1957 to Memorial Sloan-Kettering, where a decade later he was to develop the first ever combination chemotherapy for metastatic testicular cancer.[55] It was an achievement providing a nice sexual symmetry to his research endeavours, having come up with therapeutic advances for both male and female reproductive cancers.

Shortly after that, he returned to Taiwan, as Chairman of the National Cancer Research Committee. He died in 1980, leaving behind a scientific legacy which is remembered to this day.

After Li's cure of a solid tumor, it was to be almost another decade before the next such breakthrough occurred. This time it would at least be in a climate more accepting and less acerbic. It would also be at the NCI.

XVII

The next big advance came about as a consequence of a number of smaller ones, all being pulled together for the first time. Previously, successes had been achieved typically by individuals or small groups working independently. There had been very little collaboration between institutions. Now, with many more initiatives underway at many different research centres, a more *integrated* approach was called for.

Acute lymphoblastic leukaemia in children, hitherto one of the most universally fatal of malignancies, was about to be cured by a group at the NCI. They would put together the various parts of a jigsaw puzzle, to see the whole picture for the first time.

Most of the pieces had been around for a while but one of the last to fall into place involved, of all things, the periwinkle plant.

Throughout history, plants have been a fertile source of drugs for many different medical conditions. Some, such as taxol from yew tree bark, originated from coordinated screening programmes. Others arose more serendipitously.

In 1969 for example, a Sandoz biologist, on holiday in Norway, happened to cross the mountain plateau of Hardangervidda in a rented car with his wife. They stopped frequently to take pictures and the biologist would use these opportunities to collect a small sample of soil. He couldn't help bringing his work on holiday with him.

From one of these samples, Sandoz scientists later identified a fungus *Tolypocladium inflatum,* which produced a chemical they named cyclosporine. Cyclosporine subsequently turned out to have strong immunosuppressive properties and in 1983 it was approved as the drug *Sandimmune,* for use in preventing organ transplantation rejection. By 1995 this was Sandoz's biggest selling drug, at over one billion dollars a year. Which wasn't a bad outcome from a five minute comfort break.

The discovery of the drug *vincristine* was more prosaic but ultimately just as profitable.

It was originally isolated from the Madagascan periwinkle, *Vinca rosea*. Over the years, Madagascar has been an extraordinarily rich source of drugs for both cancer and other diseases.

It's an island in the Indian Ocean, one thousand miles from north to south but with climactic variations more often associated with an entire continent. Much more importantly, it had separated from the African mainland millions of years ago and now over eighty per cent of its flora and fauna are found nowhere else on earth.

That includes the *Vinca* plant, which has been used for centuries as a folk remedy, reputedly having mildly hallucinogenic properties.

In the 1950s, studies found that Vinca actually contained up to seventy different chemical substances, many of which seemed to have biological activity of one sort or another. It was therefore an obvious place to start looking for potential new drugs.

Researchers at Eli Lilly in the early 1960s had started examining the chemical which eventually became vincristine as a possible anti-diabetic drug. They happened to notice in mice that whilst it didn't do much for diabetes, it did cause marked bone marrow suppression. Subsequent studies revealed that vincristine had beneficial effects in a mouse model of acute lymphoblastic leukaemia, suggesting it might have some value in the clinic.

The discovery of vincristine meant that there were now *four* drugs available for use in acute leukaemia. In addition to the newly arrived vincristine, there was of course methotrexate and then also two additional agents.

One of these was *Purinethol*, better known today as *6-mercaptopurine*. This was a drug developed back in 1951 by a remarkable woman called Gertrude Elion. A science graduate from New York, she had been denied an opportunity for postgraduate work, largely because of sexual discrimination, ending up working as a laboratory assistant and high school teacher instead. She later became an assistant to a former Harvard professor, George Hitchings, at what was then the Burroughs Wellcome pharmaceutical company in New York.

This was the start of a drug discovery partnership so prolific that they were both awarded the 1988 Nobel Prize for Medicine. Apart from 6-mercaptopurine, the pair were responsible for drugs used successfully to treat malaria, organ rejection, gout, bacterial and viral infections. It was Elion's work which would eventually lead on to the AIDS drug AZT.

6-mercaptopurine acted by blocking the synthesis and function of chemical groups called *purine nucleotides*. These form the basic building blocks of DNA and RNA. Through doing this, it disrupted the entire genetic organisation of a cell, stopping it from replicating and functioning effectively.

Animal testing showed 6-mercaptopurine to have value against a range of leukaemias and lymphomas. This led to early clinical testing in the 1950s, which produced some short lived remissions in acute leukaemias. When combined with other agents, it still has a place in cancer medicine today.

The final member of the drug quartet was the steroid *prednisolone*.

The natural steroid *cortisone* had been identified by a group working at the Mayo Clinic in Rochester in the late 1940s. Steroids are a group of powerfully active chemicals, produced by the adrenal glands. They are essential to maintaining the body's normal function. When used as drugs, they exert a variety of effects, particularly on modulating the immune system.

Cortisone had been used to treat rheumatoid arthritis but with very unpleasant side effects. In 1950 the chemist Arthur Nobile, in the laboratories of the pharmaceutical company Schering Plough in the US, had managed to use bacteria to convert *hydrocortisone* into the steroid *prednisolone,* which had fewer side effects.

Eventually Schering Plough would be able to make prednisolone completely synthetically, thus providing a reliable, secure and standardised supply of what would become one of the world's most widely used drugs, for both cancer and many other diseases.

It was Sidney Farber again who had found, in the early 1950s, that steroids could have favourable effects in leukaemia, although they were very short lived.[56]

In 1961 a unique group had come together at NCI with the objective of taking these four drugs, each of which had some limited use as a single agent, and somehow finding a way to put them together to come up with not just a respite but a permanent cure for acute leukaemia.

Rather than fighting and falling out, the inhabitants of NCI had finally decided to come together and cooperate.

The group was led by C Gordon Zubrod who had joined NCI in 1954 as Clinical Director. He would go on to become one of the biggest names in cancer medicine in the decades to come.

During World War Two, Zubrod had served in the United States Army's Office of Scientific Research and Development, where they had developed chloroquine, the most effective drug to date against malaria. It had subsequently been widely and successfully used by the Allied Forces in North Africa and the Far East during the later stages of the conflict. This chemotherapy success against malaria had fired Zubrod with a conviction that he could achieve similar results against malignant disease.

He also applied a military level of planning to his war against cancer. This even went so far as to borrow from the experiences of senior managers at IBM on the project management of complicated technical tasks involving many differing types of discipline and skill. This was exactly the approach he intended to use in his onslaught on ALL.

Zubrod established a group called the Acute Leukaemia Task Force within NCI, with the objective of coming up with a completely new approach to treating acute lymphocytic leukaemia (ALL). It comprised some ten to fifteen scientists and clinicians, from the NCI and elsewhere, including Sidney Farber and other names that would come to prominence in years to come, such as Myron Karon, Emil Frei and Emil Freireich.

The chances of two people with such confusingly similar names being in the same place at the same time and engaged in the same task were so low, that it had to be a lucky sign.

They started by reviewing all the known data on treating ALL, generated over the last twelve years or so. Since Farber's original observations with aminopterin, studies in childhood leukaemia had been ongoing with a number of pioneering clinicians. These included names such as Jim Holland at Roswell Park, Don Pinkel at St Jude's Children's Hospital in Memphis, Joe Burchenal at Memorial Sloan-Kettering in New York, the duo of Emil Frei and Emil Freireich at NCI and of course, Sidney Farber in Boston. Many of these names are meaningless outside of cancer medicine. But for those on the inside, they are the *Beatles* and the *Stones*, mixed together.

Everyone agreed that using one drug, by itself, wasn't doing any more than just holding the disease at bay for a short while. It might buy kids an extra birthday but it wasn't going to cure anyone. Whilst everyone may have concurred on the inadequacy of drugs used as single agents, there was much less certainty about what to do to improve on this.

Work undertaken in the mid-1950s by James Holland, initially at NCI and later at Roswell Park, had shown that better responses were obtained with methotrexate and 6-mercaptopurine when used together. However, in an early example of the eventual complexity of cancer drug combinations, they had found it necessary to give the drugs *sequentially*, rather than both together at the same time.[57] Giving them simultaneously didn't produce any extra benefit. Giving them one after the other, never mind which one came first, resulted in higher remission rates, although the duration of remission wasn't prolonged.

These studies were early precursors of the principle that in cancer medicine, less was never more. A greater number of drugs were nearly always better than one alone. They also touched on what would become a significant sophistication of combination chemotherapy. They had discovered that the precise *sequence* in which drugs were deployed was as important as the total *number* used.

Today, there is an understanding of the reasons for this, based on the complicated circular kinetics of how cells divide. There is a need to hit cancer cells at different times in this cycle, with different drugs, to take maximum advantage of the cell's vulnerability. But back in the 1950s, these were simply clinical observations, although very significant ones.

Another important empirical discovery came from Jane Perrin and others at the Children's Hospital in Cincinnati. They found, in the early sixties, that injecting aminopterin, rather than giving it by mouth, which was how it had been used up until then, could produce much better results. *Injected* aminopterin could even produce responses in patients who'd become resistant to the drug *orally*, although the reasons for this were unclear. Their observations showed that the way a drug was administered could influence the results seen with it.[58]

Ironically, Perrin's work also helped spark off a divisive debate within the already factional cancer community. It was a finding which was taken as evidence by some that the full potential of single agents may not yet have been fully exploited. It provided support for those still experiencing reservations about the wisdom of more aggressive combination approaches, with the much greater toxicity that would inevitably ensue. Cancer clinicians of the period were developing an impressive skill in fashioning clinical data to support their own particular point of view.

For the Leukaemia Task Force, an additional conceptually important innovation was a realisation of the need to carry on treating leukaemia, even after the patient had achieved a response. Evidence showed that after using steroids to attain a remission, it lasted a lot longer if the patient was then treated with 6- mercaptopurine, rather than being given nothing at all. This was despite the fact that they appeared to be disease free already.

This was similar to the earlier findings of Li treating choriocarcinoma, except that leukaemia at the time had no marker equivalent to HCG. Once a patient with leukaemia went into remission, there was no way of monitoring how much disease they still had. But everyone knew it must still be there. Sooner or later the leukaemia would return, no matter how convinced you were that it had been cleared away with the initial treatment.

Overall therefore, Zubrod and his group already had a substantial body of clinical information about ALL at their disposal. This suggested the need for a combination of drugs, given in a sequence and with some of them ideally by injection. Additionally, it was important to carry on with treatment, even after the patient appeared to have responded.

But there was one other important insight that also really helped them. This however came from a different direction altogether. It arose from the work of a mathematician with a mouse.

XVIII

Howard Skipper was a pharmacologist who'd studied at the University of Florida, before being conscripted in 1941. Like many physicians and scientists who transferred to cancer research after the War, he had served in the US Army's Chemical Warfare Service. In Skipper's case, he'd been posted to Australia, New Guinea and the Philippines.

Immediately after the Japanese surrender he had been sent there as part of the Scientific Survey Group. Their task was to find out what dark secrets Japan's scientists had been working on. While there, he found himself accepting the sword of surrender from the head of the Japanese Chemical Warfare Service. That in itself might have been a career highlight for many people but Skipper hadn't even started yet.

Returning to the US, Skipper joined the newly formed Southern Research Institute, in Birmingham Alabama, where he would remain for the rest of his life. Here he developed mathematical models of how leukaemia behaved and just what it would take to effect a cure. It was a radical new idea, trying to reduce cancer to calculus.

It showed how far the *rational* approach to tackling cancer had progressed. This wasn't even experimentation in the labs. It was a model in the mind.

One of Skipper's favourite sayings was "a model is a lie that helps you see the truth."[59] The truth his mathematics showed, by a process of back extrapolation, was that it would be necessary to kill every single last leukaemia cell to effect a cure. Leaving even *one* remaining would be enough to result in a relapse.

This was only a hypothesis, which remained to be validated but it was consistent with earlier findings from animal models by two researchers from New York, Morton Furth and Jacob Kahn. They had shown, as far back as just before World War II, that implanting a single solitary leukaemia cell into an otherwise healthy mouse was enough to give it the full blown disease.[60] Just one cell. That's all it took. That's how resourceful and resilient an opponent leukaemia was. At least it helped define the magnitude of the challenge facing Zubrod's group. Total annihilation of the enemy. Nothing less would do.

However, Skipper also provided some help in solving the problem when he came up with his "log kill hypothesis" of cancer chemotherapy, in the early years of the nineteen sixties.[61] This states that any given dose of a cancer drug will kill a fixed *fraction* of the cells present and not a fixed *number*. What this means is that it is just as difficult to reduce 100 leukaemia cells down to 1 cell, as it is to reduce 10,000 cells down to 100 cells, or 1,000,000 cells down to 10,000. In each case, the decrease is ninety per cent. However large or small the number of cells you start with, there will still be the same proportion left over. And with leukaemia, even one cell remaining is one too many.

What this meant for killing cancer in general was that as a tumor became smaller and smaller with treatment, you had to carry on hitting it just as hard, if not harder. This was because you would never eradicate all the remaining cells in any one go, just a fixed proportion of them. People just hadn't realised this before. The natural tendency in the clinic had been to try to ease off on the chemotherapy once a tumor started shrinking appreciably.

But Skipper's work showed for the first time just how important it was to maintain aggressive treatment at all cost. It was now clear that you had to take the patient to the very brink of a toxic death but hopefully not beyond.

His concept would provoke a seismic shift in the approach of clinicians working with cancer chemotherapy. In the words of Vincent DeVita, himself an eminent oncologist and former head of the NCI, in 1981:

"The impact of Dr Skipper's work reverberated across the field like a whip crack and changed the field practically overnight, in medical terms, from one that relied almost totally on empiricism to a field that was heavily laced with inductive reasoning."[62]

Revolutionary though Skipper's findings were, they weren't quite enough by themselves. There was still information from a couple of other sources which needed to fall into place, to complete the picture for the Acute Leukaemia Task Force. Some of this came from the work of Dr Lloyd Law, a geneticist who'd moved to NCI in 1947.

Law had established a mouse leukaemia laboratory using newly developed transplant techniques. This had resulted, amongst other discoveries, in the most widely used of all mouse models of leukaemia, the L1210 mouse.

But Lloyd's most important contribution was to do with the mechanism by which nearly all leukaemias, if treated often enough, would eventually become resistant to a drug and stop responding to it.

This phenomenon had been known for a long time, almost since the existence of mouse models in fact. However, no one was sure whether treatment with a drug somehow eventually *altered* the cancer cells, so that they developed resistance over time, or whether some cancer cells were resistant from the *outset* and just came to the fore, once all the sensitive ones had been killed off.

Law used something called the *Luria Delbrück fluctuation test*. This was a concept from genetics so complicated that it eventually earned the Nobel Prize in Medicine for the two eponymous originators, Luria and Delbrück.

He was able to show that for any cancer drug, the mouse tumor contained sensitive and resistant cells, in varying proportions, from the very outset. The obvious implication of this was that tumors needed to be treated with a combination of more than one drug, so that cells resistant to one of them would still be susceptible to another.

This combination concept became even more important after Law also found that when he treated leukaemic mice with 6-mercaptopurine, and they eventually became resistant and stopped responding, at the same time they became *more* sensitive to methotrexate and responded even better to it. It was a phenomenon which became known as "collateral sensitivity."[63]

Law's findings confirmed the existing clinical suspicion, that the biology of tumors made it very unlikely they could ever be eradicated with just a single drug. His work provided the *theoretical* justification for combining drugs together, which had been lacking up until now. This would provide the ammunition to overcome the reticence of those who still doubted the wisdom of putting together drugs which were already overly toxic by themselves alone. At the time, the sceptics were in the majority, with combination chemotherapy being regarded with horror by most of those involved in cancer research.

Apart from one or two pioneers, who had actually tried combining a couple of drugs together in the clinic, there was a widespread conviction at the time that this sort of approach was doomed from the outset, because of the unmanageable toxicity it would inevitably incur. This was in fact a very real and justifiable fear. However, events had been moving on in the clinic to develop ways of tackling the obstacle of excessive toxicity. This would provide the final bit of the puzzle for Zubrod and his task force.

XIX

Finding that last missing piece was all down to the clinical experimentation of a physician called Emil Freireich. Looking like a young Tony Curtis and fond of sporting a bow tie, he'd arrived at the NCI in 1955. However, his journey there had perhaps been a little harder than some of his contemporaries. His parents were Hungarian immigrants and his mother worked in a sewing factory after his father died, when he was just two. He'd dragged himself into college with the help of twenty five dollars loaned by a friend of his mother and fought his way to medical school in Chicago.

Freireich graphically described the sight which met him when he eventually arrived at the NCI.[64]

"In 1955 when I began my career at the National Cancer Institute, children diagnosed with leukaemia usually lived about eight weeks. They had about a one per cent chance of surviving a year – and they had a median age of five years old at diagnosis.

The worst thing about leukaemia was not the short life expectancy but the way the children died. You see, leukaemia destroys blood platelets (the part of the blood that allows it to clot) and produces its own anticoagulant. So every child with leukaemia died of massive haemorrhaging. As a doctor in 1955, when I entered the leukaemia ward, all I saw was blood. The children were bleeding in their urine, stool, lungs and even from their eyes. They would cough to breath and spew blood as high as the ceilings. The wards were red with death."

Speaking those words in 2009, he was able to add:

"But now, thanks to years of research and the development of combination chemotherapy, leukaemia is not a death sentence. In most cases it can be cured, and in all cases we can stop the bleeding."

Freireich played the key role in developing techniques to control bleeding, through the use of platelet transfusions and to combat infection with the use of antibiotics.[65,66] The emergence of this kind of supportive care revolutionised management of the symptoms of leukaemia. It also crucially helped reduce the toxicities of chemotherapy to a point where, for the first time, patients could reasonably be expected to survive the onslaught of aggressive combination treatment approaches.

Today, platelets and anti-infectives are used all day every day in any chemotherapy unit, pretty much everywhere. No one ever gives them a second thought, so routine have they become. But without Freireich's ground breaking work in the early 1960s, the development of modern intensive chemotherapy would never have been possible. It would have killed everyone treated with it.

However, given that it was the NCI, perhaps it wasn't too surprising that Freireich had to achieve these advances in the face of bitter opposition from the majority of his haematology colleagues. They argued that children with leukaemia were going to die anyway and so why expend effort in prolonging their life and their suffering.

But Zubrod was about to address that pessimism head on. He and his team were able to complete the jigsaw puzzle, by bring together these various pieces of clinical experience and non-clinical experimentation into an integrated rationale for combination chemotherapy, based on work from Birmingham to Bethesda.

For the first time in the evolution of cancer chemotherapy, there was a scientific hypothesis supported by extensive experimental data, to justify a proposed therapeutic strategy.

This was the way it would be done from now on. A multi-disciplinary approach from the laboratory to the leukaemia ward. It was a far cry from the empirical entrepreneurialism of one or two individuals working on their own initiative, which was the way most advances had been arrived at up until now.

The end result of all this endeavour was christened VAMP, as the first of an endless series of acronyms which has ever since made cancer medicine look like a bad hand of Scrabble. VAMP was **V**incristine, **A**minopterin, 6-**M**ercaptopurine and **P**rednisolone. It was the world's first cyclic combination chemotherapy regimen.[67] It became apparent, within six months of using it in the clinic in 1963, that VAMP was living up to the high expectations riding on it.

The regimen was achieving remissions in children with ALL which were both more frequent than ever seen before and even more importantly, longer lasting than anyone could have imagined.[68] Just as critically, with the help of aggressive antibiotic and platelet replacement therapy, the patients were surviving this chemotherapeutic Armageddon.

Whilst impressive, VAMP wasn't quite the cure everyone dreamed of, although they were nearly there. The next year, Howard Skipper worked out how to cure leukaemia in his mathematical mouse model.[69] After that the human cure was only going to be a matter of time.[68] Today, childhood ALL is one of the most curable of malignancies, with the vast majority of children surviving the disease. This modern therapeutic success can trace its origins directly back to Zubrod and his task force.

At the time though, not everyone was willing to recognise VAMP as the breakthrough it undoubtedly was. In an August 1965 editorial in the research journal *Blood*, reviewing progress in acute leukaemia, William Dameshek wrote of VAMP:[70]

"Not only may this method be considered unscientific, but the initial toxic reaction may be lethal, particularly in adults. Furthermore it has not yet been shown that this treatment program offers a significant advantage over more conservative approaches. In adults two of the "shotgun" constituents (vincristine, methotrexate) are of doubtful value and may do more harm than good. In order to obtain remissions in a few cases, it is likely that the survival time of a larger number of patients may be shortened."

Overall, Dameshek was of the opinion that multiple combinations of drugs represented nothing more than "gropings, which engender little enthusiasm for long term advantages."

But the tide of opinion was against him this time. Over the next few years there were further elaborations of the VAMP approach, based on Skipper's models, to include the concept of sequential induction treatment, followed by much more intensive consolidation treatment and then finally maintenance therapy.[71] It was a chemotherapeutic onslaught, the like of which had never been seen before.

With these advances, most cancer clinicians had accepted by the early 1970s that at least a proportion of children with acute lymphocytic leukaemia were now being cured.

The numbers were nowhere near the seventy to eighty per cent survival rates routinely attainable today. But it was still hugely significant that *any* patients were being cured of ALL which was, to use Dameshek's own term, "the most feared of the "dread" diseases."[70]

The team at NCI didn't hang around though, once it looked like the VAMP regime was beginning to deliver. Emil Frei, John Moxley and Vincent DeVita turned their attention to the lymphoma cancer Hodgkin's disease and devised a combination regimen known as MOMP (nitrogen **M**ustard, **O**ncovine (vincristine), **M**ethotrexate and **P**rednisolone).[72]

This was rapidly superseded by MOPP,[73] in which methotrexate was replaced by procarbazine, a drug which had been discovered about the same time as vincristine and had shown promise as a single agent in Hodgkin's disease.

The results with MOMP and MOPP in the late 1960s were even more impressive than those with VAMP in ALL. The number of patients with Hodgkin's disease going into remission increased from effectively zero to over eighty per cent. Even more amazingly, about sixty per cent of those achieving a remission never relapsed again.[74]

By the early 1970s, along with childhood ALL, Hodgkin's disease was generally regarded as a curable condition. It became the first example of cancer of a major organ system to be curable in adults using chemotherapy.[75] Based on this pioneering work, Hodgkin's disease is today curable in over ninety per cent of patients.

But perhaps the most incredible part of the MOMP and MOPP success was that it was again achieved despite acrimonious resistance and recalcitrance from many groups within the NCI. Substantial opposition remained to undertaking clinical trials with such a radical and innovative approach.

A generation on, and with the lifesaving value of aggressive chemotherapy now incontrovertibly established, the opposition to it at the time appears hard to understand. It's almost as though the NCI should have been renamed the National Cynicism Institute. But back then, this conservatism was a reflection of the underlying fragility of the advances made so far in treating leukaemias and lymphomas.

Undoubtedly substantial and significant steps forwards had been achieved and the possibility of a cure in some cases was a very real one. Despite this, the history of cancer medicine had predominantly been one of early promise subsequently falling away, with the passage of time and the gathering of more experience.

Today, we are still faced with more failures than successes, much greater setbacks than steps forwards. Fifty years ago, the balance sheet was markedly less favourable still. There were few enduring achievements to offset the pessimism engendered by the innumerable disappointments.

Even now, it is often impossible to reach agreement on the merits of a new cancer drug, as evidenced by many of the fierce contemporary regulatory controversies over drug approvals. Trying to achieve a consensus must have been very much harder still all those decades ago. Many of the advances in standardisation of study design, imaging techniques and definitions of endpoints were still to come. This would have made it much harder at the time to interpret clinical data as it emerged.

Furthermore, information then couldn't be exchanged with anything like the rapidity and fluidity of today, thus impeding the spread of knowledge and the garnering of acceptance. The largesse and munificence of the annual ASCO meeting was at the time unavailable and unimaginable.

The climate of caution still prevailing, despite the watershed success of early combination chemotherapy, was well demonstrated by the struggle proponents of the next significant advance were to encounter.

XX

Early combination chemotherapy had shown success restricted to blood cancers, such as leukaemias and lymphomas. By the late 1960s, this had finally been extended to include a non-haematological malignancy, namely breast cancer. A combination called CMF (**C**yclophosphamide, **M**ethotrexate and **5**FU) had been developed by Vincent DeVita and colleagues at NCI.[76]

Cyclophosphamide was an alkylating agent which was a variant of nitrogen mustard. It had been developed in 1956 by Herbert Arnold and Norbert Brock at the pharmaceutical company Asta-Werke AG in Brackwede Germany.

5-FU (5-fluorouracil) had been invented by Charles Heidelberger, a biochemist at the University of Wisconsin, in the late 1950s. It worked like 6-mercaptopurine to block essential components of DNA. Today it is still the cornerstone of treating a number of malignancies, including colorectal, breast and stomach cancer. But back then little was known about its potential usefulness.

CMF therefore consisted of old drugs, now being put to new uses. In patients with widespread breast cancer, who would otherwise have a dismal prognosis, CMF was producing responses of some sort in about half the patients. A minority were even showing complete clearance of their disease.

As experience was growing with the treatment of *advanced* tumors, some were beginning to postulate that these same drugs might work better in *earlier* stage disease.

This was based partly on theoretical considerations, such as the work of Skipper and others.[77]

There was also the clinical observation that the smaller the tumor being treated, the greater the likelihood of obtaining a response. Small tumors were the most rapidly dividing, which left them most vulnerable to the

238

cytotoxic effects of the chemotherapy being used. Furthermore, it seemed intuitively obvious that the earlier the stage of the disease, the greater was the likelihood of being able to arrest its spread and progression.

In light of the favourable experiences with CMF in advanced breast cancer, a few people at NCI began to consider using it at the other end of the spectrum, in the very earliest stages of the malignancy. About ninety per cent of patients with breast cancer have only limited, locally detectable disease at the time of diagnosis. The cancer appears to be confined to the breast itself, or if it has spread, it is only as far as the nearby lymph nodes draining the breast. This is called *loco-regional disease* and is usually treated surgically, to remove all detectable tumor in the breast and surrounding tissues.

However, breast cancer is usually more widespread than it is possible to detect clinically. Because of this, many patients receiving just loco-regional treatment will have the cancer come back at some point. This happens in about a third of women with disease confined to the breast alone and in about three quarters of those in whom it has spread to the lymph nodes. Without further therapy, the *occult* disease will eventually manifest itself over time. The *micro-metastatic* tumors will grow to become clinically detectable. However, although this occurs in a significant proportion of patients, there is still a sizeable fraction who will do very well without any extra treatment. These patients will remain disease free with just loco-regional surgery.

The big difficulty is the lack of any reliable means of identifying those who will recur in the future and distinguishing them from those who will get a lucky break and remain clinically disease free. This creates a dilemma, if you want to give patients chemotherapy after surgery (known as *adjuvant therapy)*[78] in an attempt to eradicate any residual disease. If you can't tell who needs the treatment and who doesn't, then you end up having to give it to pretty much *everyone*.

This involves treating a number of patients who probably don't need the extra chemotherapy and wouldn't benefit from it, although they might well experience all the associated toxicities. To justify this, you have to be sure that most patients would relapse if not treated and that the inevitable toxicities are manageable enough to make treatment a price worth paying. You have to be confident that the cost incurred by the minority who won't get anything out of it, is outweighed by the advantages for the majority who will.

Despite this reservation, the value of adjuvant chemotherapy has been convincingly proven for a whole variety of tumor types, where it has been shown to reduce local and systemic recurrences and to improve overall survival. This impressive list of malignancies includes breast, colorectal, cervical, gastric, head and neck, pancreatic, melanoma, non-small cell lung, ovarian, bone and anaplastic astrocytoma (*a virulent type of brain cancer*).

The established place adjuvant chemotherapy enjoys in contemporary cancer medicine makes it hard to understand the antipathy towards the concept in the early 1970s, when it was first formulated. Paul Carbone and others at NCI, who were original proponents and advocates of the adjuvant approach, found they were talking to a brick wall, when it came to persuading surgeons in the US to explore the use of adjuvant combination chemotherapy in breast cancer. The resistance to the use of what were seen as toxic cocktails, of unproven value, was almost universal.

Faced with this intractable intransigence on home soil, Carbone was forced to look further afield. And it was obvious to him where he should go. Carbone made his way to Gianni Bonadonna, who was Director of the Division of Medical Oncology at the Instituto Nazionale Tumori in Milan. After studying medicine in Italy, Bonadonna had subsequently spent a number of years at Memorial Sloan-Kettering in New York and so was well known to some at least in the US oncology community.

Bonadonna was no stranger to the emerging concept of combination chemotherapy. In 1972 he had designed a superior regimen for Hodgkin's disease called ABVD (**A**driamycin, **B**leomycin, **V**inblastine and **D**acarbazine).[79] It is still the gold standard of treatment today. But more than that, he went on in 1974 to develop a treatment approach of alternating MOPP and ABVD, which became the world's first *eight* drug regimen.[80]

Clearly a man like this would be able to take a three drug combination such as CMF in his stride. It was also unlikely to perturb his surgical colleague, the pioneering Umberto Veronesi.

At the time, Veronesi happened to be challenging a number of conventional surgical orthodoxies in breast cancer, including the need for radical mastectomy and radical post-operative radiotherapy. He would subsequently achieve international fame for his work in developing more conservative and less disfiguring surgical techniques. He was therefore an ideally iconoclastic candidate to pick up the gauntlet thrown down by breast surgeons in the US.

Bonadonna agreed to visit NCI and after seeing the results of CMF treatment in advanced breast cancer, he and Veronesi committed to a randomised controlled trial of a slightly modified CMF regimen, versus placebo, as adjuvant treatment in earlier stage disease. NCI agreed to pay the Instituto Tumori for the study and it started in 1971.

Faced with the courageousness of the plucky Italians, around this time there was also some begrudging progress in the US at long last. This was due largely to the efforts of a visionary surgeon called Bernard Fisher, who was able to see far ahead of the rest of the field. He'd already conducted what was in effect an early adjuvant type trial at the end of the 1960s.[81] This had been looking at the effects of a single drug called thiopeta, which was given immediately after breast surgery in an attempt to kill cancer cells dislodged into the blood stream by the operation itself.

Fisher had recently become head of an NCI collaborative group known as the National Surgical Adjuvant Breast and Bowel Project (NSABP) based at the Allegheny Hospital Campus of the University of Pittsburgh. It had a remit, as the title suggested, to examine further the emerging field of adjuvant treatment for operable malignancies. Although he couldn't persuade anyone in the US to look at the sort of combination chemotherapy the Italians were getting to grips with, he did succeed in setting up a randomised adjuvant trial in breast cancer, using just a *single* drug. This was the agent L-phenylalanine mustard (L-PAM), better known today as melphalan.

Fisher's study ultimately involved thirty seven centres in the US and Canada, who recruited over two hundred patients between them. The women in the study were randomised to receive placebo or L-PAM, for five consecutive days every six weeks, for up to two years. In the absence of an obvious disease burden, that was a lot of chemotherapy, by the standards of the day.

In the end, this study actually finished ahead of the Italian one with CMF. The results, which showed a clear benefit from L-PAM treatment, were published in the *New England Journal of Medicine* on January 16th 1975.[82] That was just weeks after the announcements in November of the previous year that both Betty Ford, the wife of the President and Happy Rockefeller, the wife of the Vice President, were suffering from the disease themselves.

The timing couldn't have been better for Fisher. The study received a lot of attention, because of the prominence the disease had suddenly been accorded in the popular press. The similarly positive Italian CMF results were published a year later.[83] In the face of initially implacable opposition from cancer surgeons in the US, the role of adjuvant chemotherapy was now beginning to define itself, thanks to the intrepid Italians and to Bernard Fisher. In fact, the use of adjuvant chemotherapy in breast cancer turned out to be one of the biggest cancer advances of the 1970s and 1980s. It resulted in hugely impressive twenty five to thirty per cent reductions in mortality.

XXI

These early successes set off a bandwagon of adjuvant trials and Fisher in particular was in the ascendant. Over the next decade, he would consolidate the NSABP as one of the most powerful cooperative groups, able to fund larger studies than ever previously imaginable.

It was helped immensely in the early days by the passage of the National Cancer Act. This came into effect in 1971, heralding President Nixon's *War on Cancer*. It unleashed unprecedented federal funding to encourage progress in research on cancer. As a consequence of the monies flowing from this initiative, support for the cooperative group increased from just nine million dollars in 1972 to almost one hundred and twenty million dollars in 1980.

By the mid-1990s, the NSABP had enrolled almost eleven thousand patients into breast and bowel cancer trials. It had links with over five thousand physicians at almost one thousand hospitals in the US, Canada, Puerto Rico, Australia and Ireland. However, the growing sophistication and complexity of these cancer clinical trials would come at a cost. And a substantial one as far as Bernard Fisher was concerned. Particularly when, one day in July 1994, he was peremptorily dismissed by the NCI.

The NSABP was in big trouble. Its trials had grown so large that they could no longer keep track of those five thousand physicians and what they were up to. And, as it turned out, one of them, a Canadian cancer surgeon called Roger Poisson at the University of Montreal, had been up to no good. Investigations revealed that he had been responsible for fraudulently manufacturing clinical data on over one hundred patients who had been enrolled into a number of NSABP trials.

This included a particularly pivotal one in 1985, where Poisson had contributed sixteen per cent of the patients.[84] The trial in question had been comparing lumpectomy (the removal of a tumor lump from the breast, leaving the rest of it intact) to mastectomy (removing the whole breast). The results, which showed that patients did just as well with the more limited surgery, played a big role in changing the practice of many cancer surgeons towards more conservative operations.

And yet Poisson had been deliberately altering medical records and falsifying data to make it seem as though patients met all the requirements for being entered into a study, even when they obviously didn't. In some cases, this was nothing more serious than minor alterations of the dates of operations. More egregious transgressions however ranged from misrepresenting the extent of patients' cancer disease through to covering up other serious illnesses they were suffering from.

In one case, a patient's death was disguised, with Poisson pretending to see them in the clinic for another two years after they had actually passed away. Investigators found that Poisson and his staff even kept two sets of patient records, labelled "true" and "false" in French.

The whole deception only came to light after he accidentally sent NSABP two records of the same operation on the same patient. One had been substantially altered compared to the other, which recorded what actually happened. Fraudulent findings were eventually uncovered in one hundred and eleven patients over a period of twelve years.

This raised doubts over the credibility of *any* of the data from the fifteen hundred or so patients Poisson had recruited over the years. Eventually, all the NSABP trials which had involved him had to be reanalysed with his data excluded.

Poisson eventually admitted to even more fabrication than already uncovered by investigators. In return for his confession, he was expecting leniency, demanding to remain a participant in NSABP trials. In his view a "simple warning" would suffice for what he described as "silly little mistakes."[85]

Unsurprisingly, FDA took a dimmer view and in 1993 barred him for an indeterminate period from becoming involved with investigational drugs, or from receiving federal grants for the next eight years. However, he somehow managed to remain on the staff at Montreal University, although he was no longer Professor of Oncology there.

Fisher was fired not because he had done anything inappropriate but because he had presided over a research organisation which failed for over a decade to pick up on systematic fraud. There was no excuse for that. Furthermore, when it did become aware of what was happening, nothing was done for another eight months. That would have given Poisson plenty of time to destroy the evidence, had he been so minded.

Despite the deficiencies which had might have occurred on his watch, Fisher subsequently counterattacked and in turn sued the University of Pittsburgh the NCI, the Department of Health and Human Services, the National Institutes of Health and the Office of Research Integrity for defamation. He was basically taking aim at anyone in his sights. But it was worth it in the end, as the case was eventually settled out of court in October 1997. Fisher received a full apology and damages of nearly three million dollars.

It was however an unedifying experience all round, with everyone involved losing out one way or another. Particularly the patients who were unknowingly entered into clinical trials which were unsuitable and inappropriate for them.

The NSABP experience also served to show just how complicated cancer research had become by the 1980s, with the need for ever larger clinical trials and all the administrative and organisational difficulties that brought with it. Cancer trials were now so big that it was impossible to keep control of them all of the time. Complexity, confusion and occasionally outright criminality would become challenges for clinical trialists to contend with in the future.

This would ultimately generate a whole industry of compliance requirements, intended to protect the integrity of clinical data. Today, information at each centre in a clinical trial is mercilessly interrogated and tortured, to confirm its accuracy and veracity. It is always assumed guilty until proven innocent. The Spanish Inquisition could undoubtedly have picked up a tip or two from modern monitoring methods for cancer studies.

The process of checking clinical trial data at a hospital has now evolved to a point where it is not dissimilar to a police forensics team going over your house on their hands and knees. They've convinced themselves that you have a dismembered body tucked away somewhere and they are determined to find it. If you do actually happen to have something unfortunate concealed, however carefully, they *will* discover it eventually.

It is all a far remove from the Rotarian spirit which had enthused the early pioneers of cancer chemotherapy.

XXII

In addition to the associated practical problems, the growing complexity of clinical trials was symptomatic of a more fundamental issue. The successes of the late nineteen sixties and early seventies had been accomplished using relatively small numbers of patients in whom to prove the point.

By contrast, the need for much larger clinical trials in the 1980s was seen by many as confirmation of a belief that progress had slowed substantially, compared to the dramatic achievements of the preceding decades. New advances seemed small at best, requiring large trials to confirm the existence of only a marginal improvement.

Maybe this loss of momentum was inevitable. When you are starting with nothing, as was pretty much the case in the fifties and early sixties, then *anything* is going to represent a big step forwards. But with time, it becomes harder to maintain that rate of progress.

Inevitably the "easiest" targets are going to fall by the wayside faster and more frequently at the outset. After that, the struggle becomes much more demanding. The steps forward become smaller and require an ever greater effort to achieve them.

Taking stock of the first three decades of chemotherapy, by 1980 there were about ten different cancers where it was possible to use the word "curable," at least in a proportion of patients. These included choriocarcinoma, Burkitt's lymphoma, acute lymphocytic leukaemia, Hodgkin's disease, histiocytic lymphoma, Wilm's Tumor (*a childhood tumor of the kidney*), rhabdomyosarcoma (*a tumor of soft tissues and muscle*), embryonal testicular cancer, Ewing's sarcoma (*a childhood bone tumor*) and childhood ovarian cancer.

Most of these were paediatric malignancies because the most rapidly growing tumors tended to occur in children and these were the types of cancer which were turning out to be most susceptible to chemotherapy. There were still few adult tumors where a cure was possible and probably overall only about ten per cent of cancers could be considered even partially susceptible to chemotherapy.

Cures were also frequently associated with substantial permanent disability, arising from the treatment itself. Heart damage, lung damage, nerve damage were all too often profoundly disabling. Many effective treatments would subsequently go on to cause leukaemia, in a proportion of those surviving their original malignancy.

So they were cures that came at a cost. But despite that, there were still ten cancers which had become manageable in the twenty four years since the original successful treatment of choriocarcinoma. That quarter of a century had also produced a number of truly effective cancer therapies. By 1980 there were nine drugs which had been shown to be unequivocally curative, in certain contexts: nitrogen mustard, cyclophosphamide, actinomycin D, methotrexate, 6-mercaptopurine, prednisolone, procarbazine, vincristine and asparaginase.

There were a further five drugs which were probably producing cures, although it hadn't yet been completely proven. These were doxorubicin, 5-fluorouracil, cisplatin, bleomycin and cytarabine.

Progress since the end of the Second World War had been substantial. Cancer clinicians now had access to a range of drugs which were clearly providing benefit, for at least some of their patients. But maybe it was unrealistic to expect this rate of progress to continue into the next decade, when the challenge of adult solid tumors appeared so daunting. With a few exceptions, most adult tumors remained stubbornly resistant to chemotherapeutic attack.

There was a feeling at the beginning of the 1980s, that new initiatives were needed, before further inroads could be made against the disease. Although everyone knew the limitations, there was still too much reliance on mass screening of chemicals. The already prevailing disillusionment with this approach wasn't helped by recognition that most of the curative cancer drugs had been identified completely independently of screening initiatives.

They had arisen from programmes which had nothing to do with cancer. Nitrogen mustard had originated out of chemical warfare projects. Methotrexate, prednisolone and mercaptopurine came from research into nutrition, adrenal physiology and purine biochemistry respectively. Actinomycin D had been identified in the search for new antibiotics to treat tuberculosis. Vincristine had come out of diabetes research, procarbazine from a depression screening programme and asparaginase from studies in immunology.

Although at some point all these drugs had been put through cancer screening models prior to clinical testing, the fact was that nearly all of the existing useful drugs had arisen from observational serendipity, rather than organised screening.

However, it was a slow process. Corticosteroids, such as prednisolone, had first been shown to have experimental activity in 1938 and yet results indicative of a clinical cure didn't come until almost three decades later, in 1966. On average, for those drugs which had been proven to have some value, it had taken *twenty years* from the initial demonstration of experimental promise to the confirmation of clinical cure.

Henceforth, dissatisfaction with the poor productivity and protracted pathway of previous approaches to drug screening led to the gradual abandonment of the animal systems used up until that point. Primarily these had been variants of a mouse leukaemia model. The two main ones in use were known as L1210 and P388, which both consisted of a rapidly dividing tumor type.

They were popular because there was extensive experience with them. However, there was a growing realisation that their usefulness was limited, as far as slower growing solid tumors were concerned. Most drugs showing activity in these screens turned out to be clinically effective only in very actively dividing tumors, such as haematological malignancies.

In an attempt to identify more compounds of relevance to solid tumours, the mouse leukaemia model was gradually replaced.

Initially this was with nude mice, capable of growing transplanted human (*xenograft*) tumors. To begin with, the transplanted tumors included colon, breast and lung. As the technique became easier to undertake, over three hundred xenografts were eventually established. The taxane compounds, such as paclitaxel, were a major example of drugs which would eventually be identified though this new system.

Subsequently, in the early 1990s, the mouse was increasingly supplanted, for initial screening at least, by actual human cancer cells which were grown in a culture. This effectively created a tumor in a test tube, upon which the effects of new drugs could be tested. The standard screen came to consist of sixty different human tumor cell lines, derived from cancers including colon, brain, lung, melanoma, ovarian, renal, breast, prostate and leukaemia.

Later on, sophisticated algorithmic computer systems were developed. These could use the particular pattern of growth inhibitory effects displayed by an anti-cancer drug, to predict its mechanism of action.

However, with these more elaborate and demanding screening techniques, the number of compounds which could be examined actually *fell* from forty thousand to ten thousand a year, although the number of positive results remained about the same.

Despite more innovative screening techniques, very few novel compounds have arisen from this modified approach. Most of those which have been identified are variants on drugs already in existence.

After half a century of endeavour, it seemed as though screening technology might finally be running out of road.

XXIII

As it turned out though, the general decline in innovation from mass screening fortuitously coincided, in the 1980s, with the tentative emergence of what would rapidly become the era of molecular biology and the

246

beginnings of targeted therapy as a new approach to cancer control.

This point in time maybe marked the beginnings of a conceptual divergence of future cancer research.

Progress with existing non-specific chemotherapeutic agents would increasingly come from finding new ways of delivering an ever more intense generalised assault on a patient's cancer.

The targeted strategy on the other hand, was almost the opposite approach. Its advances came through novel highly selective and specific lines of attack.

The former was analogous to carpet bombing enemy positions, to produce total carnage and devastation. The later was more like infiltrating a James Bond type secret agent behind enemy lines, armed with a computer virus to take out their command and control systems.

An example of the carpet bombing approach was the use of ultra-high dose chemotherapy, in combination with stem cell transplantation, in patients with breast cancer, a technique which began to emerge in the 1980s.[86]

Chemotherapeutic regimens, such as CMF, undoubtedly improve the outcome of patients with metastatic breast disease. However, only about twenty per cent of patients show a response, in terms of tumor shrinkage and the overall survival is no more than about eighteen months. There is definitely room for improvement therefore.

It had been known since the 1970s that there is correlation between the extent of response and the amount of drug given. However, one of the big difficulties in trying to improve on existing outcomes is the bone marrow toxicity which occurs with progressively higher doses of chemotherapy. If you push the dose too high, you will kill the patient in the process.

One possible solution to this dilemma lay in another area of cancer medicine, with the advances being made in bone marrow and stem cell transplantation in the 1970s and 1980s. These were allowing patients with leukaemia and other haematological malignancies to routinely survive the ultra-high doses of chemotherapy which were needed to completely wipe out their own diseased bone marrow, prior to receiving a transplant.

Building on this knowledge, physicians treating breast cancer began to see a way they could give much higher doses of chemotherapy to patients than had ever been attempted before.

They realised they could use stem cell transplantation to rescue the patient from the subsequent life threatening bone marrow toxicity. Also, as opposed to leukaemia, where patients needed a bone marrow *donor*, breast cancer patients could be given back their *own* bone marrow, which had been collected from them prior to chemotherapy. This *autologous* transplantation, without the need for donors, made the whole procedure much more feasible.

Results from animal studies were surprisingly encouraging and in the late 1980s several small clinical studies were undertaken with this approach. The results suggested an improvement in survival in patients with advanced breast cancer. Investigators found that they could give up to *ten fold* higher doses of drugs like cyclophosphamide employing this technique, compared to when bone marrow transplantation wasn't used.

So promising were these initial trials that by the early 1990s, over forty thousand women in the US had been treated with high dose chemotherapy and autologous stem cell transplantation for advanced breast cancer.

However, as with anything in cancer medicine, nothing was that clear cut. Subsequent larger randomised trials, in the mid-1990s, of high dose versus conventional chemotherapy failed to confirm a survival advantage, at up to five years of follow up. The transplant itself had a significant mortality associated with it, as well as numerous other side effects too. What you were gaining in efficacy, you were potentially losing in toxicity.[87,88]

It was clear though that high dose chemotherapy was prolonging the time before cancer spread more widely. Twenty years after its advent in breast cancer, the exact role of high dose chemotherapy is still unclear and requires further evaluation. There is likely to be an as yet ill defined proportion of patients, with more advanced disease and highest risk, who would really benefit from this technique. The problem is that it hasn't yet been possible to clearly identify them.

High dose chemotherapy is a typical example of the current pattern of cancer advance. This is often characterised by initial promise, subsequent uncertainty and hopefully eventual future resolution.

However, it is also a testament to the ongoing ingenuity of cancer researchers, in maximising the potential of the existing tools at their disposal through slow steady small incremental advances.

As it turned out, high dose chemotherapy wasn't going to dramatically alter the outcome for anyone with advanced breast cancer. For the right patients though, it would provide an increased benefit, compared to conventional doses of the same agents.

Maybe there was only so much extra that could be squeezed out of drugs which were now all well over fifty years old anyway, however much creativity you brought to bear.

Perhaps it was to be expected that after the dramatic early advances, subsequent steps with conventional chemotherapy would be the multiple small ones which characterised the 1980s and 1990s. Like any new technology, the pace of innovation eventually slows, only to ultimately open the door for evolving new alternative approaches.

Conventional cancer chemotherapy was in many ways like the jet engine, a technology emerging at the same time in the late thirties and early forties. Initially it revolutionised manned flight and moved it into a new era. After that dramatic debut though, it was subsequently characterised by small slow progressively incremental advances and improvements.

In the context of cancer medicine however, if chemotherapy had been the jet engine propelling early therapeutic advances, the emerging area of targeted therapy would turn out to be the moon shot.

XXIV

There is no universal definition of exactly what is meant by *targeted* therapy. Many cancer drugs have a target of some sort, which has been identified over the years. Anthracyclines for example, which are as old as Methuselah in cancer chemotherapy terms, home in on an enzyme called topoisomerase II, which is vital to the control of DNA dynamics within the cell nucleus. They work by preventing topoisomerase II from functioning properly. But no one would describe anthracyclines as targeted, because they lack discrimination. They also attack the topoisomerase II of non-malignant cells, thus accounting for the dreadful range of side effects associated with their use.

To complicate things further, the novel insights now afforded by molecular biology are increasingly offering up opportunities to repackage some of the more dated molecules from the chemotherapy era. A number of old timers out there are being given a new lease of life, after being rebranded as targeted therapies.

One good example of this is thalidomide itself. For many years after the disaster of the 1960s, this remained a largely disowned and discredited drug, although it did discover a niche, following a chance observation that it produced beneficial effects in patients suffering from leprosy.[89]

Despite languishing in the doldrums for so long however, recent realisations that thalidomide has profound targeted immunomodulatory activity, as well as causing disruption to the blood supply of tumors, resulted in a remarkable rehabilitation. After encouraging clinical trials, thalidomide and analogues, such as lenalidomide (Revlimid), now have an established position in the management of a number of malignancies, most notably the blood cancer multiple myeloma.[90]

It's a dramatic redemption for one of the most notorious names in the annals of drug delinquency and testament, yet again, to the transformative power of modern molecular technology.

Targeted and *non-targeted* are therefore perhaps best considered as two ends of a spectrum, rather than being completely discrete entities. Broadly however, the term targeted therapy can be considered as comprising agents which interact at a specific point in a known signalling system of a particular cancer, to produce disruption of a key component of the cell's survival mechanisms. Their effects are hopefully more specific for the pathway which is active only in the tumour, leaving normal cells relatively unscathed.

This is in distinction to the more widespread cellular damage caused by conventional chemotherapy, which is usually much less selective in what it attacks.

Chemotherapy works largely by destroying all in its path, with as much collateral damage as necessary. The targeted approach is aimed at achieving the same effect through taking out just one or two key elements of the malignant cell, which are so vital that it can't survive without them. Success depends however on being able to identify exactly what those key elements are and then finding ways to disable them, without also paralysing normal cells along the way.

The last decade in particular has seen an exponential expansion of insights into the molecular pathways of cell control. This is offering up multiple potential points of attack, which might be vulnerable to targeted therapies.

Although employing the most sophisticated of modern scientific advances, this is however an undertaking dating as far back as the 1960s. It all began with another federal research project, known as the Special Virus Cancer Program (SVCP).

The SVCP was conceived as a research endeavour to identify viruses, which were believed at the time to be widely implicated in the development of cancer. The program failed to actually find any significant new culprit viruses but it did manage to generate a substantial number of conspiracy theories along the way.

These included a widespread belief that US authorities were attempting to develop a cancer *causing* virus as a biological weapon and also that the AIDS virus originated here, as an experiment gone wrong.

On a less sinister front, the SVCP evolved over time into what eventually became the world's first coordinated program of molecular biology, looking at the interaction between genes and tumors. This work produced much of the initial knowledge of tumor genes, tumor suppressor genes and the myriad pathways of cell signalling and cell control, which are so vital to modern research endeavours.[91]

It was to lay the ground work for many of today's advances in targeted treatment approaches to cancer.

The SVCP provided the tools that would subsequently start unlocking the targeted treasure trove. Ever since those early days and the birth of molecular biology, when the innermost secrets of the cell began to be laid bare, there has been a systematic hunt for gold, buried deep in the awe inspiring complexity of nature's evolution of the cell and the ways it has devised to keep everything under control.

This new knowledge and insight have in turn been responsible for driving the entire biotechnology revolution. In the US, the early 1990s marked the transition from cancer drug development as largely a low budget government driven research activity into a multibillion dollar high risk, high reward industrial effort.

Today, there are about fifteen hundred biotech start up companies in the US alone, all exploiting the advances of molecular biology. At least half of them work in cancer medicine, trying to repair the malignant transformations of the cell's molecular mechanisms.

Clustered in California, Boston and elsewhere, these new companies are far removed from the historical claustrophobia of the NCI in Bethesda. Europe hasn't been far behind either, with start up companies springing up overnight around university originated academic research programs.

These are modern day pirates searching for the hidden hoard, often operating at the fringes of convention and custom, as they rewrite the rules of biology and drug development. This has resulted in an unprecedented acceleration of innovation in the development of more specific and targeted anti-cancer agents, over the last two decades.

Many of these advances have already been touched on elsewhere. There are, for example, now over twenty antibodies in widespread use, for a range of solid and haematological malignancies.[92] Each is directed at a specific target on the surface of the cancer cell. Most however have to be combined with conventional chemotherapy to be optimally effective. By themselves, they can't quite do enough. Given alone, these big bulky molecules struggle to achieve sufficient traction, particularly with solid tumors.

This limitation leaves them lower down the league table of targeted techniques. To overcome this, some antibodies are now linked to radioisotopes, such as Zevalin and Bexxar for non-Hodgkin's lymphoma, or specific cellular toxins, such as Mylotarg for acute myeloid leukaemia or Adcetris for both Hodgkin's and some types of non-Hodgkin's lymphoma.[92] These *antibody conjugates*[93] have so far been most promising in haematological malignancies.

However, the solid tumor fortress is showing some signs of vulnerability at last, with agents such as trastuzumab emtansine (T-DM1) which is essentially Herceptin conjugated to a cellular toxin. This particular conjugate has recently been producing very favourable results in clinical trials with advanced breast cancer patients, who've already received Herceptin therapy.[94,95] These findings led FDA to approve the drug (known as *Kadcyla*) in February 2013.

Newer developments in molecular manipulation have also created the ability to engineer *bi-functional* and even *tri-functional* antibodies, which are basically the active portions of two or three antibodies bolted together, thus doubling or tripling the number of potential tumor and immune targets.[96] This is one of the most significant evolutions in antibody technology in the last three decades. It offers the potential to expand this therapeutic approach in a way that is analogous to the capabilities of a smart phone compared to a landline.

However, despite these promising advances with antibodies and antibody fragments, the top tiers of targeted therapy appear to be currently occupied by small molecule approaches. There are an ever increasing number of these which have shown at least early promise. Just two examples, each acting at the level of malignant mutation, are *vemurafenib* and *olaparib*.

Vemurafenib targets a particular melanoma gene defect, present in about two thirds of cases of the disease and known as the *BRAF* mutation. This is an *oncogene* which can lead to overactive and uncontrolled cell proliferation, along with resistance to cell death.[97] In patients with this specific abnormality, the drug has been producing historically unparalleled outcomes and generating a lot of excitement along the way. In a recent Phase III trial, when compared to a conventional chemotherapy drug dacarbazine, vemurafenib resulted in sixty three per cent reduced risk of death and a seventy four per cent reduction in the risk of tumor progression.[98] Furthermore, nearly half of all patients showed a tumor response of some sort.

For melanoma, which used be so high up the table of unresponsive tumors that it was almost lost from sight, these were remarkable findings. This drug was actually showing a *survival* advantage. True, it was compared to dacarbazine, a drug which exhibited modest efficacy at best, indeed if at all. Vemurafenib outperforming the comparator wasn't *exactly* setting the bar high therefore. Nonetheless it was still a dramatic development after three decades of therapeutic nihilism, as far as this particular malignancy was concerned.

Olaparib, for use in breast and ovarian cancer was proving to be no slouch either. It works through genetic abnormalities in two *tumor suppressor genes* known as *BRCA1* and *BRCA2*. These mutations can occur in a variety of tumor types, most commonly breast and ovarian cancer in women but also prostate and pancreatic cancer in men. Only about five per cent of women with breast cancer and ten to fifteen per cent of those with ovarian cancer have these inherited defects. However, individuals with BRCA1 or BRCA2 mutations are at exceptionally high risk of developing one or more cancers, often at a very early age.[99]

Olaparib inhibits a particular enzyme called PARP (Poly (ADP-ribose) polymerase) which is important in fixing DNA damage in the normal cell. It's one of many repair mechanisms but in cancer cells which lack BRCA1 or BRCA2, PARP becomes the main line of defence against potentially fatal DNA damage.[100] By taking out PARP, the malignant cell can no longer mend itself and so eventually dies of its wounds. By restricting clinical use to patients with these specific tumor derangements, response rates of forty per cent have been seen with olaparib in advanced breast cancer.[101] In late stage ovarian disease, progression free survival has been almost doubled, from five months without olaparib, to eight and a half months with it.[102] In patients with disease as advanced and as complicated as this, these are significant findings.

This kind of initial success with these more selective drugs and specific patient groupings is in stark contrast to outcomes seen in the past, in *unselected* patient populations. These newer agents therefore appear to be upping the game, as they progressively validate the targeted strategy.

It is however a slowly incremental path even the most promising agents are treading, with dangers still lurking at every turn. Both vemurafenib and olaparib reflect the dilemma currently encountered when evaluating targeted agents. The problem is that it's too early to tell whether they have the stamina to stay the course, against as seasoned an opponent as cancer. It's unclear, at the moment, whether they have the requisite longevity to maintain their impressive initial momentum.

Greater experience with vemurafenib for example has suggested that many of the early tumor responses may be of a relatively short duration. There is also a concern that prolonged treatment can lead to the emergence of a *second* type of skin cancer, called squamous cell carcinoma, in about twenty five per cent of patients. This appears to be due to vemurafenib actually *switching on* a second mutated cancer pathway, in addition to inhibiting the BRAF one it is intended to block.[103] Which just goes to show how confusing interfering with these complicated cell signalling pathways can rapidly become.

With olaparib, initial excitement has been dampened by a subsequent inability to demonstrate a survival advantage in ovarian cancer and a decision to abandon that indication.[104] This is inevitably leading to a reappraisal of how best to use these PARP inhibitors and what might be the optimal patient population with which to marry them up.

The targeted challenge is therefore still wide open. It remains to be seen which approaches will ultimately prove to have longer term performance to match the initial shorter term promise. Rather than a sprint, the race looks like turning into more of a marathon. The question is who will have the staying power.

These reservations about the more recent targeted drugs also now appear to apply to the Daddy of them all. For over a decade, pole position on the targeted track has been occupied by Gleevec, for the treatment of chronic myeloid leukaemia (CML). The question here too is whether some of the shine is finally starting to rub off.

XXV

Gleevec is the best known, most often cited and undoubtedly prototypical example of targeted technology. It even has its own biography.[105] Gleevec (imatinib) inhibits a growth enzyme (*tyrosine kinase*) which is switched into override by an abnormal protein (called BCR-ABL) which is formed in CML cells, due to structural changes in the cell's chromosomes.[106]

However, whilst Gleevec had been transformational in the treatment of CML,[107] turning it into a long term manageable disease, it is not curative in any sense. If patients stop taking the therapy, sooner or later their disease will relapse. Even if they do continue Gleevec uninterrupted, resistance to it can develop in up to twenty per cent of cases.[108]

The leukaemia cells learn over time to subtly mutate and change the structure of the growth enzyme. This means Gleevec can no longer bind to it, thus allowing uncontrolled growth to take off again.

Fortunately, there are now second generation drugs, such as *dasatinib* and *nilotinib,* which bind to the enzyme in a slightly different way. They can therefore restore control in CML which has become resistant to Gleevec alone.

Unfortunately, increasing experience with these newer drugs is beginning to show that resistance can develop to them too, in anything up to half of the patients treated. The leukaemic cells seem to possess a remarkable ability to keep one step ahead.

One of the most difficult to treat and resistant of the enzyme mutations emerging so far bears the code number *T315A*. It is caused by a simple switch of *one* amino acid (threonine) for another (alanine).

Amino acids are the basic building blocks of proteins, such as the CML growth enzyme. Given that there are over four hundred of them in the enzyme overall, this shows how easy it can be for a malignant disease to side step a new therapeutic intervention. One subtle shift is all it takes.

The binding of an imatinib or dasatinib or nilotinib molecule to the tyrosine kinase enzyme is a highly complicated manoeuvre. All the intricate structural shapes need to fit together in exactly the right conformation at the right time. Changing just one amino acid out of four hundred can throw everything into disarray.

And that is one of the potential limitations of the targeted approach. The drugs are so *precise* in their specifications, compared to conventional chemotherapy, that even a small disruption can render them potentially ineffective. It's the equivalent of driving around in a temperamental high performance sports car rather than a truck. The smallest glitch will cause it to breakdown and stop working.

So whilst Gleevec has proven enormously beneficial and changed forever the lives of the majority of patients with CML, it has perhaps at best commuted a death sentence to a life tariff, rather than setting anyone free.

Gleevec rightly enjoys a hugely significant prominence as an early validation of the targeted approach. Despite that, the limitations around its usage, which are only now becoming apparent, mean that its exact place in the parade of therapeutic advances awaits the confirmation of historical retrospect.

However, whilst the long term jury may still be out for some drugs, such as Gleevec, sentence has already been passed for others which have failed to live up to even initial expectations.

XXVI

Tipifarnib (*Zarnestra*) was a drug being developed by J&J. It was the exciting newcomer which had cornered all the elderly AML patients a few years earlier, thus crowding out AS1411.

Tipifarnib was specifically targeted to block an enzyme in cancer cells called *farnesyl transferase*. This in turn prevented activation of one of the most fundamental of all cell signalling systems, known as the *Ras/Raf/Mek/Erk* pathway, which is vitally involved in cell survival and cell proliferation. The complexity of the name gives a clue to the indispensability of the role it plays.

This pathway is mutated in about thirty per cent of cancers, resulting in overstimulation which leads to abnormal and uncontrolled cell growth. Blocking it should therefore have been a promising avenue of exploitation.

In accordance with this prediction, tipifarnib showed very promising activity in laboratory studies, which included xenograft mouse models and human cancer cell lines. It appeared to work against a variety of solid and haematological malignancies.

And yet in clinical trials, it has shown very limited anti-cancer efficacy of any sort. Tipifarnib has been ineffective against breast, pancreatic, lung and colon cancers and also multiple melanoma. Five other farnesyl transferase inhibitors have fared little better.[109]

The nearest it came to demonstrating an effect was actually in acute myeloid leukaemia in the elderly, where tipifarnib showed a modest response rate of about fifteen per cent.[110] There was however no effect on survival, leading to it eventually being rejected by FDA.

There was subsequently widespread surprise at the lack of clinical effect with a drug which seemed to be taking out such a central pathway of command and control within the cell and one which was well known to be hijacked during malignant transformation.

Tipifarnib's failure was ultimately a consequence of the enormous complexity of the checks and balances that exist within the cell, thanks to Nature's foresight. Malignant disease has the unfortunate ability to play these off against each other, thus evading the effects of the drug altogether.

As a measure of the exquisitely elaborate extent of cellular control, the Ras molecule, which is controlled by the farnesyl transferase enzyme, turns out to also be involved in *two other* pathways within the cell.

One is a cellular process called the *phosphatidylinositol 3-kinase (PI3K)/Akt* pathway, which also acts to increase cell survival.

As if that weren't enough, Ras also interacts with a protein called *Tiam1* which in turn activates other proteins, with names such as *Rac, RhoB, NFkB* and *JNK*, which all play a role in regulating cell proliferation.

In turn, many of *these* molecules are regulated within the cell by a bizarrely named pathway known for some reason as *geranylgeranylation.* Activation of this pathway produces *opposite* effects to those of farnesyl transferase.

So effectively what is happening is that Nature has evolved two interacting process of *farnesylation* and *geranylgeranylation*. Blocking the former with tipifarnib simply allows malignant cells to use the Ras molecule to alter the activity of the latter, thus overriding the drug's effects.

On top of that, although it wasn't known at the time, tipifarnib was originally developed, there appear to be about thirty *other* proteins, apart from Ras, which are directly dependent on farnesyl transferase activity and so would be blocked by tipifarnib.

The function of all of these are unknown at the moment but some act to *inhibit* cell growth. By blocking them tipifarnib would therefore have the unwanted effect of actually *stimulating* cell proliferation. In effect, tipifarnib would be pressing on the brake *and* accelerator pedals at the same time.

Basically, tipifarnib couldn't make the grade because it was *too* specific. It did block an important pathway, *farnesyl transferase* but crucially left intact all the other processes which are constantly pulsing through a cell. Its actions were effectively circumvented, due to the multiplicity of the other pathways down which the malignant cells could direct their ferocious energy. The difficulties with tipifarnib represent the dilemma of trying to find the right balance with the targeted strategy.

There is therefore a need to avoid selecting a target which is so specific that it is overridden by everything else going on in the cell, whilst on the other hand not taking out so many targets that you are beginning to overlap with the conventional chemotherapeutic approach.

That balance can be difficult to achieve, given the as yet incomplete insight that exists into the intricacies of the cellular control process.

One potential way out of this impasse however, might be by *combinations* of targeted agents, to spread the net wider as it were. That could well be the way of the future, mirroring the earlier pathway followed by the chemotherapeutic agents. As was the case back then, initial excitement over single targeted drugs may come to be displaced by a realisation that packaging them together is a far more promising avenue to pursue.

A recent example of this is the development of the so called R^2 *regimen* for the treatment of certain types of indolent lymphoma. This consists of the thalidomide derivative *lenalidomide*, combined with rituximab, an anti-CD20 antibody. Here were two targeted agents in tandem, *without* any chemotherapy partners tagging along for the ride.

This duo resulted in an incredible ninety eight per cent overall response rate,[111] prompting speculation that the end of chemotherapy was in sight, at least as far as these particular types of patients were concerned.

It might be too soon to entertain that kind of enthusiastic expectation but it is certainly a far cry from Bonadonna's eight drug MOPP and ABVD lymphoma chemotherapy combination of the early 1970s. In conceptual terms it's equivalent to using a cruise missile rather than a catapult.

XXVII

Targeting too tightly, with single agents, may therefore be one potential limitation to the current wave of molecular biology. Another is that as new molecular understandings of disease contribute to new therapeutic solutions, along the way they may actually also inadvertently create new dilemmas for drug development.

Pfizer's drug *crizotinib*, which is promising to revolutionise the treatment of lung cancer for some patients at least, is an example of the issues at play here.

Early clinical trials with crizotinib have been conducted over the past few years, in patients with lung cancer who'd already failed on two or *even three* previous sorts of chemotherapy. So these really were people who'd pretty much reached the end of the road.

And yet crizotinib was achieving *remarkable* results in this patient population. Over three quarters of those treated showed some sort of clear benefit. No one had seen anything like this before, in solid tumors this far advanced and this resistant to previous chemotherapeutic attack. It was the talk of ASCO at its 2010 meeting in Chicago.[112]

Crizotinib subsequently sailed through further clinical trials to eventually be approved by FDA in August 2011. After that, it was unfortunately burdened with the worst trade name ever invented for a drug, *Xalkori*. It sounded more like an alien life form Dr Who would go into battle against. Despite the unpromising nomenclature, its advent will however surely come to be seen as a significant milestone in the conceptual battle against the enemy.

And yet however revolutionary it may turn out to be, crizotinib will most likely play only a limited role in the treatment of lung cancer. This is because it can only ever be effective in about five per cent of patients overall.

This exclusivity is due to the way it works, through reversing the effects of a specific gene abnormality. This is known as the *ALK EML-4* mutation (or more technically the *Anaplastic Lymphoma Kinase-Echinoderm microtubule-associated protein-like 4 mutation*). A little bit like the *BCR-ABL* abnormality in CML, the ALK abnormality results in uncontrolled growth enzyme activity and runaway cell proliferation.

Crucially though, this abnormality only occurs in about five per cent of patients with non-small cell lung cancer. Which is why crizotinib is unlikely to be of much use in the other ninety five per cent. Whilst it therefore has the potential to confer a large advantage, it unfortunately has only a limited applicability.

However, the advances in molecular biology which are occurring all the time have identified about another *twenty* different genetic abnormalities which can occur in lung cancer patients, separately from the ALK one. There is therefore the possibility, at some point, of a crizotinib like drug for each of these groups too.

These developments have important implications for the way we think about the disease. Which in turn influences our approach to coming up with new drugs to treat it.

Up until recently, lung cancer has been classified *histologically*. Which means according to the types of cells physically seen when the tumor is looked at down the microscope. On the basis of this, in the past lung tumors have been divided into *small cell cancer* and *non-small cell cancer* (which has itself been broken down into further subtypes, including *squamous carcinoma* and *adenocarcinoma*).[113] This is because these are the different types of lung tissue from which the malignancy appears to arise.

In accordance with this histological classification, cancer drugs have historically been developed either for small cell lung cancer, or non-small cell lung cancer, as two distinct entities. Experience has shown that these two groups have differing sensitivities to different chemotherapeutic agents.

But the implication of advances in molecular biology is that lung cancer (as with many other malignancies) will increasingly be classified and treated according to the underlying genetic defect or defects. Already there are a significant number of global research efforts to characterise malignancies in just this way. These include the Cancer Genome Atlas, the International Cancer Genome Consortium, the 1000 Genome Project and the Genomics of Drug Sensitivity in Cancer initiative. A lot of money is being thrown at this.

In lung cancer alone, this would result in maybe twenty or so different *molecular* variants of the disease rather than just the current handful of *histological* ones.

The power of this new biology is demonstrated by its impact on the fate of a recent Astra Zeneca lung cancer drug called gefitinib (Iressa). This was a tyrosine kinase inhibitor originally developed worldwide for non-small cell lung cancer. Unfortunately, despite initial promise it didn't show a survival advantage in Phase III trials,[114,115] which led to its effective discontinuation in 2005. In the normal course of events, that would have been the end of the drug, leaving it to join the ranks of so many others which have also failed in this particular disease.

However, that isn't what happened in the case of Iressa. Astute observations at the time showed that in fact the drug appeared to be working in a small fraction of the overall patient population. These turned out to be predominantly female, Asian patients, who were non-smokers and whose cancer was of the non-small cell *adenocarcinoma* variety.

At first sight, this appeared quite a hotchpotch of unrelated characteristics. However, subsequent insights revealed that the unifying finding in patients with these diverse features, was a higher than normal probability of bearing a lung cancer gene mutation called the *EGFR* mutation.

Epidermal **G**rowth **F**actor **R**eceptor is a structure on the surface of the cell, which is linked to a tyrosine kinase growth enzyme inside the cell. When a mutation occurs (as happens in about fifteen per cent of lung cancers), the growth enzyme runs out of control thus allowing the cancer to proliferate and spread.[116]

Armed with these new findings, Astra Zeneca subsequently conducted another trial with Iressa, in over twelve hundred lung cancer patients, *all* of whom had clinical characteristics indicative of the EGFR mutation. The results of this study, known as IPASS (**I**ressa **P**an **As**ia Study) were dramatic. Overall, three times as many patients treated with Iressa were progression free at one year, compared to a control chemotherapy group of carboplatin and paclitaxel. In patients proven to have the EGFR abnormality, Iressa by itself was substantially superior to chemotherapy (and vice versa for those without the mutation).[117] Iressa thus became the first ever targeted therapy to outperform a chemotherapy control group in a solid tumor. It was a watershed moment in the evolution of cancer therapy.

Iressa was also the first example of a drug failing to demonstrate a benefit, when developed along conventional histological disease lines but which was subsequently shown to work when the newer principles of molecular biology (and gene mutation) were applied. Just as importantly, on the basis of these results, Astra Zeneca were able to get Iressa approved for use in lung cancer patients in whom it could be shown that their tumor carried the EGFR mutation. Molecular biology had allowed them to rescue a drug which otherwise would have died a conventional death back in 2005.

However, the opportunities afforded by this molecular biology bonanza come with a price tag attached. By fractionating cancer patients into progressively smaller segments, on the basis of more fundamental understandings of the underlying disease process, molecular insights are at the same time both clarifying and complicating the challenges now facing cancer researchers.

Lung cancer, for example, in the future may well come to be regarded as multiple different diseases, based on differing genetic mutations at play. The same is true for most other malignancies too. The more we seem to understand cancer, the more diseases it actually appears to become. Whilst this creates the opportunity to uncover more effectively tailored drugs, such as crizotinib or Iressa for differing variants, it also means that *overall* the drug development burden will increase substantially.

There will be a need to find different drugs, uniquely suited to *each* new lung cancer type. Rather than buying clothes off the peg, with a couple of sizes covering everyone, they will instead now have to be exquisitely handmade, with a number of fittings along the way, costing a lot more and taking much longer.

The explosion of molecular pathways of malignancy, combined with a profusion of promising pharmacological agents with which to explore them, represent a potentially enormous dilemma. There will, in the future, be an almost infinitely competing demand for the finite development resources available. This creates the risk of actually *slowing* down the rate of progress for new anti-cancer approaches, as we struggle to search through all the possibilities on offer, trying to sort out the handful of more promising *Gleevecs* in amongst all the unproductive *tipifarnibs*.

We will find ourselves chipping away at the biotechnology gold seam, having to sift through bucket after bucket of slurry, to find the nuggets of precious metal they contain. Ironically, the problem today may therefore be one of having *too* much information and *too* many drugs for evaluation.

In the future, it will become progressively more challenging to evaluate so many candidate compounds through the conventional pathway of Phase I and Phase II, let alone Phase III, clinical testing. It's simply too demanding. There aren't enough patients or patience to permit this, with the levels of statistical probability we have applied in the past.

The problem is though that we haven't yet worked out a better way of doing things. That still has to come.

This is all in dramatic contrast to those pre-war pioneers, so handicapped by the very dearth of available agents. It shows how far we have come but also how much further we still have to go.

XXVIII

It is impossible to summarise even the last five years of cancer drug research in the concise way the entire preceding century permits. There is simply too much which has happened on every front, including small molecule chemicals, large molecule antibodies, small and large molecules conjugated, immunotherapy, gene therapy, targeted and non-targeted approaches, mono-therapy and combination strategies.

The sheer scale of this human endeavour is an unprecedented challenge to contain and control.

However, a few decades more will be needed before history can judge whether the 1980s represented a turning point in our efforts against cancer. Did this mark the beginning of the decline of the heavy industry of chemotherapy and the emergence of the ascendant new technologies? Or would molecular biology eventually run out of steam, like so many previous advances which had sooner or later lost their initial momentum?

Looking back at the history of man's struggle against cancer, we had already been fighting it for about seventy years before Richard Nixon launched his *War on Cancer* in 1971. For the first thirty years or so, the battle seemed to move at about the same rate as the stagnant trench warfare of World War One. After that, it picked up a definite pace which has increased ever since, although characterised by frequent advances which have subsequently degenerated into routs.

Today, it is possible to attack the disease with military precision, using sophisticated guided weapons. But cancer is still such a formidable enemy that the battle sometimes seems more like street combat, fighting hand to hand for every inch of ground.

In 1971, Nixon urged that "the time has come in America when the same kind of concerted effort that split the atom and put a man on the moon should be turned towards conquering this dread disease."[118]

The current frenzy of molecular targeting is the closest thing so far to that concerted effort sought by Nixon. If the analogy were nuclear physics, then cancer research has definitely reached the point of splitting the atom. It may even be possible to fashion the components of a nuclear weapon.

The challenge in the future will be to assemble the bomb, without it blowing up in the process and then choosing the optimal target to launch it against. Maybe that will one day be the way in which we eventually win the battle, or at least negotiate a truce.

XXIX

From the overall perspective of the long history of the war on cancer and the innumerable casualties along the way, the loss of ASA404 would seem no more than one more bombed out building in yet another city under siege. Except that it had been our home. And so it was a lot more personal than that.

Maybe amonafide or even AS1411 would fare better. But if there were one thing history was telling us, it was that we were up against an enemy which was endlessly ingenious and which fought hard and dirty, taking no prisoners. It was also much better equipped than us, with a seemingly endless supply of munitions.

So you wouldn't really rate the survival chances of AS1411 or amonafide much higher than those of a World War One trench trooper.

But we are also increasingly seeing that it is an enemy with vulnerabilities and you could occasionally score a surprise hit or two, if you were lucky enough. So we couldn't write them off completely either.

But those were events which would unfold in the future. For the moment, we had enough to grapple with in the present.

SIX

GET OFF OF MY CLOUD

Antisoma's one remaining drug seems to be faltering. Can they keep it alive? A look at the complexities and compromises of clinical trials in cancer.

I

The Icelandic volcano Eyjafjallajökull had been dormant for over two centuries. Until it started to rumble back into life in the spring of 2010 that is.

Reaching a height of over sixteen thousand metres and with a crater four kilometres wide, the volcano was topped by a huge ice cap covering an area of one hundred square kilometres. When it eventually erupted, the molten rock, at a temperature of about one thousand degrees centigrade, met the frozen ice and the resulting plume of steam and pulverised material was blasted into the atmosphere above Iceland. The coarser components fell rapidly back to Earth but the fine particles formed a cloud which was to persist for weeks to come.

Most people outside of Iceland had never heard of Eyjafjallajökull. They would have remained happily ignorant too, had it not been for that enormous cloud of volcanic ash which started billowing out of it in early April and then drifted southwest towards Europe.

Enveloped in a blanket of potentially damaging dust, European airspace rapidly became a no fly zone. Flights to and from most airports in the UK and mainland Europe were cancelled day after day between April 15th and April 23rd, during what became the largest air traffic shut down since World War Two. The closures would end up leaving five million passengers stranded around the world. The disruption was worse than after the September 11th attacks of 2001.

But whilst millions of others were inconvenienced beyond description and with passenger groups and airline bosses railing against the draconian air traffic enforcement, for us at Antisoma it would perversely turn out to be a blessing in disguise.

By now, the amonafide (AS1413) Phase III study was well on its way to the target of entering all patients by the end of August that year, with about three hundred or so already in the trial. With the tortuous acronym of ACCEDE (**A**monafide **C**ytarabine **C**ombination **E**valuating **D**rug Efficacy) this study aimed to recruit a total of about four hundred and fifty patients.

263

They were divided into two groups, who received either amonafide or the standard leukaemia drug *daunorubicin*, in either case combined with *cytarabine*, another widely used and well established agent.

The patients being entered into the ACCEDE trial all had something called *secondary* acute myeloid leukaemia (sAML). Most of the time, acute leukaemia is something which occurs out of the blue. You weren't exactly expecting it and had no reason to suspect that Nature had singled you out for the massive dose of bad luck that was coming your way.

It might begin with the chance observation that you'd started bruising a lot more easily, or that your gums kept bleeding when you cleaned your teeth. You'd been absolutely fine up until then. Nothing wrong with you for years in fact. You couldn't even remember the last time you'd gone to see the doctor.

But the next week, you did go to see him about it. You were worried now. And the week after that, your life was turned upside down forever, as you found yourself in the leukaemia unit of the nearest hospital that had one. You were plunged headlong into an alien and alienating world where nothing was familiar, everything was frightening and all the normal points of daily reference in your life had disappeared.

It suddenly *really* didn't matter anymore that you couldn't afford to pay this bill, decide where to go for that holiday, you needed a new car, your boss was a bastard, your partner didn't love you, you didn't love your partner. Whatever. In an instant you'd trade where you were now to have all that depressing daily detritus back again. Except there was no way back. You'd passed a point of no return.

That's *de novo* AML, leukaemia which occurs without any obvious explanation and which accounts for the majority of new cases. However, in about a third of patients with AML, the condition is a direct consequence of *previous* illness the person has suffered from. It doesn't just occur out of nowhere, after years of good health. This is known as *secondary* AML and it can arise either from preceding bone marrow disease, which evolves over time into leukaemia, or from treatment in the past with certain types of cancer chemotherapy for an earlier malignancy.

There are a number of bone marrow disorders, collectively known as *myelodysplastic syndrome (MDS)*[1] which result in bone marrow failure, a bit like leukaemia itself does. However, many patients with mild MDS manage quite well, getting along with the help of the odd blood transfusion now and again and can lead relatively normal lives. But at the other end of the spectrum, there are a group with much more serious disease, called *high risk* MDS. This can become so bad that it actually turns itself into acute leukaemia.

These patients account for about half the cases of secondary AML that occur. The other half are caused by previous treatment with cancer chemotherapy drugs themselves, particular two types known as *anthracyclines* (including doxorubicin, daunorubicin and idarubicin) and *alkylating agents* (of which nitrogen mustard was the first example but also including more modern agents such as cyclophosphamide and chlorambucil).[2] Large amounts of radiotherapy can also result in sAML.

Anthracyclines and alkylating type drugs are widely used to treat a whole range of tumor types. However, in about twenty per cent of people given them, they go on to cause leukaemia (amongst other haematological malignancies) usually about five years or so later. The reason why some people draw a short straw and develop this complication, whilst the majority don't, remains poorly understood.

The cancer drugs appear, in susceptible people, to initiate damage to the chromosomes of the blood forming cells in the bone marrow. Eventually, after a number of years, this genetic derangement manifests itself as acute leukaemia. This is known as *treatment related* secondary AML and the commonest example of this is patients who have received previous breast cancer treatment, where both anthracyclines and alkylating agents are extensively employed.

Secondary AML, whether it is due to previous MDS or prior *leukaemogenic* chemotherapy, is a devastating disease. For patients who have already battled through one life threatening condition, it can be the final blow to then be diagnosed with leukaemia and moreover to learn that one is a direct consequence of the other.

It's an example of just how merciless Nature can sometimes be, in selecting out some people for particular punishment. Just when they thought they'd actually beaten cancer, they are suddenly back to square one and having to start all over again. It just doesn't get more unfair than that.

Whatever its origin, sAML is a formidable disease, because it is even harder to treat than *de novo* AML. Which is saying something. Firstly, the patients can't tolerate aggressive therapy that well. Their bodies have already taken such a battering from their previous condition and the treatment given for it, that they just can't cope with much more. They have too much damage already to their bone marrow, heart, liver and other organs, all of which are targeted by the anti-leukaemia drugs themselves.

And then there is the issue of the psychological fortitude needed to get through the kind of physical assault leukaemia treatment entails. Previous rounds of debilitating chemotherapy and prolonged periods of hospitalisation can readily deplete the limited supplies of mental energy any one person can call upon.

On top of that, the particular disease characteristics of sAML give patients a worse prognosis from the outset. Arising as it does from a background of previous disease and prior drugs, sAML is doubly dangerous compared to its *de novo* counterpart. It is biologically a more aggressive and malevolent malignancy and responds much less well to conventional leukaemia therapy. So both *patient* and *disease* characteristics interact to make sAML one of the greatest of therapeutic challenges. There isn't another malignancy out there which is harder to treat. Which is what made amonafide so interesting as a new drug.

II

Amonafide had started off life at Knoll Pharmaceuticals. This was originally part of the German company BASF Pharma. It was taken to Xanthus by the founders there, who'd left Knoll when the pharmaceutical giant Abbott acquired BASF at the end of 2000.

Amonafide worked in a similar fashion to anthracycline cancer drugs, to inhibit an enzyme called *topoisomerase II*. This plays a vital role in cell division, by allowing the DNA double helix to unwind, prior to dividing and replicating itself. Blocking the enzyme effectively puts the cell's chromosomes in a straightjacket and paralyses the normal cell cycle. Unable to divide, the cell dies.

Originally, amonafide was intended for use in solid tumors, where it was tried in a range of malignancies, including breast and prostate cancer. Unfortunately, it turned out to be disappointing in these indications, largely because it was too toxic, particularly causing profound bone marrow suppression.

However, whilst that sort of toxicity was unacceptable as a *side effect* of solid tumor treatment, it was exactly the kind of *efficacy* needed in an anti-leukaemia drug, as these actually worked, by and large, through wiping out the bone marrow. And so capitalising on their initial misfortune with amonafide, the people at Xanthus went on to undertake some early clinical studies in patients with end stage haematological cancers, such as leukaemias and myelomas. Here they found that amonafide was producing effects in cases so far advanced that they were almost beyond improvement.

Encouraged by these preliminary results, North Shore Hospital in Long Island, subsequently undertook a study of amonafide combined with cytarabine in patients with advanced leukaemia, including both *de novo* and secondary AML. They found that seven out of fifteen patients with sAML showed a response to the amonafide and cytarabine combination. At just under fifty per cent, those results seemed much better than any other treatments available at the time for the disease.

Not that there were exactly a lot of alternatives. Because there was little else around, the treatment of sAML was pretty much the same as for AML generally. The standard approach was to use a combination of an anthracycline combined with cytarabine, to try and get the patient into remission. This was somewhat counterintuitive, given that anthracyclines were actually one of the biggest *causes* of treatment related sAML. So you were effectively treating a condition with a drug which had helped cause it in the first place. But that just served to emphasise the lack of agents there were to choose from and therefore potentially how beneficial amonafide might turn out to be.

No one though was really sure just how useful the standard anthracycline and cytarabine combination was in sAML anyway. Because it was a relatively rare disease, there were only *two* published leukaemia studies in the whole world, which specifically separated out patients with sAML. All the other trials either didn't mention it at all or if they did, just lumped sAML together with *de novo* disease.

These two studies had been run by the collaborative South West Oncology Group (SWOG) and they were both over ten years old now.[3,4] And so the findings then might not be that relevant to the results achievable today, given all the improvements in supportive care which have occurred over the intervening decade. With that caveat, they indicated the standard approach was producing remission rates of about twenty five per cent. If that were really true, then the results from North Shore showed that amonafide was doubling this.

That was an exciting and dramatic prospect and enough for Xanthus to invest heavily in an eighty patient, single arm, Phase II study of amonafide and cytarabine in treating sAML. This ran from 2006 to 2007 in the US and when the results were eventually available,[5] they showed that the amonafide combination was indeed producing a forty five per cent response rate, which was very similar to that seen in the previous Phase I trial. It would probably have been higher still, except that about twenty per cent of the patients appeared to be dying early on, due to toxicity of the drug combination.

These results were very encouraging. A doubling of the response rate wasn't exactly something you saw that often with new drugs in leukaemia. The difficulty however was that Xanthus hadn't been able to afford to do a *randomised* trial, comparing the amonafide combination to the standard anthracycline one. That would have doubled the number of patients in the study and they just couldn't finance it. They were living hand to mouth as it was, unable to secure further funding.

Compared to the *old* SWOG studies the outcome was much better with amonafide. The problem was that no one knew what sort of remission rate the standard treatment approach might produce in a new trial conducted *today*. There was a distinct possibility the results would turn out to be that much better now, just because the general level of medical care had improved so much over the years which had gone by. There was a good possibility that amonafide might prove to be little better than the modern version of what was already available.

There was also the twenty per cent mortality to consider. That *was* a bit of a concern. There was no information from previous clinical trials about what the early mortality of an anthracycline combination in sAML might be. At least nothing we could find. No one seemed to have specifically looked at this before.

In *de novo* AML, the early death rate was about ten to fifteen per cent with anthracycline treatment. If the same were also true in secondary AML with anthracyclines, this would obviously be lower than the figure Xanthus had experienced in their trial. If the amonafide combination were really causing a higher number of fatal toxicities, that would inevitably weaken the outcome of any direct comparison with an anthracycline in sAML. If the patients were dying before they had a chance to respond, that wasn't exactly going to help your cause.

It was clear therefore that Xanthus would need to undertake a Phase III study, directly comparing amonafide against an anthracycline, to address all these reservations. Putting the contestants in the ring together was the only way to find out whether amonafide really had anything to offer. Pitted head to head, could the new contender land a big enough punch to take out the established veteran? And that is what eventually became the ACCEDE trial.

Xanthus managed to enter a handful of patients, before they ran out of money. The study subsequently stalled until Antisoma arrived to the rescue in the middle of 2008, riding into town with saddle bags full of cash to revive the flagging programme.

And now, almost two years later, we were about three quarters of the way through the trial. With the loss of ASA404 just a month earlier, amonafide had now assumed a much greater importance to us. It was a potential lifeline and we were clutching at it with all our might.

Before ATTRACT I had fallen apart, amonafide had almost been a luxury we were indulging ourselves with, because we could afford it. It was an expensive programme and a high risk one. This was mainly because there were no randomised Phase II data with the drug and so a much higher than normal chance that it would end up showing no efficacy advantage in the Phase III trial.

Additionally, there was a lingering concern about just how safe amonafide really was and whether it might turn out to be too toxic, with further experience of it in the clinic. These things were always a fine line and it was too early to tell which way the scales would eventually tip.

But now we no longer had ASA404, amonafide had changed from being a treat to becoming a staple item, an everyday essential. It was all we had left, apart from AS1411. Which pretty much meant it was all we had left. It was the bread on our table, the fruit in our basket.

Given this new found pre-eminence, there was simply no way we could permit anything to happen to the ACCEDE study. Barring a catastrophe, it had to be allowed to gracefully proceed to its conclusion in the early part of the following year, when the initial results would become available. Actually, even if there were a catastrophe, it still somehow had to get to that point. It would buy us the best part of twelve months of relative stability, in which to do something to revive our failing fortunes.

But if anything happened to ACCEDE along the way, we would be dead. We had barely survived ASA404 going down and were just about keeping our heads above water. Anymore setbacks though and we would surely be dragged under.

And the big problem we now faced was that there was already something tugging at our heels, in the shape of a Data Safety Monitoring Board (DSMB) meeting for the ACCEDE study. It had long been scheduled for just a few weeks' time, in late April, in Chicago.

There were four members of this particular Board. Three were leukaemia clinicians and there was one statistician, all from leading US medical centres. None were directly involved in the ACCEDE trial but each was familiar with amonafide. Their job was to review the safety data emerging from the study at regular intervals along the way, to make sure that one drug combination wasn't turning out to be unacceptably toxic, relative to the other pair of drugs.

But the difficulty we had wasn't so much the ash cloud, which was making it look increasingly unlikely that we would be able to get out of the country and meet them in Chicago. It was something much more troublesome than that.

III

DSMBs are a normal feature of most Phase III studies involving drugs which are expected to produce a reasonable amount of toxicity. Their job is to make sure that any emerging safety concerns during the study are considered and addressed, if necessary by changing the design of the trial or, in extreme cases, stopping it altogether.

Unlike a Data Monitoring Committee, they don't have a formal remit of reviewing *efficacy data*, in the sense of conducting an interim look. They will however take whatever efficacy data might be available at the time into account, when making a determination of any particular safety issues. Obviously, if a new drug looks like it is producing encouraging effects, then they are likely to be more tolerant of any toxicity than if there were no hint of it doing anything useful at all.

When you are dealing with drugs and diseases as dangerous as AML and the treatments used for it, then DSMBs become an inescapable part of life. The amonafide DSMB had already met two or three times earlier on in the

ACCEDE trial. Whilst these occasions weren't exactly plain sailing, there hadn't been any real show stoppers either.

We had always taken the DSMB very seriously, as they had the power to terminate the study if they felt patient safety could be compromised by carrying on. We were taking them *even* more seriously now, because there was no way we could contemplate them doing that. And for the first time, there was a real risk that they might just try to.

The trouble we were facing, as far as the upcoming DSMB meeting was concerned, was that we couldn't actually tell them how many patients were dying due to amonafide side effects. Nearly all leukaemia drugs carry a substantial mortality as one of the complications of using them and amonafide was no exception.

We knew it was something they wanted to know. The problem was that we didn't have the answer ourselves.

All approaches to leukaemia treatment involve a balance, The powerful nature of the drugs you have to use, combined with the debilitating effects the disease has on the individual concerned, mean that unavoidably a number of patients are unable to survive the intensity of the treatment. They succumb to what is termed *treatment related mortality*.

This is usually defined as those deaths occurring within the first thirty days of receiving treatment. They are most often due to consequences of bone marrow suppression caused by the drugs, such as uncontrollable bleeding or overwhelming infection. These are however exactly the same complications arising from the untreated leukaemia itself. Which means it is sometimes extremely difficult to separate disease from drug as the culprit.

Despite that, death within the first thirty days of treatment is conventionally assumed to be due to drug toxicity, unless there is some very obvious other explanation for why a patient may have died. There aren't many of those though. When you're marooned in the middle of a leukaemia unit, you are unlikely to be run over by a bus or stabbed to death by a lunatic run amok. Deaths occurring *after* thirty days are more likely to be due to factors other than drug toxicity alone, most probably as a consequence of the disease itself, particularly if the patient isn't responding to the therapy.

With advances in intensive care, improvements in supportive medicine and greater understanding of how to best use the leukaemia drugs themselves, the treatment related mortality in AML in general has slowly declined over the years. However, it can still be as high as ten to fifteen per cent for existing standard treatments, depending on just how ill any given patient is at the outset.

The trade off is that the other eighty five to ninety per cent of patients don't die early on, with a significant proportion benefiting from a response to treatment and achieving remission of their disease. This opens the way to potentially curative approaches for them, further down the line. So *overall,* you have a better chance of surviving the treatment and benefiting, than you do of being killed by it.

There is also the not insubstantial consideration that no treatment at all is a certain death sentence, sooner or later. And usually sooner. So in many ways, there isn't much to lose from taking your chances with therapy.

Patients faced with such a ghastly decision doubtless see it in terms that are less black and white however. Particularly given that assessing the risk treatments represent, is complicated by the difficulty of predicting just who might end up in the ten to fifteen per cent marked with the black spot. It's hard to separate them out from the other eighty five to ninety per cent, who will make it through into the happy space.

Obviously there's the odd clue, now and then. If you are very ill at the outset, with some other complication such as liver or heart disease, you're less likely to withstand treatment. Or if your disease is so advanced that your blood has practically turned to jelly because of all the leukaemic cells in it, then that doesn't bode well either. But essentially, for the majority of patients, whether they're going to pull through the first thirty days is pretty much a lottery, determined by the random hand of fate. Is the Haematologist in the Heavens on your side or not today?

Treatment with *any* leukaemia drug is a dangerous proposition, with a possibility of it killing you. However, that doesn't make it any easier to determine what might be an acceptably *higher* treatment related mortality for a new drug, such as amonafide, compared to existing ones. At what point does a higher chance of dying early on cease to be justified by a greater probability of having a response, if you make it through?

Which is the better bet, a drug with a ten per cent chance of treatment related mortality and after that a thirty five per cent chance of a response, or a different drug with a twenty per cent chance of treatment related mortality but a fifty per cent chance of a response, in those who survive the treatment itself?

Do you take a greater chance of dying now, in return for a higher probability of responding later on? Particularly bearing in mind that without a response, the disease is going to kill you anyway. That's one game in the casino where you hope to never find a free seat at the table. But it's the one patients with AML have no choice but to play.

However, it becomes an even more complicated calculation than that. Assuming you survive the treatment and achieve a response, that isn't by itself going to stop you dying of the disease. You haven't won yet. It's more like you've made it through to the quarter finals. You still need to go on and receive more intensive chemotherapy, or a bone marrow transplant. Or both. Neither of these come with any guarantee of success and each also carries a significant risk of death.

And whilst without any treatment you are going to die, it might not be for a couple of months, rather than in the next thirty days. You might also be able to slip away more in a manner of your choosing, rather than the anonymous awfulness of a hospital, with all the attendant indignity and impersonalisation that represented.

There is no objective answer to this sort of risk-benefit question. Individual patients and their clinicians have to work out what is best in their particular case. Inevitably this is an emotional process, based on personal preferences and fears, as much as facts and figures.

Some patients will take any chance and incur any risk, however small the resultant possibility of a response. They just don't want to give in. Or they are simply too afraid to let go. Others might think *"Sod it. I'm going on a cruise with whatever time I've got left."* The majority though find it impossible to know what to do and which decision to make. There is no way for them to rationalise the probabilities on offer with different drug treatments.

It was a similar dilemma for members of the DSMB, looking at the collective outcome from the ACCEDE trial to date. The data might be objective but the interpretation of it couldn't be anything other than subjective. You were making a value judgement here. There wasn't a computer algorithm to turn to for an answer.

Which was another way of saying that the members of the DSMB were going to be hard to predict, as far as we were concerned. Just how would they react, if the mortality with amonafide was worse than with daunorubicin. We'd have liked some advance idea of how they might see things. Not least because there was a distinct possibility amonafide might be more toxic than we were expecting. Which didn't exactly boost our confidence in the drug's prospects. Or our own.

IV

At the beginning of the ACCEDE trial, we had assumed the amonafide combination would have about a twenty per cent early mortality at worst. That's what we'd seen in the Phase II study and we didn't have any reason to believe it would be any different now. We didn't know what the figure should be for the daunorubicin comparator arm but somewhere between ten and fifteen per cent seemed to be as good a guess as any, based on what happened in *de novo* AML.

As long as the results weren't too different from these assumptions, then we would probably be OK. We would be able to find a way past the watchful eye of the DSMB. We didn't actually have anything concrete to support this supposition but it's what our instincts told us.

They had met a couple of times previously. But on those occasions, the numbers of patients in the study had still been relatively small and so it was difficult to form an accurate impression of what was really going on. Attention at the earlier meetings had also been diverted by a different issue with amonafide. It seemed to be causing the same QTc heart rhythm disturbance which also characterised many other cancer drugs. Ultimately this turned out to be a manageable complication but it initially consumed a lot of time and effort, trying to understand the extent and severity of the problem.

However, in Chicago things would be different. With over three hundred patients in the study, it would now be possible for the first time, since the trial had started back in June 2007, to get a good idea of just how the early mortality and overall safety in the two treatment groups was stacking up. That's certainly what the DSMB members were expecting to see. Were earlier reservations about amonafide justified, or had it in fact gone on to redeem itself? Just what was happening, now that we were well over half way through the largest ever randomised clinical trial in secondary AML?

Our problem was that we just didn't know.

Our best guess was that early mortality could range from just under twenty per cent to just over thirty per cent. Neither end of the spectrum was good but one was obviously much worse than the other. The DSMB could probably live with around about twenty per cent but a figure of thirty per cent would be too high. It would mean the ACCEDE study was over there and then. And with it the future of Antisoma. We had to decide which was the correct figure. There was a lot riding on it after all. One would keep us out of jail, the other put us in the grave.

At first sight, it may seem strange that we couldn't accurately work out the mortality in our own trial. Doctors and nurses tend to notice things like dead patients lying around and so there shouldn't be too much ambiguity in getting the body count right.

But it wasn't that easy. We had become trapped in an intricate web of modern clinical trial methodology, in a way which would have confused and perplexed the chemotherapy pioneers of half a century earlier. Theirs had been more straightforward times, allowing them to tackle problems with an insouciant simplicity. By contrast, we now inhabited a world where even the simplest of issues could rapidly become shrouded in a cloud of complexity.

V

As a patient moves through a clinical trial, from start to finish, they generate an enormous amount of clinical data about their experience of the safety and efficacy of the drug they are receiving. All of this has to be recorded at the time, for use later on. The clinical data for each individual patient is captured at the hospital in a series of customised forms, which the clinician has to fill in.

Collectively, these are known as the patient's *Case Record Form* (CRF) which, for a demanding study, can often end up the size of a set of dictionaries. It documents and details every aspect of a patient's involvement in the trial. The CRF becomes an impersonal and impartial chronicle of this most terrible journey they are undertaking, as they struggle to survive the disease and its treatment. Inevitably, this ends up as a hugely complicated dossier.

The complexity arises partly because quite a number of people will be involved in filling it in, such as the main doctor, his assistant doctor, study nurses and so on. Each tends to add their own particular shade of ambiguity to anything they write down.

In some cases, it's possible to reduce things to a tick box exercise. (*Is the patient still in remission? Tick yes or no*). However, much of it requires free text (*Describe the course of the patient's multi-organ failure after they developed sepsis*).

Trying to get people to tick a box accurately is surprisingly difficult. Giving busy doctors free rein to write down whatever comes into their heads, is an invitation to omission, obfuscation and opaqueness. It usually serves to confuse as much as it clarifies. Doctors aren't natural bureaucrats. Anyone who has ever read a set of hospital records will know that. Attempting to decipher an ancient Egyptian papyrus would be a less daunting task.

Increasingly, CRFs are becoming electronic (known as *eCRFs*). This means the hospital fills them in using a computer or handheld organiser and then transmits the data online directly into a central database, which is collecting and compiling CRFs from all the patients in the trial, wherever in the world they may be.

In the early days of eCRFs it was possible to use this as an opportunity to hand out laptops to hospital staff, on the pretext that they otherwise wouldn't have access to computer facilities. These thinly disguised gifts could do wonders for morale and patient recruitment. For a doctor at an institution in Latvia or Lithuania, a present like that was a big deal.

Today though, when even kids living in caves have Nintendos, it doesn't have anything like the same impact. You're also not allowed to give anything away anymore. It's heavily frowned upon as a potentially inappropriate inducement. In fact, in the current climate of stringency, even providing a clinician with a free cup of coffee at a meeting can attract a level of opprobrium usually only reserved for a child snatcher at a pillow party.

Electronic CRFs are a big advance over paper ones, which require the staff at the hospital to laboriously complete them with a pen and then post or fax them back to the central site, where the data are entered into the database, equally laboriously. Paper CRFs are Bakelite black and white TV. Electronic ones are high definition plasma screen. The ACCEDE study was paper based.

Some clinical studies are short and simple, for example examining a week's worth of treatment with a new antibiotic for pneumonia. In these cases, the hospital might wait until the patient has finished the trial altogether before filling in the CRF and sending it back. The amount of information involved will be small and it's easy to tackle the forms all in one go.

For a more complicated and protracted study (such as ACCEDE, running over two years) there would be a need to fill in bits of the CRF on a more ongoing basis, in order to keep on top of the workload. That way, you avoid having to remember events which may have taken place some considerable time in the past. It's very hard to recall how many days a patient's skin rash lasted, when it occurred two years ago. You have to keep track of events as they are happening, to have any chance of recording them accurately.

There were no rules however and different hospitals worked at their own different pace. Inevitably though, given the amount of work to fill them in and the tedium involved, completed CRF pages always lagged behind a patient's actual progress through the trial. So any information there may have been in the central database on a particular patient, based on CRFs which had been completed and sent back, was usually a couple of months or so behind what was actually happening in the clinic. It was an inherent inefficiency in the clinical trial process.

Given the complexity and volume of clinical trial data, enormous numbers of inconsistencies, errors and omissions creep into completed CRFs. These can range from illegible writing, through to parts of the CRF not being completed, through to things that just don't match up. Examples from previous Antisoma studies included a male patient with a positive pregnancy test and someone else apparently developing a serious side effect three weeks after they had been reported as having died.

There was also the occasional oddity, such as a patient from France, who'd also had gender reassignment surgery in the past. The hospital hadn't ticked male or female in the relevant box of the CRF. No one could decide which one to opt for. Then there was another patient from the US, whose CT scan check box hadn't been ticked. It turned out that at three hundred and fifty lbs, he was too fat to fit in the scanner. The motorised trolley couldn't take his weight. And that was despite the wasting disease he was suffering from.

However, clinical trials require absolutely every *i* to be dotted and every *t* to be crossed. In duplicate, if not triplicate. When it comes to clinical data, there is no room for incompleteness or inconsistency, irrespective of how irrelevant it may be, or irrational its origins. These rigid regulatory requirements have about as much flexibility as your average fatwa. Achieving this level of compliance requires a devotion rarely experienced outside of a cult.

Sophisticated computer programmes within the central database pick up these anomalies in the CRF and automatically generate queries about them. This is a process known as *data cleaning*. Hundreds, if not thousands, of these *Data Clarification Forms* (DCFs) can be thrown up and sent back to the centres involved, in order for them to complete the missing or clarify the confusing. If not handled properly, this deluge can easily overwhelm and potentially antagonise medical staff at a hospital.

Resolving these queries usually involves digging out hospital records, often from many months if not years ago, and trying to work out where the answers lie. The hospital then has to send this information back to the central database, where it will be re-entered, a process which may then lead to a whole new set of queries that need to go back to the hospital again.

These can be queries about an incomplete answer to the original query, or an entirely new query arising where one didn't exist before, as a consequence of clarification of a previous query. *(Missing information A, provided to answer query B, could now turn out to be inconsistent with existing information C, thus leading to a new query D to resolve it)*. This exercise in iterative ping pong could in theory go on forever and usually only the intervention of some external deadline forces the cessation of this impossible quest for perfect precision.

This tortuous process had implications for us, trying to sort out data to provide to the DSMB. The information we needed for the ACCEDE study was out there, trapped in the desks and drawers of one hundred and fifty different hospitals scattered over every continent on Earth. The staff in all these institutions were doubtless doing their best to keep up to date with CRFs from ongoing patients and with the influx of DCF queries about patients from the past.

However, given all their other more pressing daily clinical commitments, as well as three or four other clinical trials they may also be involved in, the ACCEDE paperwork inevitably slipped down their list of priorities. If you've just spent five hours of your afternoon in a busy outpatient clinic, dealing with disease and disappointment, then the last thing you're looking forward to is a couple of hours of clinical trial form filling, the equivalent of completing your tax return a hundred times over.

And so when we looked in our own centralised database, to find out information on early deaths, we knew that what was in there would be out of sequence with what was happening in the real time world. Also, the more data that came in, the more the queries that were being generated because of it and so the less confident we were about the reliability and accuracy of what we did actually have. It was always like that when a trial was still running. It was a process of constantly trying to catch up. Like a dog chasing its own tail.

Because of the painfully protracted nature of the normal clinical data pathway, your database is always out of synch and out of date. Although this might not be ideal, it usually doesn't really matter, as far as most of your clinical trial data is concerned. If you don't have a completely contemporaneous and accurate summary of how many headaches have been recorded so far in your study, then you could probably live with that. There's no real reason why you would need to know such a thing until the end of the trial. Come to think of it, there's probably no real reason why you'd need to know it even then.

But if there were something really serious happening with your drug, like a heart attack or someone going blind or something terrible like that, then you would obviously want to know about it pretty much straightaway. You couldn't wait months and months whilst this sort of information ground its way through the normal data process, with all the urgency of an undertaker.

To deal with this, a parallel more expedited mechanism has evolved to address really important safety data which may emerge during a study. This is a process called *serious adverse event* reporting and it is a requirement of regulatory authorities all around the world to have such a system in place, for pretty much all clinical trials. *Adverse event* is just another way of saying *side effect* and the term *serious* adverse event (SAEs) refers to a side effect which is so significant that you have to know about it as soon as possible.

Obviously SAEs include deaths, as you can't really get anything more serious than that but they also have a particular regulatory definition. The legal determination of what makes an adverse event serious is:

"Any untoward medical occurrence at any dose that results in death; is life threatening; requires inpatient hospitalisation or prolongation of existing hospitalisation; results in persistent or significant disability or incapacity; is a congenital birth defect or anomaly."[6]

It's a wide ranging description which clearly came out of many hours of gruelling committee work somewhere along the line.

Most regulatory bodies want to be informed fairly immediately about these sorts of side effects, with new experimental drugs. When regulators wake up in the morning, the first thing they think of is *thalidomide*. Usually the rest of the day doesn't get any better for them either. Unless proven otherwise, they remain convinced that all new drugs are poisonous chemicals, which are toxically dangerous to public health. They are probably right some of the time.

For fatal or life threatening events therefore, there is a requirement to report them within *seven days* of the company first becoming aware of their existence. For all other types of SAE, the reporting period is fifteen days.

Regulatory authorities are very hot about meeting these obligations, as they are particularly anxious to maintain an eye of their own on the safety of new drugs under investigation. If you don't keep to these timelines, they can put you study on *clinical hold*.[7] This means you are forbidden to enter any more patients into the trial until they say you can start again. It's the regulatory equivalent of the naughty chair.

You want to avoid being sent there, if at all possible.

VI

Clinical holds are bad news. No one likes that to happen. Your study loses momentum, your drug is tarred with the assumption that something has gone badly wrong and companies have to put out press releases which can send their share price tumbling. In the US, FDA have the power to put people in prison for ignoring clinical holds and so you can't get round them by doing that.

On the other hand, when you report SAEs as you are supposed to, you can still be put on clinical hold if the regulatory authority is concerned by what it is seeing. And so sometimes you can't win.

In order to meet the demands of these timelines and to avoid regulatory retribution, there is a particular mechanism which clinical trials use, when dealing with SAEs. This is called the CIOMS form.

CIOMS stands for something called the *Council for International Organisations of Medical Sciences*, which is somehow vaguely connected to the World Health Organisation.[8] No one seems to know what it really does but despite the lack of any discernible purpose, its form has persisted and become the standard document used by all pharmaceutical companies and regulatory agencies for initial reporting of SAEs.

When something serious happens to a patient in a clinical trial, the hospital is supposed to immediately record preliminary information in one of these forms. They are designed to be simple and easy to complete and are only a couple of pages long. The CIOMS form is then faxed or e-mailed to the sponsor pharmaceutical company, who can at that point start the clock ticking to pass it on to regulatory agencies. As the serious adverse event unfolds, the hospital provides updates on additional CIOMS forms.

At the *same time*, the hospital still has to fill in information about the serious adverse event in the relevant CRF pages for the study. These are then fed into the normal data management process, so that the information will eventually end up in the central database along with all the other adverse events from the study, serious or otherwise. The central database always remains the final *matter of record* for the trial. The CIOMS form is therefore a *parallel* mechanism, which bypasses the slow moving more formal one, for those occasions when you can't afford to hang around.

To keep track of all the CIOMS forms in a trial, particularly those involving updates of ongoing adverse events, they are normally entered into a database separate from the main centralised clinical trial one. This is known as the *pharmacovigilance* (PV) database. Pharmacovigilance is the discipline of drug safety monitoring, which has become so elaborate that it is now a career in its own right. From the early fledgling days post-thalidomide, it has grown in size and complexity to spawn an entire industry. These days there are even some sad souls who have ended up as *professors* of pharmacovigilance. It's a testament to human ingenuity though, that they've managed to carve an academic discipline out of something which intellectually appears to be relatively unchallenging. It does however remain something of a mystery what they do all day long, after they've had their mid-morning muffin break.

Pharmacovigilance databases can rapidly become large and complicated. This is especially so in a trial involving a clinical condition like AML, where it is likely that most patients will experience a number of SAEs during the study, just by the nature of the disease itself and the treatments involved. Some of these side effects can go on for weeks and weeks at the hospital, as the patient either recovers or gets worse. Supplementary CIOMS forms therefore need to be issued on a regular basis, to document what is happening.

The complexity is magnified further by the need to report SAEs, not just to the regulatory authorities in the country where it happened but also to those of every other country taking part in the study. Any resulting feedback needs to be recorded too.

At Antisoma, there was a full time person employed just to look after pharmacovigilance activities. Simon was a bluff, what you see is what you get, no nonsense northerner from Hull. In appearance, he was a cross between Nosferatu and Noggin the Nog, which somehow suited his grim daily task of tracking death, disease and debility.

Although in theory it should have helped, the existence of the ACCEDE pharmacovigilance database actually caused us even *further* problems in trying to work out what the safety data was really looking like. This was because of a complicated triage process SAEs had to be put through, after they had been reported. For each SAE, this involved trying to work out whether it was both *related to* and also *unexpected for* the drug in question.

If something serious happened to a patient in a clinical trial, you had to try to determine whether being in the study actually had anything to do with it. This is because the definition of an SAE is very wide ranging. It includes for example *anything* which results in hospitalisation of the patient. Someone in a clinical trial could be hit by a lorry whilst out shopping and end up in hospital with a broken leg. That technically would meet the definition of a serious adverse event, due to the resulting *hospitalisation*.

However, this is unlikely to have anything to do with the clinical trial. Although it's not impossible either. There have been cases of drugs causing sedation as an unexpected side effect and resulting in accidents as a consequence.

Because of this ambiguity, someone needs to decide whether a particular SAE is to some extent *related* to being in the trial or not. That judgement is usually left to the clinician looking after the patient, on the basis that they are the one most likely to be in possession of more of the relevant facts than anyone else.

Conventionally, the likelihood of a drug being responsible for an SAE is broken down using a WHO five point scale:[9]

Unrelated; Unlikely; Possible; Probable; Definite.

However, clearly this determination can sometimes become quite arbitrary.

Being run over by a heavy goods vehicle would usually be considered *unrelated* by the vast majority of people. But it would be more difficult to decide about an eighty five year old patient, with a past history of heart disease, who has a heart attack twenty minutes after receiving an injection with an experimental drug not previously known to be associated with cardiac side effects. The judgement call there is a much more complicated one and not all physicians would reach the same opinion, about whether or not the drug had a role to play.

In a study such as ACCEDE, with a large number of hospitals and involving many different clinicians, there was inevitably a diversity of interpretation, when it came to deciding which SAEs were related and which weren't. This was compounded further, depending on whether the suspected culprit was amonafide or daunorubicin.

Daunorubicin was a well established drug, with all the hospitals having extensive experience of it. There was therefore a tendency to give it the "benefit of the doubt" and assume that SAEs *weren't* related to it.

Conversely, there was a much higher index of suspicion with a new and much less well known and understood drug, such as amonafide. There was therefore a higher propensity for deciding something *was* related to it. Which was understandable really. You're instinctively more comfortable with the familiar, whilst being more wary of the unknown.

Importantly though, physicians often don't report SAEs which they've decided aren't directly related to the drug in question. If it wasn't caused by the drug, then why worry about it any further and also incur all that paper work involved in dealing with it.

This however creates a problem with studies involving both an established and an experimental drug. There tends to be an *under reporting* of SAEs for the former, because less are determined to be related and conversely an *over reporting* for the latter, where guilt is more readily assumed. Many cancer clinical trials experience this problem.

The disparity is however exacerbated further because, in addition to deciding whether an SAE is related, you also have to work out whether it is *expected* or not.

A regulatory authority isn't really interested in hearing about SAEs which it is already familiar with. Its primary concern is to keep abreast of emerging *new* safety signals about a drug. It doesn't want to receive the seven hundred thousandth report of severe diarrhoea with daunorubicin for example. But it does want to hear about *unexpected* SAEs, whether they are occurring with an experimental drug or a well known one.

An unexpected event is defined, rather circuitously, as one which the regulatory authorities aren't already aware of for that drug. They may have learned about a particular side effect in the past from other sources, either through existing product information, for a marketed drug, or from previously submitted safety summaries for an experimental one. In that case, they aren't interested in having any more reports on it.

For an established mature drug, like daunorubicin, there will obviously be a more extensively documented collection of side effects already in existence, than could possibly be the case for a recently arrived experimental one, like amonafide. Consequently, the potential range of *unexpectedness* will be that much wide for the experimental drug, again encouraging greater reporting of SAEs.

The way SAEs are classified therefore, creates an inherent reporting bias *against* a new drug, when it is being compared with an older and better known one. The only way to avoid this is to have a double blind trial, where no one knows which drug a patient is receiving.

But that isn't always possible for technical reasons. Many drugs have characteristic side effects which are difficult to disguise. Doxorubicin, for example, is a widely used cancer drug, which also happens to turn the urine bright red. Which tends to be a bit of a giveaway when trying to blind a study. It would have been easier to hide Abu Hamza at a Police Federation dinner dance.

The ACCEDE trial wasn't double blind because it had been impossible to come up with a placebo which exactly matched amonafide. And that resulted in a significant limitation of our pharmacovigilance database. Clinicians were more likely to report immediately serious events occurring with amonafide, rather than with daunorubicin. All serious adverse events for both drugs would eventually make their way to the *centralised* database, although that would probably take quite a long time. In the meantime though, there was a greater likelihood of them being judged reportable and so end up in the pharmacovigilance repository, if they were occurring in patients receiving amonafide.

This meant that at the end of the study, when the centralised database was complete, there might be a serious side effect, say death or kidney failure or heart attack or whatever, that was actually occurring with a similar frequency between the two drugs. However, if you looked along the way at the pharmacovigilance database, it could *appear* to be occurring more frequently with amonafide, because clinicians were reporting it sooner for that drug compared to the other one, daunorubicin.

But until the trial was complete and all the data had been collected, it was impossible to know whether the pharmacovigilance database was potentially misleading or actually giving an accurate picture of how things were.

And that was our difficulty with the DSMB. The early mortality for amonafide was coming in at about twenty per cent, with data from the centralised database. But when we looked at it from the pharmacovigilance source, the figure was just over thirty per cent. To further complicate things for ourselves, we had a third database of early mortality, which we had cobbled together from a variety of informal sources. These included records of recent telephone calls with, or visits to, participating hospitals, which sometimes contained additional information not yet available elsewhere. This gave us a result somewhere in between the other two.

So we didn't really know what we should be telling the DSMB. The difference between twenty per cent and thirty per cent was an *absolute* difference of only ten per cent but in *relative* terms, one was fifty per cent greater than the other. Moreover, the higher figure for amonafide mortality was almost *double* what we were seeing for daunorubicin. In clinical terms these were significant differences.

If we gave them the lesser figure, from the centralised source, that would probably be low enough to keep the study alive and on track. *Probably.* But there was a danger it could be *underestimating* the eventual mortality rate, if the PV figure subsequently turned out to be an accurate one.

However, if we used the much higher result from the PV data, we risked *overestimating* what the eventual difference between amonafide and daunorubicin might be. And we would also be blowing up the study in front of our faces.

It was that classic drug development dilemma of trying to guess half way through a study, what was going to happen at the end. It must all have been a lot simpler in the days of Farber and Li and Zubrod, when they managed to get on with small things, like curing cancers, without a form in sight or a database in existence.

And, as if all this uncertainty over the malleable mortality wasn't bad enough, to make things even worse, the DSMB were expecting to see some *efficacy* data too. Which would have been fine, except that we didn't have anything we felt we could give them.

It was just too big a risk.

The safety data was bad enough but at least we had some idea of what it looked like. The problem with the efficacy results was that whilst it was alright for the DSMB to have this information, we wouldn't be able to see it ourselves. They would have to keep it a secret from us.

As the sponsor, we weren't supposed to look at the results until the very end of the study. Even though the study wasn't a double blind one, we had to effectively remain *blinded* to the results. There was a need to artificially distance ourselves from them.

That's how it always worked in big clinical trials. It was a measure to minimise the possibility of anyone being tempted to try and manipulate something along the way. It was another thing regulatory authorities were very hot on. They were constantly on the lookout for any infringements, convinced that even the smallest temptation would prove too strong to resist.

We would have to deal with the efficacy data at arm's length, through a third party. So we'd find ourselves having no idea what we would be handing over to the DSMB. Which was a step too far for us, given just how precariously we were currently poised on the precipice. This could be enough to tip us over the edge.

The three hundred or so patients currently in the ACCEDE trial was a decent enough number. It would give a reasonable idea of how the response rates were looking between the two groups. Any comparison wouldn't be conclusive at this stage but it could certainly end up influencing the DSMB. Particularly if there was little difference between the amonafide and daunorubicin arms.

If we weren't seeing anything at this stage, it was improbable that would change dramatically by the end of the trial. It was unlikely that amonafide could pull away and make a break for the finish line, at this stage in the race.

The biggest problem though was that we didn't have much confidence in the *reliability* of any of the efficacy data. We had found out the hard way, from the earlier Phase II study with amonafide and from our previous experiences with AS1411 in AML, just how difficult it was to pull together all the different pieces of information needed to determine something as complex as response rates. Particularly when the study was still ongoing and data was flowing all over the place, as it washed back and forth between the sites and the database.

Working out whether a patient had responded or not was a composite of different pieces of information, all of which came from differing places in the database. These had to be married together and then checked and rechecked, to detect and resolve the inevitable inconsistencies, anomalies and complexities of interpretation occurring along the way.

It was like trying to assemble a particularly intricate item of flat pack furniture, without an instruction sheet. Or any tools that fitted. It took you a while to work out how all the pieces went together. Along the way you probably had to undo it once or twice and begin all over again.

And we hadn't started this work yet. It wasn't even scheduled to commence until later in the year.

It wasn't something you could really do on an ongoing basis, as and when information trickled in. You had to wait until a significant body of data had accumulated and then look at it in its entirety. That way, you could pick up patterns and get some sense of how consistent everything was looking. This in turn allowed you to define the inconsistent outliers, which is where you needed to focus most of your attention.

Until you had amassed a decent core of information to define what appeared to be *normal*, you couldn't start to separate out the *abnormal* results. Which were the ones you would need to investigate further and explain away.

We had only just reached this point with the ACCEDE database. If we'd started looking at it any earlier, we'd have probably been struggling to make too much sense of it. Which meant that we weren't really ready for the DSMB just yet. That however was our problem, not theirs.

And it was a big problem for us. If we had reservations about the risk of what the DSMB might make of robust and reliable results, then it would be an even greater danger to provide them with unreliable and potentially misleading data, which hadn't been cleaned up or sense checked yet.

It was as though the DSMB were expecting to see a jigsaw of the efficacy data. It might not be complete right now but enough would be in place for them to get a good idea of the final picture. But in reality, we hadn't even taken the lid off the box and got the pieces out yet.

The situation was very different from studies which have specified up front that a *formal* interim look at the efficacy data will take place part way through, as had been the case with ASA404. In these cases, everyone has planned from the outset for the need to collect and collate the ongoing efficacy data at a fixed point during the trial's progress. It is built into the mechanics of the study, from the moment it starts. If necessary, the trial can even be slowed down for a while, to allow the interim process to complete.

Knowing in advance what is coming and when doesn't avoid all the difficulties of pulling the data together but it can certainly significantly help. Including a formal efficacy interim look is like conducting a scripted interview. It's fairly predictable. You know what questions will be asked and when, although obviously you can't guarantee what the answers might be.

In contrast, for studies without a scheduled interim look, such as ACCEDE, you essentially take whatever you can lay your hands on, when the time comes. Gathering efficacy data from these trials is more akin to a radio phone-in. There is no certainty whether anyone will call at all and if they do, how long they're likely to talk for. It's much more random and haphazard. You may have enough material to pull a show together or you may be really struggling to come up with anything half decent. With amonafide, it didn't look like we had that much to broadcast. Certainly not enough to keep the listeners entertained.

At the time, we were also sensitive about the efficacy of amonafide for other reasons. Recently, two differing AML studies had been published, both in the same September 2009 issue of the prestigious *New England Journal of Medicine.*[10,11]

Whilst having a somewhat parochial title, the New England Journal is the world's foremost and most highly regarded medical publication. Only the best and most original of research make it on to those august pages. Which means it tends to have the greatest impact and the highest profile.

And these two publications had certainly made an impact. Both were large trials in AML, one from the US and the other Europe, comparing treatment with cytarabine, which was given with daunorubicin at a dose of either forty five mg/m² or ninety mg/m².

What they both found was that the higher dose of daunorubicin was much more effective but without being more toxic, than the lower dose. This might not sound like the most earth shattering of events but it made waves within the leukaemia community. It was the equivalent of a road safety study unexpectedly concluding it was actually better to drive at twice the national speed limit on motorways.

Up until then, most people had been employing daunorubicin at the forty five mg/m² dose level, widely regarding this as the standard of care. Which included us in the ACCEDE trial, because in 2007 when the study started, that's what nearly everyone was using.

However, these two publications were now showing you could give twice this dose and get much better results, without killing everyone in the process. The implication was that even if we showed amonafide to have superior efficacy, people could argue we had used what now looked like an inappropriately low dose of daunorubicin and so the results didn't mean very much.

There were a few straws to clutch at though. The New England Journal studies were looking at *de novo* and not secondary AML. Also, some of the data suggested the benefits might not be so marked in older patients with worse disease characteristics. These were two of the hallmarks of secondary AML. The findings might not be directly relevant to the ACCEDE trial therefore.

However, it was impossible to escape the inference that we were now potentially *undertreating* patients in the daunorubicin arm of the study. If that really were the case, it would skew any comparison between the two groups unfairly in amonafide's favour. That's certainly what a lot of people told us, including a number of clinicians involved in the study.

There wasn't really anything we could do about it now however. The trial was too far advanced to make any fundamental changes to it.

There was a danger though that clinicians might become reluctant to continue entering patients into the study, because of concerns over the daunorubicin dose we were using. This was a particular worry, given that a number of the investigators who'd participated in the two New England Journal studies were also taking part in the ACCEDE trial too.

But as it turned out, recruitment of patients wasn't too badly dented by the emergence of these new findings. This may partly have been because the data wasn't *directly* derived from patients with secondary AML. There was therefore some wriggle room to argue over exactly how relevant it was.

That may have been the rationale in the US but ACCEDE was also being run at various hospitals throughout the world. Many of these were in markedly less affluent regions of Central and Eastern Europe, where the cost of drugs, even comparatively cheap ones, was a big issue.

Here they were getting the daunorubicin for free, by virtue of being in the ACCEDE trial. The clinicians were probably grateful for the opportunity the study afforded them to treat patients at any dose level of daunorubicin, whatever the New England Journal may have to say about it. In the former war zone of Tbilisi, where we had one centre, pragmatism would always prevail over perfectionism. The same went for many other places too.

But what it did mean was that at the end of the study, we would *really* need to show a superiority of amonafide over the dose of daunorubicin we were using. Even with this, some critics would inevitably argue that events had moved on and our results were outdated or possibly even irrelevant. But given a decent improvement in response rates with amonafide, there was sufficient ambiguity around the applicability of the New England Journal findings for us to be able to fight our corner.

However, without an unequivocally better outcome, we would be really struggling to capitalise on the ACCEDE results. This was particularly so as we had plans, if amonafide showed an advantage in secondary AML, to develop it in other haematological malignancies too. In that case, the issue of the daunorubicin dose might well be harder to duck.

The whole New England Journal issue was an example of how advances in medical practice could overtake and potentially derail a lengthy clinical trial. By the time it actually completed, the design could have been rendered outdated, with the results suddenly of questionable relevance.

There has been more than one example in cancer medicine of a new drug completing an expensive and time consuming Phase III trial, only to find that the world has moved on, medicine has progressed and it needs to be repeated all over again to take account of this.

However, we were fairly confident we could avoid this fate. There was enough room for manoeuvring, should we need it later on.

Also, there was never a complete consensus on anything to do with AML and eventually there was bound to be the emergence of disagreement of some sort, over the conclusions from these two studies. Sooner or later, something would rock the boat.

Despite that, the last thing we needed at the moment was a DSMB sifting through our incomplete efficacy results, in the midst of a debate over whether we even had the right dose level of comparator drug.

So we felt a compelling need to sit on the efficacy data from the ACCEDE trial. If it wasn't accurate, combining it with the potential mortality rates we were seeing for amonafide would create too volatile a situation. It would be throwing petrol on the fire.

But the DSMB were expecting something that much was clear. They knew we hadn't exactly been sitting around playing *Warhammer* all day long, since the last time we'd met them. They would want to see some progress with collecting the efficacy information from the study.

The best, or rather least worst, course of action was probably to come clean and explain the genuine difficulties we were having, in collecting and cleaning up the efficacy data. If we could paint a picture of inaccuracies and inconsistencies lurking at every turn of the page, maybe we could convince them it would do more harm than good to look at results which were clearly in such a parlous state of imperfection. It was a fairly accurate portrayal of what was going on, after all.

The biggest risk with doing this though, was the DSMB politely telling us to f**k off and not come back until we had sorted out the problem and had something to show them. In the meantime they might decide to put the study on hold, which meant we wouldn't be able to carry on recruiting patients.

We had no idea how likely an outcome this might be but whatever happened, it was probably less risky than letting them have the existing data, without us knowing what we would be handing over. So we didn't really have that much choice.

The clock wasn't exactly on our side either. We didn't have much time left to come up with a better plan.

VIII

The news reports on April 15th were carrying stories that Gatwick, Heathrow and other regional airports were planning to close for a couple of hours later in the day. The cloud of volcanic ash was descending on us from Iceland. No one took much notice of this to begin with. It looked like a minor annoyance at worst. Later in the day though, the initial airport closures were slowly evolving into a complete shutdown of UK airspace. The situation was far more serious than anyone seemed to have anticipated.

It was obvious that this was going to create problems for us. The most immediate one was how we were going to get to the DSMB in the US the following week. We'd been thinking for some time that we really needed a face to face meeting. It would give us the best chance to present our case and try to steer a safe passage through the subsequent dissection of the data.

This seemed all the more important now because it suddenly turned out that none of us, who would be at the meeting, had ever actually met any of the DSMB members before. Up until this point, relationships with them had been handled exclusively by our most senior clinical person in the US.

Based in Boston, Bill Lundberg was a graduate of both Stanford University in California and also the world famous Massachusetts Institute of Technology. He'd trained in oncology at Harvard Medical School, where he still held a clinic at the Dana-Farber Cancer Institute, no less. He was thin, ascetic looking, with a self-deprecatory gentleness, that for some reason always reminded me of a monk in a monastery. Bill had this wonderfully infectious passion for cancer medicine and clinical trials, almost as though these really were his religion.

He also seemed to be on first name terms with just about everyone in the US leukaemia community, including all the members of the DSMB. Under his deft and diplomatic guidance, previous meetings had run amazingly smoothly, with us comfortably weathering the odd hiccups that had occurred along the way.

This was in no small part due to Bill's ability to engage with individual members on an equal professional and intellectual footing, earning their respect as well as their goodwill along the way. With his unique mixture of passion, pragmatism and personability he was the ideal person to get us through this critical upcoming meeting.

The only problem now was that he'd just announced he was leaving us.

Bill had originally been with the Xanthus organisation, when we acquired them in the middle of 2008. He had been in charge of all their clinical activities. Since the merger he had been running everything in North America for the newly enlarged Antisoma. However, he had recently decided to accept a position as Chief Medical Officer with a small newly formed Boston based biopharmaceutical company.

He'd actually announced this a few days *before* the ASA404 interim look disaster and the timing of his decision subsequently created an aura of prescience, which only added to his already substantial reputation for canniness and cunning.

We were all really pleased for Bill on one level. We'd have probably gone with him, given the chance. But his departure would now leave a very big hole. It couldn't have come at a worse time either. In the weakened state we were in overall, we would never attract anyone of Bill's calibre to join us as a replacement. In fact it was doubtful we could attract anyone of any calibre.

However, despite all the immediate demands of his new job, Bill had kindly and generously offered to act as a consultant to us, over the fast approaching DSMB meeting. It was a typically magnanimous gesture of his and served to emphasis just how much we would miss him.

It was obviously helpful to have Bill remaining in the background, particularly as he had such a good grip on the history of the relationship but it still meant that at the actual meeting, the DSMB would be facing an Antisoma team it didn't really have the measure of.

From our side, the mutual lack of familiarity was a handicap, in trying to work out how to angle the meeting to our best advantage. Running this sort of event was something we usually gave quite a lot of consideration to. You are bringing together a group of very intelligent and highly articulate individuals, to consider issues of considerable complexity and, in our case, almost certainly controversy. On these occasions, the debate can be very difficult to control, with a tendency to unpredictably veer off in different directions. The train of thought comes to resemble the path of the ball inside a pinball machine, flipped this way and that with surprising rapidity and randomness.

This is generally the last thing you want, when navigating something as contentious as clinical data. You have no idea and even less control over who will suggest what next and who else is likely to agree or disagree with it. If you're not careful, this can quickly end up in dangerous territory, where unwelcome suggestion and supposition suddenly gain traction and support, before you can nip it in the bud.

Often you can reach the very verge of moving on from a discussion, where you thought you'd achieved the outcome you were hoping for. Then someone suddenly throws a speculative spanner in the works, which everyone else eagerly grabs hold of and the whole debate starts off all over again.

To minimise this liability, you have to control the discussion. Which can be difficult, when you are dealing with professionals whose enormous capability is sometimes matched only by their own ready appreciation of it. You have to keep things short and succinct. People need to be cut off before they have a chance to get up a head of steam behind whatever unhelpful initiative it is they appear to be developing.

You must keep moving on at all cost. The more delay and deliberation, the greater the chance people will start changing their minds or procrastinating.

However, if you want to hurry and harass people it obviously helps if you already know the individuals you are dealing with and how they behave as a group. And that was an insight we would no longer have, after Bill's departure. Which was another reason for thinking it would be best to sit around a table with our intellectual adversaries and look them in the eye. Whilst at the same time gauging whether there was any scope for blinkering them a little bit.

But with Eyjafjallajökull now kicking off and threatening to disrupt everything, we had to look at alternatives. An obvious one was to postpone the whole thing. After some deliberation though, we decided we really needed to know the outcome now. We couldn't carry on with a possibility hanging over us, however remote, of the study being stopped by the DSMB. It would be impossible to entertain any sort of corporate life, with something like that lurking in the background, ready to stab us in the back at any moment. It would be much better to find out where we stood, as soon as we could.

If we couldn't meet with them though, we would need to come up with a pretty good Plan B.

IX

A few days later, we sat down in London to look at the data we were pulling together for the meeting. There was a lot of it. Clinical trials always generate enormous amounts of information and this one was no exception. There weren't just the deaths, although those were by far and away the most important thing.

We also had to account for all the other *non-fatal* serious adverse events which had occurred. The DSMB would want to know about those too.

Usually in an exercise like this, you take all the SAEs and then group them together, according to which part of the body they had affected. This is known as the MedDRA *Organ System Classification*.[12] A stroke or an epileptic fit would be classified as *central nervous system* adverse events. Diarrhoea or a stomach ulcer would become *gastrointestinal* adverse events, pneumonia, or a clot on the lung, would go under *pulmonary* adverse events. And so on. The idea behind this was to reduce the sheer volume of SAEs down into some sort of manageable format.

To put the serious adverse events into context you also want to include a summary of the *non-serious* ones which occurred in the same organ system classification. For example, if you found that amonafide was causing liver damage as a serious adverse event in five per cent of patients, you would also want to know in what additional proportion it was causing less marked liver damage. That way you could get a more accurate picture of its total liability for injury to that particular organ.

Just to make things as confusing as possible, the classification of side effects draws a distinction between *severe* and *serious*. For example a headache can be severe but is rarely serious. On the other hand, a stroke, however mild, would always be considered a serious occurrence.

The term serious has the specific working definition mentioned earlier (*resulting in death; is life threatening; requires in patient hospitalisation or prolongation of existing hospitalisation; results in persistent or significant disability or incapacity; is a congenital birth defect or anomaly*).

The *severity* of side effects with cancer drugs is categorised according to something called the CTCAE system (*Common Terminology Criteria for Adverse Events*) produced by the US National Cancer Institute.[13] This divides them into five grades of *severity*:

1 (mild); 2 (moderate); 3 (severe); 4 (life threatening); 5 (fatal).

As is almost inevitable with two classification systems drawn up by different committees, which clearly never met, there is an overlap between the two. Side effects of Grade 4 or 5 *severity* would also automatically qualify as *serious* because there is a shared definition between the two categories.

When trying to work out the severity of a particular adverse event, it is usually fairly easy to decide whether it is life threatening or fatal. However it is often much harder to distinguish between mild, moderate and severe. In an attempt to achieve standardisation, the CTCAE system comprises a comprehensive manual, with detailed descriptions for most toxicities (headache, heart attack, haemorrhage, whatever) dealing with how to grade their severity.

Grade 1 vomiting for example, would be one episode of being sick within a twenty four hour period (despite having received anti-nausea pre-treatment). Grade 2, is between two and five episodes, Grade 3, six or more episodes and/or the need for intravenous fluids and Grade 4, vomiting so severe it requires more extensive intervention, including intensive care if necessary.

The big advantage of everyone using the same system, which they pretty much do, is that it makes it much easier to compare safety results across different studies.

DSMBs generally want information about adverse events of Grade 3 or higher severity. They are the ones that represent a real threat to the patient.

We needed therefore to prepare an extensive summary of these. Given that we were dealing with a life threatening disease and some seriously ill patients, who were being treated with some very toxic drugs, it wasn't surprising that we had accumulated a fair number of Grade 3 or higher toxicities for the DSMB to have a look at.

These included numerous effects arising as consequences of both amonafide and daunorubicin wiping out the bone marrow. Mainly these were infections and bleeding. There was also substantial diarrhoea and other gastrointestinal damage, as well as nerve toxicity and allergic reactions.

Amonafide appeared to be more toxic to bone marrow than daunorubicin and was also associated with some particular effects on the heart, including disturbances of its normal patterns of electrical activity. It wasn't exactly a clean bill of health for the drug. Overall though, both agents were exceptionally unpleasant. You would really have to be backed up against a wall, to consider having that sort of thing pumped into you. But that's AML all over.

We hadn't finished yet though, with our dismemberment of the data. There were many more ways in which safety information was usually further broken down, to try to understand it better. It was like interrogating a suspect. If you kept at it long enough, sooner or later he'd crack and tell you what you wanted to know. Safety data was just the same.

One thing you were constantly looking out for were any identifiable patient characteristics, which helped predict whether they'd be more likely to suffer a particular side effect. To help find this out, it was normal to analyse side effects, or at least the serious ones, to see whether their frequency was influenced by a range of factors. These usually included age, the severity of the AML, which country the patient lived in, how long since their leukaemia had been diagnosed, their ethnic origin, their sex, and so on. We could just as easily have included their star sign too.

We would also normally look to see how the pattern of serious adverse events was influenced by something called the patient's *performance status* (PS). The PS is essentially a functional assessment of how disabled the patient is by their malignant disease. Inevitably, there are at least two different performance status systems in use.

The *Karnofsky scoring system* was described as long ago as 1949 by David Karnofsky, a pioneering cancer specialist from Memorial Sloan-Kettering Hospital in New York. But the more widely used one today is the ECOG (*Zubrod*) system, originally developed in the 1960s by Gordon Zubrod from the NCI. He must have squeezed it in during a spare moment or two, when he wasn't busy coming up with the cure for childhood leukaemia.

The ECOG scoring system is divided into five categories from PS 0 (*fully active and able to carry out all normal activities*) to PS 5 (*dead*). Most patients entered into cancer clinical trials are PS 1 or PS 2 (*PS 2 basically being ambulant and up and about for at least fifty per cent of the day*).[14]

The vast majority of trials try to avoid at all cost patients of PS 3 or above (*PS 3 being bed ridden for at least fifty per cent of the day*). This is because although the PS score is an incredibly simple and blunt tool, particularly compared to the complex techniques of modern cancer clinical trials, it is also surprisingly predictive of how well or badly an individual is likely to do, when treated with a new experimental agent.

Patients with a PS greater than 2 never do well. It's not their lucky number. They inevitably fare extremely poorly in clinical trials, with a higher likelihood of early death or serious non-fatal toxicity and a low probability of showing any sort of response. It's surprising that a measure as crude as whether or not someone is bed ridden for more than half the day, turns out to have the same sort of prognostic power as some of the most complicated recent advances in the molecular biology of cancer. Performance status is therefore an analysis which is usually undertaken when trying to understand the pattern of toxicity of a drug and so this was something we knew we would have to provide.

By the time all these various analyses were complete, we'd cut the ACCEDE safety data more ways than a Las Vegas casino croupier could split a deck of cards. If we weren't careful, there would be more than enough information to keep the DSMB busy until Easter and beyond.

And on top of all that, we had spent a lot of time on a detailed presentation for the DSMB of why the efficacy data currently had more loose ends than a Baghdad rug weaver and so was too unreliable to share with them. This had unavoidably required a lengthy exposition of the intricacies of clinical data management, as well as a number of real life patient examples of where the data just didn't add up at the moment. We had more than enough of those to choose from, we reasoned. And so why not share our burden with them a bit.

All in all, it was about as exciting as an accountancy office party but it got the point across, with a certain murderous monotony.

X

So we had pretty much everything covered by now. There was a very comprehensive safety summary, which if we chopped it any more, would turn into the computational equivalent of confetti. And as for the lack of efficacy data, we at least had an extensive explanation, even if it didn't quite amount to an excuse. Which just left the question of what we said about the early mortality with amonafide. Twenty per cent or thirty per cent? Survival or suicide?

We had a clear clinical, corporate, moral, ethical and probably legal responsibility to provide the DSMB with everything we could about the emerging safety profile of the ACCEDE study. There weren't any circumstances that could justify holding back on anything. That was crystal clear.

Even so, it would be unbelievably convenient if we could just give them the twenty per cent mortality figure and forget about the rest. It was still quite a high number and definitely greater than the daunorubicin group. However, it was no worse than what had been seen previously in the Phase II trial and therefore already tacitly accepted by the DSMB. But the thirty per cent number would be game over. Despite the implications though, we couldn't just give them the lower figure, without also telling them of the higher one. Could we?

The thought hung in the air for a long moment. *No.* We couldn't do that. The future of the company might be riding on it, but no one would have been prepared to compromise the probity and professionalism which we hoped characterised everything we did.

No mileage there then.

We sat around the table of whichever meeting room we were holed up in.

"We'll never get all of this over to the DSMB," said Albert in his normal clipped observational tone. "They won't be able to take it all in. I'm not sure we can and we know it backwards."

He had a point, particularly as we only had about three quarters of an hour scheduled at the meeting for us to run through everything. And it had just taken us five times longer than that, despite already being quite familiar with the data by now. There wasn't much we could do about it though. This was complex stuff and we had an obligation to ensure that they had all the available information at their disposal.

As we sat around mulling things over, an idea slowly started to crystallise, out of all the nebulousness. Things might just end up playing to our advantage. If the DSMB were smothered with statistics and drowning in data, maybe the detail could be lost in the deluge.

It was an old legal tactic. The defence team would *haystack* the prosecution by handing over such an enormous amount of pre-trial discovery information that their opponents would struggle to discern the wheat from the chaff, in the limited amount of time available before the trial proper kicked off.

Maybe we were inadvertently doing the same thing. Amonafide was on trial for its life, after all. If the sheer amount of evidence presented to the court ended up confusing the case, then we couldn't really be blamed for that. Well, not too much.

A plan of action began to emerge from the gloom. We would give them *absolutely* everything we had. Right down to the most diminutive digit and the very final fraction. We didn't want them to choke on it but it would certainly be difficult to digest everything.

The challenge of communicating all this information to the DSMB probably wasn't going to be helped by the fact that we'd eventually decided a few days earlier to hold the meeting by phone, with each member at their respective institution. If we weren't able to get to Chicago, they didn't really want to travel all the way there either. These were busy people after all.

Telephone conferencing however was far from ideal for issues of any complexity. It was often a woodenly rigid and inflexible means of communication. There was no emotion, no *empathy* over the phone. It was an inefficient way of dealing with things, acting like a dam to the flash flood of information we had to share with the DSMB.

To overcome this, we would also have to run a web based real time presentation of what seemed to have grown to about six hundred PowerPoint slides by now. They would access them on their own computers. Meanwhile we could gather together over the video link between London and Boston, making it that much easier to coordinate our own actions. It would fortuitously give us an important psychological and logistical advantage.

We had a lot to convey, in a limited period of time and through an imperfect channel of communication. Rather like the ash cloud of Eyjafjallajökull, there was the danger of a fog cloud of complexity descending on the DSMB meeting. Maybe one or two things would slip through in the ensuing lack of visibility.

It was probably our best hope. Come to think of it, it was our only hope.

XI

There were two last things we needed to do, before the actual DSMB meeting. One was to check the precise nature of the legal relationship between the two of us, just in case things came to a showdown and a standoff. This was contained in a document called the DSMB Charter, which detailed very clearly their responsibilities and our obligations.

Looking at this, it appeared that the DSMB only had the power to *recommend* that the ACCEDE study be stopped, should they reach the point of making that particular decision. They didn't actually have the ability to terminate the trial *themselves*. They couldn't really do that anyway, as they didn't "own" the study. Antisoma did.

The DSMB lacked the information and infrastructure necessary to execute a task of such magnitude. Only we were in a position to contact the one hundred and fifty or so participating hospitals around the world and start shutting things down. However, although we may be the only ones who could actually press the *stop* button, it would in practice be impossible to refuse to accept a recommendation from a duly constituted DSMB to halt a study on safety grounds. There was absolutely no precedent for that.

So we *really* needed a recommendation from them to continue with ACCEDE until the end of the trial. Anything less and we wouldn't have much room for any legal manoeuvring.

No pressure there then.

The final task before the big day was to prepare a press release, announcing the termination of the ACCEDE trial on the recommendation of the DSMB. Just in case it came to that. We had to be ready for the worst.

It made grim reading. It was like finalising a last will and testament before undergoing a particularly gruesome operation, where there was no guarantee of making it through.

We hoped it would remain forever firmly tucked away in the bottom draw of Glyn's desk. But you had to be prepared for anything. ATTRACT I had taught us that.

XII

The day of the DSMB meeting was a strangely quiet one. Our Chiswick Park Headquarters were on the flight path to Heathrow and would normally have been subject to the constant roar of jet engines, preparing for their final approach. But the skies were empty of planes, instead being full of volcanic ash.

The meeting was scheduled for three pm London time, seven am in California and ten am on the East Coast.

We'd had a few message of good luck from those who knew it was happening, including one from Ursula characteristically telling us to just get on with it. Glyn was unusually subdued during the morning, constantly clasping his hands together as though he'd only just noticed them for the first time. Daniel had a copy of the draft Doomsday press release on his desk, heavily annotated in red ink.

Those of us who would be involved in the meeting convened in the board room at about two thirty and established a video link with Boston. For once the images were crystal clear, the sound sharper than usual.

Normally, our video equipment tended to depersonalise the people on the other end, giving them a subtle puppet like quality. It resembled conferencing into Tracy Island and having a discussion with the Thunderbirds team.

On this occasion though, it was as if we were all in the same place. There were about eight people altogether. Only two or three of us would be doing presentations, the rest were there ready to deal with any specific questions or issues which arose.

Shortly afterwards, the disembodied voices of the DSMB members came wafting into the room from the speaker console on the table. With gravelly sounding gravitas, the Chairman brought the meeting to order. A silent prayer and we were off.

We set the scene by briefly running through the history to the study, since its inception. We didn't miss the opportunity to remind the DSMB just how valuable many leukaemia experts considered the ACCEDE trial to be, for secondary AML in general, never mind anything to do with amonafide itself. It was going to be the largest randomised trial ever undertaken anywhere in the world in this particular patient group.

As well as information on amonafide, it would also provide a unique understanding of the safety and efficacy of daunorubicin and cytarabine, in a contemporary clinical context. This was important, given that the daunorubicin combination was the most commonly used treatment for sAML, despite the lack of well conducted clinical trial data to support this. Hence the value of ACCEDE.

Of course the DSMB could only really consider what was best for the patients in the study at the moment but we wanted to introduce this bigger dimension into their deliberations, if we could. Maybe the greater benefit of ACCEDE for leukaemia medicine in general, would help tip the balance in our favour. It might make the DSMB more inclined to give us the benefit of the doubt and let the study run to its completion. Well, it was worth a try anyway.

Next, we moved on to the data from the study itself. The slides were being fired off with the rapidity of a Bren gun spitting out bullets. We started off running through the non-fatal toxicities of the two treatment arms.

Thud, thud, thud, thud, thud, thud.

The gun blasted away. Out shot the slides documenting all the poisonous side effects, the terrible chemical consequences of having to be treated for such a dreadful disease.

This went fairly smoothly. There was a lull in the shooting. People were prepared to accept that amonafide had a somewhat greater toxicity burden. That was the price you had to pay, for the possibility of the greater efficacy we were expecting to see. When we eventually had some efficacy results to look at that was.

We wanted to tackle this thorny issue next and had decided in advance that Fredrik would run through an inevitably complicated exposition of the difficulties we were facing, in collecting all the efficacy data together.

Fredrik Erlandson was one of our cancer clinicians, based in London. He was one of the kindest and gentlest people anyone could ever work with. He was a calming influence, in even the headiest and most volatile of atmospheres which occasionally descended on Antisoma. Unfortunately he too was to leave us later in the year, to return to clinical practice in his native Sweden.

A former soldier and world champion free fall parachutist, he was well used to hurtling towards a hard impact at great speed and so was ideally suited for this particular task. More importantly though, with his measured and considered, slightly accented tone of voice, he sounded just like a clinician delivering some bad news to a patient, in a way which left no choice but to accept it, however reluctantly. Which was exactly the way he presented things to the DSMB.

They seemed to take it in their stride. Doubtless in part they had been bludgeoned into submission by Fredrik's remorselessly anodyne and exhaustively extensive explanation of the data management process and all its vagaries. After twenty minutes of Fredrik's disembodied voice, delivered with his steady unvarying cadence, running through slide after slide on the algorithmic complexities of clinical audit and quality control, it would have been surprising if they hadn't slipped into a hypnotic state of somnolent suggestibility.

Whatever the explanation, they seemed to have accepted, with varying degrees of reluctance and resistance, the suggestion that the efficacy data wasn't worth handing over. Like many things in life, the more you worry in advance about the prospect of something, the less awful it eventually turns out to be in reality.

That certainly seemed to be the case here. We had worried ourselves into a paroxysm of torment about this issue before the meeting. And yet it had sailed through on an almost calm sea, suffering only the odd buffeting along the way. Fredrik had certainly done an excellent job.

Which only left the problem of treatment related mortality. Explaining the differing numbers we had for amonafide early deaths required us to once again take the DSMB down the reluctant road of database construction and the differences between centralised and pharmacovigilance ones. The Bren gun sprayed away again with its rapid fire.

Thud, thud, thud, thud, thud.

It never paused for reloading. The slides kept coming in an overwhelming onslaught.

But by now, the DSMB seemed to have had enough of being under fire. They were predominantly a group of physicians, used to seeing clinical data. They were interested in the *product* not the *process*. They seemed, by this point in the proceedings, to have also accepted the general proposition that the ACCEDE trial was a work in progress, a moving target.

Placing too much emphasis on the mortality data when the trial was still under way, would be like trying to take a picture of a fast moving object. It would come out all blurred while it was in motion. The only way to clearly capture it was to wait for it to come to a halt. That was when everything would finally fall into focus.

Like a speeding bullet, a clinical trial was most dangerous whilst it was still in full flight. It was only when it had lost all momentum, that you could safely grasp hold of it.

But they did get the clear message that overall, the early mortality was worse with amonafide but we weren't sure if it was just a little or rather a lot. We tried to give them some comfort with this ambiguity by analysing the pattern of amonafide mortality, broken down according to the individual countries involved in the study. The US centres seemed to do best, with a lower overall death rate in both treatment arms, although there were still numerically more in the amonafide one. Other countries, notably some parts of Central and Eastern Europe, seemed to be having much higher death rates than the US, for both treatment groups.

We had in fact recently closed down one country, Georgia, altogether as there was an enormously high early death rate here. This appeared to be due to a lack of available drugs to help support patients through the worst effects of the treatment. Unless the patients paid out of their own pockets, they didn't get the drugs they might need to save their lives.

We made a big play of having shut down Georgia on our own initiative. We hoped it would create the impression that we were more in control of the mortality issue than was really the case and that somehow, it was predominantly a problem originating in countries other than the US. This shouldn't of course make it any less of an issue. A dead patient was as dead in Georgia, as they would be in Georgetown.

But it was another thing to throw into the mix. Bringing up the vagaries of foreign clinical practice, in far flung geographical territories, probably wouldn't help simplify the interpretation of things for a group of clinicians such as the DSMB, used to hospitals with the best facilities immediately available at all times.

There was a pervasive parochialism about some of the Americans we dealt with. Although highly educated and hugely skilled, it often seemed that their horizons stopped at the geographical boundaries of the North American landmass. They didn't appear to have much interest in, or understanding of, what happened beyond that point.

Of course that was a sweeping generalisation. For all we knew, the DSMB members may have been some of the most cosmopolitan people you'd ever want to meet. But even so, they would probably still struggle a bit to fully understand the overall relevance to the ACCEDE study of a higher mortality occurring at hospitals in a completely different hemisphere from Houston or Honolulu.

But we would find out what they thought soon enough. Up until now, we had kept firm control of the meeting. But the pendulum was about to swing in the opposite direction.

XIII

So far, the DSMB had listened a lot but said little. We hadn't really given them the opportunity to. However now our guns fell silent, as we reached the end of what we had to share with them. We had hardly stopped talking for the last forty five minutes, keeping up a relentless and remorseless barrage of information.

Our case seemed to have gone down reasonably well. When it came to the toxicity issue, there was a feeling we'd sown *reasonable doubt* over the true extent of amonafide's culpability and that this should be enough for an acquittal. But now it was out of our hands.

The DSMB ran itself in two parts, with an initial open meeting, involving us as the trial sponsor. After that, there was a closed gathering with just the DSMB members, where they had a deliberation amongst themselves and then reached a decision about what to recommend. We didn't exactly like the idea of the closed session but there wasn't much we could do about it. That was how all DSMBs worked.

The best we could hope for was that, wearied by information overload and the contradictory complexity of some of the data, they would take the path of least resistance and give us the benefit of the doubt. After all, the study was well over half way through and was due to finish in only another four months or so.

They were only offline for about half an hour in the end but it seemed a lot longer as we sat around, wondering whether we had done our job well enough. And then they were back, their distant voices filling the room with preambling pleasantries.

"*Come on,*" we silently mouthed.

And then...there it was. They *were* going to let us carry on.

Yes the early mortality was an issue they had obviously discussed. Whatever the figure might be, it wasn't exactly supporting amonafide's case. And *yes* the lack of efficacy didn't help either. *But* they accepted the safety data was immature and incomplete and so potentially misleading at this stage. That made it harder to rely on. Particularly as it *was* an important study for a number of reasons.

On balance, amonafide remained a drug with potentially useful efficacy in a disease bereft of that many treatment choices. The safety profile we were presenting was acceptable in that context.

So the recommendation was to continue with the trial. What's more, they were happy for us to carry on to the end of the study. They didn't see the need to meet again as a DSMB, prior to having the final results towards the end of the year.

We looked around the room at each other, in confusion. Had we somehow reconnected to the *wrong* meeting? We couldn't quite believe what we were hearing. Everyone stared at the phone. We waited for them to stop the macabre joke and tell us they were shutting down the study.

But instead, the other end of the line was now all bubble and banter about who would be at ASCO in the summer and other cancer chit chat. They'd clearly already moved on in their minds. We weren't about to do anything to hold them back. With an almost unseemly degree of haste, we drew things to a conclusion in a profusion of platitudes and promises to let them know when the study eventually came to an end.

The phone dropped back into its cradle with a sharp tap, like a judge's gavel bringing court to a conclusion.

It was the best outcome we could possibly have hoped for. It was like coming up from the bottom of the deep end and suddenly breaking the surface into the clear breathable air above.

It had been sink or swim time. And now we were swimming again.

We went to find the others and tell them we were still afloat.

XIV

Sometimes the unexpected seemed to be the only thing you could expect in drug development. The sheer unpredictability of it all. The important could suddenly become the irrelevant, the footnote be precipitously projected to the forefront. An hour and a half earlier, we had been working ourselves into a frenzy that we would never get through the DSMB. Now they didn't want to see us again, until we had finished the study and had some real results to show them. Had we worried too much, or just done our job better than we'd anticipated?

It was quite likely that the members of our DSMB were undertaking the same role for other companies, with other trials in AML. Perhaps they were seeing even more complicated pictures there. Or maybe they were just that much more worldly wise to the pitfalls of clinical trial data in AML than we were. They had years of accumulated insight, compared to our relative innocence and inexperience. They'd seen any number of AML drugs come and go in the past and must have developed a sixth sense by now, of when something uncomfortably out of the ordinary was sitting in front of them.

But we didn't know and it didn't matter now. The ACCEDE study had been nodded through and would go on to complete recruitment. Depending on the eventual results, maybe amonafide would even make it and become a useful drug. At least it looked as though Antisoma would now survive long enough to actually find out.

We filed out of the room, still not quite believing our luck. We would have to wait a few days for the official minutes of the meeting, before it was all confirmed in black and white. But it looked like we were out of the woods, for a while at least.

For the first time in over a month things looked a little brighter. Maybe there would even be planes in the sky again soon.

Being able to carry on with the ACCEDE trial would provide us all with a much needed psychological boost and serve to show the rest of the world that we still had a heartbeat. In fact shortly afterwards we even found a suitor who seemed to want to hold our hand, even if it was only to take our pulse.

Their name was Oxford BioMedica.

SEVEN

YOU CAN'T ALWAYS GET WHAT YOU WANT

**An unlikely suitor appears on the scene. What are they really after from
Antisoma? It looks like a dangerous advance.
How strange can two bedfellows be?**

I

Oxford BioMedica was a biotechnology company which had started life in
the late 1990s, under the guidance of its founder, Professor Alan Kingsman.
At the time, he was a gifted academic in the Biochemistry Department at
Oxford University.

Having originally studied in Birmingham and Edinburgh, he
subsequently spent two years in California, in the late 1970s, learning about
the emerging science of *gene cloning*[1] and *genetic engineering*.[2] These would
later form the basis of *gene therapy*[3] which promised a revolutionary new
therapeutic approach to many of the most intractable of diseases.

He was present at the very beginning of the molecular biology bonanza.
This was the time of the fledgling first steps of what were now multibillion
dollar companies, such as Genentech and Amgen. Back then, they'd just
been a group of gifted individuals starting a company for the hell of it.
Now, Kingsman thought, perhaps he could do the same thing in the UK.

His research had given him technical skill in exploiting gene structure
and function and additionally a wealth of experience with manipulating
viruses. These would eventually become the vehicles used to deliver
therapeutic genes. Alan and his wife Susan, also an academic, intended
establishing a company which could turn theoretical gene therapy into
clinical reality.

Ever since Crick and Watson had unravelled the structure of DNA in
the 1950s, researchers had been dreaming of gene therapy as a therapeutic
possibility. The people at Oxford BioMedica hoped they might be the ones
to finally bring all the strands together.

In theory it sounded so simple. All you had to do was take a disease,
caused by an abnormal gene and replace it with a healthy one. Game over.
Of course, in practice it would turn out to be infinitely more difficult than
that, for everyone involved in the area.

With a focus in cancer and neurology, the company had enjoyed all the
usual ups and downs of a biotechnology start up. However, like the rest of

us, they had struggled on through thick and thin. Then, just when it looked like things were going so well, they suffered a massive setback in the middle of 2008. Their most advanced project had failed in a Phase III clinical trial in kidney cancer.

This wasn't actually even a gene therapy product but instead a cancer treating *vaccine* called TroVax. The technical problems of gene therapy were taking longer to resolve than anyone had imagined. TroVax, which had been around when the company started off, ended up becoming the front runner. But now it had stumbled and fallen.

They had never really seemed to fully recover direction after that. Like many small companies, the idea of a partner was probably attractive for them. Now they were at our door, perhaps sensing a kindred broken spirit.

At first sight, it didn't appear there were many synergies between the two of us. We were both in cancer, so there was that of course. But we were very uncertain of the science they were embracing. TroVax was a vaccine approach to cancer, which most of us simply didn't believe in at Antisoma. It was one of the house rules that vaccines couldn't work by themselves. Cancer had too many defence mechanisms which it could deploy against such an attack.[4]

Furthermore, with TroVax now firmly parked in the wings, trying to convalesce, the mainstay of their company had become gene therapy, which was a hugely complicated challenge. It was an area we had previously vowed to avoid at all cost, fearing it still had too many obstacles to overcome. Or maybe we just didn't understand it enough. It was Star Trek stuff to some of us. *Gene therapy*, rather than *Gene Roddenberry*, seemed the Final Frontier, and we weren't quite ready to be beamed up yet.

It didn't seem a particularly promising start for a potential first date.

II

If we had reservations about this therapeutic approach, it wasn't really that surprising. Having been around for quite a while, it had managed to accumulate a very colourful past. Which was probably only to be expected, given that the story of gene therapy actually all started, somewhat implausibly, with John Travolta. *The* John Travolta. More renowned for his role in films such as *Saturday Night Fever* and *Pulp Fiction*, Travolta's contribution to molecular medicine has to date gone largely unacknowledged and overlooked.

Whereas in fact, along with all the scientists, geneticists, barrier breaking biologists and clinicians, he was one of the technology's earliest protagonists. Travolta's seminal contribution to the field consisted of a 1976 made for TV film, *The Boy in the Plastic Bubble*, in which he starred. This was a drama based on the life of a real patient called David Vetter, whom he played.

Vetter suffered from a rare genetic disorder known as *severe combined immune deficiency syndrome* or SCID.

This disease and patients like David Vetter would eventually mark the beginning of the entire gene therapy journey. It's where everything started. Along the way though, gene therapy would, over the years, turn out to be much more *Vincent Vega* than *Tony Manero*.

SCID was also known as Glanzmann-Riniker Syndrome, thymic alymphoplasia or alymphocytosis. When a disease has that many names, you can be pretty sure it isn't going to be a good one. And this was certainly the case with SCID.

Due to an inherited genetic defect, it leaves the sufferer with no functioning immune system to speak of. All their white blood cells, the body's normal defences against attack, are either absent or ineffective. They are therefore susceptible to potentially fatal infections, arising from even the most innocuous of sources. Any bacteria or virus could overwhelm and kill them.

To survive, Vetter was reduced to living in a plastic bubble. He was forced to remain in permanent isolation from the outside world and the dangers lurking everywhere therein.

In real life, he died at the age of twelve, after a failed bone marrow transplant from his sister. Ironically, it was her attempt to save him that ultimately caused his demise. An undetected viral contaminant in the bone marrow spread like wild fire through his defenceless body and killed him.

Just prior to his death, he became so ill that he had to be taken out of the bubble, allowing his mother to hold him for what had been far too few occasions in his tragically short life. Before he lapsed into a fatal coma, one of the last things he asked for was a Coca Cola. He'd seen it advertised on television over the years but the difficulties of trying to sterilise one had prevented him ever tasting it. His doctors couldn't even grant him that innocuous wish.

It wasn't much of a life really.

Which is presumably why in the film, he doesn't die so young. Instead, he lives long enough to eventually fall in love with Gina, his next door neighbour. Ultimately, he has to make a decision. The choice is between leaving his protective cocoon, thus risking an almost certain death, or staying where he is and dying of a broken heart instead. He chooses to take his chances and the film ends with him emerging from the bubble and the two of them riding off on her horse.

The storyline of The Boy in the Plastic Bubble accurately captured what would turn out to be the ethical dilemma the early days of gene therapy came to represent. Whether to swap one situation, fraught with uncertainty and danger, for another with equally parlous prospects. Whether to take your chances with a disease left untreated, or to give gene therapy a go and hope for the best.

Gene therapy was too late for the real David Vetter though. Sadly this also meant TV audiences were denied the sequel, *Bubble-Trouble, The Bubble-less Boy* or something along those lines.

However, not much more than a decade later this approach would attempt to provide a cure for SCID and many diseases like it. That's what the potential of gene therapy represented. It would finally allow patients to escape from their metaphorical bubbles. It offered a possible solution to people with incurable diseases, who were often living unimaginably debilitated lives as a consequence. If they were prepared to take the risks involved that is.

III

The basic idea of gene therapy was a simple one. There are about two and a half thousand diseases identified so far, including a number of cancers, which are caused directly by defects in a single or limited number of genes.[5] In total, conditions which can be traced back to a single gene defect account for about five per cent of all childhood hospital admissions. One of the best known, for example, is cystic fibrosis, which affects the lungs and other parts of the body.

In theory, all you need to do, to deal with these conditions, is to manufacture a normally functioning gene and then introduce it into the patient, in place of the defective one.

Genes basically exist as templates to make proteins, which are required for the body to function normally. After putting in a working gene, it should then take over and restore normal levels of whichever protein the defective gene couldn't make. This should then reverse the entire disease process, leading to a clinical improvement. But as with many things in medicine, the simplicity of the theory is often matched only by the complexity of the translation into reality.

The world's first proper experiment with gene therapy was performed on September 14th 1990. It was the brainchild of Dr W French Anderson, who was a geneticist at the US National Institutes of Health. A black belt in Taekwondo, he was used to sticking at something until he got what he wanted. And what he wanted now was to extend the success scientists had enjoyed with inserting new genes into plants and animals, by exploring the technique in humans too. And he had found the perfect patient to try it out on.

Ashanti de Silva was a four year old, who also happened to have a form of SCID, the same disease which had killed David Vetter. She lacked the gene responsible for making an enzyme called *adenosine deaminase*, without which her body's defence system couldn't function adequately. This left her susceptible to overwhelming infection at any moment.

The only conventional way of saving her would have been a bone marrow transplant. However, no suitable donor could be found, leaving her with no obvious alternative options. Life in a plastic bubble was no life at all, as David Vetter had so depressingly demonstrated. Her desperate parents, Raj and Van de Silva, eventually agreed to an experimental approach, which would lead to their daughter making medical history on that day in the middle of September.

She ended up at the US National Institutes of Health in Maryland, under the care of Drs Anderson, Michael Blease and Kenneth Culver. There she was treated with a technique which involved removing her white blood cells, which were the site of the defective gene. The missing gene was then inserted into them in the laboratory, after which the modified cells were returned to her. She had just become the first person to ever undergo gene therapy.[6]

This exploratory approach appeared to have some success, with little Ashanti subsequently able to enjoy a more normal life, involving less of the isolationist restrictions she had suffered from previously.[7] News of this ground breaking event shot around the world, generating an enormous amount of media hyperbole. W. French Anderson quickly became known as the "Father of gene therapy."

Unfortunately, much like the subsequent early experience with gene therapy itself, he would later crash and burn, receiving a fourteen year custodial sentence in 2007 for crimes unrelated to clinical research.[8] But back in 1990, Anderson could do no wrong. He had broken the scientific sound barrier.

But the procedure was far from a cure. The treated white blood cells couldn't go on to form other healthy white cells and so when they died, after a few months, the new gene perished with them.

This meant that the whole process had to be repeated every three months or so, with all sorts of attendant technical problems and practical difficulties. But it was a start. A big step had been taken from the laboratory to the clinic. Since the crossing of that 1990 threshold, almost two thousand human gene therapy studies have been conducted. Many involve potential anti-cancer approaches, aiming to replace a defective or damaged gene implicated in the mechanisms of malignancy.

But initial progress was disappointingly slow. And as if that weren't enough, in 1999, disaster rocked the whole gene therapy world.

IV

Seventeen year old Jesse Gelsinger spent Christmas Night 1998 in the intensive care unit of the Tucson Children's Hospital in Arizona. His blood ammonia level was six times what it should have been. That was bad in anyone's book. This time he survived. But only just. It had been close.

Ever since the age of three, Jesse had suffered with the symptoms of a genetic disease, present with him since birth. He had a disorder known as *ornithine transcarbamylase deficiency (OTCD)* which occurred in about one in eighty thousand births. It wasn't exactly common therefore.

The resulting lack of the enzyme *ornithine transcarbamylase* prevents the liver from breaking down ammonia, a toxic by-product of the body's consumption of proteins. The build up of ammonia in the blood leads to delayed development, seizures, comas and liver damage.

Existing treatments consisted of a low protein diet and various drugs. These scavenged up nitrogen, which was the main chemical component of ammonia. If that didn't keep things at bay, the only remaining option was a liver transplant. Jesse though had fared relatively well so far, with a combination of diet and drugs. He'd grown up as a reasonably normal teenager, although frequent hospitalisations had resulted from lapses in dietary discipline or drug compliance.

A few months before his Christmas dance with death, Jesse and his family had learned, through their local specialist Dr Randy Heidenreich, of an experimental trial being run at the University of Pennsylvania. This involved patients with OTCD and utilised the promising new approach of gene therapy. The Gelsingers were definitely interested but potential patients had to be at least eighteen to participate. It would therefore have to wait for now.

However, the subject came up again the following April, during a routine metabolic clinic visit and this time things looked more promising. Jesse's family were already planning a visit to New Jersey in June, by which time he would have turned eighteen and be potentially eligible for the study. And so on June 18th, the day of Jesse's birthday, the family flew up north, ready for an appointment a few days later with the clinicians running the trial.

V

Pennsylvania Hospital, located at 800 Spruce Street in the middle of Philadelphia, enjoyed the distinction of being the nation's very first hospital, founded in 1751 by Benjamin Franklin and Dr Thomas Bond. It was now home to one of the most advanced medical experiments ever undertaken. And Jesse Gelsinger was about to become part of it.

Dr Mark Batshaw was a paediatrician who'd helped devise the study that would eventually go so catastrophically wrong. He held a lifelong interest in developmentally disabling diseases and had ended up as a world expert in *urea cycle disorders,* such as OTCD. He'd been the first person to develop the low protein diet approach to the treatment of OTCD and had also been the head of the team which originally devised the currently used drug strategies. So no one knew more than Mark Batshaw did about diseases like Jesse Gelsinger's.

As a super-specialist though, he mainly saw patients who were much more severely affected than Gelsinger. In a bad case of OTC deficiency, a new born child would become comatose within a couple of days of birth. Many suffered severe brain damage. Half died within four weeks and a further half of those surviving would die within the next four years.

These were the kinds of patients for whom gene therapy was the hope of the future. To try and make this a reality, Batshaw was working with another gene therapy enthusiast, Jim Wilson, who was Director of the Institute for Human Gene Therapy at the University of Pennsylvania. At the time, this was the largest academic gene therapy program in the whole of the US. Wilson had state of the art laboratories, nearly three hundred staff and an annual budget of over twenty five million dollars.

Wilson and Batshaw's earlier laboratory experiments had proven promising, in OTC deficient mice. These had survived for months, even on a high protein diet, after having a normal gene introduced into their livers. In contrast, the untreated mice died almost immediately. In all, they conducted more than twenty mouse studies to test the efficacy of their gene delivery approach, as a prelude to finally trying it out in humans.

They also undertook extensive safety testing in mice, baboons and rhesus monkeys. These experiments didn't go quite so well though. Three monkeys had died of a blood clotting disorder and severe liver inflammation. They had however received a stronger than normal version of the virus which was being used to deliver the normal gene to the liver. The amount of virus administered was also about twenty times higher than the one intended for human use.

It was therefore difficult to decide how relevant the animal findings really were.

The particular virus planned for the clinical trial was called an *adenovirus.* One of the problems though, was that no one had ever injected this directly into the blood stream before. Which made it hard to work out just how people might respond. To take account of this, Batshaw and Wilson were proposing to inject the virus directly into the blood supply to the right lobe of the liver itself. That way, if damage did occur, hopefully the liver's other left lobe would be left unaffected.

However, this wasn't exactly a straightforward solution. There was a possibility of serious bleeding arising from the procedure and also the risk of severe liver inflammation, which might lead to the need for a transplant or even result in death.

Given these substantial risks and as yet unproven benefits, there was an ethical and clinical issue of which patients with OTCD would be the most appropriate for this sort of clinical trial. Very sick babies, with the most severe form of the disease, would have appeared obvious starting candidates. They would seem to have the least to lose and the greatest to gain.

But there was a significant ethical issue with these patients. Many of those involved in setting up the trial contended that the distraught and distressed parents would be incapable of making an informed decision over their child's participation. They wouldn't be in a position to take objective account of all the risks involved.

VI

The ethical and moral dimensions of human participation in clinical research have spawned a whole academic branch of medicine called *bioethics*. Those involved spend most of the day deliberating the difficulties around willing participation and informed consent for activities such as clinical testing.

Informed consent is an issue which has assumed much prominence in modern clinical trials, whether in cancer or any other area of medicine. It is based on a proposition that it's essential to make potential participants in a clinical trial aware of the risks involved, which may be very high. It's also necessary to give them an appreciation of the likelihood of deriving any benefit, which may be very low.

Without having ensured informed consent and documenting a patient's agreement to participate based upon this, it is simply not permissible to include an individual in a clinical study. Breaching this requirement is regarded as one of the most fundamental of all violations of the principles of clinical trials. Usually regulatory authorities will refuse to consider any clinical data generated from patients where this has occurred. It is therefore something which is taken extremely seriously.

The preoccupation amongst bioethicists with this issue can ultimately be traced back to the enforced Nazi medical experimentation of World War Two. Some of them seem to still believe that only the existence of an informed consent form stands in between all doctors and the otherwise irresistible temptation to initiate unauthorised and unacceptable experimentation on the unwary, at every possible opportunity.

However, many modern clinical trials are technically very complex. It can be extremely challenging to reduce the issues involved to a simplicity which an average person could readily understand, without inadvertently refining out all the relevant detail along the way. This would obviously be an even bigger difficulty with something as novel and sophisticated as gene therapy. Particularly in the context of a child suffering from a potentially terminal illness and a distraught parent having to decide what might be in the best interest of their offspring.

Trying to explain the fundamentals of astrophysics, using only a Punch and Judy show, would probably have been a lot easier.

Arthur Caplan was Emanuel and Robert Hart Professor of Bioethics and Director of the Centre for Bioethics at the University of Pennsylvania. He was an enthusiastic man, who was passionate about bioethics. This was the same Arthur Caplan who ten years later would exuberantly describe synthetic life (detailed in Chapter Five) as one of the most important advances in the history of mankind. He was inevitably drawn into the debate over the ethics of the proposed OTCD trial. He had a view on everything and was much in demand.

As with any academic discipline, in bioethics there was always a danger that the means would become more important than the end. And certainly discussions on informed consent often seemed to generate much heat and light, whilst resulting in little of subsequent substance. It was frankly difficult to understand exactly how bioethicists might occupy themselves all day long with the issue. When it came down to it, informed consent wasn't that difficult a concept to define and debate.

But they somehow happily managed to do so and their views were important influences in the deliberations surrounding complicated issues, such as experimental gene therapy.

Caplan's eventual advice to Batshaw and Wilson, on the ethics of their OTCD study, was to steer well clear of severely affected children, even though these were the ones in theory most likely to benefit. The potential difficulties in obtaining *informed* consent from the parents were just too great.

Instead, he counselled them to focus their efforts on stable adult patients. People like Jesse Gelsinger, who were more capable of understanding what they were getting themselves into and making their decisions accordingly. However, this was also the group with milder disease. Otherwise they would never have survived that long in the first place. They therefore had less to gain from taking part.

Whilst Gelsinger's OCTD was bad, it wasn't so bad that the gene therapy would make a huge difference. Any effects were also likely to be short lived. In the month or so after the infusion, his immune system would hunt down and destroy the virus carrying the gene, thus removing the opportunity for it to continue incorporating into liver cells. The truth was that if he agreed to take part in the study, he'd be doing it largely for the potential benefit of others in the future.

His main contribution would be helping the technology to progress and evolve. There might not be that much in it for him at all. Any benefits would be transient at best. He would be exposed to all the risks but few of the rewards. That was the ethical dilemma. It wasn't an easy circle to square.

However, Caplan's views eventually prevailed and the trial became one involving adult patients only. The next step was to submit the study to the *Recombinant DNA Advisory Committee (RAC)* for approval. The RAC had been set up in 1974, by the National Institutes of Health, in response to growing public concern over the use of recombinant DNA material to undertake genetic manipulation.[9]

The popular conception had become one of Frankenstein monsters, incubating in bubbling chemical cauldrons, with deranged scientists hovering in the background. The truth probably wasn't quite that bad but to allay these fears, the RAC was charged with vetting all studies involving gene therapy. They were supposed to weed out the mad professors hell-bent on the destruction of civilisation as we know it. Just in case they might otherwise go unnoticed.

By 1999 though, it had become increasingly redundant as a regulatory force, with most of these responsibilities having been appropriated by FDA. Despite that, passage through the RAC was a box which still had to be ticked for studies involving gene therapy.

A proposal was therefore made to them for the OTCD trial. The plan included eighteen adult patients, divided into six groups of three, each group receiving a higher dose of DNA than the previous one.[10] It all seemed fairly straightforward, on paper at least.

The RAC duly ticked their box and everything was finally in place for the great experiment to commence.

VII

The first patient was scheduled for treatment on April 7th 1997. Jesse Gelsinger was to be the eighteenth and last patient. He would also turn out to be the youngest.

Gelsinger and his family met with the clinical team on June 22nd, to talk through the practicalities. On the study day itself, he would be sedated, after which two catheters were to be carefully placed in his liver. One would go into an artery supplying blood to the organ and one into a vein draining it away again. The gene carrying virus would be delivered into the liver by this route.

Afterwards, he would have to remain completely immobile for eight hours. It was imperative that he didn't move at all. This was to minimise the risk of a clot breaking away from the site of the infusion. If that happened, it could lodge in the lungs and kill him. There would also be some flu like symptoms for a few days afterwards and a small possibility of inflammation of the liver.

The biggest danger was a week after the infusion, when a biopsy of the liver would have to be undertaken. This was needed in order to obtain some tissue for Batshaw and Wilson to determine whether the normal gene had managed to establish itself into the rest of the DNA of the liver cells.

The biopsy was a procedure which involved pushing a long hollow needle through the skin on the right side of the abdomen and then carrying on upwards towards the chest, hopefully ending up in the liver. The trick was to avoid all the other major body structures unhelpfully situated along the way. The needle was then pulled back out, usually with a core of liver tissue embedded in it.

This is normally done at the patient's bedside, without X-ray guidance or any other help. It relies on the skill of the person performing it and their knowledge of the internal anatomy of the body organs. A bit of luck doesn't go amiss either.

The big danger lies in inadvertently hitting a blood vessel and provoking a catastrophic haemorrhage. The liver is a uniquely vascular organ, as it possesses a dual blood supply. It has an artery and vein like other organs but also an *extra* supply from something called the *hepatic portal vein*. This delivers blood from the intestines, so that the liver can deal with all the nutrients and toxins contained therein. It is this unusually abundant blood supply which makes a liver biopsy so much more dangerous than a biopsy of most other organs.

Gelsinger was told there was about a one in ten thousand chance of the biopsy killing him. It didn't seem that huge a risk but it had to be set against the fact that he would be unlikely to gain much benefit from taking part in the trial. But that was fine with Jesse. He wanted to do something for others, just as others had done a lot for him over the years. Which were admirably altruistic intentions. Although probably not worth dying for.

And so he signed up for the trial. His participation was scheduled for the autumn. In fact, an opening arrived sooner and so on September 9th Jesse returned to Philadelphia. This time he was by himself as his father, Paul, a self-employed handyman, couldn't get away from work. He was going to fly up a week later, to be there for the liver biopsy. The two of them would then return together to Tucson.

VIII

Treatment with the OTCD gene therapy started on Monday September 13th. Jesse was to receive the highest dose given so far, with the exception of one previous female patient, who'd been given the same dose and done reasonably well by all accounts.

Everything with the technique seemed to go uneventfully and the procedures were all completed by lunch time. That evening though, he felt profoundly nauseated and was running a high temperature. No one was overly concerned however. They'd seen this with other patients in the past. Jesse's father phoned and they talked briefly. Neither had any idea that it was to be their last conversation.

The next morning, Jesse's condition had worsened and he was obviously

313

jaundiced. The medical staff were more concerned now. This wasn't something they had seen before with previous patients. They became even more concerned when tests suggested that his blood's entire clotting system had gone into melt down. He appeared to have a condition known as *disseminated intravascular coagulation* (DIC).

This can occur as a consequence of many serious illnesses, including cancers, severe infections, major trauma and liver failure. It results in all of the body's clotting factors being used up. There is uncontrolled formation and breakdown of clots in random blood vessels, throughout the patient's different organs, often damaging them irreparably in the process.

This would be life threatening for anyone. Not that many patients actually survive DIC. The situation was even more dangerous for someone with OTCD, as it would result in large amounts of ammonia being produced. Their liver would be unable to cope with that at the best of times. And this was about as far from the best of times as you could get.

What was actually causing the DIC was a mystery though. No one was sure what to do next.

Events rapidly took an ominous turn. By lunchtime on Tuesday, just twenty four hours after the infusion, Gelsinger was in a coma. Kidney dialysis was started in an attempt to remove some of the accumulated ammonia and other toxins. This seemed to buy a breathing space with his condition stabilising, although the doctors had to put him into a deeper coma with a ventilator machine breathing for him.

But on Wednesday, things started to slide again. His lungs had become so stiff with fluid that even with a ventilator doing the work, not enough oxygen was getting to the rest of his body. They considered a liver transplant but Jesse was in too bad a condition to be a candidate for something as traumatic as that. There was no way he could survive the operation. Things were desperate now and so the doctors reached for desperate solutions.

Extra corporeal membrane oxygenation (ECMO) was something most physicians would have read about at medical school but never actually seen in use. It was a technique similar to the heart lung bypass procedure used in open heart surgery, except that it was used at the bedside, rather than in the operating theatre. ECMO utilised a device, about the size of a washing machine, which was plumbed into the patient to form a circuit so that blood flowed from the body, through the machine and then back to the patient.

The machine helped out the heart and lungs by doing the hard work of pumping and breathing. It was mainly used in neonatal medicine with very small sick babies, where it was often quite successful. Experience with adults though was much more limited and much less predictable. But with not much to lose by this stage, they hoped it might buy some time. Time being in very short supply by then.

However by Thursday, Jesse's father, who'd been at the hospital since

Tuesday morning, knew they had lost the fight. You didn't have to be a doctor to work that one out. Jesse had developed *multi-organ failure*, a feared complication of severe systemic illnesses. It was characterised by progressive failure of the liver, kidneys, heart and lungs. He was retaining so much fluid that he had swelled up beyond recognition. There was nothing left of the Jesse Gelsinger of less than a week ago.

The next day, tests showed, to the surprise of no one who could see him, that Gelsinger was brain dead.

At two thirty in the afternoon, on Friday 17th, after all the machinery had been switched off, he was pronounced dead. With him in that room, died much of the early promise of gene therapy. The hope and the hype were to be replaced by hysteria and hyperbole over what had gone so wrong.

Seven weeks later, Gelsinger's ashes were scattered over the peak of Mount Wrightson which ranged ten thousand feet above Tucson. At the same time, people were beginning to poke through the ashes of the OTCD gene therapy experiment, trying to finds clues explaining why things had unravelled in such a disastrous fashion.

It appeared that Jesse had died due to a severe immunological reaction to the adenovirus, which had been used to deliver the gene to the liver. Naturally occurring adenoviruses are common pathogens in man and account for some ten to fifteen per cent of upper respiratory tract infections, such as coughs, colds, tonsillitis, conjunctivitis and ear infections. The vast majority of people recover spontaneously from these sorts of illness, without any kind of immune consequence.

It seemed therefore that the genetic manipulation of the adenovirus, which was necessary to incorporate the human gene for ornithine transcarbamylase, had made it much more *immunogenic*. The virus had somehow become more recognisable to the immune defences and it had turned into a more provocative stimulant of the immune system.

But if that was the case, why hadn't there been any earlier clues or warnings, during the OTCD programme, about something as dramatically dangerous as this? As it would turn out however, there did appear in retrospect to be a number of warning signals. One way or another, they were all overlooked or ignored.

IX

The death of a volunteer in a clinical trial, especially a teenager who could have been expected to live for many more years despite his disease, inevitably provoked a huge amount of private and public scrutiny. This ranged from internal investigations by both Pennsylvania Hospital and the Children's National Medical Centre (where Dr Batshaw was based at the time), all the way through to a series of investigative reports by the Washington Post.

At the same time, there were multiple investigations by federal regulatory agencies, including the Office for Human Research Protections,[11] the NIH and FDA. On top of that, the whole case ended up in front of committees from both the US Senate and House of Representatives and also the United States Attorney for the Eastern District of Pennsylvania. Everyone wanted to have their say on a case as unprecedented as this one.

Perhaps the most telling investigation was the one undertaken by FDA. FDA may have many faults and multiple critics but one thing they excel at, more than any other organisation on Earth, is investigating a clinical trial where things have gone wrong. As part of their Bioresearch Monitoring Program, they have specialist teams with the ability to take something as hugely complicated as a clinical study and deconstruct it into thousands of small individual constituent steps, which are then put under the microscope and examined in intimate detail.

Two of FDA's foremost forensic experts, Mike Rashti and Dr Thomas Eggerman spent most of December and January at the Institute for Human Gene Therapy. They had taken a big bag of fine-tooth combs with them. Ultimately their findings, at the end of this exhaustive investigative endeavour, were disturbing. They also reached markedly different conclusions from the historical perspective of Jim Wilson, one of the people eventually most implicated in what went wrong.

Almost a decade after Gelsinger's death, Dr Wilson reviewed his experiences in an essay entitled "Lessons learned from the gene therapy trial for ornithine transcarbamylase deficiency," appearing in a relatively obscure journal called *Molecular Genetics and Metabolism.*[12]

In it, he concludes that:

"The hyperaccelerated translation to the clinic that occurred in the field of gene therapy in the 1990s was driven by multiple factors including (i) a straightforward if ultimately simplistic, theoretical model indicating that the approach "ought to work"; (ii) a large population of patients with disabling or lethal diseases and their affiliated foundations harbouring fervent hopes that this novel therapy could help them; (iii) unbridled enthusiasm of some scientists in the field, fuelled by uncritical media coverage; and (iv) commercial development by the biotechnology industry during an era in which value and liquidity could be achieved almost entirely on promise, irrespective of any actual results."

In other words, what went wrong was the result of everything, except Dr Wilson himself. Although to be fair to him, Wilson's article did capture the combustible excitement of the era and a possible generalised under estimation of the biological potency of the new technologies emerging at this time.

FDA and others disagreed with this relatively blameless version of events though. Their investigations had uncovered a number of worrying errors and omissions in the study.

These included poor documentation, inaccurate and delayed reporting of adverse events and other safety findings to FDA, incomplete adherence to the requirements of the study protocol, inclusion of patients who strictly weren't eligible for the trial, poor training of clinical staff and failure to notify FDA of important animal toxicology findings. This sweeping indictment showed how adept FDA were at this sort of forensic analysis but also just how bad the actual conduct of the OTCD trial had in fact been.

It subsequently emerged that two patients early on in the trial had developed Grade 3 liver damage. This was one grade short of being "life threatening." However, the study was continued, despite the fact that, according to the wording of the protocol, the trial should have been stopped if any *one,* let alone two, patients experienced this level of toxicity.

Another patient was entered into the study, although they had results from laboratory testing which should have excluded them. This was despite a telephone conversation at the time with FDA, when the Agency specifically rejected a request from Dr Wilson to remove this particular restriction from the protocol.

It also transpired that the inclusion of Gelsinger, as the *second* patient in the sixth dose level group, was a violation of a verbal agreement with FDA. Male patients were only supposed to be included as the *third* person at any dose level. The first two patients should have been females, as there was evidence that they were, for some reason, less susceptible to toxicity than male ones. It was safer to start with them. If anything went wrong, it was likely to be more manageable.

Furthermore, patients volunteering for the study, including Gelsinger, hadn't been told about those three monkeys who'd died in toxicology testing, of what now sounded very much like disseminated intravascular coagulation. They hadn't therefore been informed of the consequent risks this might represent to them, if they participated.

In light of these anomalies and aberrations, in November 2000, FDA wrote to Wilson. Steven Masiello, Director of the Agency's Office of Compliance and Biologics Quality summarised their case.[13]

"You repeatedly and deliberately violated federal regulations in your capacity as an investigator in clinical trials with investigational new drugs, specifically an adenoviral vector. These violations form the basis for the withdrawal of your eligibility as a clinical investigator to receive investigational new drugs."

He then proceeded to list almost *sixty* violations Dr Wilson was responsible for in the OTCD study. It was a very long letter. Masiello concluded by informing Wilson that, unsurprisingly, FDA were considering banning him from taking part in future clinical trials in the US.

Another significant finding which came to light was a potential conflict of interest some of those involved in the study may have faced. As it turned out, both Wilson and the Institute for Human Gene Therapy had substantial financial ties to a private gene therapy company called Genovo. Genovo had an involvement in adenovirus technology, similar to that being used in the OTCD trial and hence an overlapping interest in it. Genovo also had deals at the time with two larger companies, Genzyme and Biogen Idec, broadly encompassing gene therapy for liver diseases.

Genovo ultimately turned out to be a valuable asset. It was sold in August 2000 to a Seattle based company called Targeted Genetics for sixty seven million dollars.[14] Dr Wilson personally made thirteen and a half million dollars in Targeted Genetics stock from the deal, as a thirty per cent shareholder in Genovo.

At the time, no one came out and suggested that such a *potential* conflict of interest, between clinical research and commercial reality, might compromise the medical judgement of an investigator running a clinical trial. At the very least though, it added to the complexity of the final picture which was emerging.

Following the FDA investigation, the Department of Justice eventually brought civil charges against Wilson and Batshaw, the University of Pennsylvania and the Children's National Medical Centre. Inevitably, given that so many organisations were now taking part in picking over the pieces, events were moving at an extremely slow pace.

It wasn't until February 2005 that a semblance of resolution finally emerged, when the government reached civil settlements with all involved. Some kind of compromise was probably inevitable, given the complexity of the subject under prosecution and the bewildering number of parties involved on either side of the case. At the end of all this though, there was still no one who stood up to take responsibility for Gelsinger's death. As part of the settlement, the FDA proceedings against Wilson were dropped. Events appeared to have reached an inconclusive conclusion.

Wilson resigned as Director of the Institute for Human Gene Therapy in July 2002. However, he remained at the University of Pennsylvania and also continued to run a lab in the Department of Pathology and Laboratory Medicine. This has so far identified well over a hundred different variants of adenovirus, which might one day turn out to be more suitable candidates for gene delivery than the one used in the Gelsinger OTCD trial.

X

Despite all of the investigation and recrimination following the OTCD disaster, no one has ever fully resolved whether the death of Gelsinger was caused by a failure of the conduct of the clinical trial, or the underlying technology, or a combination of the two. The answer is probably that both contributed, although it will never be known for sure.

The adenovirus that was used in the OTCD trial was given, at least to Jesse Gelsinger, at a very high dose of about 10^{14} viral particles in total. In other words, or rather other numbers, that is:

10x10x10x10x10x10x10x10x10x10x10x10x10x10 viral particles.

Which is a *lot* of virus and such a dose would probably contain a high number of non-viable viral fragments. These would be like a red rag to a bull, as far as the recipient's immune defences were concerned. It could partly explain the massive immune reaction that ensued.

So excessive viral delivery may have been one issue in the OTCD trial. Another was how well each patient's liver was working at the time they received the infusion. About ninety per cent of an adenovirus load, injected directly into the blood stream, would be taken up by the liver. Which meant that the probability of the virus spreading throughout the rest of the body would be low. However, for a patient with a damaged liver, who maybe couldn't deal quite so efficiently with that kind of onslaught, the chances were much higher that the virus would disperse and disseminate, in the process provoking the immune system to attack back.

One of the concerns FDA had, when looking in detail at the Gelsinger death, was that immediately before the fatal infusion, when the doctors checked the ammonia levels in his blood, they found them to be significantly higher than normal. This indicated that his liver wasn't working as well as it should be.

But because his ammonia levels were much lower, when they had been measured three months earlier, at the time Gelsinger had visited Pennsylvania Hospital to sign up for the trial, the doctors went ahead anyway. That was all the protocol for the study required. The patient's ammonia levels had to be reasonably normal at the time they were first checked over for entry into the trial, not necessarily at the time when maybe it mattered the most, when they were on the table, about to receive treatment.

Maybe if the study had been designed differently, to test the patient's liver function more rigorously, then Gelsinger would have been excluded from taking part and none of the subsequent events would have unfolded. But then again, even if the protocol had included this kind of consideration, if the clinicians involved were ignoring other restrictions that were proving inconvenient, it's unclear whether they would have taken this requirement any more seriously.

Furthermore, even if the safety problems were partly down to a poorly designed trial, it was still clear that the gene delivery technology itself had a role to play. After all, those three monkeys that died were all in perfectly good health before they received the adenovirus infusion.

In hindsight, maybe Gelsinger's death could have been avoided but retrospect is an easy perspective through which to view events. In defence of the clinicians involved, although some at least of their actions would appear to have been indefensible, they were at the forefront of an incredibly complicated technology, for which there was virtually no previous experience. It's clear that the biological power at their disposal was simply not sufficiently understood by them at the time. When you are exploring completely unknown terrain, it's easy to stumble and trip.

The potential of gene therapy however was so enormous, that it would go on to survive this major setback and others that were still to come. The disaster of the OTCD trial was, to paraphrase Churchill, not the beginning of the end but definitely the end of the beginning. The earliest days had been a period where excitement and expectation clearly exceeded reality and rationalism. There had been, as Jim Wilson described, a *hyperaccelerated* rush into the clinic. Following the OTCD events in Philadelphia, all that came to an abrupt end. Subsequent progress around the world would be more painful and protracted.

However, whilst the pathway may suddenly have become harder to navigate, the final destination remained one which people were still desperate to arrive at. The problem lay in working out how to actually get there.

XI

The end of this initial era of optimism was further hastened by another major setback at the beginning of 2003. This was after FDA stepped in and halted all US gene therapy trials, involving another virus delivery system.[15] This one was based on *retroviruses*, which were a different approach from the modified adenoviruses employed previously. FDA had identified three US trials which were similar to one in France that all of a sudden appeared to be going badly wrong.

The retroviral technique was being explored in a French clinical trial at the Hôpital Necker Enfants Malades in Paris. The study, which had started a couple of years earlier, once again involved using gene therapy for severe combined immune deficiency disease. The investigators were following similar approaches to that adopted previously with Ashanta de Silva at the NIH in the US. The main difference was the use of retroviruses as the delivery mechanism.

They were also targeting a slightly different form of the disease, known as X-linked SCID, which is caused by a mutation in something called the IL2RG gene. This abnormality prevents the gene from producing a number of proteins essential for normal immune function. In this case, replacing the abnormal gene actually seemed to have worked well, with ten out of eleven children demonstrating reconstitution of their previously non-existent immune systems. This was allowing them to go on and enjoy essentially normal lives. To all intents and purposes they were cured.[16]

However, it was to become a story without a happy ending. Two of the children in the trial went on to develop a leukaemia like condition, about three years later, with one of them dying of it.[17] This complication was simply too great a risk, relative to any benefits the gene therapy treatment might offer. No parent would take those kinds of odds. It was also the event which prompted FDA into suspending related US trials.

The exact role played by the retrovirus was unclear. However it seemed as though the leukaemia was a consequence of some kind of genetic instability, caused by the vector itself. The symptoms of the leukaemia didn't become apparent for about two and a half years after the gene therapy had been given. But when the clinicians involved looked back over blood and bone marrow samples they had collected during the study, it became apparent that leukaemia like abnormalities were present as early as twelve months from the start of treatment. In both children, the leukaemic cells contained an exact copy of the genetic material of the retrovirus which had been used. It had become incorporated into the cells' chromosomes.[17]

Leukaemia is a disease characterised by chromosomal and genetic abnormalities. In these children, the inserted retrovirus must somehow have disturbed the genes already present on the chromosome, tipping them into a malignant malfunction. It was a potent demonstration of just how exploratory this technology was and how poorly characterised and unpredictable the risks really were.

Interfering with biological processes at the fundamental level of the gene was not as straightforward as it may have originally appeared. As with most things to do with gene therapy, it appeared to be one step forwards and two or three steps back.

The blighted reputation the technology was developing wasn't exactly helped when yet *another* patient died in a gene therapy trial in 2007.

Jolee Mohr from Illinois was a thirty six year old mother, with a five year old daughter. She suffered from rheumatoid arthritis and although disabled, was managing to lead a fairly normal life with conventional treatment. She was an active gardener and frequent volunteer at county fairs. A photograph the day before she received the gene therapy, showed her in a bikini on a speedboat.

And yet she succumbed to overwhelming fungal disease, after taking part in the trial with an *adeno-associated virus*. This was yet another virus vehicle, carrying a gene designed to reduce inflammation in arthritis sufferers. It was injected directly into the affected joint. Somehow though, the therapy appeared to have wiped out the entire immune system, leaving her wide open to fatal infections. With her body unable to defend itself, she died of multi-organ failure.

Ironically, the company running the trial was the same Targeted Genetics from Seattle, who'd acquired Genovo seven years earlier.[18]

Subsequently it transpired that the entire study had been intended to assess the *safety* of this particular gene therapy, with no real prospect of the participants deriving any benefit. Jolee's husband, Robb, claimed she had been unaware of this at the time of agreeing to take part in the trial. That was despite signing a fifteen page informed consent document, which was supposed to provide her with all this information. It was however far too complex for her to take it all in.

As with Jesse Gelsinger almost a decade earlier, the death ignited a public debate about the ethics of gene therapy. The technology was on trial, as was the way in which studies with it were being conducted.

Inevitably Arthur Caplan, the bioethicist from Pennsylvania, popped up during the debate. His view, in amongst all the emotive hysteria, was however a well balanced assessment.[19]

"If research is to advance, including gene therapy but also embryonic stem cell research and other novel therapies, then someone has to go first, after all the animal testing and lab work have been done. Those first subjects face very real risks, including death. But there is nothing anyone can do to completely eliminate those risks."

With three deaths in three different trials, it was all too evident that the risks of gene therapy couldn't be eliminated. Caplan provided a bleak assessment of what had been achieved so far.

"The irony of gene therapy is that despite its name, it has achieved little in the past decade in terms of therapy but has, rather, been associated with serious problems, including deaths."

However, like all those involved with the technology, he remained a proponent of carrying on.

"Jolee Mohr's death is a horrible tragedy. It should not, however, end research on gene therapy, which may be the only way to treat a variety of ailments and diseases. That death should, however, cause us to re-examine whether we are adequately protecting the heroes who help medicine make progress."

The research has continued since then and measures to protect patients have improved. However, because of all these setbacks, to date no gene therapy has received FDA approval. There is in fact only one approach which has ever reached the market. And that was right the way around the other side of the world, about as far away as you could possibly get from the disasters of the US. It was in China, as it happened.

Gendicine was approved by the State Food and Drug Administration of China (SFDA) in 2003, for use in patients with head and neck cancer. This is an unusually common malignancy in that country, with over three hundred thousand new cases diagnosed each year. It generally carries a very poor prognosis despite treatment with surgery, usually combined with chemotherapy or radiotherapy.

Gendicine was developed during a five year clinical programme by a company called Shenzhen SiBiono GeneTech, based in Shenzhen in Southern China's Guangdong Province. Most of the clinical work was undertaken at the Beijing Cancer Hospital. That's not a fun place to spend any time in.

Gendicine uses an adenovirus to deliver a gene called the *p53 tumor suppressor gene.*[20] In normal cells, as the name suggests, this plays a vital role in preventing abnormal cellular growth but it is often defective in many tumor types, allowing them to proliferate uncontrollably.

The drug is injected directly into the tumor mass itself, which is the most effective way of delivering the viral vector to the cancer tissue.

Whether Gendicine actually works or not is difficult to determine. It doesn't help that much of the clinical data is published only in Chinese. There are also some substantial differences in design and interpretation between Chinese clinical trials and those conducted in more western territories.

Over there, the doctors have a tendency to give the drug and then decide amongst themselves whether it seems to be working or not. It involves a lot of smoke filled rooms. They don't appear to have a need for the restrictive statistical rules or awkward advisory panels we have burdened ourselves with in the West.

However, it does appear, on the basis of the evidence available, that Gendicine combined with radiotherapy could possibly be producing higher response rates and more prolonged disease free intervals than radiotherapy alone.[21] That said, it isn't in use anywhere else in the world. The data just isn't credible or convincing enough. The fact that it appears to work in China is no guarantee of the same thing happening elsewhere.

In fact, five years later a small biotech company called Introgen Therapeutics, based in Austin, Texas, tried unsuccessfully to pull off something very similar in the US. They filed with FDA in 2008 for approval of Advexin, which was also an adenovirus based p53 gene therapy for head and neck cancer.[22]

Despite the striking similarity to Gendicine, FDA wouldn't even accept the application for review. They weren't going to waste their time reading the submission, let alone give any consideration to approving it.[23] In their opinion, there were just too many deficiencies and unanswered questions.

The only thing left open to Introgen was to file for bankruptcy shortly afterwards.

For this kind of very advanced technology, FDA appeared to be building a Great Wall around themselves, at the same time as the Chinese were busy forging ahead. China stole a march again, two years after Gendicine, when they approved the world's first *oncolytic virus* in 2005. A company called Shanghai Sunway Biotech was given marketing authorisation for a virus known as H101.

Oncolytic virotherapy was a slightly different approach from gene therapy.[24] It still used an adenovirus but this time without a therapeutic gene inserted into it. Instead, the virus was modified to attack cancer cells and destroy them directly, through the process of viral replication itself. The virus would insinuate itself into the cell and literally blow it apart, having stimulated a frenzy of destructive self-division. The clever twist though, was that the alterations to the virus meant it couldn't replicate in normal cells. The non-malignant tissue was therefore left well alone.

H101 was also intended for use in head and neck cancer and seemed to double the response rate from forty per cent to an incredible eighty per cent, when it was added on top of conventional chemotherapy.[25] This seemed impressive but again, no one outside of China was sure what to make of the data with H101.

It didn't help that it was virtually identical to another oncolytic virus called Onyx-15,[26] which had belonged to the American biotech company Onyx. Unfortunately, it had been unceremoniously dumped by them part way through Phase III trials. This had gone on to create an erroneous impression amongst many that Onyx-15 didn't work.

However, the real reason for the discontinuation was that Pfizer had acquired Onyx's development partner at the time, the pharmaceutical company Warner Lambert, in 2000. Subsequently, the programme had failed to survive a rationalisation of the merged companies assets. Unable to find the funding themselves, Onyx had been forced to abandon a study which might otherwise have provided a definitive answer as to whether or not this approach had clinical efficacy.

Had the West therefore missed a trick with Onyx-15, or had the Chinese tripped up with H101? Like Gendicine and gene therapy, the waters remain muddy and murky.

Gene therapy therefore still awaits the ultimate validation of a US or European regulatory approval. In cancer at least, this still appears a long way off. Despite that, gene therapy remains an enormously active area of optimism and research. In parallel with the targeted therapeutic revolution of the 1980s, the emergence of gene therapy in the 1990s is a consequence of man's ability to take the fight against cancer (and other serious diseases) to a higher level of sophistication, based on the new biology of the molecular era.

The promise of the approach, battered and bruised though it may be, is attested to by the sheer number of trials that have been undertaken so far. Between 1989 and 2012, there have been a staggering one thousand eight hundred and forty three gene therapy clinical trials worldwide, with more than three and a half thousand patients having been treated. Two thirds of the studies have been in cancer, with the rest involving vascular diseases or AIDS and other infectious diseases.[27]

The gene therapy train now has an almost unstoppable momentum. The fervent hope of all those involved is that another catastrophe doesn't derail it yet again.

XIII

Against this background of pitfall and promise, success and setback, where did Oxford BioMedica fit in and what did they want with us? And more to the point, what might we be able to get out of them?

The biggest problem with gene therapy appeared to be in actually *delivering* the gene, in a safe way, to wherever its ultimate destination in the body was. And that was where the OBM people thought they had an angle. And not just an angle. More like a protractor, loaded with promise. A whole geometry set in fact.

If you wanted to cure a disease, such as a particular cancer, with gene therapy then first you needed to sort out which genes were missing or had malfunctioned, to cause the disease in the first place. That was becoming easier with time, given that cancer was increasingly being characterised as a disease of disordered genetics. Assuming you had identified a single gene defect, then you would next need to manufacture a normal copy of that gene. This again has increasingly become a relatively straightforward technology.

The Human Genome Project[28] now already nearly a decade old, has identified the structure of all of the twenty one thousand or so normal genes that a human possesses. The public availability of this database, and recent US legal rulings that genes can't be patented, because they are essentially products of nature, makes it easy to access the information necessary to work out how to manufacture any given gene.

Putting genes together in the test tube has also become a routine laboratory procedure. Well, at least if you happen to be a highly skilled molecular biologist with decades of experience and expertise.

So those were the easy bits. The struggle was in transporting the gene to its target. You couldn't just inject the gene by itself into the blood stream and hope for the best. It would be exposed to all sorts of destructive forces, such as the enzymes lurking there, waiting to specifically eat up any stray DNA they may come across.

And then there was the problem of how the gene would know where to direct itself to, assuming it survived long enough to have to worry about that. Even if, by chance, it did somehow arrive at the right place in the end, there was still the challenge of how the gene would manage to get into the cell and find its way to the nucleus in the centre, where all the other genes were located.

Despite all these theoretical limitations, the *naked DNA* approach had in fact been tried out in the clinic. Attempts had been made to deliver genes by themselves. Unsurprisingly, the results were disappointingly bad. The gene definitely needed some help on this incredible journey and fortunately nature seemed to have a solution to hand. This was the *virus*.

Viruses are the cause of a whole host of human diseases ranging from the trivial, such as the common cold, to the decidedly serious such as smallpox or AIDS. What they all have in common however, is that the virus *alone* can't divide and reproduce. By itself, it is effectively biologically inert. To be able to propagate, a virus has to infect a person and then insert itself into the host's own DNA. It then subsequently uses that machinery to divide and reproduce itself.

It is a pretty neat trick of nature. The virus can travel light, without having to carry around all the machinery of replication. It then invades and hijacks the host, turning it into a factory to manufacture millions of viral progeny, which can go on to infect other cells in turn.

Whilst viruses are normally detrimental and dangerous pathogens, their ability to penetrate a foreign cell and insert their own genes are exactly what's needed in gene therapy. It offers a way of actually delivering a gene to its final destination.

Much endeavour has been directed therefore at trying to modify viruses by removing most of their own genes, especially the ones associated with disease. This then leaves room to replace them with the human gene of interest. After that, it's possible to inject the manipulated virus into the patient, leaving it to travel to its ultimate destination. Here it penetrates into the cell and inserts its whole payload, including the desired human gene, into the host's existing gene structure.

Having done this, the remaining viral genes (the ones you didn't remove at the outset) send signals to kick start the process of genetic replication. This is exactly the same as if it were a normal virulent pathogen. The host's cellular machinery then obligingly manufactures multiple copies of all the inserted genes, producing large numbers of the desired one along the way. And that is exactly what you want.

The technique of using viruses to deliver human genes like this, is called *transduction*. If you can pull it off effectively, then that should be more than enough to allow gene therapy to do its job.

There is however an art to manipulating the viruses, which are technically called *vectors*. The skill is in finding the right balance. Emasculate a virus too much and you run the risk of reducing its ability to invade target cells and insert itself into them. On the other hand, it you don't weaken it enough, the virus might retain its original disease causing properties and run amok, once injected into someone.

That was aside from all the potential problems of the major immune response viruses and viral particles were capable of provoking. These could have fatal consequences, as was so graphically shown by the cases of Jesse Gelsinger and Jolee Mohr. Whatever approach you tried therefore, it probably wasn't going to be straightforward.

The difficulties with optimising viruses have spurred research into other approaches to the tricky problem of delivery.

One of these consists of coating the gene in an artificial lipid sphere called a liposome, which is then capable of passing the gene through the outer membrane of target cells. There are innumerable other innovative approaches too, even including the creation of an artificial forty seventh chromosome (in addition to the forty six we normally have) which would be able to carry an enormous amount of genetic information.

However, the diversity of these different approaches is probably a reflection of the inadequacy of each one individually. Currently the viral approach to delivery, imperfect though it may be, remains the general focus of attention. That was certainly the case at OBM, where they had developed a unique expertise in this most challenging of technologies.

A whole variety of different virus types have been tried as gene delivery but most experience has been with four particular classes. These differ mainly in terms of how much genetic material they normally contain and what its detailed structure is like.[29]

Retroviruses are a group which includes the AIDS virus, *adenoviruses* cause coughs and colds, *adeno–associated viruses* are a broadly similar group, although not normally causing diseases in man and *herpes simplex viruses* are responsible for cold sores, amongst other things.

Each has technical advantages and disadvantages, with proponents and detractors variously vying for supremacy. The biggest difference between them is the extent to which the viruses take over the host machinery and exactly how much of a trace they leave behind in the host's own chromosomes.

OBM were firmly in the retroviral camp. They were working on one particular group of viruses within the overall retroviral family. These were called *lentiviruses*. They had the theoretical advantage of being able to carry a large amount of genetic information, thus allowing the transport of more than one gene, if necessary. This made them useful in diseases which might have a multigenetic origin. They were also very efficient transducers, as they could hitch a ride on to both host cells which were actively dividing and also those which weren't.

This was a potentially very useful characteristic, as some other virus types could only survive and replicate in host cells that were in the process of division already. They couldn't infect stationary or static cells. It was an important distinction because some parts of the body, such as the liver, were in a constant state of division, replication and repair, whilst others, such as the brain, had cells which were normally quiescent and non-dividing. Viruses without the lentiviral flexibility wouldn't be able to work in these more dormant places.

The other big upside of being able to get genes into non dividing cells was the possibility of producing a much longer lasting effect than the very short lived responses, which had plagued gene therapy so far. In rapidly dividing cells, it is harder for the viruses to introduce their invading genes in an orderly and stable way into the host chromosomes. That task is much easier to achieve in cells which are quiescent. It's like trying to jump on to a fast moving treadmill. It's much harder to do than stepping on to one which hasn't started moving yet.

Inserted genetic material is more stable and will survive for much longer in non-dividing cells. There is therefore the possibility of producing an adequate effect with just one course of gene therapy. This is in marked contrast to the multiple treatment cycles which appear to have been required so far in more active tissues.

OBM had a leading edge in the use of lentiviruses in gene therapy and a broad platform technology around this, which they called *LentiVector*. They hadn't however applied any of their technology to cancer, which was generally a rapidly dividing disease. Instead they were aiming at something called *Parkinson's disease* as the starting point for their lentiviral lift off.

This was a different proposition altogether, presenting challenges all of its own.

XIV

Parkinson's disease is a neurological condition, first described by the London physician Dr James Parkinson in his 1817 publication, *An Essay on the Shaking Palsy*. Occurring mostly in people over fifty, it is an incurable and progressively worsening condition characterised by uncontrollable tremor, rigidity and slowness of movement. Usually starting as nothing more than an inconvenience, it could, over a number of years, end up in complete incapacity and a wretched loss of bodily control.

The remorseless nature of the disease is still best depicted by Parkinson's original description of a patient in the grips of its terminal stages.[30]

"As the debility increases, the tremulous agitation becomes more vehement. It now seldom leaves him for a moment; but even when exhausted nature seizes a small portion of sleep, the motion becomes so violent as not only to shake the bed-hangings but even the floor and sashes of the room.

The slops with which he is attempted to be fed, with the saliva, are constantly trickling from the mouth. The power of articulation is lost. At the last, constant sleepiness, with slight delirium and other marks of extreme-exhaustion announce the wished-for release."

This was a serious and unpleasant condition. It was palsy *plus*.

The underlying cause was degeneration of a particular nervous pathway within the brain called the *nigro-striatal system*. This was a part of the central nervous system vital to the initiation and control of movement. For reasons that weren't full understood, in Parkinson's disease the nigro-striatal nerve cells (neurones) slowly died away over time. They stopped producing an important chemical transmitter called *dopamine*, which was essential for keeping the brain's movement control centres working. This lack of dopamine was responsible in turn, for all the terrible symptoms of the condition.

Treatment consisted mainly of trying to replace the patient's missing dopamine, in the hope of restoring a normal flow of electrical activity in the affected areas of the brain. This was far from perfect though. The dopamine like drugs that were used had to somehow travel all the way to the nigro-striatal area, which was buried deep in the base of the brain. Their effects were also short lived and so patients needed to take them a number of times a day, sometimes as frequently as every couple of hours.

The best way to deliver these drugs would have been to administer them directly into the brain, at the site where they were actually needed. But it's not possible to go around injecting things into peoples' heads five or ten times a day. Instead, the drugs came as pills or tablets which were swallowed, after which the chemicals had to make their way through the stomach to the blood stream and on to the brain.

This meant it was necessary to give a *large* amount of drug at the outset, to have a chance of a *small* amount reaching its final distant destination in the depths of the brain. It was like trying to fill a thimble with water from a hose pipe, held on the other side of the room. There was going to be a lot of spillage before it was full up. And that *spillage* was the problem with the dopamine drugs. The vast majority of any given dose didn't make it to the brain, seeping out into the rest of the body instead. This resulted in a range of serious side effects, which limited the value of the drugs in improving the patient's overall lot.

Things were made worse by another big problem which occurred, when trying to treat neurological conditions, like Parkinson's disease. This was something called the *blood brain barrier*. Because the brain is both so valuable and so vulnerable, nature has evolved to cloak it in multiple mantles of protection. One of these is a physico-chemical blanket wrapped around

329

the brain and protecting it from toxic chemicals getting in from the blood stream. This blood brain barrier is a sort of Hadrian's Wall keeping invaders at bay.

Whilst it is very effective at doing this, in the process it also prevents a large number of useful drugs penetrating into the brain from the bloodstream, thus substantially limiting the ability to treat diseases occurring there.

Dopamine is unfortunately one of the drugs which are blocked by the blood brain barrier and so it can't be used in patients with Parkinson's disease. Instead, there is a need to employ a closely related drug called *L-Dopa*. This has the big advantage that it can get into the brain. However, it also has the distinct disadvantage that it then has to be converted into dopamine to actually work. Once in the brain, L-Dopa can be turned into dopamine but *crucially* only by the neurones of the nigro-striatal system. They alone have the necessary chemical mechanism to perform the transformation.

But these are also the very nerve cells dying away, due to the underlying Parkinson's disease. The more these neurones degenerate and disappear, the less dopamine the remaining ones are able to synthesise and so the less effective the L-Dopa becomes. This results in a terrible paradox. As the patient's condition progresses and they need drug therapy more and more, at the same time their brains become less and less able to benefit from it.

Patients with advanced Parkinson's disease therefore tended to end up substantially disabled and out of time, as far as treatment options were concerned. This made them ideal candidates, for something as experimental as gene therapy. They had little to lose and any benefit they derived could only be a bonus.

Well, at least that was the theory.

XV

OBM were running a Phase I trial in France with Parkinson's patients, using their gene delivery technology. Because the brain wasn't a rapidly dividing tissue, it should be a suitable candidate to maximise the potential advantages of the lentiviral approach.

They had somehow even managed to load not one but *three* genes into their lentiviral vector, which was no mean achievement. The whole thing, the virus along with the genes, was called *ProSavin*. The idea was that the newly delivered genes would re-establish the damaged neurones ability to synthesise dopamine.

In monkey models of the disease (where the monkeys underwent surgical destruction of the nigro-striatal system, to mimic the spontaneous degeneration which occurred in patients) a single injection of ProSavin had

330

improved symptoms for up to twenty four months. That was an impressive effect in anyone's book. There was no doubt about that.

But it came with one big cost attached. The ProSavin virus had to be injected *directly* into the site of the nigro-striatal system in the brain. There was no other way to get it there. And unfortunately, these neurones were situated deep down in the brain, making the procedure an intricate neurosurgical process. It was bad enough in monkeys but a hugely more complicated proposition altogether in patients.

This was one of the biggest problems with all types of gene therapy. Getting it to the right place. Once it was where it was meant to go, the virus vector could penetrate the cell and hijack the genetic machinery inside. But first it had to be delivered to whichever part of the body happened to be harbouring the damaged or missing genes. This was a challenge of variable dimensions, depending on just how accessible any particular body part might be.

In the case of a condition like cystic fibrosis, (a gene defect affecting many parts of the body but predominantly the lungs), the virus could be given as an aerosol breathed into the chest, in just the same way as other drugs for lung disorders. For an eye disease, the virus could be injected directly into the back of the eye. Not something for the squeamish to dwell on but nevertheless still a straightforward procedure.

In the OTCD trial in Philadelphia, the virus had been delivered by injecting it into the main artery supplying the liver. Not quite so straightforward but still a relatively manageable undertaking in skilled hands. And of course for many malignancies, it was possible to inject directly into the tumor itself. That's how Gendicine was being used, to treat head and neck cancer in China.

But injecting into the depths of the brain? That was something else altogether.

This would involve performing a procedure known as *stereotactic surgery* on the brain. If it sounded complicated, that's because it was. But it did allow access to deep structures, far down in the depths of the cerebral chasm, with a pinpoint precision.

The technique involved immobilising the patient's head, by attaching a metal frame to it using pins pressed firmly against the bones of the skull. After that, the frame was bolted to the operating table so that any movement of any sort, however small, was physically impossible. The surgeon then drilled a tiny hole, about the size of a piece of spaghetti, through the skull and into the brain itself.

These were the easy bits. The harder part was guiding a long needle through the metal frame and the hole in the skull and then all the way down into the brain to access the nigro-striatal system, hopefully avoiding damaging everything else it might encounter along the way.

To help achieve this, the patient's head is scanned, just before the operation, taking advantage of highly advanced imaging techniques, which use the head frame as a fixed point of reference. From this, a three dimensional system of internal coordinates of the whole brain, relative to the head frame, can be calculated with the help of sophisticated computer programmes.

Again using the head frame as a reference, the surgeon can then work out *external* coordinates for where he wants to get to *internally* and guide the needle accordingly, working to a sub millimetre accuracy.

You could think of it as a very advanced form of orienteering, with the head frame as a kind of three dimensional compass. But obviously the penalties for getting lost are a lot higher.

This technique formed the basis of the OBM clinical study with ProSavin. Patients would have the virus injected directly into the brain, using stereotactic surgery. In the hands of those skilled enough, this is relatively straightforward, at least in neurosurgical terms. It is however obviously a different proposition from swallowing a handful of tablets every day, which is what these patients had been used to up until then.

Which may be why the trial had been progressing at a *very* slow pace. There was a certain amount of effort required to convince patients to undergo an operation in the depths of their brain, with all the risks that entailed, for an experimental treatment which had no guarantee of leaving them with any benefit.

But nonetheless, OBM had been plugging away since the end of 2007, when the trial started. By the time they turned up at our door, in the summer of 2010, there were about six patients in the study, who'd been treated at higher doses of ProSavin. More importantly, all six seemed to have tolerated the treatment without anything disastrous happening, which was always a good sign where gene therapy was involved.

Those who'd entered the study early on had now been followed up for getting on for a year and a half and some were showing promising signs of an improvement in their condition.

All in all, it wasn't a bad story to be able to tell. ProSavin seemed to have something going for it, despite the vestigially early stage it was at.

OBM also had four other programmes involving their lentiviral technology. These were all for eye disorders, where the gene carrying virus would be injected directly to the back of the eyeball.

Two were for very rare causes of blindness called Usher Syndrome and Stargardt Disease. Another was to prevent rejection after corneal transplants, in people with cataracts. The final one was for something called age related macular degeneration, which was a major cause of blindness in older people. These programmes were known respectively as *UshStat, StarGen, EncorStat* and *RetinoStat*. Together they formed an interesting portfolio, with much potential promise. However, none of them had reached the clinic yet, making it hard to assess their prospects.

Later on, OBM would also unveil an additional LentiVector programme called *MoNuDin*, aimed at treating the degenerative disorder motor neurone disease, whose most famous sufferer is Stephen Hawking. It showed the diversity with which their technology could be directed.

And so here was a company with what might well be the leading edge technology in gene therapy anywhere in the world and with five or more programmes on the go. And yet it was struggling to achieve the recognition it should have commanded with the capital markets. OBM wasn't a blooming company, in that sense.

Admittedly, gene therapy was a long haul, for investors as well as everyone else. There had been many setbacks in the past. This created an aura of doubt and scepticism around even the brightest of stars in this particular firmament. But on the other hand, it was also a technology which many people felt was poised to come of age and put its troubled history behind it.

There was even the prospect of the first ever *Western* gene therapy approval. AMT Biopharma was a Dutch company which had recently submitted a gene therapy product for approval by the European regulatory authority, the EMA.

Glybera aimed to replace a missing gene in a disorder called Lipoprotein Lipase Deficiency (LPLD). LPLD led to the absence of a protein necessary for breaking down fat globules in the blood stream. This could result in inflammation of the pancreas, diabetes and heart disease, amongst other complications.

At the time, *Glybera* appeared to be struggling a bit with the regulators but were it to eventually be approved, then this would undoubtedly be a big boost for the whole gene therapy sector, Oxford BioMedica included.[31]

And yet despite the promise seemingly just over the horizon, OBM was having a hard time. Like many other biotech companies, it was handicapped with a market capitalisation much less than it appeared to deserve. At times, this has been as low as thirty to forty million pounds. Given that it had about sixteen million in cash, this meant that all its technology put together was only being given a value of somewhere between fifteen and twenty five million pounds by the financial markets.

In other words, they didn't rate the company's prospects too highly. It was quite a lot like Antisoma in fact. And like Antisoma and many other companies, its depressed market capitalisation meant that Oxford BioMedica was struggling to raise any new money.

It's sometimes impossible to understand why the markets favour some companies and discriminate against others. One might get a much higher valuation than the next, when at first sight there wouldn't appear to be much to distinguish between them. But *sentiment* is often what seemed to drive the assessment of small biotechnology companies, more than anything else. And some of us had our own theory as to why the prevailing sentiment had been going against Oxford BioMedica in the recent past. It was, we felt, in large part down to a drug called TroVax.

XVI

TroVax was a vaccine, which expressed something called the *5T4 tumor antigen*. 5T4 was a protein which seemed to exist on the surface of many tumor cells but not on most normal ones.[32] It was analogous to nucleolin, in the case of AS1411. 5T4 should have been a flag, waving loud and clear that it was attached to a malignant cell.

Under normal circumstances, it would have alerted the immune system to its presence from miles away. However, tumors were able to deploy a variety of techniques to hide themselves from the body's immune defence system and so most of the time the 5T4 antigen went unnoticed and undetected, along with the associated malignancy. That's where TroVax came in.

The idea was that the 5T4 antigen on TroVax would activate the immune system to finally become aware of the 5T4 marker on malignant tissue. This would in turn initiate an attack on tumors carrying the marker on their surface, thus causing their eventual destruction. It would be as though TroVax were turning up the 5T4 volume on the tumor to a point where the immune system could finally hear it.

At Antisoma, we had generally been sceptical that the vaccine approach could work in cancer and we had stayed well away from it. There was no doubt that on the occasions when the body's immune defences did detect a cancer, they could mount a robust attack on it. The fact that this can occur spontaneously was one of the factors which had complicated our interpretation of the findings with AS1411 in kidney cancer. But these events were few and far between. We believed that tumors were so good at disguising and hiding themselves from the various components of the immune system, that even the added boost a vaccine might add wouldn't really help very much.

Maybe that was why there has only ever been one *therapeutic* vaccine approved for use in cancer, anywhere in the world. And that was in Russia, which doesn't really count. It's true that in the US, FDA have approved two vaccines for use in the *prevention* of cancer. Infection with the viruses Human Papilloma Virus (HPV) and Hepatitis B Virus (HBV) are implicated in the development of cervical and liver cancer respectively. Vaccines against these two viruses are used to prevent the infection and hence the subsequent risk of cancer.

But that is a very different proposition altogether from a *therapeutic* vaccine, directed against an already established tumor. Once a cancer had put down roots and started growing, it became a much harder biological target than trying to stop it germinating in the first place. Dealing with an existing tumor was effectively unproven territory for a vaccine. The fact that the Russians had their hands on one didn't really change that proposition too much.

Oncophage (vitespen) was a vaccine expressing a tumor marker called a *heat shock protein.*[33] These are normally occurring proteins, which are markedly elevated in many malignant diseases. A vaccine against them, such as Oncophage, might therefore make the cancerous cells more vulnerable and less viable.[34]

Oncophage was approved in Russia early in 2008 for patients with kidney cancer. It's intended for use in the very early stages of the disease, at the time it is first detected and the cancerous kidney is removed. The surgeon has to send part of the tumor to Antigenics, the US company to whom Oncophage belongs. They then use this tissue to manufacture a vaccine, specific for that particular individual's tumor characteristics.

This personalised vaccine is then subsequently returned to Russia to be administered to the patient. All of this shuttling back and forth makes Oncophage quite cumbersome to use in practice. These logistical difficulties with it aren't helped by the fact that outside of Russia, it's unclear how well Oncophage really works.

It didn't show any overall efficacy in an original Phase III trial in kidney cancer.[35] It also failed in a large skin cancer study.[36] Any apparent benefit in patients with kidney disease was only discovered after extensive *retrospective* examination of the study results.[37]

Going back over the data with a fine-tooth comb is an irresistible temptation after a big study has failed, on all the criteria which had been defined for it upfront. It's nearly always possible to pick out a subgroup which appears to have responded more favourably, if you try hard enough.

But this sort of exercise rarely cuts ice with a regulatory authority. They would argue that any such findings are likely to be nothing more than chance associations and usually of questionable clinical significance anyway. Coming up with data, after the event, showing your drug appears to work in left handed Librans, who are over six feet tall and have at some point in their lives lived in Milwaukee, isn't going to rescue a trial which has failed in all other respects.

And that was the problem with Oncophage. The results suggesting it worked in certain subsets of patients were dredged from the data in a way that convinced no one, except apparently the Russians. Antigenics must have had a fleet of trawlers working on it day and night. Oncophage was rejected outright by the European regulatory authorities in 2009. Similarly in the US, FDA had indicated that Oncophage was unapprovable, on the basis of the existing trial results. Even Antigenics' CEO, Garo Armen conceded in an interview in early 2010 that "the easiest thing for us right now would be to abandon Oncophage...but we have a moral responsibility."[38]

He didn't however make clear whether that responsibility was to patients or to Antigenics' shareholders. The latter group must have been somewhat puzzled as to what there was to show for the hundreds of millions of dollars invested so far in Oncophage.

So TroVax wasn't on the firmest of grounds, as far as the general approach of therapeutic vaccines was concerned. There wasn't exactly a lot of precedent. The jury was still definitely out. Except possibly for some of us at Antisoma. We'd already made our minds up some time ago that we didn't really rate TroVax. For as long as anyone could remember, if things were looking bad for us, we could derive comfort from reminding ourselves that it could be even worse. Whatever had gone wrong, at least we didn't have TroVax.

It was our lodestone, dragging us back to realism and reality.

XVII

Now and then, you just develop an antipathy to a drug in development, despite the fact that it's probably no better or worse than lots of others you have to deal with. In a world which should be driven by empirical observation, sometimes emotional overtone could come to exert just as big an influence.

Maybe it was the subjective uncertainty that complicated trying to decide whether a cancer drug was doing any good or not. Or maybe it was just a gut reaction. Sometimes you had an instinctive feeling that a drug wasn't going to make it. There wasn't any one thing you could point to. It was a composite of any number of small things, each of which individually you could probably live with but collectively they just coalesced into something that didn't resonate with you. These feelings may be irrational but sometimes they become irresistible too.

And they were the feelings some of us had about TroVax.

To be fair though, we had to acknowledge that as far as vaccines in general were concerned, the ground had shifted *slightly* in the last few years. There was some movement, at least as geologists would define that term.

In early 2010, FDA had approved a drug called *Provenge* for use in prostate cancer. It was a therapy which involved removing immune cells from the patient's blood, incubating them with certain prostate tumor proteins in a test tube and then returning the now activated cells to the patient. Once safely back home, they then went on to fire up the entire immune system.

Many people had started referring to this as a vaccine. It was however probably better described as a *cellular therapy*,[39] in that it entailed quite a lot of *ex vivo* manipulation of the patient's own immune cells. It differed therefore from vaccines, which you injected into the body and then left to their own devices.

Nevertheless, it was in the same broad arena and it was the first time FDA had approved something like this. They did so on the basis of a study showing that Provenge produced an overall survival of just under twenty six months, compared to a placebo group where survival was about twenty two months.[40]

Despite this seemingly impressive outcome, Provenge has struggled to gain acceptance, something which hasn't been helped by the ninety thousand dollar price tag. More fundamentally though, a significant number of clinicians are now questioning just how well Provenge actually works, if at all.

The argument being put forward is that it did better than placebo largely because the placebo group *underperformed*, rather than Provenge outperforming.[41] For some reason, those receiving placebo lived for a significantly shorter period than you'd normally expect for a group like that. If you did the study again therefore, you might see no difference a second time around. It's currently an unresolved controversy but it hasn't helped to put vaccine therapy on any firmer footing.

Whatever the real merits of TroVax though, Oxford BioMedica had spent a year and a half, up to the summer of 2008, running a large Phase III trial with it in patients with advanced kidney cancer. Called TRIST (TroVax Renal Immunotherapy Survival Trial) it was a study involving seven hundred and thirty three patients at over one hundred hospitals in the US and Europe.

It was looking at whether the addition of TroVax improved survival, when it was given along with one of three possible standard first line treatments these patients would have received anyway. The short answer was that it didn't and in the summer of 2008, OBM announced that the study's DSMB had recommended amending the trial to stop any further vaccinations with TroVax. An interim analysis of the data had suggested virtually no possibility of success.[42]

The DSMB did however recommend continuing to follow up the patients, minus the key TroVax component, as the data might still end up showing something scientifically useful. It wasn't quite clear exactly what that might be though.

Naturally, this didn't come as much of a surprise to many of us at Antisoma.

We weren't to know at the time, that a year and a half later we'd be in an even worse position with ASA404. But there was one big difference between us. When ASA404 fell apart with the ATTRACT I trial in lung cancer, we had little choice but to give up there and then. We grimly accepted what had happened and tried to move on. But OBM didn't seem to be able to do that with TroVax. They still felt there was something which could be retrieved from the fallen trial.

Despite the TRIST study having failed in its primary endpoint, OBM took the data and tortured it to pieces, trying to get it to give up a glimmer of something more positive. They must have put it on the rack, applied the thumbscrews and attached some electrodes all at the same time.

With most forms of torture, if you persist for long enough eventually you will elicit a confession of some sort. And so it was that almost a year after the initial DSMB decision, OBM revealed in July 2009 that they had discovered a small sub group, within the overall patient population, who appeared to do better on TroVax and to survive longer, compared to the group that didn't receive it.[43]

These included patients judged to have a more favourable prognosis at the outset, who had received the specific cytokine drug interleukin-2 as first line treatment and also had blood laboratory tests indicating good bone marrow function. It was unclear whether they'd ever lived in Milwaukee or not.

They were also able to subsequently come up with something called the "immune response surrogate" as a composite formula for predicting patients who might do well on TroVax.[44] It appeared to share the same basic principles as many of the techniques widely available to help pick the winning Lottery numbers each week.

To be fair to OBM though, maybe they had identified a genuine group, definable by these characteristics. At least some of this new information came from an analysis of differing patient subsets, which had been prospectively agreed up front. It was also biologically plausible that a drug reliant on the immune system, such as TroVax, would do better in patients whose bone marrow was in better shape. They were likely to have a more intact set of immune cells, capable of killing off the cancer. Even FDA conceded that point back in 2009.[43]

An alternative interpretation however would be that these were simply chance associations thrown up by going through the data too many times. If you stare into the darkness for long enough, sooner or later you'll start to believe you can see something out there in the shadows. And to some of us, TroVax still looked as though it belonged in the shadowy world inhabited by Oncophage.

The only way to tell for sure would be the passage of time and the generation of a significant new body of *prospective* clinical data. Which is what OBM may have been hoping for when they started an exploratory Phase II study in prostate cancer, just about the time we started talking to each other, back in late 2010. You had to admire their loyalty.

Unfortunately this study eventually came to an end in the autumn of

2012, when OBM finally gave up the ghost, after the trial struggled to recruit enough patients.[45] There were just too many other competing treatment choices around now. Seemingly, even those with terminal cancer and few other remaining options couldn't be persuaded to spend any of their precious remaining time on TroVax. Even the promise on offer from the *immune response surrogate* didn't seem to be sufficient compensation for them.

However, in the random roulette that is cancer medicine, there is always an argument for another throw of the dice and so TroVax is still under investigation in colorectal cancer, in a clinical trial being run by Cardiff University in the UK.

Never say never is a useful mantra in cancer medicine.

Despite the fact that hope never dies, to some of us at Antisoma, the drug appeared to be a millstone around their neck, which they'd be better off dumping. However, TroVax had a strong emotional energy behind it at OBM, just as AS1411 did at Antisoma. The 5T4 antigen itself had been discovered by scientists from CRUK, who were founding shareholders in OBM, way back in 1996. TroVax was part of the family jewels therefore, present for as long as anyone could remember.

That made it all the harder to get rid of, given the integral nature of its contribution to the very foundations of the company. In a situation like that, it would have been difficult to raise the question of whether TroVax may have had its day.

Or possibly that had nothing to do with it. Perhaps OBM just had access to the same crystal ball that seemed to inform some of our decisions about AS1411. Maybe in the long run their faith would be vindicated. We couldn't know but from the outside some of us were struggling to understand their strategy around TroVax. OBM's lacklustre share performance certainly suggested that for investors, the experience with TRIST hadn't exactly turned into a tryst either.

Furthermore, things weren't exactly helped either for OBM or us by the problems with *Ark*.

XVIII

Ark Therapeutics was another emerging gene therapy company. It was based in London, just off Oxford Street and also in Kuopio, which was in the middle of nowhere in Finland. Kuopio was best known as the home of the national delicacy, Finnish Fish Pastry. There wasn't much else that went on there. It was the kind of place where people spent a lot of time with reindeers.

The significance of Ark was that like the rest of us, it too had recently experienced the major setback of a spectacular Phase III failure. This one involved its biggest gene therapy programme, which was called *Cerepro*. Cerepro was otherwise known by the mouthful of *sitimagene ceradenovec* which was, as the name suggested, an adenovirus vector based gene therapy.[46] It was aimed at treating a highly malignant and exceptionally unpleasant brain tumor called a glioma. Patients stricken with this normally only survived months, whatever you did. It was a desperate diagnosis with an even worse prognosis. It was therefore another ideal candidate for gene therapy.

The Cerepro approach required the initial neurosurgical removal of the glioma, as would usually happen anyway. After that, the adenovirus vector was injected directly through the walls of the resulting cavity, into the surrounding *healthy* brain tissue. The virus carried a gene which became incorporated into the normal adjacent brain cells, causing them to start producing an enzyme called *thymidine kinase*. By itself this didn't do anything useful but the trick was to then give a drug called *ganciclovir* about five days later.

Ganciclovir was usually used to treat serious viral infections. When used alone, it wouldn't have any effect on a brain tumor. However, when it came across thymidine kinase, it was converted into a highly toxic molecule, which killed off actively dividing cells but left non-dividing ones alone. Because normal healthy brain cells didn't divide, they escaped unscathed. But any proliferating glioma cells, left behind after the surgery, were wiped out.

In theory, that should prevent the tumor from growing back again, which was the biggest problem with trying to treat the disease. However carefully the original tumor was resected, it was impossible to remove all of it without causing unacceptable damage to surrounding brain tissue. The microscopic fragments left behind inevitably resulted in the glioma re-establishing itself, usually within only a matter of months.

The real innovation of Cerepro was that the genes were introduced into *healthy* cells. Here they could continue working, almost indefinitely, to produce cancer killing chemicals. This was different from most gene therapy approaches, which were targeted at the *cancer* cells themselves. Which meant that when the cancer cell was eventually killed, the gene died with it. Cerepro was therefore a variant on the normal gene therapy approach of aiming to *replace* a defective gene in diseased cells with a normal one. Instead in this case, an *additional* gene was introduced into normal cells, resulting in the production of an extra substance, the enzyme thymidine kinase.

It was a great idea. The only problem was that it didn't seem to actually work that well.

Ark had completed a large Phase III, two hundred and fifty patient glioma trial, called the ASPECT study.[47] They claimed this showed that treatment with Cerepro delayed the onset of death or the need for further surgery, whichever came first. Both appeared to be useful effects of the drug, as neither event was exactly a welcome development. They submitted these results to the European regulatory authority, the European Medicines Agency (EMA), in 2008, hoping for approval to market Cerepro in the EU.

The EMA weren't overly impressed. The effects with Cerepro were lasting a little longer than forty days and forty nights but not by that much more. For a variety of technical reasons, largely related to the design of the ASPECT trial, the EMA were also insisting that another large Phase III trial would be needed, to get a better understanding of what Cerepro was really doing.

Ark initially protested loudly but eventually bowed to the inevitable and withdrew their EMA application at the beginning of 2010.[48] They didn't even bother submitting it to the US FDA. Without the funds themselves to do anything further, Cerepro was drowning and Ark were definitely marooned. They had enough remaining cash to tread water but that was about it.

And so there was now a triumvirate of wounded companies with a recent Phase III cancer catastrophe but which hadn't yet bled to death. Antisoma, Oxford BioMedica and Ark. All in the same boat, as it were. Each was discredited in the market place, trading at company values which gave little recognition to the remaining assets and each had enough cash to survive in the short term but not enough to get to a place of safety. If we were all in the same boat, then it was probably a lifeboat with enough fuel to escape the shipwreck but not enough to get to landfall.

Because the three companies were in a similar predicament, their prospects became lumped together in people's minds. It was as though they were all tied together by one leg. Whichever way one moved, it tended to drag the other two along as well. If one said they were going to pull off this or that and it didn't happen, then the ensuing disappointment and disillusion washed over the other two as well.

The obvious question now being asked was whether the three companies would be stronger if put together, rather than remaining apart. Could one, plus one, plus one add up to more than three?

It was certainly possible. We may all have had the same weaknesses, borne of failure but on the other hand, we also had differing strengths. Antisoma was still sitting on a Phase III programme with amonafide and those were always in short supply. Oxford BioMedica possibly held the key which would one day unlock the door to the riches of gene therapy. And Ark had the...*Kerraboot*.

In an act of extraordinary corporate diversity, in addition to dabbling in the science fiction of gene therapy, Ark also produced a range of wound care products. For some unfathomable reason, this included the *Kerraboot* which was a novel wound dressing that looked like a cross between a Christmas stocking and a ski boot. It was used for conditions like foot ulcers, frostbite, burns and the like. There were also other bizarrely misshapen items, such as the *Kerraglove*, the *Kerraped*, the *Kerraheel* and the *KerraMax* for application to various other parts of the anatomy.

These products might not have enjoyed the allure of more leading edge technologies but they were at least tangible objects you could see and point to. They weren't just promise and possibilities for the future, which is what the rest of us dealt in all day long. But of even greater importance, Ark also possessed something much more substantial that you could point to. They were the proud owners of a biological manufacturing facility in Kuopio, which was fully equipped to handle live viruses and produce gene delivery vectors for both itself and also third parties, on a contract manufacturing basis.

So we each had something to compliment the other. But even so, a love triangle was never going to be straightforward. Perhaps the more obvious arrangement would have been a relationship between OBM and Ark. But they didn't seem able to dance in time together and were forever treading on each other's toes. They just couldn't get a rhythm going. Just as opposites were supposed to attract, maybe in some strange way they were too similar to get on.

Both were squeezed together in close alignment in the gene therapy space, although with competing viral vectors. And from an investor perspective, putting together two companies, each with a similar core technology, might end up actually magnifying risk as much as mitigating it.

And so for one reason or another, it made sense for Oxford BioMedica to at least talk to us. It was part of the Brownian motion by which biotech companies constantly come into contact with one another, in the perpetual search for synergy and growth.

XIX

Glyn had already met John Dawson, OBM's relatively recently appointed CEO, a couple of times during June and July to sound each other out. CEOs of biotechnology companies did that all the time. Running one was often like an endless round of speed dating. There was nothing out of the ordinary in it. Things hadn't necessarily gone that well though. Partly this was because some of us were worried OBM appeared mainly interested in our cash.

Like all biotechnology companies, they were struggling to find other means of getting their hands on any. At that time, investors seemed unwilling to put funds into them at any sort of reasonable price. Like the rest of us, they were therefore looking for less direct ways of getting some new money. They may well have seen us as a very big piggy bank, ready to be raided.

That said, they did display some interest in amonafide. After all, a Phase III programme in full swing wasn't something you would lightly walk away from. But in many ways it would probably suit them just as well, if amonafide fell apart when the initial results became available. If that happened, there would be even more cash for them to grab. We wouldn't have to spend however many millions it might have been on keeping the US and European regulatory submissions moving forwards, with no guarantee of eventual success. Instead, that money could go straight into their pockets.

From our point of view though, there were just a couple of problems with things panning out that way. Firstly, if amonafide failed and OBM ran off with all the money, then they certainly wouldn't need Antisoma coming along for the ride. We definitely didn't like the idea of that. If we had any choice in the matter, we wanted a merger which didn't involve us all being shown the door. We could live with one or two strategic sacrifices but not with all of us falling on our swords.

Even if amonafide survived, OBM was the bigger company with the larger market capitalisation and it was reasonable to assume that John Dawson would come out on top as CEO, if we got together. Glyn was too woven into the fabric of Antisoma to contemplate a personal future without it. At least for the time being. He had the proprietorial passion of all good CEOs. None of the rest of us could blame him for that. In fact we wouldn't have respected him as much, if he'd seen it any way other than naked self-preservation. He was our man and we were rooting for him.

The other stumbling block was that we believed Oxford BioMedica would have to issue OBM shares to acquire Antisoma and its cash. We weren't sure how well that would sit with existing Antisoma shareholders. If they wanted to own shares in Oxford BioMedica, there was nothing stopping them going out and buying them directly. And very few had done this.

In fact there was a very limited overlap between our largest shareholders and theirs. So would we really be doing our investors a favour by spending a lot of our time and their money to essentially just swop their Antisoma shares for Oxford BioMedica ones, which they didn't appear to want in the first place?

And so throughout the early summer, we were endlessly evasive about OBM. We'd end up chasing round all sorts of other companies, here, there and everywhere. Companies we wouldn't really want to touch with a bargepole. Companies who didn't want to touch us with a bargepole. Companies with drugs for diseases we'd never even heard of. Companies with no drugs at all.

It didn't matter, as long as it wasn't Oxford BioMedica.

And it probably didn't help, given the delicacy of our internal dynamics, that Eric had suddenly decided he really liked the sound of Oxford BioMedica.

There had been an understated tension between Glyn and Eric for a while. It had probably been a good thing to begin with, a sort of constructive challenge between the two. Eric was fresh and new to the company whilst Glyn was, *well*, entrenched. There were bound to be some sparks between the arriviste and the ancien régime. The roles of CEO and Finance Director were those with the greatest degree of overlap, particularly in a public company like Antisoma. Inevitably friction points would develop between the two positions. But recently, the differences had started to become more obvious.

A month or so earlier, at the beginning of summer, Glyn and I were wandering one afternoon around Berkeley Square, in the middle of Mayfair. We were on our way to meet a hedge fund manager, in what would prove to be an ultimately unsuccessful attempt to extract an enormous sum of money, as an investment in some wheeze or other we had up our sleeve at the time. But we were early and so we ambled around the square, in and out of the Bentley and Porsche showrooms.

We were chatting, in the strained sort of way which seemed to characterise most of our dealings with one another, when the conversation turned to the immediate future and whether Eric or someone else might one day want to make a play for the CEO role. We were after all in parlous times and anything was possible.

"You can't trust anyone anymore," I muttered, running my eye covetously over a gorgeous jet black supercharged Bentley Continental GT, sitting proudly and imperiously in the window of the Jack Barclay showroom. But I already knew that, because Eric and I had chatted a few times about our corporate strategy, or, from some people's perspective, the seeming lack of it. It was a conversation most of the senior management had with one another now and then, given the circumstances we were in.

It was a tense time at Antisoma, obviously, and like many of us, Eric seemed perplexed about what direction we were heading in. Part of it was that Glyn and Eric seemed to have very different management styles.

Eric appeared to like sorting things out on the spot, there and then, even if it meant that the impact of his remedies didn't always have the opportunity of being tempered by the passage of a little bit of time. Eric was a hanger and a flogger. Probably even if you hadn't done anything wrong. By contrast, Glyn was a liberal appeaser, made of less stern stuff. He liked to stay his hand and keep all his options open.

But Eric also had a sense of urgency to him. He could feel that time was running out and that if we were ever going to act to regain control of our fate, it had to be sooner rather than later. In fact, anytime right about now would do nicely.

Although it might risk pissing off Glyn, Eric liked the idea of Oxford BioMedica, not because he thought gene therapy was the way of the future but because straightaway he could see cost savings. And potentially big ones. More than anyone else, Eric could see, almost on a daily basis, our precious cash slipping away through our fingers and he was desperate to conserve it. Left to his own devices, Eric would have fired most of us there and then, shut down the Boston side of things and moved us all out of the now admittedly overly palatial London offices we were rattling around in. He'd have us in a lock up, on the wrong side of Heathrow, in the blink of an eye.

You could see his point of view. Eric felt the need to act. He was a hard headed businessman, who regarded coming to work every day as war. And right now we definitely had a battle on our hands to stay alive. In his eyes, the rest of us were nothing more than a bunch of leisurely libertines, incapable of mounting a defence, let alone going on the attack.

He was worried that we would dance around any possibility which Oxford BioMedica might represent until it was too late and they found someone else they liked the sound of better.

Apart from the synergies, consolidations and cost cuttings that his spreadsheets showed him, Eric liked the OBM idea because it would be a catalyst. It would be doing *something*. It would snap us out of the somnolence he feared we were slipping into. It was also not impossible that it might put him in *de facto* command, if things went the right way.

He could see a structural symmetry in the two companies getting together. Were we to merge, we could obviously rationalise all the duplicate functions, such as communications, finance, business development, the Board, administration, IT and so on, saving a lot of money along the way. Eric's idea was to keep our development teams intact, located somewhere in London and leave the rest of the company in Oxford. We could then keep amonafide going, if it was still alive and probably take over their development programmes too. They didn't seem to have many people of their own to do that sort of stuff.

The fact that we knew fuck all about gene therapy or neurology didn't bother us too much. It couldn't possibly be worse that trying to develop a cancer drug. As a combined entity, we would also have a new story to tell to investors and maybe we could even raise some cash into the bargain. Looked at like that, it didn't sound too bad an idea. As long as you put to one side the fact that by and large we didn't rate TroVax, we didn't really know what to make of gene therapy, there were two CEOs potentially vying for one position and we suspected all they wanted from us was our cash. They also had a well established senior management and so it was unclear how much room there would really be at the inn for the rest of us either.

The more Eric warmed to the idea of OBM though, the more Glyn seemed to cool down. Glyn preferred to keep all his options open for as long as he could. He didn't like to commit until he had to. If Eric's preference was to strike whilst the iron was hot, Glyn was more comfortable building the fire slowly until he felt the temperature was just right.

However, given that we weren't exactly fighting off approaches from elsewhere, the internal momentum to at least meet with them grew to a point where we all eventually had to bow to the inevitable. Glyn agreed to invite the Oxford BioMedica people down to London to swap some information.

It didn't sound very much, the idea of just getting together for a chat. But once you let someone get their foot in the door, then you never knew how far open they might manage to push it. Also, psychologically, it was like starting an affair. It didn't matter how small the initial move was, it was the fact that you'd done *anything* at all that really counted. Fundamental boundaries had already been transgressed. It was impossible to then step back within them.

XX

One day in August therefore, a small contingent from OBM duly arrived at our offices in Chiswick, having taken the train down from Oxford. There were four or five of them, with John Dawson leading the way of course.

We sat on opposite sides of the table, eying each other up. They probably weren't that interested in hearing about amonafide and we weren't exactly desperate to learn more about TroVax. We were there thinking: *Well, how might this work out. He seems alright but I'm not sure I could work with that one.* That sort of stuff. Were they human, did they have our sense of humour? Was there cohesiveness?

We were all very different individuals at Antisoma but most of the time we glued together pretty seamlessly as a team. Well, up until recently at least. Were they the same? Most eyes were on Glyn and John of course but more so on John. If this thing was ever going to work, he would most likely be the one having to orchestrate it and keep it all hanging together. Did he look like he could do that?

He wasn't giving much away.

The OBM contingent were an impressive team. They certainly knew their stuff, as became apparent very early on. But there wasn't exactly a huge amount of energy or drive emanating from their side of the table. Their finance person didn't say a single word throughout. Perhaps he was too busy amortising all our visible assets. Or maybe they were all just tired after the journey.

Admittedly, they weren't on home turf and it was an away match. However, they'd definitely been up for the fixture and we at least expected them to play an aggressive attacking game, with their captain leading from the front. But instead of a good old kick around and a bit of contact sport, it was more like a game of Christmas cribbage, with a group of unfamiliar elderly relatives.

But then the biotechnology industry was largely populated by relatively anodyne individuals. It was that kind of business. It wasn't very rock and roll, most of the time. The colourful ones tended to come to prominence for all the wrong reasons.

Like Sam Waksal. He'd been the founder and CEO of ImClone in the US, which had developed what was to become the best selling cancer drug Erbitux,[49] after it was eventually approved by FDA in 2004. Waksal ended up receiving a seven year prison sentence and three million dollar fine in 2003 for insider trading, securities fraud, bank fraud, obstruction of justice and perjury. He had failed to make public that FDA were about to reject Erbitux in 2001, the first time it was submitted to them. He'd received a tip off in advance and had used the information for the personal gain of himself and others, by selling a whole load of stock before the price collapsed. Household names in the US, such as Martha Stewart, were dragged into the ensuing controversy and Waksal became the subject of widespread public notoriety, if not infamy.

Then there was Lars Bildman, former CEO of the American division of Swedish company Astra, before it became Astra Zeneca. He was accused in 1996 of diverting over two million dollars of company money for personal use, including improvements to *three* of his houses. He simply had the same contractors who were working on an extension to Astra's Westborough, Massachusetts headquarters, do the work for him and then bill Astra for it. He later attempted to cover it up by destroying company documents and trying to persuade the contractors to do the same.

And that was without the allegations of wild partying, yachts, fifteen hundred dollar top end prostitutes and firing older female employees, in order to replace them with much younger ones. A pretty normal day at the office in fact.

Bildman eventually found himself on the end of a fifteen million dollar lawsuit from Astra USA, as well as a string of sexual harassment charges from disgruntled former staff members. According to Astra court documents, Bildman attempted to avoid complicity by concocting "tales of conspiracy involving ex-KGB agents and competitors...in a last-ditch effort to distract attention from the real wrongdoer, Bildman himself."[50] It was too lurid a story to be credible though. It sounded even worse than having to deal with FDA or the EMA.

Bildman also landed a twenty one month prison sentence in 1998, after federal authorities charged him with thirty five counts of fraud and tax evasion. Astra were caught up in the mess too, eventually having to pay out almost ten million dollars in 1998, to settle charges brought by the US Government. At the time, this was the largest sexual harassment case in the entire history of the Equal Employment Opportunity Commission.

The last anyone had heard, Bildman was living in Vermont on Social Security.

The bad boy list was probably topped however by Jonathan Nyce, CEO of the New Jersey biotech company EpiGenesis. He was sentenced to eight years in prison in 2005 for killing his thirty four year old wife Michelle, whom he'd originally met as a Filipino pen pal. He clubbed her to death in his garage with a baseball bat, after it turned out she'd been having an affair with the family gardener. He then tried, very ineptly, to disguise it as a car accident, by leaving her body at the wheel of their SUV, which he'd driven down an embankment and into a creek. It was intended to look as though she'd slipped off the adjacent icy road.

Unfortunately he failed to notice that he'd left a trail of footprints in the snow, when getting out from the passenger side and running away. Maybe he was in too much of a hurry, as he'd only been wearing a tee shirt, pyjama bottoms and a pair of moccasins. It presumably didn't take detectives too long to figure out that things didn't quite add up. The major head injuries to the victim, from such a minor motoring mishap, were also a bit of clue. Nyce managed however to carry on at work as though nothing unusual had happened. It was a class act in dissimulation, arguably one of the most essential qualities in any biotech CEO. Although not usually to the point of *literally* trying to get away with murder.[51]

These were some of biotech's more memorable individuals. So maybe it was just as well that we were a much more restrained group. It was safer that way. Although it did make it harder to get to know one another. We weren't exactly *partying*.

Which was important, as nothing was really gelling on a human level. From their point of view maybe that was irrelevant. After all, the things they were probably most interested in seeing were our bank statements, not us.

But from our side, where we were looking to use this as an opportunity to build up something again, something self-sustaining and regenerative, then it did matter.

Having spent as long as we decently could sizing each other up, we eventually got down to business, with us presenting our pipeline and them theirs. And what they had to share was scientifically interesting. There was no doubt about that.

With TroVax, most of us had already written it off in our own minds and whilst they were duly enthusiastic about its future, we were sceptics.

Even if they'd said they were selling their own children into slavery to personally keep TroVax going, it wouldn't have cut much ice with us.

Their gene therapy programmes were a different proposition. We were being afforded a glimpse into a future world of unimaginable innovation and technical accomplishment.

We were really keen to hear more.

The OBM people had a video of their star patient from the ProSavin study in France, with *before* and *after* sequences.

The film showed a scene prior to treatment, of a small wizened old Frenchman sitting dejectedly, hunched up in an armchair. He did actually have a beret on, as if to provide an extra degree of authenticity. Upon being asked to get out of the chair and walk to the end of the room, it was as though the video had suddenly switched to slow motion or even freeze frame. We'd all have grown beards by the time he'd reached his destination, if the filming hadn't ceased long before then. Point made. This patient was very severely impaired.

The contrast with the post treatment sequence was dramatic. This opened with him lounging in the same chair as before but now with all the insouciance of a man fully in control of himself and his destiny. Upon being asked to complete the same task as previously, all you saw this time was a blur of motion on the screen, as he launched himself from the chair and sprang across the room. A French farmer couldn't have run any faster, on being told there was another EU farm handout on offer.

It was certainly a striking improvement. It was a tantalising one too. Could one fast moving Frenchman really represent the difference between decades of disillusionment with gene therapy and the possibility of progress at last?

But it was only one person. The history of gene therapy was after all littered with promising prototype patients, who'd subsequently turned out to be erroneously encouraging, compared to subsequent disappointment, if not disaster.

The whole lentiviral programme seemed to add up to no more than a handful of individuals who'd been treated with ProSavin. We were convinced they were going to tell us about some more patients they had tucked away somewhere. That they were saving up, to surprise us with and help break the ice. A sort of house warming gift as it were. But that really seemed to be all they had. How was it possible to make any sort of judgement based on so little information, we thought.

We were genuinely disappointed. We wanted to be enticed and enthralled further. But the limited extent of clinical data on offer amounted at best to an emollient for our itchy enthusiasm. It was a starter, whereas we had anticipated being served up something far more substantial to get our teeth into. In fact, it wasn't even a starter. More of a *mis en bouche*. At least it was a course with an appropriately French title though.

As for the other projects, none of these had even reached the clinic yet. So no crumbs there.

And yet here we were at Antisoma with a large development team, one Phase III drug, amonafide, nearing the end of the largest ever study conducted in that particular disease and a late stage Phase II agent in AS1411. It was a groaning platter, by comparison. We might as well have started roasting a whole pig on a spit, right in front of them, to emphasise the disparity.

And they had TroVax, which wasn't exactly a Feast of Plenty. More like gnawing at a bone. And basically not much else. Certainly not enough.

They didn't seem far from going *hungry*.

Maybe the paucity of their pantry was staring us in the face all along but we somehow needed to hear it from them, for it to develop the clarity it now had. And yet because of the craziness of the financial markets, they had a higher valuation than we did and were probably anticipating a sixty-forty or even seventy-thirty division in their favour, in any merged company.

Well, *sod that for a game of soldiers* was the general gist of the discussion, after they'd gone. One or two people might have used slightly stronger language. Maybe a fifty-fifty split as a minimum, we thought. Surely that was reasonable. But nothing less. And it wasn't just that their cupboard seemed barer than Mother Hubbard's. The other issue was whether we could work together as a combined team.

We weren't yet convinced the best bet was to put our fate and that of our shareholders, in their hands. As Shakespeare put it, far better than we ever could,[52]

"*Let me have men about me that are fat. Sleek headed men, such as sleep a-nights.*"

Like Cassius, OBM had a distinctly lean and hungry look and as Caesar pointed out, "*such men are dangerous.*"

They had probably left with similarly ambivalent, although less poetic, sentiments about us.

Maybe we were being overarchingly arrogant. After all, if you looked at it dispassionately we didn't exactly have the best track record of steering a company, having managed in the last few months to erase as much shareholder value as Oxford BioMedica might ever have done. And maybe also we were walking away from a really cheap ticket to ride, right at the very front, right in first class, on the gene therapy juggernaut. It might still be stuck in first gear but it had to get up some speed eventually. And OBM had some consummately clever people capable of driving it.

Or perhaps we just weren't desperate enough yet, in our own minds. We *were* in a parlous state. Obviously. But we still had six months to go, until the ACCEDE results would become available and force our hand. Maybe we had convinced ourselves that there was still time for another opportunity to come along. Something which was a better fit. For whatever reason though, the spark wasn't there with OBM and without that you're never going to be able to set things on fire.

XXI

But in any event, we knew they wouldn't go away. Seventeen million pounds of our cash was worth waiting around for, even if it was just on the off chance. If amonafide eventually fell apart we were certain they would be straight out of the blocks the next day, with an offer for the company which we would then be duty bound to consider.

In the apocalyptic context of a post amonafide failure, they might suddenly seem a lot more attractive to our Board and investors than they did now. Especially if there were nothing else on the table at the time. In the emotive and volatile environment, which would inevitably follow amonafide failing and our share price falling right through the floor, a firm offer by someone like OBM would have the huge advantage of providing certainty and direction, at a time which would otherwise be characterised by chaos and drift. As a management team we could lose control of events very rapidly in a situation like that, giving OBM a clear run.

And so if at all possible, we needed to have a few more merger proposals worked up and in our back pocket, ready to pull out just in case we needed to counter a resurgent Oxford BioMedica, at some point in the future.

We were now at the end of August and we would know where we stood with amonafide by the end of January. That didn't leave long to find a new best friend to start playing with. Just in case we ended up in desperate need of one. So we had our work cut out and with time clearly not on our side, there was only a certain amount we could do to determine the course of events.

And there were a couple of things lurking just over the horizon, which we were to discover we couldn't influence at all.

One of which would turn out to be the United States Food and Drug Administration. They were suddenly threatening to bring down one of the biggest beasts in the biotechnology jungle. It was a dramatic development, which would have an impact on everyone else involved with new cancer drugs, ourselves included. Now no one could feel safe anymore. Events occurring three thousand miles away in North America would have ramifications reaching all corners of the biotechnology universe.

At least it put our own problems into perspective.

EIGHT

SHATTERED

The rise and fall of the world's best selling cancer antibody. A look at the ephemeral nature of many cancer advances. An insight into the unpredictability of the drug approval process.

Having a drug reach the market is the single dream, shared by everyone in biotechnology. Just the possibility of it is enough to counteract the innumerable nightmares caused by all the other drugs that fall by the wayside. But the biggest nightmare of all is the possibility of losing a drug, once it has made it through. The prospect of having a drug withdrawn, after it has become comfortably ensconced in the market place, would cause even the most battle hardened biotechnology veteran to buckle at the knees.

Once a drug has survived the arduous journey through the development jungle, it ought to be safe and secure when it emerges on the other side. If it didn't perish along the way, it should be allowed to prosper now. But nothing is forever in cancer medicine. Now and then, drugs end up being forcibly ejected from the market, despite their best attempts to cling on for dear life. New data can emerge about the safety or efficacy, which puts them in a worse light and forces a reappraisal of their viability. It's like having parole revoked and being sent back to prison.

On the rare occasions when this happens, it's the biotechnology equivalent of a natural disaster. Moreover, when it affects the world's biggest biotechnology company and involves their best selling and most successful cancer drug, it's an earthquake measuring a ten on the Richter scale. The reverberations and aftershocks are felt *everywhere*. No one and nothing are safe. The ensuing tsunami sweeps away all in front of it.

In the summer of 2010, biotechnology was facing its worst ever humanitarian crisis. There was a very real prospect that Avastin, one of the most widely used cancer drugs in existence, might lose its position in the market place. The unthinkable looked like it might become the unavoidable.

It is difficult to accurately convey the enormity of this development. If *Avastin* wasn't safe, then absolutely nothing else was either. It represented a threat to the very viability of future drug development in cancer. Having reached the face of the gold seam, the mine was in danger of being blown up. Who'd want to carry on prospecting, when confronted with hazards like that. It was like spending all your life paying off the mortgage and then have the bank decide to repossess your home anyway. Except that in this case, it was a house worth several billion dollars.

The outcome of the Avastin saga was to have wide ranging consequences for everyone. That included companies attempting to develop new cancer drugs, physicians for whom they were intended and patients hoping for a final drink in the Last Chance Saloon.

Unlike most acts of God though, it didn't happen out of the blue. The history of Avastin in breast cancer is a tale of prolonged conflict, struggle, treachery, despair and despondency. If it were a novel it would probably be *War and Peace*. Maybe without the Peace though. It's a story so epic that, like Tolstoy's masterpiece, it can be subdivided into four chronological books, each telling their own tale.

Book One

I

Avastin was an antibody which destroyed the blood vessels supplying tumors, causing them to shrink and die. In most cases, it worked best when combined with other anti-cancer agents, particularly chemotherapy ones. Although it acted by a different mechanism, it produced effects on the blood vessels similar to ASA404. However, it had the distinct advantage of having already been approved by FDA for use in *five* different cancer types altogether. The first one had been colon cancer in 2004 and then after that, lung cancer, breast cancer, kidney cancer and finally a particularly nasty form of brain cancer called *glioblastoma multiforme.*

Overall, it was a revolutionary drug. No other biotechnology product had such a wide range of uses. Although it didn't actually cure anyone of their cancer, it clearly arrested the spread of the disease and bought patients valuable time, something they would otherwise fast be running out of.

And yet in 2011, its fate in breast cancer was on the line, despite there being a total of three Phase III trials supporting its value in this disease. The drug was widely used in over eighty four countries around the world. But in the US, it was suddenly fighting for its very existence. Its enemy was none other than FDA and ODAC. Patients and clinicians alike looked on in horror as the conflict unfolded. There was a very real possibility they were about to be deprived of the world's bestselling cancer drug.

II

The regulatory story of Avastin in breast cancer stretched back to 2007, when ODAC met to review data on an original clinical trial, called E2100. This had begun life as a collaborative study, initiated by the Eastern Clinical

Oncology Group (ECOG). If they'd known what trouble was in store for later on, they may never have started in the first place. But at the time, it seemed an important study to help define the role of Avastin in one of the commonest of all malignancies.

The study consisted of about seven hundred women with advanced breast cancer, who were receiving treatment for the first time for their metastatic disease. This is known as *first line* or *front line* therapy. Three hundred and fifty patients were randomised to receive the combination of Avastin and the already widely used chemotherapy drug paclitaxel and about three hundred and fifty to receive paclitaxel alone.

Breast cancer is broadly divided into two groups, known as HER2 positive and HER2 negative.[1] HER2 is an abnormal marker, present on the surface of breast cancer cells in about twenty per cent of patients. It is part of a signalling mechanism which promotes cancer cell growth and division. HER2 positivity is usually associated with more aggressive disease and a worse prognosis than a HER2 negative status.

Genentech already had the hugely successful antibody Herceptin, which was used, in combination with chemotherapy, in HER2 positive disease. Avastin was aimed at women with HER2 negative cancer. The two drugs would complement each other nicely. Assuming of course that Avastin was approved by FDA.

The primary endpoint of E2100 was progression free survival (PFS). This is the amount of time that passes, following treatment, before the patient either dies, or their breast cancer starts to spread and get worse. It's whichever one occurs first.

At the time, two previous Avastin approvals had been on the basis of showing an improvement in the very demanding primary endpoint of overall survival. These were for colon cancer, in 2004 and lung cancer in 2006.

However, previously in *breast cancer* FDA had been willing to accept less stringent endpoints as the basis for approving two other drugs, for the same broad indication as the E2100 trial (first line treatment of advanced disease, in combination with paclitaxel). These were Genentech's own Herceptin (trastuzumab) in 1998 and Lilly's Gemzar (gemcitabine) in 2004.

In the previous twelve months alone, FDA had also approved two additional drugs for second line use in breast cancer. These were Tykerb (lapatinib) from GSK and Ixempra (ixabepilone) from Bristol Myers.

These four drugs were all approved on the results of either PFS or a related endpoint called *time to disease progression* (TTP). TTP measures the amount of time which passes before the breast cancer spreads (and so, unlike PFS, doesn't also take account of whether the patient dies or not).

Additionally, trastuzumab demonstrated a survival advantage as a secondary endpoint,[2] whilst gemcitabine just failed to confirm a survival improvement (as a co-*primary* endpoint) at an interim analysis but did do so subsequently at a final analysis.[3] However, neither drug had formally proven this, as a *primary* endpoint, at the *time* of the original approval.

And so, with the precedent of drugs which had made it through regulatory review in the recent past, PFS for breast cancer looked, at least on a balance of probabilities, like a well established primary endpoint. Everything should therefore have been straightforward for Avastin and E2100. It was looking like another home run for the drug.

This was especially so, given that the final results of the trial showed a hugely impressive fifty two per cent prolongation of average PFS in the Avastin combination arm (11.3 months), compared to the paclitaxel alone arm (5.8 months). Also, nearly fifty per cent of patients had tumor shrinkage with Avastin, compared to about twenty two per cent in the other arm of the study.[4]

Most clinicians and patients would be more than happy with a drug that seemed to work that well. They were better results than anything else out there. Things became harder to interpret however, when there turned out to be *no* difference in survival between the two groups of women. Both were living on average for about twenty five months. There was also a twenty per cent higher incidence of serious side effects in the Avastin arm, with two per cent of patients being judged to have died directly due to the drug itself.

Ultimately FDA didn't really know what to make of all this. Avastin had met the primary endpoint, of improved PFS, without which the study would be dead and it also appeared to be shrinking tumors. But it was quite toxic, apparently contributing to the death of some patients and not prolonging survival in the rest. It showed the problems often encountered, when trying to interpret cancer clinical trial data and some of the difficulties regulators faced. Things never quite added up. What you gained here, was lost there. Working out the profit and loss, whilst trying to balance the books of cancer accounting, was often a complicated and confusing calculation.

III

To make matters worse, FDA were unhappy about the way in which progression free survival had been calculated in the study. They were very unhappy in fact.[5] Sometimes, even a seemingly objective hard endpoint could have ambiguity surrounding it.

PFS is the amount of time before a patient either dies, or their cancer spreads. It ought to be straightforward to work that out. But the first problem is how you decide whether the cancer has got worse and spread or not. If the tumor happens to be a large lump of visible disease, such as a melanoma deposit in the skin, then it's fairly easy to figure out what is going on. Nothing more complicated than a ruler is usually required. However, normally tumerous deposits are invisibly hidden away, somewhere unhelpfully deep within the body. Assessing what is happening there requires something a little more sophisticated than the contents of a pencil case.

To tackle this problem, at the beginning of the study you would take radiological scans (either CT scans, or more usually MRI ones) of the body. These would generate images showing whether there were any tumor masses, either at the site of the original breast cancer, or in the places it commonly spreads to, such as the skeleton, the brain, the lungs and the liver. You can then count the total number of tumor deposits and also measure the size of the bigger ones.

Usually scans are repeated at intervals during the study, typically every six or eight weeks. By comparing these new ones with those taken at the very beginning you can, in theory, work out whether any new tumor deposits have appeared, or whether any existing ones have got bigger. Both of these would be evidence of the cancer having taken a course for the worse.

Although this sounds simple, in reality it is often less straightforward. Firstly, you have to work out whether what you are seeing on a scan is really tumor, or actually something else. Scars from previous surgery, foci of former infection and things such as that can easily look just like a tumor deposit, potentially catching out the unwary. Dead tissue at original tumor sites can also sometimes look confusingly like residual disease. However, assuming you can deal with this and make the correct distinction, you then have to decide whether what appears to be a tumor has got bigger, stayed the same or shrunk down to become smaller.

This isn't always problem free either. Each time the patient has a scan, their body and the scanner may be in a slightly different alignment from the last time and so the images produced may similarly have slightly different perspectives. In turn, this can complicate the accuracy of the measurements of size that you make. Although small inconsistencies, they can sometimes exert a more significant influence on determining tumor dimensions.

Also things aren't helped by the fact that alterations in tumor size are often quite small to start with. A couple of millimetres here, a fraction there. It can be extremely difficult to calibrate these changes with confidence. There is in fact a whole category of tumor images seen on scans, which are known as *non-measurable lesions*. This refers to deposits of disease which are simply too small to measure at all. All you can really say is whether they are there or not.

Deciding whether a scan shows individual tumors to be changing in size and if so in which direction, is frequently a subtle act of judgement and differing people looking at the same scans might well reach differing opinions over what is actually happening. There is a lot of ambiguity and more than a little art involved.

If you can actually measure a tumor with some degree of reliability, then you still have to consider what constitutes a meaningful increase in the size. Is it five, ten or fifteen per cent, or some other figure? Do you look in just one dimension, or bi-dimensionally (usually two measurements at right angles to one another)?

How much does a tumor have to shrink for this to be important? Should it halve in size, disappear altogether, or some other permutation? What do you do with a tumor that starts shrinking and then begins to grow again but not to the size it was originally? Or, how do you assess patients who have some metastases progressing, whilst others are shrinking at the same time. What is the state of play in a case like that?

These are just some of the complexities created with anatomical imaging, such as CT or MRI. A whole different league of creativity is required when interpreting more *functional* imaging such as PET, or nuclear medicine scans. If CT and MRI are photographs then functional images are more like abstract paintings. Even experts in the area often refer to them as "blobograms." Working out what they are telling you is not dissimilar to finding yourself on the judging panel for the Turner Prize.

To help with these sorts of issues, objective guidelines for assessing tumors were developed about ten years ago, by an international group of oncologists and radiologists. These are known as the RECIST criteria (standing for **R**esponse **E**valuation **C**riteria **I**n **S**olid **T**umors).[6] They are an evolution of an earlier set of World Health Organisation (WHO) guidelines. RECIST criteria, in one variant or another, are used in pretty much all cancer clinical trials and have helped to standardise approaches to determining changes in tumor size. But despite this, there are still other complications to deal with.

Most patients in clinical studies get scans about every six or eight weeks. It's just not logistically possible or economically feasible to undertake this sort of exercise with any greater frequency. But if a scan shows that a tumor is bigger and has clearly progressed when compared to the preceding scan, do you assume that the growth happened immediately after the last scan, or immediately before the current one, or half way in between the two, or something else.

Depending on how you approach this, potentially six to eight weeks could be added to or subtracted from the time to progression. Which for many solid tumors, as was the case for Avastin in advanced breast cancer, is usually just a few months anyway. The scanning *interval* can therefore have a substantial impact on the results reported for a new drug. This can become particularly confusing if different trials with the same drug deal with this issue in different ways.

Even determining the time before a patient dies during a clinical trial can sometimes be harder than it might first seem. Do you start counting from when they first enter the trial? That can often be two or three weeks before they actually start receiving study treatment. Particularly if they need a number of investigations and tests first. Or should it be from when they start treatment, or from when treatment ends?

It can all make a difference, especially in very aggressive malignancies, where the patients don't live very long. Working out when they have died is usually easy, if they had a fast moving cancer and have quickly passed away in hospital. But sometimes in advanced cancers where the patient might still typically live for a couple of years (such as ovarian or prostate cancer) clinical trials often rely on phoning the patient or their family at home. You have to do this at regular intervals, say every few months, to see whether they are still alive or not.

Inevitably, in this situation you lose contact with some of the patients sooner or later. They move away to other areas, start attending other hospitals, go into a hospice, or just disappear off the face of the earth altogether. And so you are never really sure if they are still alive and if not, when they actually died.

Given all of this variability, it can sometimes be difficult to accurately measure something such as progression free survival, even though this is seemingly an easily quantifiable parameter. For this reason, it is not uncommon in cancer trials to have efficacy endpoints which involve scanning (such as response rates and PFS) double checked by an imaging specialist who hasn't actually been directly involved in the trial. This is exactly what we'd done with AS1411 in kidney cancer. It allows a consistent review of all scans across all centres taking part in a study.

This means you then end up with two different determinations of PFS. There is an *investigator* assessment, which comes from the doctor actually treating the patient in the trial in hospital. And you also have an *independent* assessment, performed by someone not associated with the study. They usually look at the scans without knowing which treatment group the patient was randomised to.

However, even the independent assessors could disagree amongst themselves. In the case of E2100, there were two independent radiologists reviewing the scans. They actually managed to disagree in nearly half of the cases. They couldn't decide amongst themselves whether the scans showed that things were getting worse, improving or staying the same.

This then required a *third* radiologist to become involved. Fortunately, he was able to agree with at least one of the other two, in ninety five per cent of cases. It was almost like a party game, some sort of ghastly cancer variant of charades.

Normally independent reviews come up with lower figures for response rates and PFS than do those from investigators. This is because the latter often know which treatment group any individual patient is in. Either it's an open study anyway, or they can work it out from characteristic side effects, which give away the treatment assignment in blinded studies. They are more inclined to be overly generous in their assessments, giving experimental treatment combinations the "benefit if the doubt" when making these sorts of judgements. The independent reviewers are, in theory, more likely to have a higher degree of objectivity.

In the case of the E2100 study, FDA were concerned that there was a very high discordance between the independent and the investigator review of PFS events.[5] They were disagreeing in about fifty per cent of cases. Normally this figure would be more like ten or fifteen per cent in most cancer trials. Furthermore, almost a third of patients appeared not to have been followed up sufficiently well to allow an accurate determination of progression or death.

Unhelpfully, on top of that, ten per cent of the patient scans were lost or had gone missing during the study and so weren't available for an independent review. Incredibly this happens a lot in clinical trials in cancer medicine.

In the case of E2100 though, FDA were lucky to even have two sets of scan assessments to worry about. When the trial had originally been designed by ECOG, they had included just investigator readings. The independent review had only been added at a later date, after Genentech took over the reins.

Despite Genentech's generosity with the additional review of the scans, all of the methodological issues about PFS, along with the lack of a survival advantage and the extra toxicity of the Avastin arm, worried FDA a lot. They didn't like loose ends and there were more here than you could count on the hands of someone from Fifteen Finger Land. It eventually led to them referring the whole study to ODAC, to see if they could pull it all together.

IV

The Committee eventually met on December 5th 2007 to consider things further. This time, they convened at the Hilton Hotel in Gaithersburg, another bleak Washington suburb. Only ten members of ODAC had been available for this particular meeting to begin with. Even they had to have a holiday sometimes. Additionally, there had been bad weather for days beforehand, with heavy snowfalls overnight in the Washington area. Gaithersburg was even bleaker than normal.

Many people were delayed getting to the meeting, due to appalling traffic conditions. One member, Professor Ronald Richardson from the Mayo Clinic in Rochester Minnesota, would never actually make it at all. He was trapped when snow disrupted flights throughout the North East of the US.

ODAC could influence many things but the weather wasn't one of them.

In keeping with the inclement conditions, things didn't seem too promising for Avastin with ODAC from the outset. The drug hadn't shown a survival advantage in the E2100 trial. That meant everything was going to revolve around whether PFS, in its own right, was considered a sufficient endpoint to confirm clinical utility.

The value of PFS was an enormous controversy in cancer medicine and the committee were already divided over it. It was an issue which would come to dog the entire Avastin debate for the next five years.

As far back as June 1999, FDA had asked ODAC's views about the general acceptability of progression free survival in metastatic breast cancer.[7] At that time the committee had voted unanimously twelve-zero that it wasn't a sufficient endpoint for the approval of a drug in that setting. It didn't get more clear cut than that. Their view had been that drugs needed to show a survival advantage, as a minimum requirement for approval.

With that line in the sand having been previously drawn, Avastin was already facing an uphill struggle in the current ODAC meeting. And that was before a single word had been spoken or slide projected.

This time around, ODAC was chaired by Professor Maha Hussain, an oncologist at the University of Michigan, whose main interest was prostate cancer. Some may have regarded her as a surprising choice. She had presumably never treated a patient with breast cancer in her entire professional career. However, FDA must have had their reasons for selecting her, opaque though they may have been.

After formally opening the meeting, she wasted no time in reigniting the debate over PFS. In her opinion it was a poor endpoint, because it didn't reliably predict overall survival.[8]

"There have been examples where early positive indications (in PFS) didn't translate into a survival advantage. If anything, early therapy with drugs resulted in worse survival," she expanded. "Therefore if you ignore the survival, and you just go by response, or progression free survival, you would actually have put harmful drugs on the market."

Presumably this wasn't exactly what the Genentech people in the room were hoping to hear, in the opening remarks of the meeting. There was nothing like getting things off on a positive footing.

Natalie Portis of Breast Cancer Action, a San Francisco based patient advocacy group, was the patient representative on ODAC. She was in complete agreement with the chairman. From the outset, she was against both the drug and the study.

"It's a very painful reality that metastatic breast cancer is not curable and I don't think we should just say, "Well dear, try this," if there isn't meaningful data to support it. And in this study, there is missing data, there are inconsistencies, and I feel very uncomfortable about this," she said.

Her group had in fact written to FDA on November 29th, just a week before the ODAC meeting, urging them to deny approval for breast cancer drugs which hadn't been shown to extend survival or improve the quality of life. And then, just two days before the meeting, on December 3rd, they had issued a statement strongly suggesting that FDA should reject the Avastin application. It didn't exactly look as though she was going into the meeting with an open mind.

However, despite unanimity in the past, not all ODAC members agreed this time around.

"From the patient perspective, I think PFS is a very meaningful endpoint in first, second and third line therapy," said Joanne Mortimer, a Professor of Medical Oncology at the City of Hope Comprehensive Cancer Centre in Los Angeles.

"Outside of trastuzumab (Herceptin) I don't believe that any chemotherapy alters overall survival. This just reflects that we don't know who the subsets are, who truly benefit from each of these different therapies."

She was supported by another committee member, Gary Lyman from Duke University Medical Centre in North Carolina.

"There is no question, amongst my colleagues and myself, that PFS is clinically meaningful," he stated.

This was just as well because, in his opinion, it was actually going to be difficult to show an effect on survival for a first line drug like Avastin. This was due to the influence of subsequent treatments, given *after* the failure of first line therapy (called second or third line treatment and so on).

"Many of my patients, after the first line approach, go through five, six, seven additional regimens and that just adds enormous noise and can cloud the survival differences of a first-line regimen." The question of whether it was actually even possible to dissect out a survival advantage, was to recur throughout the years of the subsequent Avastin debate. The problem was how to go about measuring something you couldn't necessarily detect.

The differences of opinion shown by this initial skirmishing weren't going to help the committee members in their job of reviewing a trial with as complicated a provenance as E2100. It had definitely been around the block a few times, on its journey to Maryland.

V

By the time it eventually arrived in front of FDA, this was a study which had accumulated quite a lot of baggage along the way. That never helped in a situation as contentious as this one was already shaping up to be.

At this point in the ODAC meeting, the history of E2100 was outlined by an FDA presenter Dr Lee Pai-Scherf, who had the impressively long title of *Medical Officer, Division of Biologic Oncology Products (DBOP), OODP, OND, CDER*. This seemed to be a rather long winded way of saying that she was a clinician from FDA.

The study grumbled into life in October 2001, when ECOG sent details of it to FDA. The Agency however would later assert that at this time there was no mention of the trial possibly being used by Genentech for regulatory purposes, in the future.

The first patient was entered into the study in December 2001. Although ECOG was coordinating the trial, other investigative consortia took part and contributed patients along the way.

At the time, Genentech was actually involved with a different study with Avastin (combined with another cancer drug, this time called capecitabine) also in the treatment of advanced breast cancer. This trial, called AVF2119, eventually failed in September 2002, when it didn't meet the primary endpoint of PFS.

Perhaps anticipating this coming setback, in May 2002 Genentech first indicated to FDA that they were now intending to use the E2100 trial, to support regulatory approval for Avastin. FDA subsequently claimed that upon hearing this, they had sent two letters to ECOG, pointing out concerns with the trial's endpoints and proposed statistical analysis. However, they apparently never received a reply.

Meanwhile, E2100 completed recruitment of patients in May 2004. In October, FDA wrote to Genentech warning them again of reservations over the acceptability of some of the E2100 endpoints, particularly those to do with PFS.

The seeds of subsequent discontent had clearly been sown early on. For some reason though, none of the parties involved seemed to be listening to one another. It wasn't an auspicious start.

In April 2005 the preliminary results became available from the trial, showing an impressive PFS of 10.9 months for the Avastin plus paclitaxel arm and only 6.1 months for the paclitaxel alone arm. This was based on the investigator assessment of the scans and other patient data.[9]

This difference seemed so promising to Genentech, that they decided to make the results public later that month and subsequently present them at the May 2005 ASCO meeting. Here the data actually received a standing ovation from the crowded room. Things were looking pretty good for Avastin and E2100.

Avastin was heralded by oncologists as a potentially significant advance in the treatment of breast cancer. By comparison, the only other similar drug approved at the time was gemcitabine, which barely managed a two month improvement in Time To Progression when combined with paclitaxel.[10] It just showed what a desperate disease advanced breast cancer was.

For the next year, Genentech ploughed through the laborious process of collecting and collating the enormous amounts of information from the trial. In May 2006 they were ready to submit it all to FDA, for them to review and hopefully approve the drug.

However, it wasn't going to be that simple. In September, FDA wrote back claiming there were a large number of discrepancies in the data. Most notably there was a lack of *independent* radiological review of the scans and that the submission was unacceptable because of this. In the enclosed world of the oncology community this was a dramatic development.

When the study had originally been put together, ECOG had foreseen a need only for investigator assessments Up until then, FDA had never required independent reviews of scans from cooperative group studies. Instead they had been happy to work with investigator assessments alone. Now they suddenly seemed to be altering the rules of the game. There was an implication in some quarters that they no longer had complete confidence in the objective independence of these groups. The close collegiate collaboration of yesteryear seemed on the brink of being irreparably ruptured.

But that was FDA and they had the power to change their minds, if they felt like it. And in this case they clearly did. Genentech ultimately had little choice but to go back and arrange for all seven hundred and twenty two patients' worth of scans to be reviewed independently. This was when they realised that ten per cent were now missing and that over one third of the patients hadn't even been fully followed up, as they should have in the first place.

But somehow all of these anomalies, when resolved, didn't alter the eventual PFS advantage. If anything, they seemed to *improve* it even further. The final, independently verified, figures stood at 11.3 months versus 5.8 months, in favour of Avastin.[4] The difference of 5.5 months was even greater than the preliminary 4.8 month superiority, which had everyone on their feet at ASCO two years earlier.[9] They'd have been swinging from the chandeliers at this final data.

Flushed with pride and enthusiasm, Genentech eventually resubmitted all the reworked data to FDA in August 2007. They were thinking that surely they had done enough by now to demonstrate the benefits of Avastin, in breast cancer. Maybe not beyond all reasonable doubt but certainly way beyond a balance of probabilities.

After all, the drug had already been approved in Europe in March 2007 on the basis of the E2100 results.[11] Over there, PFS was widely regarded as an acceptable endpoint. The Europeans couldn't understand what all the fuss was about on the other side of the Atlantic. However, here they were, just before Christmas, having to defend the relevance of PFS to both FDA and a sceptical ODAC.

And it wasn't just PFS their opponents were unhappy about. There was also the issue of that softer endpoint, *quality of life.* If Avastin wasn't increasing survival and the actual *quantity* of life for a patient, then many held that it should at a minimum be improving the *quality* of whatever time remained.

The tools available to measure quality of life in cancer trials were fairly crude though. Mainly they consisted of questionnaires, which had to be filled in by the patient or their carer. If you were in the grips of terminal cancer, this was, as much as anything else, an opportunity to unburden yourself and document your woes.

Often the paperwork ended up painting an unduly pessimistic picture of how things really were. Frequently this made it difficult to capture an improvement in a patient's well-being with a new drug.

Perhaps unsurprisingly, the E2100 trial had been unable to demonstrate a benefit for Avastin. There was no clear evidence that the drug was improving the quality of life for the patients receiving it.

In theory, it shouldn't be that difficult for a drug to show some kind of benefit, in terms of how patients perceived their lot. In advanced breast cancer, you weren't exactly starting with a high baseline. However, improvements in overall well-being, due to better disease control, could often be offset by the toxicity most drugs brought along with them. That double edged sword of good and bad activity, combined with the bluntness of the tools available to measure such a subtle balancing act, had effectively stabbed Avastin in the back, as far as quality life outcomes were concerned.

The problem was framed by a question from ODAC Chairman, Maha Hussain.

"If a patient is not living better, which you have shown us they are not, and they are not living longer, how does this translate into clinical benefit? I'd argue that these patients' quality of life went *down*, not *up*. You didn't show that they are feeling better and you didn't show that they are living longer," she concluded.

It was a strong argument, going to the heart of the weakness in the E2100 data on this point.

"What we have demonstrated in this trial is not a quality of life *improvement* with paclitaxel and Avastin but the fact that it *declined* less than in women who received paclitaxel alone," responded Dr Eric Winer, who was Director of the Breast Oncology Centre at the Dana-Farber Cancer Institute in Boston. He had also been a presenter on behalf of Genentech earlier in the meeting.

It was a masterly statement of semantics surpassing science. If Avastin wasn't actually enhancing anyone's dying days, then maybe it was at least arresting the inexorable decline the patients were going through. It might not make things better but on the other hand, it might slow down the rate at which they got worse.

Sometimes in cancer medicine, that was as good as it was ever going to get.

"But the real issue is, does PFS in this setting translate into an improvement in quality of life?" he continued, moving on swiftly. "I actually believe it does, because in a substantial number of patients, one is avoiding moving to a new therapy, with both a physical and psychological trauma."

It was another subtle line of reasoning. Although patients' overt quality of life might not be improved by Avastin, they could still derive considerable comfort, due to the familiarity which came from the prolonged period of treatment possible with it.

Many patients were profoundly disturbed, when one therapy failed, by the prospect of moving from a treatment whose side effects they had got to grips with, to another they didn't yet have the measure of. If Avastin was prolonging PFS, it could delay that fateful day.

The disorientating and disturbing world of cancer chemotherapy was one example of where familiarity didn't necessarily breed contempt.

The exchange over the quality of life issue was a vignette of the ping pong nature the proceedings had developed.

The meeting settled into a steady rhythm, with the two opposing camps of ODAC-FDA and Genentech continuing to snipe away at each other. The debate on the meaning of progression free survival and quality of life could have continued indefinitely. The answer was that no one knew the answers.

Left to their own devices, the participants would undoubtedly have carried on their deliberations until long after dark. The meeting was beginning to resemble the proceedings of a leisurely amateur debating society. There seemed to be no more at stake than a degree of academic antagonism, which would have been happily at home on the high table of any university dining room.

But ultimately reality had to intervene and time ran out. The ODAC members needed to vote, for or against approving Avastin in breast cancer, on the basis of everything they had heard. And given the wide ranging, often contradictory nature of the various views expressed, it was inevitably going to be a close run thing.

Eventually, ODAC voted five to four *against* approval. It was a close call but still sufficiently clear cut to be decisive.

Chairman Maha Hussain summarised the panel's deliberations. These included misgivings about the discrepancies in imaging interpretation, worries about missing data, and reservations over the relevance of PFS, the absence of a survival advantage and concerns over the toxicity profile. Pretty much everything to do with the study in fact.

The same day, Natalie Portis's Breast Cancer Action Group sent out a laudatory message *applauding* the recommendation.[12]

But she wasn't quite there yet.

Book Two

I

FDA retreated to Rockville for further deliberation. In the light of their eventual decision, it must have been quite a lot of deliberation. The midnight oil would have been bubbling rather than just burning. Finally, on February 22nd 2008 they announced, to widespread surprise, that they were actually going to *approve* Avastin in breast cancer. This was based on the E2100 trial, despite all their own reservations and the negative ODAC vote.

Regulators usually marched to a predictable rhythm. Most of the time, you could be pretty sure which direction they were headed in. But now and then, they would catch you off guard and veer off at a tangent. This appeared to be one of those occasions.

It was a commendably decisive act and one which should have gained them widespread support. If only they'd subsequently stuck to their guns, that is.

"We wanted to have the regulatory flexibility to approve effective drugs where there isn't overall survival," Dr Richard Pazdur told a press conference.[13] He was the man who more than anyone else would have taken the final decision over Avastin. He also conceded that lengthening progression free survival "may be a direct clinical benefit in itself," although survival remained the "gold standard."

Others agreed.

"I think it's just a matter of time before a survival benefit is documented," said Amy Tiersten, a Professor at New York University, in a statement she may have later lived to regret.[14] She also volunteered that she routinely used Avastin for her breast cancer patients, even though it wasn't yet approved for this.

Genentech had previously estimated that anything up to ten thousand breast cancer patients in the US were already receiving Avastin. This was a widespread practice, known as *off label use,* where a drug is prescribed for a disease different from the one for which it is actually approved.

Clinical practice is usually years ahead of regulatory rulings and doctors use drugs as their clinical experience guides them. This leads them into new territories and it can take the regulators inordinately long periods of time to catch up. This is particularly so in cancer medicine, where all oncologists are experimenters and risk takers. Hence the extensive off label use of most approved cancer therapies.

Because Avastin was already approved and hence widely available for colorectal and lung cancer, it was easy for doctors to prescribe it for a patient with breast cancer, if they were so minded. And clearly very many were.

One of these was Gabriel Hortobagyi, who provided one of the most forthright of all statements on the FDA decision. His is one of the biggest names of them all in the US breast cancer community. Gabriel Hortobagyi is to breast cancer what Elvis had been to rock and roll. The King. But obviously without the capes and costumes.

Professor Hortobagyi was originally from the Universidad Nacional de Colombia. He is now Chairman of the Department of Breast Medical Oncology at MD Anderson and an international expert on breast cancer. He's one of the most famous in the world probably, with an astonishing six hundred and fifty scientific papers and one hundred and forty book chapters to his name.

His view was very clear, as he explained at the time.[14]

"I believe FDA did the only appropriate thing with bevacizumab (Avastin) in breast cancer – approve it. It is going to be increasingly rare to find significant survival differences with new drugs in the metastatic setting, unless we are willing to do increasingly larger clinical trials, which would limit our ability to evaluate new drugs.

Breast cancer is treated with all available drugs in sequence. Therefore, a single patient might receive eight to ten different treatments during her life with metastatic disease. When you introduce a new drug, it will become part of one of those eight to ten treatments. So even if the new drug doubles the duration of control of the disease, it will affect one tenth of the survival for that patient.

To detect that statistically you need thousands of patients. In addition, overall survival duration will be affected by the other seven to nine drugs the patient will receive during the rest of her life.

PFS, on the other hand, is a direct measure of the effect of the drug under evaluation."

That was endorsement indeed. Where Hortobagyi led, many others inevitably eventually followed. Overall, most medical experts in the field seemed to be in agreement with him. Their views were well summarised by Kathy Miller, the E2100 lead clinical investigator from Indiana University School of Medicine.[14]

"There is no cure for metastatic breast cancer, so it is important to control the disease as early and for as long as possible. Now, with bevacizumab plus paclitaxel, we can increase the time a woman's cancer is kept under control."

However, not everyone was prepared to line up behind the received wisdom at MD Anderson and elsewhere. There was vehement opposition to the Avastin approval in some quarters. Interestingly, much of this emanated from patient advocacy groups, leaving many observers surprised that these organisations were coming out against a drug which should offer *more* choice to women who would, sooner or later, start running out of options.

In the US, these groups are more developed and more vocal than in Europe. They can trace their heritage back to the pioneering AIDS activists, nearly a quarter of a century earlier. They have become a powerful constituency with political clout and their views matter.

In most cases, their views on Avastin seemed very clear.

"We believe they have lowered the bar," said Fran Visco, president of the patient advocacy group National Breast Cancer Coalition Fund (NBCC).[14] Their stated mission was, amongst other things, to reject popular thinking and stand up to challenge the status quo.

"Our goal is to get the best treatments out to patients that really will be effective and safe," she continued. "This particular circumstance will not advance that goal."

The NBCC president had in fact written an open letter to FDA, just three days earlier, urging them again not to approve Avastin. It captured the views of many of the patient groups, who'd set their minds implacably against the drug.

"FDA plays a critical role in protecting the public health by setting high evidentiary standards for clinical utility," the letter ran.[15]

"In the first line metastatic (breast cancer) setting, it is the hope of consumer advocates that the research effort aims to improve survival and eventually lead to cures. We believe that lowering the standard for drug approval will undermine the quest for advancement in treatment and for cures, as we will lose the ability to determine whether new treatments truly save lives."

Not all the patient collectives were completely aligned though.

Robert Erwin was from the Marti Nelson Cancer Foundation, a patient advocacy group based in Northern California and named after his wife, who died of breast cancer in 2004.

He wrote a supportive letter, at the end of January, addressed to both Richard Pazdur at FDA and also David Schenkein, who was Senior Vice President of clinical haematology and oncology at Genentech. This reaffirmed his organisation's belief in the overall value of the E2100 trial.

In his group's view, an improvement in PFS was "clinically important for metastatic breast cancer patients even with equivocal survival results," and that the data represented "a clinically important improvement in quality of life."[15]

The supporters and detractors of Avastin were equally vocal in promoting their own particular view of events. In the weeks after the FDA announcement, the debate showed no signs of diminishing. So what had happened between the ODAC vote in December and the FDA decision in February, to influence The Agency's thinking on the E2100 trial?

Well, two things probably.

II

In the vital breathing space that couple of months gave them, Genentech had been busy in the background with two other Avastin breast cancer trials. These were called AVADO and RIBBON I. RIBBON I wouldn't complete until much later in the year but on February 12th, just a week before the FDA decision, Genentech issued a very timely announcement of the preliminary results of the AVADO trial.[16]

AVADO, which was a very similar trial to E2100, met the primary endpoint, which was PFS again. Whilst actual results weren't given in the press release, Genentech had already provided them to FDA. This time around though, the improvement in PFS appeared to be much *smaller* than in the E2100 study. However, taken together results from the two trials seemed to give FDA the confidence they needed to go against ODAC.

Later on though, this would become a subject of intense disagreement between the two camps. Genentech's position was that FDA had approached them for the results because, in the Agency's words, they "didn't want to go out on a limb,"[17] and issue an approval, on the basis of E2100, if the other two studies then turned out to be a bust.

Genentech would subsequently appear to interpret this as tacit *acceptance* of the AVADO results by FDA. As they said at the time the AVADO results were initially released, "we have *shared* the AVADO data with the FDA to *assist* the agency in assessing the risk and benefit of Avastin in this patient population."[16] It did seem to imply that Genentech thought they'd bared all in front of the Agency.

However, FDA later maintained that, at the time of the E2100 approval, Genentech had provided only twenty four slides summarising the AVADO data. It was no more than a teasing peek at best. No one, they insisted, could have assumed they would endorse a study on the basis of something as cursory as that. Everyone knew they couldn't act on anything less than a truck load of paper.

This was one of many misunderstandings between FDA and Genentech which would progressively muddy the waters, eventually turning them into a murky soup of mutual suspicion.

Despite the additional data from AVADO, FDA had also hedged their bets. They'd opted to give Avastin *accelerated* rather than full approval.

This decision was based on PFS in the E2100 trial, as a surrogate for overall survival. Following approval, Genentech were required to submit survival data from the AVADO and RIBBON I studies, as and when the information became available.

By doing this, FDA had effectively kept all options open, giving them the opportunity to reverse their decision later on, depending on what the eventual survival data looked like. In fact, they had gone one step further and given themselves even more room for manoeuvre.

As would crucially emerge later on, the intent of the wording of the accelerated approval obligation on Genentech and the consequent expectations of FDA, were not exactly crystal clear.

The phrasing of the actual approval letter from FDA to Genentech was a masterly exercise in regulatory ambiguity.

"Approval under these regulations requires, among other things, that you conduct adequate and well controlled studies in order to further define the clinical benefit to patients."[18]

Clinical benefit was a phrase whose absence of clarity was matched only by the abundance of controversy over its interpretation. Decades of debate had failed to delineate what measure best captured something so nebulous. FDA could have meant almost *anything* by those two words.

Over time, Genentech would contend that the spirit of what FDA intended, as a condition of granting accelerated approval, was simply to confirm the improvement in progression free survival seen in the earlier E2100 trial. The only requirement, as far as overall survival was concerned, was to demonstrate, in AVADO and RIBBON I, that this wasn't *reduced* by treatment with Avastin. They didn't have to show that it was actually *improved*.

That certainly appeared to be Genentech's understanding, following a number of further discussions with FDA, following receipt of the initial letter bearing the welcome news of the accelerated approval. The fact that FDA had apparently left themselves some wriggle room over this, seemed to have slipped by them, in the magic of the moment.

FDA would subsequently claim they were perfectly entitled to insist on seeing an improvement in survival and that the phrasing in their letter was entirely consistent with such an expectation. It's what they'd meant all along. They just hadn't actually *said* it in the letter. As past masters in the art of ambiguity, they were consummate craftsmen with linguistic contortions such as this.

Whatever Genentech thought, FDA were convinced they had retained the right to see a survival advantage. Whilst they were willing to take a step forwards with Avastin for now, they were also confident that they'd staked out a secure line of retreat, if they needed it later on.

The subtle nuancing of the differing positions between the two camps encompassed all the smoke and mirrors ambiguity of a Cold War diplomatic dispute. But with the completion of AVADO and RIBBON I, some of that smoke would eventually begin to clear.

And that ultimately was why the Genentech people were once again to find themselves at the Hilton Hotel in Gaithersburg.

This time, it was on a July morning in 2010.

After a three year wait, the survival data from AVADO[19] and RIBBON I[20] were finally available. And FDA didn't like what they were showing. They didn't think the requirements, laid down at the time of the original accelerated approval, had been met. At least not according to their view of the world.[21] Maybe, they were concluding, it was time for a rethink about Avastin's future.

Having shown some courage under fire with their initial decision to approve the drug, they were now feeling uncomfortably exposed. They weren't exactly a battle hardened force after all. With one eye on their escape route, they had decided to call in ODAC once again, for another look at Avastin in breast cancer.

In the intervening years, since the earlier ODAC meeting in 2007, Avastin had managed to establish a firm footing as a breast cancer agent in the US. It now accounted for over a billion dollars a year in revenue. Depending how things went, these new ODAC deliberations could therefore have very costly consequences for Genentech. For Avastin, it was breast or bust time.

III

AVADO (standing for **A**vastin **A**nd **Do**cetaxel) was a trial which had started entering patients in March 2006. It finished recruiting nineteen months later, in October 2007. RIBBON I (**R**egimens **i**n **B**evacizumab for **B**reast **On**cology) entered its first patient in December 2005 and the last one two and a half years later, in July 2008.

However, once a trial has finished putting patients in, it can take a long time to subsequently work out the survival data, telling you whether more patients have died in one arm of the study compared to the other.

The only way to accurately do that would be to follow up every patient in the study, until eventually they had all died. Once everyone is dead, it's easy to compare how long they lived for.

However, it's not practical to follow up every single patient for the rest of their lives, dogging them like some expectant agent of the Grim Reaper.

This is especially true in a context such as first line treatment of metastatic breast cancer. In this situation, as the E2100 trial showed, patients were living *on average* about two and a half years. By definition this means that a lot of patients must have been living quite a bit longer, although this would be balanced by those who died more quickly. It's simply too long a period of time to keep track of something as unpredictable as the life expectancy of a group of people scattered all over the world.

You have to compromise therefore.

Which usually means trying to follow up patients for about two years. Anything extra is a bonus.

Obviously, in a trial of fixed duration, if you recruit patients earlier, then they can be followed up for a longer period than patients who come into the study further down the line. The more time you have to keep tabs on patients, the greater is the possibility of them dying, whilst you still have a watchful eye on them.

This allows you to maximise the number of deaths you record, which in turn will give you the most accurate picture of overall survival.

The difficulty with patients still alive at the end of your trial is that you don't know whether they would have died the next day, or stayed alive for another five years, had you been able to follow them up indefinitely. This means you have to make *assumptions* about how much more they would have lived, if you'd only been able to keep track of them for longer.

As soon as you start making these kinds of best guesses, you inevitably begin introducing arbitrary subjectiveness into that otherwise most objective of all cancer endpoints. Death itself.

That is why survival data tends to have greater accuracy in more rapidly fatal conditions, like AML. There will be fewer patients still alive at the end of your follow up period. That leaves less patients still needing to be accounted for. Dead patients are always easier to deal with in clinical trials. It's the ones who are still alive who tend to cause the problems.

Obviously you keep a tally of the numbers of patients dying as your trial progresses. However, only when the last patient has completed their follow up, alive or dead and this information has been added in with that of all the other patients, can you draw a final conclusion about survival. Your data is then said to be *mature.*

Even after that, it takes a number of weeks to collect all the data, which in the case of RIBBON I involved over twelve hundred patients from twenty two countries. Then there is a need to check the information is all accurate and nothing is missing. Which is never the case. There are always enormous amounts of absent and inaccurate data, which have to be looked into and resolved. That can take a considerable period of time.

Subsequently, everything has to be entered into a computer database and then sophisticated statistical programmes are required to make sense of it all. The whole process can be a painful and protracted one, spanning many months.

Genentech had finally submitted the survival and other results of the AVADO and RIBBON I trials to FDA on November 16th 2009. The

Agency had been busy analysing them ever since. The data was more complicated than in the E2100 trial though and took longer to work through.

The E2100 trial had only about seven hundred and fifty patients and two treatment groups. These were Avastin, at a dose level of ten mg/kg (that is ten mg of Avastin for every kg the patient weighs) combined with paclitaxel, or paclitaxel alone.

AVADO also had about seven hundred and fifty patients but had three treatment groups. One was docetaxel (a drug similar to paclitaxel) alone, another was docetaxel and Avastin (at a dose level of fifteen mg/kg) and the third was docetaxel and Avastin (at the lower dose level of seven and a half mg/kg).

RIBBON I was by far and away the most complicated of the three trials, with just under one thousand two hundred and fifty patients. It consisted of *six* groups altogether, looking at three standard types of breast cancer drug with or without Avastin added on top.

One group received *either* the breast cancer drug capecitabine[22] alone, *or* capecitabine and Avastin. There was a second treatment group who received a taxane[22] drug with or without Avastin and a third group receiving an anthracycline[22] drug with or without Avastin.

Given the labyrinthine nature of the AVADO and RIBBON I trials, it would inevitably take FDA a while to work through all the data. However, it quickly became apparent that in both studies, Avastin had failed to demonstrate the sort of improvement in PFS which had proved so persuasive in the E2100 study. In fact in these latter two trials, Avastin didn't seem to be doing very much at all.

This was a finding *no one* had been expecting. It left everyone scratching their heads, wondering what was going on.

IV

In AVADO, the average PFS was 7.9 months for the docetaxel alone group and about 8.7 months for the two Avastin groups. The results showed that the higher dose level of Avastin didn't seem to have fared any better than the lower one. Neither seemed to be doing very much.

In RIBBON I the average PFS was 5.7 months for capecitabine alone compared to 8.6 months for the Avastin and capecitabine group. PFS was 8 months for patients receiving taxanes or anthracyclines alone, compared to 9.2 months when Avastin was added in.

These were disappointingly small differences.

PFS had been the primary endpoint of both AVADO and RIBBON I and whilst statistical testing indicated that both trials had formally met this endpoint, the difference made by Avastin was just too small to have any real meaning for either clinicians or patients. Especially as Avastin seemed to be adding substantially to the toxicity of the various treatment combinations, causing problems with bleeding, high blood pressure, infections, poor wound healing and quite a few cases of bowel perforation, a couple of which were fatal. These were side effects which seemed much more pronounced than those seen previously in the E2100 trial.

Survival was a secondary endpoint in the two studies but obviously still a very important one. Avastin failed to show a survival advantage in *any* of the treatment groups, in either of the trials. Patients were living on average about twenty five months, whatever treatment they received.

Worryingly however, in RIBBON I some patients seemed to be surviving for a *shorter* period, if they received a combination with Avastin, as opposed to one without it. There was a similar finding in the AVADO trial, where average survival was slightly lower in the Avastin groups.

The cause of this survival imbalance was never fully explained. Genentech argued, somewhat disingenuously, that patients in the *non*-Avastin arms had somehow lived longer than expected, for a group with disease that advanced. This had therefore negated the survival advantage Avastin would otherwise have demonstrated, if they'd only behaved as they were supposed to and died earlier on.

It wasn't much of an argument, especially as they couldn't find any explanation for this apparently greater longevity in the groups not receiving Avastin. It was the best they could come up with though.

However, no one was really buying it. Certainly not FDA, who were understandably more inclined to the view that Avastin was causing a greater number of fatal toxicities, resulting in shorter overall survival in patients receiving the combination therapies. The toxicity was predominating over the efficacy.

And so no wonder FDA felt a need to refer all of this to ODAC. They were now faced with three large trials in the first line setting, with a drug which appeared to meaningfully prolong PFS in one study but not the other two, had failed to extend survival in any of them and appeared to result in an excessive toxicity, which was directly contributing to the deaths of at least some of the patients.

In other words, it was difficult to decide whether Avastin was really providing a benefit or not. Had the time finally come for FDA to remove the breast cancer approval, on the basis of these findings. If not, what should they do instead?

The confusion wasn't helped by the fact that the reason for the differences in PFS between the three trials was unclear. Obviously each was using slightly different permutations of drug combinations. That could have something to do with it. Genentech would later try to use this particular argument to support their case for Avastin. But there were also some important variations in the design of the various studies. Those could be playing a role too. This would subsequently become FDA's chosen line of reasoning.

E2100 was on *open* study. The clinicians involved knew which treatment combination each patient was receiving and whether it contained Avastin. AVADO and RIBBON I were *double blind* trials, which meant that the various drug combinations were disguised to all look the same, so that no one knew who was receiving what.

Another difference was that E2100 used both investigator and independent review of the scans whilst AVADO and RIBBON I used only investigator assessments. The double blind nature of the studies made it more acceptable to have just the one.

E2100 involved only hospitals in North America, whereas the other two were international studies using cancer centres over a range of countries and continents. In an ideal world, it shouldn't make any difference whether a cancer trial is conducted in Missouri or Moscow or Mumbai or Montreal or anywhere else. However in practice, it is frequently surprisingly difficult to reproduce the same findings in different geographical territories involved in the same trial.

This regional diversity can occasionally be due to something identifiable, such as genetic or other variations, whereby different ethnic groups respond in slightly different ways to the same drug.

Or it could be accounted for by differences in the level of sophistication of hospitals in various parts of the world. This could be in things such as making an accurate diagnosis, being able to deal with potentially fatal toxicities of drugs, training in reading scans and so on.

Even regional disparities in mundane activities, such as the level of hospital record keeping, or the ability to follow up out patients for prolonged periods of time, could all contribute to geographical variability.

However, more often than not there isn't anything tangible which can account for these sorts of difference. They are just part of the unpredictable complexity of modern cancer studies.

It's like the enormous extremes of the Eurovision Song Contest. What's rhythm in one country is ridicule in another. You can't begin to explain it.

Which is why most regulatory authorities like to see some component of major clinical trials being conducted in their own territory, as a condition of considering a drug for approval. It gives them confidence that they're not being led astray by untrustworthy foreigners.

Despite all these possible explanations, there wasn't a clear reason why three Avastin trials had three different results for PFS. Even if they were at least all in the same direction of positive improvements.

And so the big question, on everyone's mind, was what ODAC would make of all this. It was time to see what Avastin's overall survival was looking like.

V

Out of the thirteen ODAC members at the latest July 2010 meeting, seven had also been present at the December 2007 one. The rest were new to the debate. The Chairman was ODAC veteran Wyndham Wilson. As a blood cancer specialist from the NIH, he wouldn't have been everyone's first choice to tackle this difficult breast cancer debate. But again everyone presumed FDA must have an explanation for it. They just weren't telling anyone else.

His opening remarks struck a note of pessimism which was to become characteristic of the way he liked to get an ODAC meeting in the mood.[23]

"This is a very difficult question, because we are being asked to evaluate whether or not an indication for Avastin should be removed," he explained, as he kicked the meeting into session.

"These confirmatory trials are large and they have not been able to show a survival advantage. They all show a very small benefit in PFS and also they show toxicity from Avastin, which can be life threatening and can lead to death in some patients. And so I think the question we need to ask ourselves at this point is how comfortable do we feel allowing this indication to remain?"

There was a little bit of initial skirmishing amongst some of the members. It was as though they were limbering up before the main event.

Jean Grem, an expert in gastrointestinal malignancies from the University of Nebraska, wasted no time in reminding FDA that they ignored the 2007 ODAC recommendation not to approve Avastin. Knowing what they did now, had that clearly been a mistake, he helpfully deliberated.

At least he was making his own voting intentions clear from the outset.

"We do not think we made a mistake here," responded Richard Pazdur from FDA.

"Believe me, we do not look at this as a mistake and it's not now a judgement on our past approval of the drug," he claimed.

However, many believed that was exactly how FDA were seeing it. And now they were here to vindicate themselves.

Dr Pazdur outlined the FDA pitch.

"We had data in 2008. We have more data here. And that's what we are looking at. There is a far more comprehensive picture here of the role of Avastin than we had in 2008.

FDA questions whether the magnitude of PFS improvement, observed in the AVADO and RIBBON I trial, confirms the magnitude of PFS improvement and the initial enthusiasm of these findings observed in the E2100 trial. This initial enthusiasm again resulted from a fifty two per cent increase in progression free survival with an observed 5.5 month difference observed when Avastin was added to paclitaxel.

The magnitude of treatment effect is clinically important, providing a measure of delaying symptoms from tumor progression and must be weighed against drug toxicity. In 2010 we now have a more comprehensive understanding of Avastin's role in the initial treatment of metastatic breast cancer compared to the 2008 approval. We will be asking the committee to re-evaluate Avastin's risks and benefits in this clinical setting."

Professor Wilson picked up the thread.

"I think we just have to be very aware that the goal of medicine is first to do no harm. I think the burden of proof is that a drug is helpful, not that it doesn't make people worse.

And we have definite evidence that Avastin causes serious and life threatening side effects: small numbers, but if you are the one, then that's not where you want to be. I think the Good Housekeeping seal of approval is important, and I think it needs to reflect what the data shows."

Most people though, were hoping the clinical content of the meeting would be at a more fundamental level than the health tips contained within *Good Housekeeping*. Certainly Genentech were anticipating a demanding debate. They had brought along no less than three of their own medics, along with a biostatistician. Each was going to make a presentation in defence of the areas of concern identified by FDA. Genentech were taking no chances this time and had also brought along Gabriel Hortobagyi, in person.

They had first go at presenting to ODAC and Dr Sandra Horning, Senior Vice President of Haematology/Oncology at Genentech, started for them. She had only been with the company since September 2009, having previously spent 25 years as a Professor of Oncology at Stanford University School of Medicine in Palo Alto, just down the road from the Genentech Headquarters in South San Francisco.

"I'm eager to be joining Genentech," she had said at the time.[24]

"I look forwards to working with an extraordinary team, and external collaborators to continue and extend the leading position of Genentech in advancing cancer care."

And this morning looked like being her opportunity to do just that.

"We look forwards to sharing and discussing our study results with you," she began. Which probably wasn't strictly true, given the uphill struggle Genentech suspected they were facing.

"There are three key elements to our presentation today. Firstly, we will demonstrate a reliable, consistent and significant improvement in progression free survival in each of our studies. Secondly, we will show that safety in metastatic breast cancer is well characterised and consistent with the broad physician experience of Avastin across oncology.

We believe that Avastin, combined with chemotherapy, is an important option for physicians and metastatic breast cancer patients to consider. We will review the largest data set *ever* submitted for first line metastatic breast cancer, more than twenty four hundred patients in three randomised controlled trials."

She never got round to saying what the third element was. Maybe she was in too much of a hurry to lay her cards on the table.

"Whilst the perfect clarity we would all like in every subset is elusive, we find the *totality* of the data consistent and clinically meaningful, allowing physicians and patients to make informed choices.

Today we will take you to the clinic to convey what it means to physicians and patients to have the option of Avastin and why the observed benefit is meaningful for women with metastatic breast cancer. That is how clinical benefit is defined by each patient and disease setting.

There's an extensive experience with Avastin for us to call on in oncology. This experience allows us to put the studies under consideration today in metastatic breast cancer into perspective, with regard to efficacy, combined ability with multiple chemotherapies, and safety.

Avastin has been approved for six indications.[25] Within these indications, 5-FU, irinotecan, oxaliplatin, carboplatin, paclitaxel and interferon (*all established anti-cancer drugs*) have been partnered with Avastin."

She pointed out that overall data were available for more than thirteen thousand patients in completed clinical trials. In total more than eight hundred thousand patients had been exposed to Avastin in clinical studies, or as a marketed product. That included more than ninety thousand patients treated for metastatic breast cancer alone.

She then went on to remind the committee of Genentech's involvement in breast cancer generally, as evidenced by the range of drugs it had in development. They were running a total of ten Phase III trials in the disease, involving more than ten thousand patients. That was a substantial commitment in anyone's book.

Dr Horning wanted to comprehensively establish the credentials of both Genentech and Avastin. The message was clear. Unlike ODAC, where virtually no one had direct experience of breast cancer, Genentech knew what they were talking about. This was what they did all day long. Instead of pontificating on committees, they were out there, developing new drugs and trying to make a difference.

Having made her point and hopefully captured a bit of higher ground along the way, she handed over to her colleague, Dr See Phan.

He was a Senior Medical Director and his job was to give an overview of the detailed data from each of the three Avastin trials separately and also with the data from all three pooled together. His was a highly technical presentation, full of clinical trial complexity. His sentences were stuffed with phrases such as *Kaplan-Meier curves, hazard ratios, forest plots, confidence intervals* and *p values.*

Just a one minute extract from his twenty minute slot, revealed his enthusiasm for the minutiae of methodology.

"The hazard ratio of 0.48 represents a reduction of 52 per cent of the risk of progression or death. Median PFS increased from 5.8 to 11.3 months, a 5.5 month difference. These Kaplan-Meier curves show the overall survival from E2100. In the lower left of the graph are the median overall survival and one year survival rate. There was a median of 35 months of follow up with approximately two thirds of the events having occurred. The hazard ratio of 0.87 favors the Avastin arm, although the difference was not statistically significant."

That was enough to leave everyone hoping the coffee break wouldn't be too far off.

However, having examined in exquisite detail the efficacy and safety data from all of the trials, individually and collectively, the inescapable conclusion from Dr Phan's presentation was still that there was *no* evidence for Avastin improving survival. There were also disturbing suggestions that it might in fact be making it worse, in selected groups of patients. You just couldn't get away from that fact, however complicated the language you used.

After a short presentation by Dr James Reimann, a Genentech biostatistician, on issues around the statistical techniques used to examine the primary endpoint of progression free survival, all eyes turned to the star presence of the morning, Professor Gabriel Hortobagyi.

The biggest act in town was about to take the stage.

VI

Bearded and engaging, he had a quiet air of authority about him. Like the King himself, he was also a natural performer.

Professor Hortobagyi warmed up with a review of the intricacies of the molecular biology of breast cancer. Despite the complexity, this must have come as something of a respite to the audience, after the preceding arcane abstractions of clinical trial methodology.

Working the audience, as though it were the Bellagio rather than Bethesda, he soon had them in the palm of his hand. Sizing up the room and seizing the moment, he marched straight on to the thorny issue of survival. It was time to grapple FDA's major bone of contention.

"Overall survival remains a reliable and hard endpoint. However, over the past thirty years, phase three trials that have shown a survival benefit have been exceeded many fold by trials without an overall survival benefit.

Demonstrating survival benefit in the metastatic breast setting is difficult because of the long median survival of patients, the use of multiple subsequent lines of treatment and crossover designs that attenuate or hide the survival effect of first line therapy."

(Crossover studies have two treatment groups, say Drug A and Drug B. When patients initially randomised to Drug A start to progress, they are swapped to Drug B, to give them something else to try. For patients this kind of design is attractive, as it increases treatment possibilities within the study. However, the interpretation of survival becomes complicated, because it will now be influenced by contributions from both Drug A and Drug B).

"Recent publications indicate that overall survival benefit is most likely seen with treatment regimens closest to the end of life, when subsequent treatments are limited and expected survival short. Very few clinical trials have shown significant improvement in overall survival in metastatic breast cancer, despite the introduction of dozens of new agents."

However, he did point out that overall survival in metastatic breast cancer had been creeping up over the years. This paralleled the successful commercialisation of an increasing number of anti-cancer agents. Each alone probably made a small difference but cumulatively the effect was a noticeable one.

"Today more than thirty drugs are available for managing metastatic breast cancer. While all agents have demonstrated anti-tumor activity, very few of them have documented survival benefit. However, the aggregate addition of these agents to our armamentarium resulted in a gradual and continued prolongation of overall survival of metastatic breast cancer, over the past three decades."

If survival was so difficult to document, then what about PFS? Professor Hortobagyi now began to move away from the abstract nature of clinical trial results, to the effects of new drugs at the level of the individual patient, bringing a more personalised perspective to the deliberations. He was like a barrister trying to *connect* with the jury.

"Improvements in PFS result in significant delay of disease related symptoms and avoidance of the psychological consequences and inconvenience associated with disease progression and changing therapy. The great majority of patients prefer the comfort of ongoing disease control, with the same continued therapy, to the uncertainties of multiple changes of treatment. Therefore from the perspective of the treating physician, prolongation of PFS can be, and is, highly clinically meaningful.

Having multiple therapeutic options is important to patients and physicians alike. Different treatments have different safety patterns and convenience, leading to different levels of compliance and therapeutic benefit. For patients, having more than one option and the ability to decide which is best for them represent important benefits. In this light, Avastin is not just one more interchangeable therapeutic option but a new tool to enhance disease control...in the management of symptomatic, bulky or rapidly progressive disease."

He went on to illustrate this proposition with a couple of real life patient examples. It was important not to lose sight of this *individual* personal dimension. This was particularly so, when confronted by the enormity of the impersonal *collective* clinical data, which a drug development programme represents.

Clinical trials typically lump together the data from hundreds or thousands of patients. They then look at the *average* of what outcomes occur across all of those patients. This is obviously important, to help get a clear understanding of what is happening *overall*. However, it runs the danger of overlooking *individual* responses, which can become drowned out in the averaging up that occurs.

After all, when you go to see your own doctor, he makes an individual determination of what is the best treatment for you alone. He doesn't wait until he has collected a thousand patients with the same condition as you and then work out what is best on average for all of them. And similarly, the aggregate nature of large clinical trials can often become divorced from the individual context of daily clinical practice.

By introducing some personal colour into the proceedings, Professor Hortobagyi was sowing the seeds of the idea that there were *clearly* some patients who were doing very well, all thanks to Avastin. Never mind what the collective data showed.

This *individualisation* of responders would subsequently become the strongest plank in the platform of the Avastin proponents.

As fate would have it, a succession of real life patients would obligingly stand up and promulgate exactly this message, in the subsequent public session of the meeting. It was almost as though Professor Hortobagyi had somehow managed to choreograph them into playing a role in the unfolding drama he was masterminding.

Having done his job with characteristic consummate professionalism, he handed the baton back to Dr Horning, to close the Genentech case. She largely reiterated what she had already stated at the outset, concluding:

"We believe Avastin combined with chemotherapy provides clinical benefit for metastatic breast cancer and deserves to be an option for the experienced oncologist to discuss with their patients, who can then make an informed choice.

For those of you who are not treating metastatic breast cancer patients on a regular basis, Dr Hortobagyi has provided scenarios where he and many physicians using Avastin today consider it to be helpful in gaining disease control.

While every patient's decision making will be individualised with her physician, we believe Avastin is an important option for physicians and patients to consider. And the extent, quality and consistency of the data presented here today facilitates meaningful discussion of benefit and risk, offering patients with HER2-negative breast cancer an informed choice."

She'd somehow managed to finish on *exactly* the right note. Informed choice and the right to it, were to become predominant themes in the subsequent stages of the Avastin adventure.

For the benefit of the wider audience, she'd also managed to helpfully remind the ODAC members of their overall lack of familiarity with treating breast cancer patients. This was in sharp contrast to Professor Hortobagyi, who was apparently surrounded by them at all hours of the day and night.

The Genentech team must have felt they had demonstrated that the weight of experience was on their side of the room. They *knew* what they were talking about. The unspoken inference was that the other side clearly didn't.

VII

The spirited Genentech defence was then followed by a much more laborious counter presentation from FDA, highlighting their concerns over the three trials. This was again given by Dr Lee Pai-Scherf, who had made the FDA presentation on the E2100 trial at the earlier ODAC meeting, at the end of 2007.

Obviously, none of the data in the trials had changed since the Genentech presentations of a few hours ago. Inevitably there was therefore a substantial degree of repetition, although FDA examined the safety profile of Avastin in greater detail because this was an area where they clearly had real reservations.

This was their big issue. Was the toxicity of Avastin simply too great to be justified by the relatively modest benefits.

"With the (*small*) margin of improvement in PFS and no improvement in survival, it is very important to consider the impact of Avastin related adverse events on a patient's quality of life," said Dr Pai-Scherf.

"You have heard me several times saying that the addition of Avastin to taxane, anthracycline, and capecitabine resulted in an overall increase in Grade Three to Five adverse events and serious adverse events.

When metastatic disease in a patient is *not* symptomatic, the delay in time to progression accompanied by treatment related toxicity, may not increase the patient's quality of life. The toxicities observed in AVADO and RIBBON I are well known to Avastin. The most common are Grade One or Two bleeding with epistaxis (*nose bleeding*) or mucosal bleeding. They were reported in more than fifty per cent of patients. And hypertension *(high blood pressure)* can occur in one out of five patients with Avastin.

However, serious adverse events such as haemorrhage, gastrointestinal perforation, fistulas, arterial and venous thromboembolic events, wound healing complications, left ventricular *(heart)* dysfunction, nephritic syndrome *(kidney disease)*, neutropenia *(bone marrow suppression)* are all events associated with Avastin. They are not as common but they certainly carry a high risk of morbidity or death. And they certainly do not improve patients' quality of life."

Which seemed to be points difficult to argue with. That was, after all, a lot of toxicity. FDA had scored a good point here.

"As you heard," Dr Pai-Scherf continued, "there was no improvement in overall survival in any of the three randomised controlled studies for metastatic breast cancer. But of concern is the fact that the hazard ratio *(a measure of survival)* favors the (non Avastin) arm in AVADO and the taxane/anthracycline cohort in the RIBBON I trial."

What she was effectively saying here was that none of the Avastin arms showed an *improvement* in survival and moreover it actually appeared to be *reduced,* when some of the patients received Avastin in AVADO and RIBBON I.

It wasn't a very strong signal but *any* suggestion that the drug might be worsening mortality was a powerful point for the prosecution to get in.

"So in conclusion," she finished up, "the key issue is the risk-benefit analysis."

And so there it was again. That risk-benefit, efficacy-safety balance, which framed any consideration of a new cancer drug and any determination of its usefulness. It was as impossible to avoid, as it was to objectively define what it meant. Dr Pai- Scherf left the concept floating in the air, like a school teacher who has just set a particularly demanding essay topic. *Risk-benefit. Discuss. You have one hour.*

After she had sat back down, there was an hour or so of questioning from the panel to the various presenters. They knocked the data backwards and forwards, toying with it from various angles but failing to really find anything new. The facts, which had by now been exhaustively presented, were after all fairly straightforward. The interpretation of them was however another matter altogether. That would have to come later on.

VIII

After a well deserved lunch break, the pace changed and there was an hour of open public hearings. This was a session when anyone, who'd registered their intentions in advance, could take the floor and air their views. These were usually patients or patient advocates, who'd developed strong opinions about the drug in question. However, the forum was also available to any other members of the public who felt particularly motivated to get something off their chest.

This time around, it was a fairly restrained event. Certainly compared to future Avastin occasions, which would degenerate into verbal abuse of FDA and ODAC. In months to come, as the Avastin saga unfolded further and people became more desperate, with tempers that were more frayed, the niceties of public debate and discussion would be increasingly discarded to one side. But for the moment at least, the rules were being observed.

The first to speak was Paul Brown, who was presenting a statement on behalf of the National Research Centre for Women and Families. This was a patient support group, based in Washington DC. They specialised in making medical information accessible to patients and their families.

Part of their self-imposed remit was to testify before various federal bodies about "programs and policies that need to be changed and about unsafe medicines and other products that need to be taken off the market and out of our homes and communities."[26]

It wasn't really a surprise to anyone therefore which direction they would be coming from.

"We had hoped that new research would support the FDA's decision to give Avastin accelerated approval for first line breast cancer treatment in 2008.

The drug showed promise in an open label trial, in terms of progression free survival but not overall survival. These two trials indicate the drug has much more modest effects on progression free survival than was claimed in 2007 and no improvement in overall survival. In fact the (non-Avastin) patients tend to do better in overall survival. Simply put, the patients are dying of other causes related to serious adverse reactions, such as heart attacks, strokes and gastrointestinal perforation.

Even when these are not fatal, it has a terrible impact on a cancer patient's quality of life. Metastatic breast cancer is not curable and most people live less than two years. So if treatment can't prolong survival, then the focus needs to be on quality of life.

Avastin does not improve either quality or quantity of life of breast cancer patients. It may shorten survival and it certainly harms the quality of life. In 2007 this advisory committee recommended against approval for Avastin, but FDA approved it anyway.

We urge you to set the record straight. Send the FDA a clear message that this committee is putting public health first. It is clear that the benefits do not outweigh the risks and that the indication for treatment of metastatic breast cancer should be removed."

Mr Brown couldn't have made his opposition to Avastin any clearer, if he'd leaned over and tattooed it on Richard Pazdur's forehead.

However, no sooner had Mr Brown sat down, than up popped breast cancer patient and Avastin user, Patricia Howard. She had a very different message to send to FDA.

Mrs Howard had been diagnosed in 1993 and treated initially with chemotherapy and radiotherapy, before being declared cancer free. She now recounted the positive tale of her encounter with Avastin. Although suffering from a terminal disease, she appeared to have all the time in the world to share her story with the captive audience.

"In 1999 my husband and I decided to retire from teaching. I was cancer free. A few years later we decided to purchase a home in Florida. We were to be snowbirds. I decided then that I would seriously take up the sport of golf. I entered lessons in our local club. One day, when I was at the lessons, I pulled back the club and I could hear something crackle and crunch in my lower back. If you've seen me swing a club you'd understand what followed.

My husband took me to a local hospital. They diagnosed what they thought was a pulled muscle. The pain persisted. I went back a week later to that same hospital and they decided to do a CAT scan. The diagnosis came out what they thought. I had a broken rib. As I said you should have seen me swing that club.

But they also thought I might have mesothelioma (*a rapidly fatal kind of lung cancer*). In a panic I called my oncologist and he guaranteed that he would set up the necessary appointment with a thoracic surgeon and all necessary testing would be done in New York. But I still had to get through Christmas with my children. As I opened that box of new golf outfit, through my tears I wondered if I would live to see the day to wear it.

I did return to New York and a lung biopsy was performed. And in fact I was diagnosed with incurable metastatic breast cancer to my left lung. The course of action started off with Femara (*a hormonal treatment used in breast cancer*) and many of the like with known results. During that I was experiencing a lot of difficulty with breathing. Walking up a flight of stairs became an extreme effort. I constantly felt like I had an elephant on my chest.

We went through many emergency visits as an outpatient to have Sloan-Kettering (*a New York cancer hospital*) withdraw the fluid in my lung. It got to the point where the cancer was showing some itty bitty growth and so the lung specialist decided to insert a pleurex catheter (*a tube placed into the chest cavity*) as an outpatient. I walked around with that coiled around my abdomen for months. The visiting nurse would come every other day and draw the fluid from my lung. This was not a fun situation but we had to get through it.

They decided at that point to offer me the opportunity to enrol in a clinical trial using the drugs Avastin and Abraxane (*a form of paclitaxel*). I willingly agreed. The infusion was on a Monday. By Friday the fluid in my lung had dried up. There was evidence that the tumor was shrinking. My quality of life was not the greatest. My golf handicap plummeted (*sic*). I was tired. But I saw my way through two years of using Abraxane and Avastin.

At the end of that year the neuropathy (*painful nerve damage, which is a side effect of paclitaxel*) became unbearable and so he decided to change my course of action to Avastin with the inclusion of the pill Xeloda (*capecitabine*). I was to get an infusion of Avastin every three weeks and Xeloda pills on a week and off a week.

Well, let me tell you, that completely changed my quality of life. I've been known to come out of the chair after the infusion of Avastin and get on the golf course and play eighteen holes of golf. My golf handicap has plummeted instead of risen. I think that I can thank Avastin for enjoying the birth during that time of my granddaughter Charlie, who lives in New York, and my grandson Jackson, who lives in Atlanta. Another one is on the way in September.

I can thank Avastin for giving that quality of life that I can continue to shop and dine with my friends. I can thank Avastin for the fact that I can play four and five days of eighteen holes of golf. I can thank Avastin for – I can look across the table at night at my husband with the hope of knowing that we will be spending many more years together. We just celebrated our forty third wedding anniversary. I only hope that I could know that you will continue to manufacture this drug for myself and all the other women around me. Thank you."

The panel could probably have spent the rest of the afternoon being drawn further into Mrs Howard's personal life. Her testimony powerfully served to capitalise on the human dimension to the Avastin debate, which Professor Hortobagyi had sought to develop earlier on. Many others also took to the stand to tell their personal stories of how Avastin had turned their life around, after all other chemotherapies had failed to bring their disease under control.

The testimonies ranged from the mundane to the moving. They all had a common theme though. Avastin had worked for them, whatever the clinical trial results might suggest to the contrary. It was difficult to avoid the conclusion that Avastin was doing something dramatic, in at least some women. In time, these patients would become known as the Avastin "super-responders." The problem was that no one seemed to know how to identify them in advance. That would make it impossible to select out the patients most likely to benefit from treatment.

As if to emphasise this difficulty, the last speaker in the public session stood up to knock Avastin firmly back down again. Roberta Gelb was a name straight out of the annals of James Bond villainy. She was in fact a breast cancer survivor and a member of SHARELeaders, another patient advocacy group for breast and ovarian cancer. Their members had been meeting monthly for the last ten years to discuss research results and controversial issues in breast cancer.

"Last month two of our members died of metastatic breast cancer. One of them was only thirty six years old. Both were passionate advocates who used their experience to make differences to the lives of others.

SHARELeaders has had ongoing discussions on the research results for Avastin coupled with the hope that after accelerated approval was given, rightly or wrongly, further clinical trials would show clinical benefit, overall survival or sufficient progression free survival with quality of life.

This was not the case.

Avastin should not be approved as first line treatment for metastatic breast cancer. The members of SHARELeaders advanced several different lines of argument for their decision."

Their main reasoning lay around the lack of clear survival or quality of life benefit for Avastin. That was their biggest objection. SHARELeaders also had more generalised reservations, about whether progression free survival should ever serve as a credible endpoint in breast cancer research.

"We survivor advocates strongly believe that overall survival, without compromising quality of life, must remain as a primary goal of research. Some believe it's the only goal. We want drugs that extend our lives and not merely the length of time until progression of our disease.

Overall survival as an endpoint also enables us to know what late toxicities may arise with longer term use of the drug or even after the drug is no longer being used.

The Avastin results failed to show overall survival or any clinically meaningful progression free survival. There were critical toxic and unacceptable side effects and little quality of life data.

Any risk-benefit analysis would strongly suggest that Avastin should not be approved at this time."

Although Ms Gelb had ended things on an unequivocally negative note, opinions overall were balanced.

Most individual patients who'd made the journey had done so to speak out in favour of Avastin. None were there to recount an adverse experience. Opponents however would later cynically argue this was because patients who'd died of the drug weren't exactly able to step forward to talk about the experience.

That was certainly the view of most of the patient advocacy groups. These were surprisingly united in their antagonism to Avastin in particular and any drug in general, if it hadn't shown a clear survival advantage.

The big question was which camp most closely represented the wider patient population. Was it the grouping of individual patients, who felt they owed their continued existence to Avastin. Or did the various advocacy groups have their collective finger more firmly on the popular pulse. Despite the fact they often had their own vested interests to promote and axes to grind.

IX

With time now moving on apace, Professor Wilson tried to summarise the discordant views arising from the proceedings so far.

"What we are here to judge is whether or not there is a clinically meaningful, from a patient's point of view, quality of life *et cetera*, between the patients who received Avastin versus those who didn't.

And in considering that, one has to take into account what the risks are and there definitely are risks on the Avastin arm that are not there on the other arm. Then one also wants to take into account whether or not these risks are translated into a late *decrease* in survival.

I think from a scientific point of view what we can say is that we have no evidence that there is any survival advantage. I think we don't have any strong evidence that there is a survival disadvantage to the Avastin arm. But clearly no signal that Avastin is improving outcome.

So I think the focus now has to be on are we dealing with a clinically significant improvement in progression free survival and is this offset by the increased risk associated with this agent."

And that neatly framed the dilemma now facing the ODAC members, as they came to the all important issue of *the voting*.

There were four questions in total that FDA had submitted to ODAC but only one of them really mattered.

The first two questions related to whether or not the results of the AVADO and RIBBON I trials represented a favourable risk-benefit analysis for Avastin, in their own right.

The third question, obviously dependent on the answers to the earlier ones, was whether AVADO and RIBBON I provided *confirmatory* evidence of the clinical benefit of Avastin seen in the E2100 trial.

And then there was the real clincher. If the answer to Question Three was "No" then FDA wanted to know "Should the indication for metastatic breast cancer be removed from the Avastin label?"

Members of the committee voted by pressing one of three buttons at the bottom of their microphone, marked "yes," "no" or "abstain." The totals were electronically displayed on a monitor next to the chairman. It should have been a foolproof system.

The results, when they came, were unequivocal. The panel seemed to be pretty much thinking and acting as one.

Voting for the first three questions was thirteen-zero unanimously negative, with the exception of Question Two, about the value of the RIBBON I study, where the vote was twelve-one.

The outcome of the vote over Question Four and the removal of metastatic breast cancer from the Avastin approved indications, was a foregone conclusion by now.

"Let me read into the record the voting results: "*Yes*" twelve, "*no*" one, "*abstain*" zero," revealed Chairman Wilson. It was all over, bar the shouting.

The committee had come down twelve-one against continuing the approval of Avastin in metastatic breast cancer. Not unanimous, as some ODAC votes have been in the past and would be in the future. But nevertheless, it was still a very unambiguous message to FDA.

"Just so we don't all get bored," continued Professor Wilson, with the nearest he ever came to an animated gesture, "I'm going to start from the left hand side now and have you state your name, your vote for the record, and the reason for your vote."

This was regulatory transparency in action.

"Natalie Portis. (*Patient Representative*). I voted yes for all the reasons that we've been talking about, that these further studies did not give us reason to believe that this was effective, does not prolong life and even progression free survival. If it is of value as a surrogate it's very limited and there still remain serious adverse effects to patients."

The next member of the committee appeared confused about how she had voted.

"Virginia Mason. (*Executive Director, Inflammatory Breast Cancer Research Foundation*). I'm the lone yes vote which may sound a little strange after the other no votes. I mean I'm a "no" vote... excuse me.

My reason is that in the second paragraph of the indications in use (*written prescribing information for physicians*) there's a sentence that says "there are no data demonstrating an improvement in disease related symptoms or increased survival with Avastin." I can live with the fact of having that on a label and allowing the physician and the patient to make a decision if they want to take the risk of a drug that does have significant side effects but could, for that individual patient, have some benefit."

"I'm Pat Loehrer. (*Medical Director Indiana University Cancer Centre*). And I voted no. It was not and..."

"You voted yes," interjected Wyndham Wilson. Confusion reigned. "I don't know what I voted," continued a perplexed Dr Loehrer. "At least I got the right cancer."

"I voted yes," he continued. "This was not an easy vote for me because I do think for the reasons that Dr Mortimer mentioned, this was a co-operative group trial and more in the real world than some of the industry sponsored trials that are done.

So I think there is activity for Avastin in breast cancer. I think it is yet to be clarified.

I think I would look forward, if the company were so inclined to look at symptoms and see if there were a clinical benefit response as manifested by decreased pain or increased performance status, or some other surrogate marker that might be helpful. I would also welcome them to identify the particular patient population that may benefit.

I think again there's likely markers out there that I think there's been a tendency to treat as many people as possible. I think to make this a great drug, as the good to great book says, I think we need to decide who we shouldn't treat and treat those who are going to benefit."

"I'm Mikkael Sekeres. (*Professor of Medicine, Cleveland Clinic Taussig Cancer Institute*). I voted yes. The statement from FDA about accelerated approval states that it requires the applicant to conduct adequate and well controlled trials, and the sponsor certainly did that to further define the degree of clinical benefit to patients. I think that's where this fell short. At best, I think these studies may have confirmed the advantage in progression free survival but didn't go beyond that."

"I am Wyndham Wilson," said Wyndham Wilson. "I voted yes. I think that at least from ODACs voting record this is a good example of the system working. I think we got two excellent, or should I say outstanding clinical trials done in a reasonable period of time. Unfortunately they do not support the original effectiveness of the agent.

Hence, I voted to remove the indication, because I think the totality of the data does not support this being effective and therefore against the risk-benefit.

I do want to echo that there may be a subset of patients…that may benefit from this drug and in those groups this risk-benefit may well favour the patients getting this. But those are the kinds of studies which need to be done."

And so the *yes* votes kept coming.

"Jean Grem. (*Professor of Medicine, University of Nebraska Medical Centre*). I voted yes. Obviously we're all disappointed with the results of these follow up studies. But since Dr Pazdur has absolved me of guilt, I hold my head up high."

"Ralph Freedman. (*Professor of Medicine, MD Anderson*). I voted yes, basically based upon the decisions we've made with AVADO and RIBBON 1 and the substantial defects that occurred in the original trial, which I think could have contributed to physician equipoise."[27]

"Brent Logan. (*Professor of Biostatistics, Medical College of Wisconsin*). I voted yes. I felt like the reduced magnitude of benefit that we saw in these well conducted studies indicated that the indications should be removed."

"Ralph D'Agostino. (*Chairman Mathematics and Statistics Department, Boston University*). I voted yes also. I think we have a process laid down, the accelerated approval. I think we had questions, we did have substantial questions with the previous study. The sponsor did perform excellent studies.

We can say there's two or three studies that we were presented with and they did not achieve the clinical significance that we would have hoped for. They did emphasise the risk-benefit problem, the safety problems. I think the vote to remove the indication was quite consistent. Again, I did vote yes."

"Joanne Mortimer. (*Professor of Medicine, City of Hope Comprehensive Cancer Centre, LA*). I think I've already articulated why I voted yes."

"Aman Buzdar. (*Professor of Medicine. MD Anderson*). I voted yes because even though these were very good studies, they failed to confirm the finding of the initial study on which accelerated approval was given."

"Gary Lyman. (*Professor of Medicine, Duke Comprehensive Cancer Centre*). I voted yes. I still think there's something going on here with a thirty to forty per cent relative risk reduction in progression free survival but without other data imminently available, I think I would be opposed to continuing with the current label."

And finally, "Ron Richardson. (*Oncologist, Mayo Clinic*). I voted yes. I have to ask for absolution but for a different reason. I don't know that a vote of six to four or five to five would have made any difference in December 2007 but while the committee was debating the issue, I was sitting in Minneapolis snowed in for two days.

So I was not part of that decision, I think now the sponsor is to be commended for supporting the confirmatory trials. It's regrettable that we couldn't advance this field and in the end, as has been said many times, survival trumps everything and we haven't shown a survival advantage here."

Interestingly, the only vote in favour of continuing with Avastin had been from Virginia Mason of the Inflammatory Breast Cancer Research Foundation. This was a patient advocacy group located near Hermosa

Beach, a short distance south west of Los Angeles. The word *inflammatory* in their name referred to a specific type of breast cancer,[28] rather than any particularly provocative attitude they may have favoured as a group. Her position was in sharp contrast to the strident anti-Avastin posturing of the majority of sister organisations. She'd been the lone voice speaking up in favour of the individual patient having the right to determine the risk-benefit equation for themself, when deciding on whether to give Avastin a go or not.

Twelve others, including some of the country's leading experts on cancer, had voted to terminate the use of a drug which they all acknowledged was doing something useful. They just weren't quite sure how much.

It was also a drug being prescribed for breast cancer at a rate of a billion dollars a year, despite widespread knowledge of the AVADO and RIBBON I data. Genentech weren't exactly having to hold a gun to anyone's head, forcing them to write out a prescription.

It was far from clear whether the oncology community at large would agree with the decision of their august brethren, gathered in Gaithersburg to speak on their behalf.

"Okay," concluded Professor Wyndham anti-climactically. "I would like to thank all of the committee members, FDA and the sponsor for working hard and thank you and have a nice afternoon."

And so the meeting concluded at three thirteen pm.

A drug intended for the dying had just been delivered a fatal blow itself. You wouldn't put much money on its chances of survival now.

But then again, this *was* cancer medicine. When it came to oncology, nothing could be taken for granted.

Book Three

I

Despite Professor Wyndham's invitation, it was unlikely that the people from Genentech would be having a good afternoon. They traipsed out of the Ballroom and along the corridor leading out of the Hilton, on to Perry Parkway. It was difficult to take in the enormity of the defeat. Twelve-one was a resounding verdict against everything they'd been arguing for.

This was the first time FDA had consulted ODAC over the potential revocation of an accelerated approval. If they followed the recommendation of the ODAC vote, Avastin would become only the second cancer drug ever to formally lose an indication received under the accelerated approval mechanism.

The only other victim of this fate had been a drug called amifostine (Ethyol). This had been developed to prevent kidney damage, caused as a side effect of the chemotherapy agent cisplatin, when used to treat lung cancer. It lost this approval in 2005, largely because more effective treatment options had emerged to replace cisplatin.[29]

Two other drugs had also failed to survive confirmatory clinical trials, after initial accelerated approval. One, Astra Zeneca's *Iressa* for lung cancer, had been put into a restricted access programme back in 2005. It had subsequently managed to resurrect itself, through the miracle of molecular biology and establish a role in selected types of patient. The other, Pfizer's *Mylotarg* for adult acute myeloid leukaemia, had been withdrawn voluntarily by the sponsor in 2010.

Neither of these were therefore technically revocations.

In theory, FDA had an indefinite period of grace before making a decision following on from the ODAC recommendation. However, it was widely expected they would announce their conclusion by mid-September. They had therefore left themselves about eight weeks to work out what to do.

Reaction to the Avastin news, the day after the ODAC meeting, was mixed. It certainly wasn't going to make FDA's decision any easier.

Genentech issued a somewhat restrained press release, simply saying that it was "disappointed with the committee's recommendation" and that the drug "should continue to be an option for women with this incurable disease."[30] The company stated that it would continue to discuss the data with FDA.

However, at the same time as saying this, Genentech had pretty much already removed any reference to metastatic breast cancer from the Avastin website, apart from certain legal obligations around the prescribing information for the drug.

Certainly, compared to the prominence given to breast cancer just the day before the ODAC meeting, looking at the website now, you'd never guess that Avastin had ever been intended for those sorts of patients.

It didn't send out a particularly optimistic message.

Support for Avastin came from many other quarters though.

One of them was the megalith that is the Mayo Clinic. Located in Rochester, the Mayo Clinic grew originally from the fields of Minnesota, at the end of the nineteenth century. It was built around the medical practice of Dr William Worrall Mayo and his two sons William and Charles. Today, it is the world's largest integrated medical centre, offering just about every known medical and surgical speciality.

It has flourished and propagated, just like the surrounding fertile farmland.

In fact, it is *so* big that it has also spread to two other sites – Phoenix in Arizona and Jacksonville in Florida. The Mayo Clinic in Rochester alone covers more than fifteen million square feet, and in total employs over fifty five thousand staff, eclipsing the cancer specialist MD Anderson Hospital by comparison. It has an annual budget of over seven and a half billion dollars.

The opinion of Professor Edith Perez therefore came with some weight attached to it. She was Professor of Medicine at the Mayo Clinic in Jacksonville and director of the breast cancer programme there. She was also chairperson of the Breast Committee for the North Central Cancer Treatment Group.

She clearly disagreed with her ODAC colleague from the Mayo Clinic in Rochester, Professor Ronald Richardson, who had voted against Avastin.

"The results from the AVADO and RIBBON I trials have been known for many months," she pointed out.[31] "Our practice has continued in terms of considering this agent as one of the options for patients with advanced disease. I think we need to continue our work to better identify *individual* patients who may benefit. Individualised treatment options are becoming more of a reality and so one treatment might be more effective than others, for certain patients."

Gabriel Hortobagyi from MD Anderson was much more outspoken.[31]

"Avastin is clearly active in breast cancer and there is more experience with this agent than with many, if not most, agents evaluated for metastatic breast cancer. Anecdotally, Avastin combinations can produce dramatic responses in individual patients and it is my clinical experience that responses of such quality are seldom seen with the same chemotherapy programs but without Avastin.

As a frequent user of this agent, I have found that it is very well tolerated by the great majority of patients and in very few do I need to modify the dose or schedule and in even fewer do I need to discontinue treatment because of toxicities."

He went on to acknowledge the lack of a survival distinction but was adamant that the FDA reviewer, Dr Pai-Scherf, presented the data in an unfairly biased manner.

"This either denotes ignorance of common statistical methods or an underlying agenda to place the agent in an unfavourable perspective. There were other surprising statements made by the FDA reviewer attributing certain toxicities to Avastin when in fact these toxicities are well recognised as being associated with the underlying chemotherapy *(with which Avastin was combined)*.

For instance, bowel perforations are a well recognised complication of taxanes, especially docetaxel. Angina and myocardial infarction are reported complications of capecitabine and congestive heart failure is a well known complication of anthracyclines, such as doxorubicin and daunorubicin. The FDA reviewer continuously referred to these complications as *Avastin related*, creating an artificially high mortality rate in the minds of ODAC members."

His outrage hadn't run its course yet.

"During the discussion I got the strong impression that several ODAC members had a poor understanding of clinical trials and statistics, based upon some of the questions, which were somewhat bizarre and that very few had any experience of using Avastin in the clinic. Otherwise they would have known that the frequent toxicities reported on paper caused few symptoms and actually did not affect the quality of life and then perhaps they would have seen the response and progression free survival benefits in a different light."

Furthermore:

"The sponsor complied entirely with the FDA's requests when accelerated approval was granted. However, FDA instructions were vague and the "magnitude of benefit" was never defined. Despite the fact that FDA never requested prolongation of survival, much of the discussion by ODAC members was based on this lack of survival benefit. Therefore, there was a major disconnect between FDA and ODAC.

Ultimately ODAC members acted according to their understanding of the risk-benefit ratio of the drug and recommended removal of the metastatic breast cancer indication.

I think this was the wrong recommendation, although witnessing the process I can see how inadequate instruction by the FDA, unfamiliarity with the drug and a biased presentation by an FDA reviewer led to this result."

And finally:

"I am concerned in part because this recommendation might remove an important treatment option from patients with metastatic breast cancer. I am also concerned because "clinical benefit" remains poorly defined. This precedent will set many drugs currently under development up for failure.

It would be important for FDA to clearly define expectations from sponsors and provide clear guidance to ODAC members so that disconnects such as those observed during this discussion stop happening."

It was a damning indictment of an ODAC which was seen by many as being ineffectual at best and inept at worst. It was difficult to understand how a committee with so little direct experience of Avastin could consider themselves qualified to determine its fate. The stridency of Professor Hortobagyi's views was also indicative of the apparently enormous size of the conceptual division around the Avastin issue.

This was to go on and generate an intense controversy, both within and outside the oncology community, which raged for months to come. The arguments would be fought on many levels, ranging from clinical trial design to conspiracy theory detection and involving everyone, from cancer clinicians in institutions, to cyber-columnists on the internet.

In the following weeks, the ground seemed to quickly shift away from the clinical controversies of the trial data and on to other issues. One was the cost of Avastin therapy and the influence that might be having on the decision making process.

"It's hard to talk about (Avastin) without talking about costs," Eric Winer from Dana-Farber told *The Washington Post* in August.[32] Professor Winer had been one of the ODAC participants at the December 2007 meeting, speaking in favour of Avastin.

"For better or worse, Avastin has become in many ways the poster child for high priced anti-cancer drugs."

These sentiments from specialist institutions such as Dana-Farber were echoed at the community level too. Dr Francis Arena was an oncologist from Lake Success, near Great Neck, on the North Shore of Long Island. The founder of Arena Oncology Associates, he treated a range of patients, including those with breast cancer. His philosophy was to provide "hospital-calibre care in a comfortable and warm office setting."[33] That would definitely be a bit different from Dana-Farber then.

"I think it is a travesty, a real crime that women might lose this drug," he said.[34] "Every medical oncologist had a patient on an Avastin protocol who has done extremely well. Money has become the biggest issue here, which is why there has been an incredible problem. They are shoving the doctor patient relationship aside."

Undeniably the benefit of Avastin, if it was indeed there, came at a cost. A course of therapy for metastatic breast cancer was approximately ninety thousand dollars per patient. For which there was no clear survival advantage in return. Many would go further and argue you got nothing at all for your money. Genentech subsequently countered that it had limited the annual Avastin price to about fifty seven thousand dollars, which was comparable to the cost of Herceptin (trastuzumab), Genentech's other antibody for metastatic breast cancer.

Herceptin however had the distinction of a proven survival advantage to help justify the cost. In any event, both antibodies were still very expensive, even when compared to other recent breast cancer drugs. Bristol Myer's *Ixempra* (ixabepilone) had been approved in 2007 and only cost about thirty one thousand dollars per patient with metastatic breast cancer. However, Avastin supporters would argue that drugs like Ixempra were used in a second line setting, where patients were expected to live for a much shorter period of time. That substantially reduced the cost of treating them.

FDA approval decisions are supposed, by legislation, to be limited to considerations of safety and efficacy alone. However, it would seem almost inevitable that cost considerations would have some influence on regulatory attitudes. Particularly with drugs where there was substantive disagreement over the magnitude of any clinical usefulness.

In fact, several members of Congress had written about this very issue to FDA and the Department of Health and Human Services (of which FDA are an operating division). These included the senator for Louisiana, David Vitter. He wrote to Dr Richard Pazdur of FDA on July 27th, just a week after the ODAC vote.[35]

"The decision on whether a patient should use a possible life extending drug is a decision that should be made solely between a doctor and a patient, not a government panel. I find it outrageous that a government panel would put a price on those precious months for the families that are living through the trauma of losing a mother, wife, sister, daughter or aunt. Taking Avastin off label for breast cancer treatment is essentially government rationing.

I am not suggesting that Avastin is a perfect drug but it has a proven record of effective treatment for some patients when used along with chemotherapy. Lacking any safety concerns, we should not deny patients access to a treatment which might extend their lives and their time with their loved ones."

His letter came to an end, in a crescendo of dramatic hyperbole:

"I shudder at the thought of a government panel assigning value to a day of a person's life. It is sickening to think that care would be withheld from a patient, simply because their life is not deemed valuable enough. I fear this is the beginning of the slippery slope leading to more and more rationing under the government takeover of healthcare that is being forced on the American people."

An editorial in the Wall Street Journal, on August 18th 2010 was much more brutal.

"Unless the FDA leadership overrules its own experts, the 40,000 women killed by breast cancer each year will be denied an important clinical option."[36]

It pointed out that the original requirement of FDA, after the accelerated approval of Avastin, was to show an improvement in progression free survival, with an obligation only that overall survival was *not impaired*.

However, FDA "later unilaterally redefined its regulatory expectations devising a pretext to undermine Avastin. The terms of ODAC debate are set by instructions from FDA staff reviewers and in round two they suddenly emphasised topics that had been resolved in round one, such as the lack of overall survival benefit and safety issues such as toxic side effects."

The editorial raged on:

"Whilst ODAC is ostensibly independent, it is in practice a creature of FDA and the FDA's political masters in Congress. The Agency appoints the rotating ODAC members, which is like a prosecutor choosing his jury. The Agency's oncology leaders – led by cancer drugs chief Richard Pazdur routinely stack the panel with people who share their dislike for industry and accelerated approval."

The article pointed out that in recent years FDA had tightened conflict of interest rules so much, that the ODAC members often had no specific expertise in treating the disease they were considering a drug for. That explained why so few of the ODAC panellists had firsthand experience of treating metastatic breast cancer themselves.

Most of the physicians who *really* knew about breast cancer and were experts in the disease, tended to have been hoovered up as consultants to pharmaceutical companies active in the area. They wanted the best advice they could get for their development programmes. It also gave them a handy pool of captive clinicians to call on at tricky times, such as tense ODAC debates for example.

FDA had dealt with the potential problem of impartiality this might have created by appointing ODAC members who couldn't conceivably have a conflict of interest. The fact that they had achieved this by diluting out anyone with anything more than a passing knowledge of the disease area, so that no pharmaceutical company would want them anyway, seemed to have been overlooked in the process.

Unfortunately it meant that in the quest for probity and propriety, proficiency had been an early sacrifice.

The *WSJ* continued, objectively:

"So here we have government anointed medical patriarchs, substituting their own subjective view of Avastin's risks and costs for the value that doctors and patients recognise. If Avastin is rescinded, thousands of dying women will lose more than proverbial false hope in the time they have left. They will lose a genuinely useful medicine.

The Avastin mugging is really an attempt to undermine regulatory modernisation like accelerated approval that offends FDA's institutional culture of control and delay. It is also meant to discourage innovations, like Avastin, that the political and medical left has decided are too costly, with damaging implications for the next generation of cancer drugs."

The article concluded with the reminder that:

"Cancer survival rates have improved gradually over the last several decades, thanks in part to improvements at the margin, like Avastin. ODAC's advice is not binding and it would be a hideous injustice if the Agency came down once more on the wrong side of a life and death question."

With the Wall Street Journal fanning the flames, the Avastin debate continued unfolding, with typically American multimedia transparency. Disagreement developed in the press, on TV, on blogs, in patient forums and pretty much everywhere else too.

Josh Turnage was a nineteen year old from Madison, Missouri. His mother Christi Turnage, a forty eight year old nurse, had suffered from breast cancer since 2006. A year later, it had spread to her right lung, making her disease incurable. Technically, this was called *stage IV disease*, where the cancer had spread way beyond its origins in the breast. Amazingly though, following treatment with Avastin, she was now twenty seven months progression free.

He made a seven minute and forty one second video about her fight with breast cancer, which somehow seemed to crystallise the personalisation of the national debate. It sparked a huge amount of attention. Shot in a couple of hours, with a camera borrowed from his local Broadmoor Baptist Church, the video featured stills and footage of his mother and her family. There was nothing more to it than that. But it seemed to do the job.

In it, Josh points out that "My mom is living with stage IV, not dying of stage IV. My family and I are just asking that the FDA help my mom to continue this way."

Josh's mother, and a family friend, whose wife also had stage IV breast cancer, started a petition and the YouTube video led to six thousand and five hundred signatures against FDA removing the Avastin approval.

"This drug is a miracle drug for some patients with metastatic breast cancer," said the petition.[37] "(*Stopping the drug*) would be a huge disservice and death sentence to people with metastatic breast cancer who are responding well to this medication. Every patient will have a different response to Avastin but every patient should have a right to choose. Let breast cancer patients have the choice of a medicine that may hold our cancer at bay and allow us hope that we will be around when a cure is found."

The petition was featured prominently on a number of news channels, often alongside profiles of other breast cancer patients, who were also doing exceptionally well on Avastin. This was accompanied by regular media allusions to "death panels" restricting access to a lifesaving drug, despite the absence of any evidence that it actually did this.

The emotive individualisation of the controversy continued in many different ways. About the same time as the emergence of the Turnage petition, Patricia Howard, who had spoken at the previous month's ODAC meeting, giving her own testimony on the value of Avastin, gave an interview to Newsday, a New York news outlet.[34] By now, she had become something of an amateur expert on the drug.

"Yes, women do die while on the medication. That does happen," she said. "Yes, some women do not get past the first year but some of us are thriving." Recalling the ODAC meeting, she continued, "I was the lone soldier speaking for patients who need this drug. One doctor got up during the meeting and said, 'This drug gets women only to first base and we want a home run.' I felt like jumping up and saying I don't mind just being in the ballgame. I am alive."

The *WSJ* kept up the pressure, with an article on Thursday September 16th 2010 by a breast cancer sufferer called Geraldine Satossky. It came out just a day ahead of the anticipated FDA decision date. The piece was entitled:

"My battle with cancer and the FDA. By Friday regulators may withdraw the drug that's keeping me alive."[38]

The sixty seven year old cancer victim from Reston, Virginia, recounted her harrowing eleven year battle against breast cancer, which included a mastectomy, a liver resection and endless rounds of chemotherapy. She was now facing her third relapse of the disease and only Avastin and capecitabine seemed to be providing any hope. Even her own oncologist had told her she was "in big trouble" now. But despite this, two out of four tumors in her liver had started to disappear within days of commencing Avastin.

That was three and a half years ago.

"Today, I am not just living life, I'm enjoying it," she explained. "While I get tired more easily than I used to, I can take part in just about all normal activities. I can go out to dinner with my husband. I can visit friends."

Like most victims, she went on to express her bewilderment at FDA's reservations over the seemingly limited efficacy and excessive side effects of Avastin, concluding that, "I'm proof Avastin works."

As someone who'd experienced more chemotherapy than many, she was also well qualified to point out that, "all cancer treatments are risky and they all come with side effects...but the worst side effect is death, and that's guaranteed to happen when cancer isn't treated."

She ended by conjecturing that maybe better treatment approaches would eventually materialise. However, until then, "Avastin is all I have. And I want to live."

IV

Whilst these emotive arguments could be disproportionately persuasive, not everyone appeared to be in favour of Avastin. This included many oncologists treating other types of cancers, who were increasingly speaking out against it.

"Avastin was not as promising as once hoped," wrote Dr Michael Cummings from Chatham Massachusetts, in response to the Satossky article.[39]

"We now spend seventeen and a half per cent of GDP on health care, most of it wasted on care that doesn't work. Somehow we must find a way to get more bang for our buck. Sentimental pieces like this do not help that process. I would prefer to see the *Journal* roll up its sleeves and offer advice on how to solve this morass before it drowns in a tsunami of waste."

Nearly ninety per cent of cancer specialists and other healthcare professionals, who voted in an online survey in September on the highly regarded Medscape Medical News website, felt that the FDA decision to withdraw the Avastin breast cancer indication was the correct thing to do. The poll was organised by Howard West, a medical oncologist with an interest in lung and prostate cancer, at the Swedish Cancer Centre in Seattle. He pointed out that in lung cancer for example, nearly *all* new drugs have been approved on the basis of survival alone and so why should breast cancer be any different?[40]

"It is hard for me to understand why we should have different acceptable endpoints for accepting wildly expensive medications depending on whether they are treating one cancer or another. It is hard to look at the oncology landscape and not think that society basically feels that some cancers are simply more worth treating than others."

It was a deliberately provocative position to adopt but clearly some were beginning to believe it might be true.

Additionally, most of the breast cancer patient advocacy groups remained steadfastly opposed to continuing the approval of Avastin.

Musa Myer, herself a breast cancer patient since 1987 and coordinator of *AdvancedBC.org*, a Manhattan based advocacy group, wrote an open letter to FDA, urging it to act upon ODAC's recommendation.

The San Francisco based advocacy group *Breast Cancer Action* claimed prominently on its website that, "BCA was the only breast cancer organisation to put patients first by actively opposing the use of Avastin for metastatic breast cancer, because of its failure to improve overall survival or quality of life, its side effects and high price tag."[41]

In all the heated controversy, maybe one of the most balanced views came from a third advocacy group, *Susan G Komen for the Cure*. This was the world's largest grassroots network of breast cancer survivors and activists. They issued a statement on August 17th, jointly with the Ovarian Cancer National Alliance. *(Avastin was also extensively used for ovarian cancer, although not actually approved for that particular indication)*. The Dallas based group, named after breast cancer victim Susan G Komen and founded by her sister Nancy Brinker, acknowledged that:[42]

"The benefits of Avastin overall are modest for women with metastatic breast cancer. However, we do know that for some women Avastin offers a greater benefit – but we do not yet know how to determine which patients will experience greater benefits. We have much to learn about the drug and how individual patients respond, such as why some women receive greater benefit while others do not.

Moving into the world of personalised medicine, cancer treatments will be more tailored to the characteristics of patient's individual tumors. Yet due to the current state of the science, we don't always know which patients will benefit most before a drug is made commercially available. As with all medicines, we encourage a thoughtful discussion between a woman and her doctor that carefully considers the benefits and the risks."

Acknowledging that FDA would most likely withdraw the Avastin approval, the statement continued:

"We hope that drug manufacturers will continue to develop medications for the treatment of metastatic breast cancer and would not want this decision to mean that drug development for breast cancer comes to a crashing halt. We will only succeed in finding new treatments for cancer by bringing new drugs to the clinic.

We call on stakeholders – government, private industry, academia and the non-profit community – to invest in the development of biomarkers and new drugs and to get new technology and treatments to patients' bedsides as safely and as quickly as possible. Further, we hope women who are currently receiving Avastin for metastatic breast or ovarian cancer continue to have access to the drug and that third party payers will continue to cover it."

This was a pragmatic view of the situation, which stood out for its reasonable modesty, in amongst the extremes of hyperbole colouring most of the rest of the debate. Unlike many of the more zealous proponents and opponents, it recognised a middle ground.

The overall evidence for Avastin's efficacy was modest, in most people's book. However, hidden within that anonymity of the average, there was clearly a sizeable sub group of women who were deriving substantial benefit. The challenge now was to find ways of identifying them. Surely that had to be a more sensible approach than burying the drug altogether and depriving *everyone* of it.

V

However, many views still being expressed were much less temperate than this. There appeared to be no end in sight for the firestorm of controversy engulfing FDA. Given this, the Agency did what they did best and procrastinated. They announced on 17th September that they would be delaying a statement on the Avastin issue until December 17th 2010.

They gave no reason for this though. Maybe their dilemma seemed so obvious, there was no need to spell it out. They were paralysed by indecision, caught in the middle of an argument they couldn't contain or control.

This decision, or rather indecision, itself provoked a further round of controversy. The delay "has left the breast cancer community in limbo," said Kathy Miller from Indiana University and the original lead investigator on the E2100 study.[43]

Whilst she acknowledged that FDA were likely to be criticised whatever they did, "leaving us in limbo is the worst possible decision they could have made. What do we tell our patients? There is now even more uncertainty over whether or not to use Avastin in breast cancer. To put a new patient on this drug could lead to problems with reimbursement if the decision in December revokes the breast cancer indication but not putting a patient on this drug could be seen as "short-changing" her if the decision is in favour of the indication."

Professor Miller, like many others, also wondered just what was taking FDA so long. The information from the AVADO and RIBBON I studies had been available for over a year and there was no new information likely to emerge between September and December.

Those of a more conspiratorial inclination noted that the delayed decision was now conveniently after the US midterm elections in November. Many in Congress had been lobbying FDA to keep the breast cancer indication. Presumably they wouldn't want an unpopular decision coming out any time soon, if it might adversely influence voters' intentions.

However, despite the sustained intensity of the preceding five months, the fury of the debate abated somewhat during the run up to the December 17th FDA deadline. Maybe everything that could be said, already had been, by then. The protagonists' passion had been spent.

VI

In the end, FDA revealed their hand a day earlier than expected, on December 16th.

They had finally come down in favour of *removing* the breast cancer indication for Avastin, on the basis that the benefits seen didn't outweigh the risks involved. These included high blood pressure, bleeding and haemorrhage, perforations in the nose, stomach or intestine, heart attacks and heart failure. A fairly comprehensive litany of liabilities, it must be said.

"The limited effects of Avastin combined with the significant risks led us to this difficult decision," said Dr Janet Woodcock, Director of FDA's Centre for Drug Evaluation and Research.[44] She was one of their most senior people. Whilst not quite at the top of the tree, she was only a twig or two below it.

"Today's decision was a difficult one for the Agency but certainly not unique," she stated. Most people weren't buying that though. The Avastin decision was in a league of its own, if for no other reason than the sheer amount of time FDA had dithered over reaching a conclusion.

The ever blunt Dr Pazdur was more direct.

"Given the number of serious and life threatening side effects, FDA does not believe there is a favourable risk to benefit profile," he told reporters at a press conference.[45] Short of poking someone from Genentech in the eye with a pointed stick, he couldn't have been more forceful in his opposition to the drug.

Less confrontationally, Dr Woodcock at least appeared to be leaving the door slightly ajar. "We encourage the company to conduct additional research to identify if there may be select groups of patients who might benefit from this drug."

The official FDA News Release indicated that "FDA is open to working with Genentech on any proposals to conduct additional studies of Avastin in patients with metastatic breast cancer, designed to identify a population of patients in which the drug's benefits exceed the risks."[44]

They were encouraging Genentech to find ways of better characterising the Pat Howards and Geraldine Satosskys. The company needed to identify these super-responders up front, rather than by waiting for them to pop up in newspaper articles, after the event.

However, they would have to pay for this enormously expensive and risky undertaking, without the comfort of Avastin remaining on the market whilst they did so. FDA couldn't have expected Genentech to derive much consolation from such a lukewarm attempt at mediation.

Despite that, the Agency must have hoped this was at long last the end of the divisions and disagreements. They'd finally managed to wrestle Avastin into a box and the lid appeared to be firmly nailed down. However as it turned out, events were far from done. There was the definite sound of banging coming from inside the coffin.

Genentech clearly weren't inclined to accept the olive branch of working with FDA, if that's what it was. Instead, the company brazenly indicated it intended to refuse voluntarily withdrawing the breast cancer indication. In the small world of those who followed the vicissitudes of US drug regulation, this was an extraordinary development.

If it had been a soap opera, it would have been the shooting of JR. Everyone was tuning in for it. There hadn't exactly been an enormous number of similar cases in the past. But previously, when FDA had actually reached a decision to rescind the approval of a drug for a particular use, the company concerned had thrown in the towel at that point and voluntarily withdrawn it from the market.

Genentech however was clearly made of sterner stuff, or at least thought it stood on firmer ground. And so in the face of Genentech's refusal to remove Avastin voluntarily, FDA were now forced into the almost unprecedented next step of issuing what was technically called a *Notice of Opportunity for a Hearing* (NOOH).

This gave Genentech fifteen days, within which to exercise the right to request a public hearing to contest FDA's decision. This was an appeals mechanism usually only made avail of by individuals about to be banned by FDA, following convictions for fraud in clinical trials, or other related misdemeanours. It would be a first for a company to go down this route.

Maybe Genentech were emboldened by the fact that, on the very same day as FDA announced its decision to withdraw Avastin, the EMA (*European Medicines Agency*) confirmed that it would remain approved for use in metastatic breast cancer in Europe. Their opinion appeared to be the exact opposite of their US colleagues.

The EMA reaffirmed that "the benefits of this combination (*Avastin and paclitaxel*) outweigh its risks and that this combination remains a valuable treatment option for patients suffering from metastatic breast cancer."[46] It was as though FDA and EMA were talking about *different* drugs. They certainly didn't appear to be talking to each other.

"We are pleased that the EMA has confirmed the benefits of Avastin in combination with paclitaxel and that Avastin will continue to be available to women with metastatic breast cancer living within the European Union," said Dr Hal Barron, Roche's Chief Medical Officer in a press release. "We believe women living in the United States should also have Avastin as a treatment option and therefore we will request a hearing with FDA," he said, throwing down the gauntlet.[47]

And just to emphasise Avastin's credentials, the Roche-Genentech press release reminded everyone that:

"Avastin has made anti-angiogenic therapy a fundamental pillar of cancer treatment today – over three quarters of a million people have been treated with Avastin so far. A comprehensive clinical programme with more than five hundred ongoing clinical trials is investigating the use of Avastin in over fifty tumor types (including colorectal, breast, non-small cell lung, brain, gastric, ovarian and others)."

It was clear that they weren't ready to give up the fight just yet. And neither were others.

Senator David Vitter, along with many other Republicans was quick to jump in.

"With this disappointing decision, the FDA have chosen to place itself between patients and their doctors, by rationing access to a life-extending drug," he said.[48]

His sentiments were echoed in a letter written by five Republican members of Congress to the FDA Commissioner, Dr Margaret Hamburg. They claimed the decision was "a large scale intrusion into Americans' lives and their personal health care decisions, that had previously been left up to a patient and their health care provider."[49]

The Wall Street Journal called the FDA decision "reprehensible" and accused the Agency of "substituting its own judgements about clinical meaningfulness for those of practising oncologists and terminally ill patients."[50]

But in reality, there was little new to say in the aftermath of the decision, that hadn't already been extensively aired in the weeks and months leading up to it. There was, after all, only so much invective which could be heaped on FDA.

The next developments would have to come from the uncharted territory of the Genentech appeal.

Book Four

I

Genentech finally responded to FDA on January 16th 2011, with a ninety eight page document signed jointly by Dr Horning, who had led the company's presentation at the previous summer's ODAC meeting and two lawyers. Michael Labson and Paul Schmidt were both from the Washington firm of Covington and Burling.

The position piece listed a number of scientific, legal and policy points which Genentech cited, in support of its contention that the Avastin accelerated approval should be maintained. Inevitably, much of this was a reworking of the data which had already been covered in excruciating length at the ODAC meeting the preceding July.

However, the company did indicate that it would be prepared to throw something new on the table. They were willing to conduct *another* Phase III trial, similar to the E2100 study and again with PFS as the primary endpoint. But this time, the trial would also be including an assessment of *biomarkers*. Genentech believed this might just be the ace in their hand of cards.

Biomarkers could potentially solve the puzzle of how to identify the so called super-responders, where the risk-benefit ratio was that much more favourable. They might provide the signpost to the middle ground and the pathway to keeping Avastin on the market.

A biomarker is something about a particular patient which can be easily measured and which suggests they are more likely to respond to a drug than another patient without the biomarker. It would therefore be a way of channelling Avastin to those women most likely to benefit from it. The marker Genentech had in mind was something called Vascular Endothelial Growth Factor (VEGF).

VEGF (pronounced VEG...F) was a chemical usually produced in large quantities by tumors.[51] It played a key role in promoting the profuse growth of new blood vessels, upon which cancer cells relied. Blocking VEGF was one of the main ways Avastin was thought to work. It therefore made sense that VEGF levels might somehow be correlated with how much efficacy Avastin was able to produce. Moreover, recent findings from a re-working of some of the AVADO data suggested patients with higher VEGF levels tended to have longer PFS results with Avastin, compared to those with much lower levels of VEGF. This information had attracted a lot of interest, when presented in December of the previous year, at the prestigious annual San Antonio Breast Cancer Conference in Texas.[52]

Maybe therefore VEGF would be a metaphorical marker pen, allowing Genentech to start joining the dots together.

If so, then measuring VEGF levels could be the answer to keeping Avastin alive in breast cancer. It might mean less women being treated in future. The drug would only be suitable for the proportion of patients with the elevated biomarker levels. But it would be a lot better than it not being used at all.

Making a concession around biomarkers, which had originally been an FDA suggestion back in December, should also have made it easier for both sides to relax their stance a little bit.

But only by a very small amount. The Genentech response reminded the Agency that, "there are fundamental differences between Genentech and FDA around the interpretation of the available data, the benefit-risk profile presented by Avastin, the consistency of FDA's proposed withdrawal...and the broader implications of FDA's actions for the development of cancer medicines."[53]

So the stakes were high. As well as the fate of Avastin, both sides had a lot of face on the line.

A month later, on February 24th, FDA agreed to the request for a public hearing. It was scheduled for June 28th and 29th. They didn't really have much choice, given the intense public scrutiny, which showed little sign of abating. By the time the June meeting came around, it would be almost four years since the first ODAC meeting had convened to consider Avastin. That was about twice the life expectancy of the patients for whom it was intended.

II

The spring and summer months, prior to the June meeting, were muted ones. FDA and Genentech were keeping their powder dry and giving little away. Activity continued on the various blogs and discussion forums but without the passion which had characterised the previous year.

The days immediately before the ODAC meeting were marked by a number of rallies and protests outside FDA and other federal buildings. Activists in favour of Avastin were doing their bit and taking to the streets.

But their demonstrations lacked both passion and momentum. No one took that much notice. If anything, FDA were probably flattered by the attention. It helped remind them that life existed outside of their claustrophobic cloisters.

For once, the Avastin meeting wasn't being held in a Hilton Hotel. Breaking with tradition, it was being hosted by FDA at their White Oak Campus in Silver Spring, Maryland. After all, there were only so many Hiltons any one person could cope with. Maybe they also felt safer on home territory.

They were certainly taking no chances. They'd given themselves an extra layer of protection by deciding to run the meeting themselves. This time, there would be no independent chairman. Well, *notionally* independent chairman.

The presiding officer was Dr Karen Midthun, who was Director of the Center for Biologics Evaluation and Research (CBER). The final decision on Avastin's future would be taken at a later date by Margaret Hamburg, the FDA Commissioner. She didn't feel the need to be at the meeting herself. Maybe her mind was made up already.

However, Dr Midthun was at pains to point out that Commissioner Hamburg had asked her to convey "How seriously she took this hearing and the need for the science to be presented and examined in an open, systematic and thoughtful manner."[54] For most people who'd had previous dealings with FDA, the terms "open" and "thoughtful" wouldn't be the first ones which sprang to mind to describe the experience. But maybe this time, it would all be different.

FDA had invited seven ODAC members, nearly all of whom had been present at previous Avastin hearings. It was a smaller quorum than the normal twelve or thirteen and had required a special dispensation from the Commissioner herself. There were the familiar faces of Ralph Freedman, Brent Logan, Mikkael Sekeres and Wyndham Wilson. Gregory Curt was again the Industry Representative and Natalie Portis was there on behalf of the patients.

The only newcomer was Frank Balis, who was Professor of Clinical Research in Oncology at The Children's Hospital of Philadelphia. It was a fair guess that he didn't see too many patients with breast cancer though.

In fact, there were only two medical oncologists on the entire panel and no one with any direct experience of actually using Avastin. Many were to subsequently question the motives behind FDA's apparent selectivity in putting this group together.

Although the ODAC caravan may have been travelling light, all the elements of the circus were now gathered, ready for the show to commence. When the curtain went back and the drama finally got underway, the opening session of the first day was devoted to pre-registered members of the public.

The majority were patients, there to speak in defence of the drug which, they were convinced, was the only thing in between them and certain death. All had a particularly strong desire to vent their views.

Each was allotted three minutes. That was about one minute, for each year of life expectancy most of them could look forward to. There was a light system to help them keep to time. It changed from green to yellow, when there was one minute remaining and then red when time was up. For most of the speakers though, the red light had started shining long before they set out on the journey to Silver Spring.

Dr Midthun was keen to point out that FDA "places great importance on public participation in this process. The insights and comments provided can help the Agency and this committee in the consideration of the issues before them."

No one seriously believed that for a moment but at least she was able to say it with some semblance of conviction. There were thirty five members of the public lined up for their three minutes of air time. Only four of them wanted to speak against the drug. These were all from patient advocacy groups, who'd previously built their opposition on foundations of immutable rock. They weren't about to change their minds now.

The other thirty one were speaking in favour and wanted to give Avastin the green light. In addition to grateful patients, there was a coalition of supporters, including representatives from advocacy groups for ovarian, colon and kidney cancer, as well as melanoma. None of these were directly affected by the decision in breast cancer but they wanted to show allegiance to sister sufferers. Many were also concerned about the wider implications of an Avastin withdrawal, for cancer drug development in general.

A number of practicing oncologists had also taken the effort to come along and speak up for maintaining Avastin. These included Dr Joseph Sparano, who was Chairman of the ECOG breast committee. This had been the group behind the original E2100 trial, which had sparked the whole controversy in the first place. Almost a decade on, he still found himself having to defend their most notorious study.

The transcript of the meeting includes a detailed index of where and when various topics were covered during the proceedings. For some unknown reason, this also documents thirty one episodes of applause and one of laughter. However most of the morning session was characterized more by tears and torment, as victim after victim took to the stand.

Many in the US never thought they would witness the day when patients were forced to stand up and openly plead for their lives.

III

These Avastin disciples had come to literally beg for a continuation of the drug which was keeping them alive. There were some common themes running through these disparate accounts of personal adversity. All were convinced, along with their physicians, that Avastin was the only thing standing in the way of a rapid demise and death.

Many of them were representatives of a sub group of patients who were now designated as the "super-responders." These were people in whom Avastin appeared to be having a definite and often dramatic effect. They stood out like a shining beacon of exuberant success, compared to the modest effects of the drug overall.

Super-responders was a phrase used frequently and freely by them. It was like the chant of a cult. It conferred them with a commonality of identity and purpose. Subsequent Genentech speakers also picked up on it too. Unsurprisingly, it wasn't a term uttered by any of the FDA representatives. Anecdotal experience was anathema to these purist practitioners of evidence based medicine.

All the speakers were adamant that the side effects of treatment were tolerable and their quality of life had improved dramatically since starting the drug. There were numerous personal accounts of how important and meaningful an increase in progression free survival could be. It translated into the birth of a grandchild, the marriage of a son or daughter, a wedding anniversary, a graduation ceremony or even something as simple as a walk with parents. Avastin might not improve survival and actually buy you extra time. But these were significant things to be able to achieve, with whatever was remaining.

Everyone acknowledged the controversy over the drug and the difficulty in interpreting the data. They all agreed there was a difficult balancing act. However, the recurring theme was that this deliberation should be left to the individual patient and physician to wrestle with. FDA had no job getting in the way and restricting personal choice. The decisions were too complicated for the formulaic approach of regulatory restriction.

Most of those speaking ended with a plea for the continued provision of the drug. These ranged from the poetic to the pitiful. Priscilla Howard was a housewife who'd been on Avastin for the last thirty two months. The drug seemed to be holding her otherwise aggressive disease at bay. Everything else so far had failed.

"I want every available weapon in my arsenal as I fight this devastating disease," she told the gathering. "As I face a frightening and uncertain future, I think of the moving poem by Dylan Thomas. I will not go gentle into that good night. I will rage against the dying of the light. And with your help, it will keep burning."

Others were more prosaic. The redoubtable Patricia Howard, a veteran of previous ODAC encounters, was there to speak again. She had the birth of yet another grandchild, courtesy of Avastin, to share with the panel. She concluded her latest autobiographical update with a direct and poignant plea.

"I ask today that you please hear my plea to continue to be that wife, mother, sister, aunt, friend and grammy for many years to come. I never thought in the United States that I would have to beg for a drug that is keeping me and many others alive. Please approve Avastin as a treatment for my disease. What if I was your wife, your mother, your sister, your friend and what if I was your grammy?"

As the panel sat back to contemplate this particular fate, others were lining up to tell stories less of affliction and adversity but more of antagonism and aggression. Many had come simply to rail against FDA and the whole absurd process that had led to them all being there in the first place.

One of the most scathing was Steve Walker, who was cofounder of the Abigail Alliance for Better Access to Developmental Drugs. This was, he explained, a "non-profit, nonpartisan patient advocacy organisation, dedicated to assisting people with serious and life-threatening diseases and unmet medical needs." They were strongly opposed to the possible removal of Avastin.

He explained to the panel in front of him.

"This hearing is taking place within a procedurally corrupt administrative process.

Dr Pazdur selects all the appointed ODAC members from the nominations submitted for these posts. He also decides when temporary voting consultants will be added to an ODAC meeting and directly selects them, no nominations or pre-screening required.

Five members of the current ODAC roster are present today. Dr Balis was selected for ODAC by Dr Pazdur after this hearing was requested by Roche Genentech and scheduled by the FDA. The rest were selected for ODAC by Dr Pazdur before the hearing was scheduled.

These facts were confirmed for me by Jayne Peterson, deputy director of the CEDR (*Center For Drug Evaluation And Research*) advisory committee office and Dr Michael Ortwerth, director of the advisory committee staff in the FDA's commissioner's office, in a teleconference last Thursday.

With the exception of Dr Balis, who is new and Dr Curt, who isn't allowed to vote, they all voted to rescind approval in the July 2010 ODAC meeting. Ms Portis, the patient representative, attended both prior ODAC meetings and voted against the indication both times.

None of the voting physicians on the panel appear to be engaged in treating breast cancer as a significant part of their clinical research or medical practice.

In March, Genentech raised serious and well founded concerns with FDA regarding the biased nature of ODAC. FDA dismissed those concerns, stating that CDER vigorously protects the independence and balance of federal advisory committees. The Abigail Alliance strongly disagrees with FDA on this point. Dr Pazdur's complete control of ODAC allows him to preordain the advice and opinions he receives from his committee, neutralizing the FDA's decision to observe separation of functions in this case and rendering this hearing effectively a sham.

To our panel here today, the patient community is going to hold everyone involved in this hearing accountable for bringing personal and professional integrity to this process. Given the circumstances, we think you should consider whether recusing yourself is the only way to do that. It's too late to do anything else."

It was probably everything Genentech had been wanting to say but couldn't. It also articulated the belief of many that ODAC was little more than an alter ego of FDA. The former existed largely to defuse difficulties faced by the latter. No bureaucrats, as skilled as those at FDA in the dark arts of political machination, would place a truly *independent* committee in their way.

Just in case anyone had missed the point, these accusations were reinforced by another speaker, Terence Kalley, whose wife Arlene was in the advanced stages of the disease. He was also the founder of the pressure group Freedom of Access to Medicines, one of the organisations behind the protests outside FDA in the past few days. Given that history, he was unlikely to hold his fire once on the stand.

"Knowing that death will come early from incurable disease is devastating. FDA has compounded this anguish by its complete indifference to current Avastin patients. FDA has treated these women as expendable innocent statistics in the face of a regulatory machine on autopilot, a bureaucracy unencumbered by any ethical controls. Your callous indifference is terrifying patients. Their anxiety is excruciating, your prolonged silence deafening."

He was only warming up though at this point:

"FDA purports to base its actions on science, in defiance of evidence and common sense. The highly unscientific and unethical handling of the entire Avastin saga cries out for congressional oversight and major FDA overhaul. The European Medicines Agency has approved Avastin. The practicing breast cancer oncologists of the NCCN (National Comprehensive Cancer Network) approve Avastin.

Can you say with certainty that all these medical experts and patients are wrong? As many issues regarding Avastin remain unresolved, requiring further research, justice and common sense dictate that you not sentence these women to premature deaths by depriving them of their life saving Avastin.

Make no mistake. This hearing is a death trial, not of Avastin but of those women who rely on it to stay alive. You are each personally responsible for the consequences of your own vote. A vote against Avastin by each of you, is a vote against thousands of women."

The rhetoric reverberated around the room. More accustomed to the dry discourse of choreographed discussion, the committee members appeared at a loss to deal with the onslaught.

IV

However, in amongst the pleading patients, angry activists, haranguing husbands and outraged oncologists, there were a few voices speaking up in support of FDA. Some of them even had their own fund of emotive tragedy to draw upon. There was enough of it to go round, after all.

Helen Schiff, for example, was speaking out against Avastin and on behalf of the advocacy group SHARELeaders. Her organisation was implacably opposed to the drug. She took the opportunity, in the final moments of her three minutes, to add a personal twist.

"Whilst I have a few seconds, just in my own name, I would like to say that for every woman here testifying, there are other women who we know – a member of our own group who bled out of every orifice in her body, Jimke Vassu. Another woman, Sandra – I can't remember her last name – in Florida who had a brain haemorrhage. So those people don't come to testify. I just want you to remember that they exist too."

She had a point. The women who were dead couldn't be there to tell their side of the story. The living were always going to be more vocal. The members of ODAC and FDA probably wanted to run over and give her a hug.

As the gruelling morning session wore towards a conclusion, the vast majority of proponents and dwindling band of those in opposition, all had their, usually highly polarized, say. The atmosphere was largely one of antagonism and accusation. Given that it was supposed to be the academic dissection of a drug, it was more like Spartacus than Socrates.

In amongst all this prejudice and preconception, there was however one balanced view, which neatly encapsulated the whole dilemma. This belonged to Bob Erwin, from the Marti Nelson Cancer Foundation. He was another Avastin/ODAC veteran.

"The FDA's objectivity and high standards are vital to individual patients and essential to public health. Anyone following cancer drug development for long has seen the retrospective data dredges that promoters of shoddy science periodically try to sneak past the FDA, often followed by diatribes

413

on the editorial pages of the Wall Street Journal, when hype fails to overcome good scientific review.

The dedicated professionals of FDA, including Dr Pazdur, are often the only significant barrier to toxic placebos in our pharmacies and twenty first century snake oil salesmen promoting false hope to desperate patients and families.

However, this is not the situation that faces us in the case of Avastin today, nor is today's challenge a matter of choosing between evidence based medicine and emotional anecdotes. Collectively, we have many years of experience with Avastin and nothing new is likely to be revealed today or tomorrow. We also know that Avastin, like many other cancer drugs, does not work for most women with breast cancer but that it does work well for a fortunate minority.

Additional clinical trials of Avastin in combination with a taxane, or any other chemotherapeutic agent, are not likely to provide meaningful new insights on the drug's effect on overall survival or progression free survival. We still may not know in advance for whom Avastin will work and for whom it will fail.

This is the critical question to which we have no answer. For whom will Avastin work? Additional questions include, why have Genentech and FDA discussed a biomarker-guided clinical trial of Avastin for months but enrolment has not begun? Why has Congress not appropriated enough money for FDA to expand its scientific staff and infrastructure to efficiently analyse and regulate drug biomarker combinations? And of course, why is the consideration of price and product performance off limits to the FDA? So many elephants and so little time.

Considering all the available evidence, our recommendation is to continue the approval of the breast cancer indication under the accelerated approval mechanism, subject however to serious carrot and stick incentives to get the necessary biomarker studies enrolled, finished and reviewed to enable better informed decisions about the ultimate fate of Avastin in breast cancer."

So many elephants. It was the most accurate statement of the meeting so far. Normally, you'd have to go on a safari to see that many gathered altogether in one place.

V

The largely rehashed content of the public session set the theme for much of the subsequent deliberations. Since the last ODAC meeting a year earlier, there was little new to say of scientific or clinical relevance. Most of the proceedings would consist of re-delineating already well defined and defended positions, which hadn't shifted in the intervening period. There were only two new pieces of information for the committee to consider. Everything else had already been exhaustively discussed.

The proposal from Genentech for a Phase III biomarker study was a recent initiative. However, it turned out to be such a new one, that they were still in the process of designing it and so couldn't give too much away. It wasn't going to form the basis for a substantive discussion and a fresh way forward. It was too embryonic for that.

The other development was a clinical study, known as Study 10. This was a large two thousand patient trial, in the first line treatment of HER2-negative metastatic breast cancer. It was important because it was very similar to the E2100 study. The patient population was the same, as were two of the three treatment arms.

One consisted of paclitaxel combined with placebo and another was Avastin combined with paclitaxel. The results from these two groups therefore had the potential to confirm or refute the impressive PFS findings seen in E2100.

The third arm was placebo, combined with a drug called *motesanib*. Motesanib belonged to Amgen, who were developing it as a potential oral competitor to Avastin. It acted in a similar way, to block VEGF activity.

And that was the problem for both Genentech and FDA. Amgen owned the data for Study 10 and they weren't sharing all the details of it with anyone else. Neither Genentech nor FDA had been afforded an opportunity to go through the raw data, stripped down to its nuts and bolts components. Only by sifting through the study at this level of micro-resolution could either be sure what the findings really were and how best to leverage them in defence of their own position. Without being able to lay bare the totality of the database, each side would endlessly accuse the other of selectively abstracting only those bits most favourable to them.

However, some of the results had been published in the medical journal *Lancet Oncology* earlier in the year. They showed a difference in PFS which wasn't that great, when Avastin and paclitaxel were compared to paclitaxel alone. It was only a month or so in duration and certainly wasn't the magnitude seen in E2100.[55]

FDA would refer to Study 10 a number of times in their presentations. For them it proved the results of E2100 were an unusual one off, incapable of replication.

On the other hand, Genentech downplayed it as much as possible, claiming FDA had selected out the worst results from the study and given these undue prominence. They also tried arguing that it was invalid to compare the two trials, due to differences in "patient demographics, tumor biology, size of the study and baseline tumor volume." Since no one had access to all the data though, neither party could claim a victory from it.

There wasn't therefore much material for either side to develop a new line of attack with. It was like two teams, which had faced each other too many times and were overly familiar with one another's players and tactics. They were wearily ready to take each other on once again but neither side were expecting any surprises.

VI

After the public sessions had come to an end, it was time for FDA to give their version of events. Although they were allocated two hours for their slot, the position of the Agency was made clear in the first two minutes by Richard Pazdur. There wasn't much need for the extra one hour and fifty eight minutes. Maybe they could have used it to build a brick wall.

"We now have five randomized trials of Avastin added to chemotherapy in breast cancer trials, involving more than three thousand five hundred patients. We have carefully reviewed this data and conclude that no trial has demonstrated an improvement in survival, no trial has demonstrated an improvement in health-related quality of life and no trial has confirmed the magnitude of benefit in PFS observed in E2100, that led us to the approval of the breast cancer indication.

After very carefully considering all the available data, we've determined that the benefits of Avastin do not outweigh the serious and potentially fatal risks.

It is not appropriate to continue accelerated approval while Genentech tries to conduct another trial to establish clinical benefit. It is likely that any new study will take years to complete and the available data simply do not suggest that a new study is any more likely to show the magnitude of benefit observed in E2100.

The Agency must show an appropriate degree of flexibility in making new promising drugs available to the American patients with serious and life-threatening diseases as soon as possible. But there is a trade off here. FDA may expeditiously withdraw approval if clinical benefit is not confirmed, in the interests of public health."

It was the same stance FDA had adopted back in December and it would steadfastly remain their position throughout the next two days. In their eyes, the only study which had shown any clinically useful benefit was E2100, with the five and a half month improvement in PFS.

This however had been a methodologically flawed study, on many levels. These shortcomings, combined with the failure of AVADO or RIBBON I to confirm the results of the earlier trial, meant that the findings of E2100 were nothing more than a chance occurrence. The PFS result was an aberrant outlier and no amount of additional studies would ever change that fact.

It was a blinkered view, which simply brushed aside all the earlier testimony from women who'd experienced prolonged benefit from Avastin, along with acceptable toxicity too.

You could almost sense Richard Pazdur stepping back and eying up the Genentech contingent, to see how they were planning to breach this particular road block. If, by some unimaginable means, they did manage to break through, he had kept his best weapon in reserve. Even if Genentech could refute the reservations about the robustness of E2100 and the degree to which it had been vindicated by subsequent trials, he still had the risk-benefit gambit to play.

It was impossible for Genentech to counter that. They could attempt to place the E2100 PFS benefit beyond any doubt. They could call Mother Theresa herself as a witness, to attest the veracity of the result. But all FDA had to do was say that the benefit, *even* if proven, just didn't justify the risk. It was a subjective stance, which couldn't easily be rebutted with facts or figures.

It was an exceptionally difficult position to fight against. It also happened to ignore what everyone had been arguing for, during the previous two hours. All the earlier speakers acknowledged that there was a difficult balancing act here. But no one thought it was anything to do with FDA. This was a deliberation which rightfully rested in between the patient and their doctor.

"I want to stress that patients are capable of making informed decisions, working with their oncologist to weigh the risks and benefits in the context of their individual circumstances," one participant, Nancy Haunty, from Seattle, had explained in the preceding public session. Maybe Dr Pazdur had been otherwise engaged, whilst she was speaking.

"My seventy six year old mother, who was diagnosed with metastatic breast cancer five months before I was, would not choose Avastin. But as a forty year old with aggressive and extensive mets (*metastases*), Avastin was a logical choice. I signed an informed consent. I understood the risks and benefits."

Ivy Ahmed, of the Cancer Support Community, framed a question which really crystallised the controversy.

"At what point should decisions surrounding risk and benefit sit with FDA and at what point should those decisions be left to a patient and his or her doctor? At what point does FDA have a responsibility to educate and empower patients with the facts and then leave the decisions to them with their eyes wide open?"

If she didn't have the answer, then Terence Kalley characteristically did.

"It should not be for you, but for my wife and her oncologist to make this life and death decision. Please just leave my dear wife Arlene alone to continue taking her medication without any interruption. Is this asking too much?"

Evidently it was indeed asking too much. The assessment of risk and benefit was the preserve of FDA and FDA alone. At least according to them. This was spelled out later on by Dr John Jenkins, who was director of the Office of New Drugs, within the CEDR division of FDA.

"In the end, CEDR's decision must be based on the available scientific data from adequate and well controlled trials. These data inform our assessments of the benefit-risk of the drug for the population of patients with breast cancer. That is our obligation under the law and we take that obligation and our public health mission very seriously."

That's how FDA saw it. They were on a mission to protect the world and nothing as inconvenient as the views of patients were going to get in their way.

What's more, they even had the law on their side. And they were going to prove it. Just in case anyone was unclear about this, their first speaker after Dr Pazdur wasn't a clinician or statistician. It was the last person you might be expecting in a debate such as this.

It was their lawyer.

VII

Abby Brandel was a lawyer from the FDA Office of Chief Counsel. She wasn't up for very long. She didn't need to be. She also came directly to the point.

"Although the shorthand for the regulatory framework we'll be talking about today is accelerated approval, an integral part of it is *accelerated withdrawal*. It's a two way street."

Except that, as far as FDA were concerned, it now appeared only to be a one way street. "The regulations authorize FDA to withdraw accelerated approval, if evidence demonstrates that the drug is not shown to be safe or effective. Either one is grounds for withdrawal. Both of these criteria are met here."

Accelerated withdrawal said it all. FDA couldn't wait to get this drug off the market. It couldn't happen fast enough for them. It made the perfunctoriness of the proceedings painfully apparent. FDA saw themselves as both judge and jury. And they had already reached a verdict, half way through the trial.

With that statement of immodest inflexibility left hanging in the air, Ms Brandel made way for the familiar figure of Dr Lee Pai-Scherf. She had the thankless challenge of reviewing, yet again, the history of Avastin in breast cancer and the data from the three main trials. It was a laborious task, presenting the prosecution evidence, after having already asked for the death sentence. If there was anything new to say, she failed to find it, instead giving an almost verbatim repeat of her performance at the ODAC meeting of a year ago. Probably any member of the committee could have given the presentation for her, so familiar were they with the facts by now.

Having lulled the audience into a contented state of pre-prandial somnolence, she was followed by her colleague from CEDR, Dr Patricia Keegan. Intriguingly, her task was to counter Genentech's arguments for maintaining the Avastin indication in breast cancer. The fact that they hadn't yet presented their case, didn't seem to come into it.

FDA had decided to use Genentech's prior written submission as a basis for attacking their entire case, a day ahead of them actually taking the stand. It seemed the wrong way round, to be cross-examining the defence case, in advance of them even making it. But this was FDA's court and they were running the trial the way it suited them best.

When it came to manipulating policies and procedures, FDA were past masters at extracting the maximum advantage for themselves. They weren't at the epicentre of Federal bureaucracy for nothing. Giving themselves this slot in the agenda was a great courtroom tactic.

It meant that Genentech had to wait until the meeting reconvened the next morning, before they could finally outline their position. Which left the ODAC members with the FDA version of events firmly in the forefront of their minds overnight.

Whilst ODAC slumbered, Genentech sweated. They may have been the most powerful biotechnology company on the planet but they were being outwitted by the procedural prowess of the puppeteers at FDA, who appeared to be pulling all the strings.

They were struggling by now and they knew it.

VIII

The next morning, Genentech unveiled Dr Hal Barron to front their presentations. He was the Chief Medical Officer for the whole of Roche-Genentech. This time they had sent their top man. Bearded, youthful looking and with an engaging smile, he was a veteran of innumerable panels such as the one confronting him now. Even so, he had his work cut out here.

As had been the case with FDA, Genentech didn't have a whole lot that was new to bring to the table. They were therefore forced to refresh arguments which had, by and large, already been extensively aired elsewhere.

Dr Barron outlined their defence, which was built around four main points of contention with FDA.

419

Essentially, Genentech's position was that the Agency had exaggerated and misrepresented the toxicity of Avastin and that furthermore, E2100 was in fact a robust trial, devoid of significant design flaws. Additionally, whilst the data from AVADO and RIBBON I might not have *confirmed* the findings of E2100, they didn't *invalidate* them either. When looked at this way, they argued, the risk-benefit could be seen in a much more favourable light.

Finally, their view of the regulations was that accelerated approval should be maintained, whilst additional trials were undertaken. As Genentech saw it, additional evidence was required before a verdict could be reached.

Dr Baron concluded his opening remarks with the statement that:

"The scientific and regulatory issues at hand call for a regulatory flexibility, a middle ground if you will, of maintaining accelerated approval. I want to emphasise that this path forward is clearly allowed by law and supported by the science. Most importantly, this path forward is in the best interests of patients. It will address a public health need to provide additional treatments for women who are suffering from this incurable disease."

"Regulatory flexibility" and "a middle path" hadn't exactly been the defining characteristics of FDA's stance so far. If appealing to these non-existent sentiments was going to be the basis of the Genentech case, they were clearly in trouble from the outset.

Their position wasn't helped by the opportunity FDA enjoyed of having already tackled most of their arguments the previous day. It deprived them of impact, creating the impression that Genentech were having a second go at something they'd failed on once already. They couldn't develop the pace and momentum, which were such an essential part of courtroom dynamics. It made them appear plodding and pedestrian.

The Agency had also already made it perfectly clear that there was no regulatory flexibility on offer. Their view was that the law required them to withdraw the drug now, because it wasn't safe and didn't work. It was God's mission and they were there to fulfil it.

There was no way they were going to agree with Genentech, not even half way.

"This unprecedented interpretation of the accelerated withdrawal standards would turn the accelerated approval program on its head," Dr Jenkins had melodramatically declared the previous day.

Furthermore, it would allow "protracted marketing of drugs which have not been shown to be safe and effective whilst sponsors take numerous bites at the apple, in an effort to confirm clinical benefit."

In case there was any lingering doubt, he continued that "such a standard could seriously undermine the integrity of the accelerated approval program.

420

It is very important that we preserve the integrity of the accelerated approval program, which has been very successfully used in oncology and other disease areas to provide early access to promising new therapies."

It was clear that for FDA, this was a fight as much about procedure, precedent and policy, as the profile of any particular drug.

It was defending an attack on the very *soul* of the Agency.

IX

In the face of such intransigence, Genentech could but do their best. Dr Sandra Horning, their breast cancer expert and Dr James Reimann, Global Head of Oncology Statistics, took to the stand in an attempt to put a new twist on some of the old facts. But they didn't really have much to play with. Unable to land a big punch, they were forced to dance around the ring, tapping away here and there, as and when they could.

FDA had overestimated the toxicity of Avastin, they contended. Unfair prominence had been given to fatalities, such as thromboembolism and heart failure, in the Avastin arm of the studies. Comparable events had occurred in the non-Avastin containing chemotherapy groups but these had been ignored. Instead FDA had played up what they called *Avastin related* deaths, when in reality they were *treatment related.* These could just as easily have been due to the paclitaxel, rather than the Avastin component of the combination.

Also, investigators had reported more deaths as serious adverse events in the Avastin and paclitaxel arm, because the safety profile of paclitaxel by itself was considered to be well known. FDA had chosen to overlook this though, because it didn't fit their purposes. This had further biased things against Avastin.

Putting the safety profile into perspective, the commonest side effects with the drug were high blood pressure and protein in the urine. No one had died of these. Furthermore, fifty million Americans got by well enough with high blood pressure and so why shouldn't patients on Avastin do so too. It was a perfectly manageable problem.

This had been confirmed by all the physicians and patients who'd talked about their own experience with the drug. Overall, the toxicity of Avastin was no worse than other treatments used for metastatic breast cancer. These could cause significant kidney, liver, respiratory and cardiac side effects, amongst many others.

Numerous drugs widely used to treat breast cancer had Black Box Warnings attached. This was due to serious concerns over their safety. The culprits included Taxol, Taxotere, Abraxane, Ixempra, Xeloda, Herceptin and Tykerb. It was quite a rogues' gallery. FDA had however kept quiet about those, whilst they had been busy highlighting Avastin's limitations and liabilities. As Genentech saw it, the picture painted of Avastin was a grotesque caricature. Surely no one could take it seriously.

Attacking on another flank, the Genentech team were at pains to establish the proven efficacy of Avastin. The combination of Avastin and paclitaxel was widely used in eighty four countries around the world. Compared to that enormous majority, surely FDA had to be in a misinformed minority of one.

After all, they couldn't even see the significance of the "super- responders" and what it was telling everyone in other countries about the importance of Avastin as a useful drug.

In an act of commendable creativity, Genentech had managed to condense the anecdotal evidence of individual patient super-responders and the widely differing overall results from the three studies, into a unifying theory. They were calling this their "chemotherapy partnering hypothesis." The proposal was that, for some reason, Avastin worked much better when partnered with paclitaxel. It couldn't be expected to have comparable efficacy when coupled with other agents, such as docetaxel or capecitabine.

That was why the results of E2100 had stood out like a sore thumb. Not because it was a chance outlier but because it was the only study in which Avastin could really be expected to show what it could do.

They had some evidence that the combination of Avastin and paclitaxel resulted in a greater overall delivery of chemotherapy, compared to other drug permutations. Patients were tolerating the regime for longer, allowing them to receive larger cumulative doses of drugs. That could be accounting for the greater efficacy seen in E2100. Especially if a higher proportion than normal of super-responders had somehow found their way into the E2100 trial, compared to the other two.

They were on thin ice though. Firstly, there wasn't that much to support the idea. It looked like something they had come up with, after the event, to conveniently fit the facts as they now stood. The data, such as it was, from Amgen's Study 10 didn't help either. That trial had contained an Avastin and paclitaxel combination and so if the chemotherapy partnering hypothesis was true, why hadn't Study 10 performed in the stellar way that E2100 had?

Furthermore, Genentech had been arguing, as recently as the last ODAC meeting, that the data supported using Avastin with multiple chemotherapy agents. Now they appeared to be backtracking.

Sensing this weakness in their defence, they had countered with an assault on yet another front. FDA had underestimated the efficacy of the AVADO and RIBBON I studies. Too much emphasis had been put on median differences for PFS rather than *hazard ratios*. FDA had done this deliberately, to create an impression that the results of these two studies were worse than was really the case.

A *median difference* was simply a measure of how much longer overall one group's PFS was than the other's. It was broadly the same thing as an average. In the case of AVADO, it was one month greater for Avastin. Medians had the advantage of being simple and straightforward.[56] However, they suffered from the limitation of representing data only from those patients who'd ended up in the *middle* of the range of possible efficacy results.

The *hazard ratio* was a comparison of the *probability* of a patient's disease progressing, in any given period of time. It was calculated from the data of *all* the patients and was therefore more inclusive than a median. A hazard ratio of two meant that a patient in one group was twice as likely to have her disease progress, compared to a patient in the other group.[57]

However, that same hazard ratio would apply, whether the PFS was two weeks versus four weeks or twelve months versus twenty four months. The clinical relevance of hazard ratios could therefore be harder to interpret.

In the case of AVADO, the hazard ratio had been 0.7, which meant there was a thirty per cent less chance of progression in the Avastin arm.

A thirty per cent reduction may have sounded better than a one month improvement. But promoting one measure over the other wasn't the strongest of arguments. Medians and hazard ratios were each a different way of looking at the same thing. Debating the relative merits of them was like two people feeling a complicated object, say a Henry Moore statue, in total darkness and then trying to decide who'd come up with the best description of the shape.

Medians and hazard ratios were both employed, because each had limitations by itself. It wasn't surprising therefore that when used together, they could lead to divergent conclusions. In Amgen's Study 10, the *median difference* between the Avastin and paclitaxel arm and the paclitaxel alone arm was similar to that seen in AVADO. In other words, not very impressive. On the other hand, the *hazard ratio* was very similar to E2100. That was a much more noteworthy result, from Genentech's point of view. Each side would inevitably pick the parameter most suited to their particular cause.

Disingenuous though it may have been, it was a ploy which helped muddy the waters and enabled Genentech to more or less accuse FDA of double standards. They reminded the audience that apart from Avastin, only one other drug had been specifically approved, for the same indication (*first line treatment of HER2 negative (or HER2 unspecified) metastatic breast cancer*) since 1980.

This was gemcitabine, which had been approved in 2004.[3] Genentech were arguing that this had been on the basis of little more evidence of efficacy than was currently available for Avastin. That was irrespective of whether you looked at median differences or hazard ratios.

Additionally, gemcitabine had also failed to show an improvement in overall survival, although admittedly it only just missed out on this. Avastin was therefore being unfairly singled out. The inference was also not lost on those listening that two drugs in over three decades, didn't exactly represent a flood of new agents to meet a clearly unmet medical need.

It was a somewhat creative claim however, given that the HER2 gene itself had only been discovered back in 1984. HER2 negative disease obviously couldn't have existed before this point, by definition. Furthermore, both paclitaxel and docetaxel had been approved in their own right in the intervening years for use in the HER2 negative patient population. In terms of courtroom drama though, it served to convey the message that maybe now was the right time for another drug to be given the green light.

That was a point reinforced by Professor Joyce O'Shaughnessy, whom Genentech had brought along as an independent clinical witness. She was a breast cancer expert, from Baylor University Medical Centre in Texas and also co-chair of the US Oncology Breast Cancer Research Program. Again, there was little for her to say, that people hadn't already heard.

Compared to Professor Hortobagyi, hers was a more folksy approach. If he had taken the stage as Othello, she was more Oprah. She tried to add some clinical flesh to the dry bones of the preceding statistical skirmishes, by emphasising the advantages she saw when using Avastin in daily practice.

She managed to shoehorn in the occasional personal patient anecdote to embellish her narrative. It helped to connect her presentation, with its credibility and clinical credentials, to the individual stories of the preceding public session the day before.

"Just last week alone, having considered all of the available options, I recommended to three patients who have metastatic triple negative cancer and who are in need of rapid relief from severe bone pain, chest wall and arm pain, and liver pain that they begin treatment with Avastin-paclitaxel."

She had an inexhaustible fund of similar stories and this helped to successfully convey the grass roots message that Avastin was an important drug with manageable toxicity. How could you consider *removing* something that relieved the remorseless and unremitting pain of large lumps of tumor, dotted all over the body?

Overall however, her testimony seemed too little and too late. It was little more than the story of one clinician and her experiences.

"It is on behalf of the women in my practice who have aggressive metastatic breast cancer and those I will unfortunately meet in the future who are best treated with tolerable and effective combination therapy that I have come to speak to you today," she concluded.

It looked thin though, compared to the fat files of collective condemnation, sitting in front of the people from FDA.

X

Genentech's case had been to establish that the clinical benefit seen in E2100 was a genuine one. There was therefore every possibility that it might be replicated in a confirmatory trial. Furthermore, Avastin had an acceptable risk-benefit ratio, because FDA had distorted the degree of danger the drug represented.

There was also, they contended, a substantial degree of laxity in the regulations. In their view, withdrawal of the current approval in breast cancer would only be appropriate if "there is no reasonable likelihood of clinical benefit and no possibility that an additional study might further characterise any existing benefit."

The fact that FDA's lawyers were at a loss to know where this interpretation of the legislation had come from, wasn't going to deter Genentech now.

The only logical way forward, they averred, was to keep Avastin on the market, whilst they conducted a follow up trial. This would prove that E2100 had been genuine all along and that the doubters and naysayers were the ones who'd been in the wrong.

Genentech had characterised this proposition as their "Middle Ground Proposal." It lay somewhere in between continued approval and complete withdrawal. Seeking the Middle Ground may have seemed a reasonable compromise to them. As far as FDA were concerned though, it was as alien a concept as something out of Middle-earth.

The trial Genentech were proposing was similar to the E2100 study. It would have the same sorts of patients and they would be randomised to receive the same treatments as in E2100. These would be either Avastin and paclitaxel combined, or paclitaxel alone. The big difference was that it would also be measuring VEGF levels.

There were two main objectives to the trial. One was to confirm the overall magnitude of effect on PFS seen in E2100. The second was to show better responses and longer PFS in those patients with higher VEGF levels. The trial would include about four hundred and fifty patients and Genentech were planning to run it in about fifty countries, mainly outside the US.

They were hoping that the biomarker component of the study would be enough to get them over the finishing line. Biomarkers were a hot topic. Everyone was trying to find better ways of selecting the most appropriate patients for any given drug. Targeted approaches were very much in vogue and normally FDA would want to be seen to embrace such initiatives. If anyone were looking for a compromise with Avastin, it also represented the best way out of the dilemma. It was therefore a strong card to play.

Genentech had two big problems though. They has argued strongly that the existing data on Avastin already clearly showed it produced clinically meaningfully better results, when combined with paclitaxel, than did paclitaxel alone. Everyone could see that, except FDA apparently. If that was the case though, how were they going to persuade patients to enter into a trial, where they might end up only receiving paclitaxel. If it really were such an inferior treatment, then who in their right mind would sign up for it.

Your chances weren't exactly great with the best that was on offer and so why accept anything less than that. Patients were altruistic in volunteering for clinical trials but not to the point of self-sacrifice. None of the Genentech team had a clear answer to that one. It was a difficult position to be in.

The more you argued that the trial was viable and would easily be able to recruit patients, the more it weaken the proposition that Avastin was clearly superior, which in itself was the justification for the study in the first place. That was a very difficult juggling act to perform.

Genentech's second difficulty was the length of time the study was likely to take. They were still in the feasibility stage of working out the logistics of the trial. Which basically meant they had no idea how much time would be needed. If it involved fifty countries though, it wasn't going to be quick. Everyone knew that.

They also still had to agree with FDA the nature of the laboratory test, which would be used to measure VEGF levels in the blood. This wasn't exactly a routine assessment and so, given the potential importance of the results, everyone had to be reassured that the technique used would be robust and well validated.

Unfortunately for Genentech, this meant they had to deal with an entirely separate division of FDA for this particular issue. The *Center for Devices and Radiological Health* were the group who would have to approve the assay used in the trial to measure VEGF levels.

They weren't known for their crazy impetuosity. These were people who liked to take their time. They could significantly delay the start of any trial, as they took forever and a day to make up their minds. It looked like FDA could have it both ways. One arm might slow down the study, whilst at the same time the other could complain about how long it was going to take. Either way, Genentech's hands were effectively tied.

The study looked like it couldn't start until at least the following year and the results wouldn't be available until 2017, at the earliest. From FDA's perspective, that would mean leaving a drug on the market for another six years, when they had already convinced themselves it didn't even deserve to be there any longer at all.

Anticipating this, Genentech were proposing to conduct an interim look at the data, whilst the study was still running. They would have an inspection of the results part way through the trial. If it seemed that Avastin wasn't holding up, they would voluntarily withdraw the drug themselves at that stage. It was a neat gambit. They would be willing to put their hands up and surrender, long before the trial came to an end. That should solve all of FDA's problems.

Unfortunately though, it would still take three and a half years to reach this stage. That was a big ask of FDA, who didn't seem to want to wait the three and a half hours the meeting still had to run. They also seemed highly suspicious of this offer from Genentech.

They knew that once a study was under way, it was much harder to stop, than it would be to prevent it happening in the first place. The reins would be firmly in Genentech's hands and it would be hard for them to wrest back control. A biomarker study with an interim look may have appeared a well thought out compromise. But from FDA's perspective, they still seemed to prefer *no way*, to any notion of *middle way*.

XI

Overall, Genentech had provided a strong defence of their case, that the clinical trial data for Avastin were compelling and there was every chance a confirmatory study would resolve any lingering doubts. They chose however to close on the personal level of the individual patient, rather than with the anonymous aggregate of clinical trial results. This was their strongest territory and it had been the firmest theme running through the deliberations so far.

It was left to Dr Barron to work the room and strike an appropriately emotive note.

He reminded his audience that:

"We have seen many slides, with many, many numbers, hazard ratios, response rates, confidence intervals, p values etc.

But what we cannot lose sight of though, is the many women behind these numbers. We have heard moving testimonials from numerous women who have described their enormous hardship from being diagnosed with this devastating and incurable disease, how grateful they are for the simple pleasures in life and how significant their unmet need truly is.

These women deserve the option to be treated with Avastin in combination with paclitaxel. Our primary objective is to preserve, in an appropriate manner, options for women with metastatic breast cancer."

It was a suitably humble end to a presentation which had been high on hype. If however there had been a hope of connecting on a human level with anyone at FDA, they were to be sorely disappointed.

The Genentech team stepped back from the stage. They had done their best. Science and sentiment were largely on their side. Now, it was time to see how well their case had gone down.

XII

Finally, the key session of the whole meeting had arrived. The fat lady was at last in the wings, getting ready to come on and sing. A journey which had begun a decade ago, with the inauspicious start of the E2100 trial was about to reach its ill-starred end.

There was a slot after lunch, when the ODAC members could discuss the issues amongst themselves and reach the all important point of actually voting. It was *do or die* time. There were four questions posed to them but essentially only two answers were required.

The first was whether the available evidence suggested Avastin had demonstrated useful efficacy, at the cost of acceptable toxicity. If the answer to this was no, then should FDA maintain the drug's approval whilst Genentech undertook their confirmatory biomarker study.

FDA had generously allocated them two hours to chew things over, just in case anyone was still in any doubt. The committee duly batted the ball back and forth a bit, in between each vote, as they revisited some of the most contentious areas one more time. But their hearts weren't in it anymore. There was only so much repetition any one person could cope with. It didn't take them long to deal with the issues on the table. Their minds were clearly made up already.

All four questions received unanimous six-zero votes against Avastin. It had only taken them half the time allocated to the session. They hadn't hung about.

Their verdict couldn't have been more unequivocal. The efficacy of Avastin was unproven and didn't justify the serious side effects associated with it. The drug should be withdrawn immediately from its use in breast cancer.

This time, there was none of the showmanship which normally characterised the end of ODAC meetings. Usually, each member would seize the opportunity to explain why they had voted as they had. But now, it was as though they were embarrassed by the indecent haste of it all.

However, ODAC member Wyndham Wilson had a final comment after the voting. He was attempting to seek an emollient note upon which to close.

"I would encourage the company, if they are in fact convinced that there is a clinical benefit here, to do this follow up trial as quickly as possible. I would also say to patients out there with breast cancer, that I hope they look at all the evidence and see there was no evidence that this drug was of help to them and not come away feeling as though an important drug, that is going to make them feel better or make them live longer, is being taken away from them."

He hadn't exactly read the mood of the room correctly though. At this moment, patients in the audience erupted into shouting and jeering. The frustration and disappointment were too much to bear. Hearing these patronising pronouncements, from a committee member who'd clearly failed to take in the public sentiment, was the last straw.

"What else do you expect us to take? We have nothing else," shouted Christi Turnage, whose petition had so captured the spirit of the moment, after the last ODAC decision a year earlier. Her outburst this time similarly reflected the bitter mood of the meeting, as it eventually disbanded. Hope had been replaced by hopelessness. There was nothing left for them, except animosity and a sense of abandonment.

XIII

However, even this wasn't yet the end of the road. The ODAC meeting was over but FDA were accepting written submissions from the public, until the end of July. After that, it would be up to Commissioner Margaret Hamburg to make the final call.

Two weeks later, the US National Comprehensive Cancer Network[58] issued a written endorsement of Avastin and paclitaxel. They were one of the nation's most influential bodies, in determining guidelines for the management of malignancies. They hadn't taken part in the preceding debates but the timing of this intervention suggested which side they were lining up with now.

Over the next month, more than four hundred written submissions from the public were made to FDA. All but four of them were in support of retaining the Avastin approval. One contained a petition with over eleven thousand signatures.

At the end of June the European EMA announced a decision to approve Avastin combined with capecitabine, for the treatment of metastatic breast cancer.[59] This was one of the treatment groups from the RIBBON I study which had the Americans up in arms. It reinforced their previous decision over the approval of Avastin and paclitaxel.

At the beginning of August, Genentech and their lawyers Covington and Burling, sent FDA a one hundred and fifty page *Post-Hearing Submission*.[60] Inevitably most of it was a resume of their position, as stated at the ODAC meeting. The message was that Avastin should stay on the market, whilst a confirmatory trial was undertaken.

The opening few sentences said it all.

"There remains an indisputable need for additional treatments for metastatic breast cancer, as was starkly demonstrated at the hearing on the proposal of CDER to withdraw the breast cancer indication from Avastin.

The public testimony, data and legal arguments demonstrate why, in the light of this need, Avastin in combination with paclitaxel should retain its accelerated approval."

Despite the intransigence of the introduction, the body of the document did however contain a few new conciliatory gestures. They were willing to restrict the use of Avastin to a much narrower population than previously. This would be patients with the most virulent forms of the disease, where alternative treatment options were most lacking.

In practice, this would be women with triple negative disease, or those with hormone positive malignancy showing very aggressive features. The risk-benefit balance would be much more favourable in these groups. They didn't exactly have much to lose.

Genentech were also offering a communication program, to make sure physicians were fully aware of the limitations of the clinical data on Avastin and paclitaxel. Furthermore, in a spirit of going the extra mile, they were also intending to produce a Medication Guide for patients. This would advise them about the serious risks of the drug and the lack of any overall survival benefit or improvement in quality of life. That way, they could make their own minds up about the risk-benefit balance.

It seemed an eminently reasonable package of proposals, which both acknowledged and addressed FDA's concerns about the drug whilst also keeping it available as a choice, for physicians and patients to make a decision over.

However, whilst Genentech appeared to be conceding some ground, they clearly weren't about to give in quietly. They seemed to have a lot of fight left in them. They sensed the weight of public and professional opinion was on their side. This left Commissioner Hamburg with a tightrope to walk.

She had an overwhelming endorsement from FDA's chosen advisers, at ODAC, to withdraw Avastin. They had given the answer the Agency so clearly wanted. And yet many were seeing this as an unfair and unreasonable action. The opprobrium was coming from many different directions. Politicians, physicians, patients and pundits were all aligned in their opposition.

However much FDA tried to bring the debate back to science and clinical evidence, the more it seemed to move away from medicine and into the realms of morality. Where did the right lie, when it came to making a decision about whether to receive a particular treatment. Was it with the patient or the paper pushers? Should it be the sufferer or the state?

Commissioner Hamburg was a career bureaucrat, with a life time service in public health administration. This was new territory for her and she can't have felt comfortable to find herself there. She was more used to dealing with issues of meta-analysis than metaphysics. She must have been struggling to find a way of getting herself and the Agency out of this mess.

Incredibly, it was another three and a half months before her decision was eventually announced on November 18th. Exactly what she was doing in the meantime, remained a complete mystery to everyone else. Maybe an entire career sheltering behind the buttresses of bureaucracy, meant it took a while before being ready to stick your head above the parapet.

FDA issued a seventy page document outlining her thinking but there was nothing new in it.[61] Whatever negotiations had been going on behind the scenes during that intervening period, there had clearly been no conceptual advance in the Agency's position from the one on display in the summer.

Commissioner Hamburg was at pains to point out that:

"Ultimately, my responsibility and the Agency's responsibility is to put aside any preconceived beliefs that I, or patients or physicians may hold, and take a hard look at the objective evidence." It didn't seem to matter that the Agency were guilty of displaying the most preconceived beliefs of any of the parties, that Avastin was guilty even before the trial had started.

One sentence, at the beginning of page three of the document, was enough to bring to an end four years of debate and division. "I conclude that the continued labelling of Avastin for metastatic breast cancer is not justified and that the approval should be withdrawn."

There was no need to read any further.

Even Genentech decided to throw in the towel at this point, announcing their acceptance of FDA's decision. There had probably been more than enough clandestine wrangling with the Agency already. With one eye to the future though, they would still press ahead with their Phase III biomarker study.[62] But they wanted to stop flogging what was now clearly a dead horse, as far as Avastin's current prospects were concerned. It was time to let the dead rest in peace. Despite the fact that the decision denied the same repose to the dying.

XV

Whilst Commissioner Hamburg's decision may have surprised few and dismayed many, it at least meant everyone knew where they stood. Even if they didn't particularly like what they now found themselves standing in.

The Avastin saga in the US is likely to have far reaching consequences, on many levels. These go way beyond the particular dilemma of patients with breast cancer. It raises questions about the role and relevance of the regulatory process in controlling the wider clinical availability of new cancer drugs.

Pharmaceutical companies will also be left pondering the wisdom of the enormous investments they have to make, if their drug development juggernaut is threatened with hitting a regulatory road block every time the finishing line is in sight.

The issues around Avastin emphasise the dilemma created by the fact that clinicians, regulators, patients, pharmaceutical companies, governmental departments and third party payers alike, have no common basis for agreeing on whether a new cancer medicine actually provides a useful benefit. This situation can only worsen, as the technologies become more targeted and the personalisation of therapies becomes more pronounced. The way we currently evaluate drugs just isn't up to the challenge.

The determination of a drug's usefulness is a balance of efficacy and toxicity and there is no simple and reliable way to measure efficacy. Endpoints short of survival are of limited value and subject to endless debate about their ultimate relevance to the patient. Improvement in survival however, is a measure which is becoming increasingly difficult to demonstrate.

We have become, in a sense, victims to the success of medical advances and medical technology. We live in an era where the modern management of the patient with cancer is hugely complicated, involving sequential usage of many different treatment strategies.

In metastatic breast cancer alone, there are about *seventeen* individual drugs which have been approved for use in the first, second or third line context. They are employed, either singly or in various combination permutations, in the majority of patients with advanced disease. The clinical complexity of cancer care therefore makes it extremely challenging to identify and isolate the effects of one particular drug, in one particular individual, on the regulatory lodestone of survival.

Even if it were possible to definitively define the efficacy of a cancer drug with just one measure, the counterbalancing interpretation of toxicity is inevitably an imprecise exercise. There is undoubtedly a spectrum of individual views about what particular level of toxicity is worth incurring, for any given likelihood of benefit.

Science and subjectivism are an unhappy partnership. That much was clear from the Avastin debate.

XVI

Even the regulators in different countries can't agree themselves, about striking the right balance. Given that, how can they ever be expected to find common ground with anyone else? In an era of increasing international harmonisation, there are still a surprising number of trans-Atlantic differences which occur, when authorities interpret the same data from the same drug in the same indication.

Avastin was made available for use in metastatic breast cancer in Europe in 2007. The drug continues to be used with benefit in hundreds of thousands of women throughout the European Community. The approval was on the basis of the E2100 data and progression free survival alone. There wasn't really any controversy over it. Certainly nothing like the anguished torment of the debate in the US. The arrival of the AVADO and RIBBON I data haven't made any significant difference to that position either.

The EMA have repeatedly reaffirmed their allegiance to the results of E2100, despite the complexities introduced by subsequent developments. In December 2010, the EMA's advisory committee, the CHMP (Committee on Human Medicinal Products) concluded that "Avastin (with paclitaxel) has been *convincingly* shown to prolong progression free survival, without a negative effect on overall survival."[63]

In the opinion of the EMA itself, in February 2011, "the results of existing studies on the combination of bevacizumab and paclitaxel are consistent and support a positive effect of therapy with a clear benefit to patients."[64]

They couldn't be any clearer than that. Well, at least by the opaque standards of a regulator.

Their conviction over the validity of the data supporting Avastin and paclitaxel was given further credibility by their decision around the same time to drop Avastin and docetaxel. After reviewing the results of AVADO, they had concluded that "the benefit-risk balance of bevacizumab in combination with docetaxel for first-line treatment of patients with metastatic breast cancer is considered to be negative."[63]

Turning against AVADO somehow made their allegiance to E2100 appear more measured and balanced.

In the middle of 2011 the EMA had gone that extra mile and approved Avastin in combination with capecitabine, showing that they were prepared to give RIBBON I a run for its money too. They announced their decision *one day* after the final fateful ODAC vote against Avastin.[59]

You might almost think the Europeans were doing it on purpose, to antagonise their regulatory relatives in Rockville.

There are many other instances, between the US and Europe, of cancer drugs which have been approved in one jurisdiction but not the other, on the basis of exactly the same data. However, Avastin remains by far and away the best or worst, depending on your point of view, example of this.

Apart from breast cancer there are now *two* other cancer indications where the US and Europe have been unable to see eye to eye on the drug.

In the summer of 2009, FDA approved the use of Avastin as a single agent to treat a hugely intractable brain tumor known as glioblastoma multiforme (GBM). This was a terrible cancer to have and a death sentence almost at the time of diagnosis.

The Agency's decision was based on just two studies, with a total of about one hundred and fifty patients. Avastin produced a response rate in approximately twenty five per cent of those treated, although the duration of effect was short lived. Most patients started progressing again, after about four months.[65,66]

However, despite these limitations, FDA recognised the graveness of the clinical situation and gave Avastin an accelerated approval. In comparison to the situation in breast cancer, they appeared to have behaved with responsibility and rapidity.

By contrast, in Europe, the EMA rejected the drug in January 2010. They found that the results "are not considered dramatic" and that the risk-benefit ratio was unacceptable, with many of the endpoints "difficult to interpret."[67] They struggled to make sense of much of the data and felt that a randomised trial was needed.

For the doomed patients and their desperate physicians, the decision by the Europeans was as incomprehensible as that of FDA to breast cancer sufferers in the US. This was a case for once of the EMA nailing themselves to the altar of randomisation and demonstrating an irrational belief in the blind faith of survival data. Semi-religious bigotry clearly wasn't the exclusive preserve of the Americans.

However, the permissive pendulum swung the other way again at the end of 2011. Just two days before Christmas, the EMA authorised Avastin, for use with chemotherapy, in the first line treatment of advanced ovarian cancer. This disease, which is the eighth commonest female cancer, accounts for over one hundred and forty thousand deaths annually. Fifteen thousand of them are in the US alone.

The approval was on the basis of two trials (known as ICON 7 and GOG 0218)[68,69] showing an improvement in progression free survival, even though in one of these studies, the improvement in PFS for Avastin was only 1.7 months.

Despite the relatively modest PFS benefits demonstrated by the two studies, the results were still highlighted as "one of the major clinical cancer advances" of 2011 by The American Society of Clinical Oncology, in their annual report for that year.[70]

It was a nice festive gift for Roche, who were able to note that the decision "marks the first major treatment advance in newly diagnosed ovarian cancer in fifteen years." And moreover, "this is the fifth tumor type for which Avastin has now been approved in Europe."[71]

However, in the absence of a demonstrable survival advantage, Genentech had already concluded, after speaking to FDA, that "we do not believe the data will support approval (in the US)."[72] Avastin in ovarian cancer was in danger of recreating the breast saga all over again. Even Tolstoy couldn't manage War and Peace *Two* and clearly Genentech didn't feel up to the task either. By now, they knew when to cut their losses and when to carry on, come what may. This was clearly one of the former occasions. It was a pity the ovarian cancer patients didn't get a say in the matter though.

Although definitely king of the controversy charts, with three top ten hits to its name, Avastin is only one amongst a number of drugs to have taken the Pepsi Challenge of this regional regulatory roulette. The Agency itself recently conducted a review of thirty five cancer drugs approved by either FDA or EMA but not necessarily both, between 2006 and 2010.[73] In those four years, the US accepted thirty two of the thirty five drugs, whilst the EMA only allowed twenty six through the door. Between them they approved twenty three in common, disagreeing on the others.

Interestingly, given their track record in the past, FDA actually approved *more* drugs than their European counterparts over this period. Understandably, the Agency couldn't help giving themselves a pat on the back, pointing out that "FDA is not in a "race" with other countries. However, we recognize it is our public health duty to approve drugs as quickly and safely as possible."[71] Despite this note of restraint, they did manage to go on and boast that their approval times were in fact faster in many instances than those of their more lackadaisical London cousins. At least according to their own analysis of the figures that is.

The most interesting findings however, in amongst all the *mine is bigger than yours* grandstanding, were the twelve drugs that FDA and EMA couldn't find enough common ground on. When they materialise, there is no particular rhyme or reason to these intercontinental conflicts. They seem to occur with a whimsical randomness that makes it almost impossible to guess which regulator is going to come out in favour or against a drug, when confronted with the same information as the other.

For example, Pfizer's leukaemia drug *Mylotarg* originally received accelerated approval from FDA way back in May 2000. It was intended for elderly patients with acute myeloid leukaemia, who'd already failed previous chemotherapy.

Why they decided to endorse this particular drug was a mystery to everyone else at the time. The last twelve years have failed to provide much further clarity.

Mylotarg (otherwise known as gemtuzumab ozogamicin) consisted of an antibody (gemtuzumab), which targeted a particular marker on the surface of leukaemia cells. It was linked to a chemotherapeutic poison (ozogamicin). The idea was that the antibody homed in on the leukaemia cell, delivering its payload of poison and thus destroying the malignancy.

Whilst an elegant theory, many people felt that in practice the clinical data with the drug showed barely discernible efficacy at best. The complete response (CR) rate was only sixteen per cent, which was pretty dismal, even for leukaemia. In fact, the sponsor at the time (Wyeth) even had to invent some new and less demanding response categories to help get Mylotarg over the finishing line.[74] That's how much the drug was struggling. And yet, in an act of uncharacteristic generosity, FDA let it through and on to the market place. They would however subsequently admit, as late as 2009, that "the approval of Mylotarg in 2000 remains a challenge."[75]

Many suspected that the spectre of Mylotarg haunted the Agency for years afterwards. Particularly as it had only ever been a non-randomised study. They felt a need to vindicate themselves and re-establish their reputation as the hard men, who played the hardest of hard ball.

The European Authorities, confronted with exactly the same data as FDA, had no problem with rejecting Mylotarg outright. It did take them until 2007 to do so though. It was a rate of progress which made FDA look almost reckless by comparison. Were they in a race, the Agency would definitely have won this one.

In the view of EMA, the effects of the drug were modest at best, there was no information directly comparing it to other potential AML treatments and it was difficult to work out whether it was having any impact on survival.

Pfizer eventually conducted a follow up study with Mylotarg, in line with its commitment, after receiving initial accelerated approval in the US. When the results became available towards the end of 2009, the trial failed to show any clear clinical benefit.[76] It couldn't even confirm the vanishingly small effect seen back in 2000. Moreover, there were *more* deaths in the Mylotarg arm of the trial. It was actually decreasing survival.

Pfizer had little choice but to voluntarily withdraw the drug completely from the US market in June 2010. That must have come as an immense relief to the Agency. The Europeans had clearly been in the right on this one.

However, FDA managed to partly even the score with the approval of ixabepilone. This was a drug from Bristol Myers, which was one of an exciting new class of agents called the *epothilones*. These worked in a similar way to the widely used taxane drugs (paclitaxel and docetaxel) but in theory, with more activity and fewer side effects.

They held out the promise of efficacy in cancers where resistance had developed to further use of the taxanes. That included many women with advanced breast cancer. The epothilones might therefore meet a real medical need.

Ixabepilone was approved for metastatic breast cancer in the US, in October 2007, for patients who had become resistant to taxane and anthracycline type drugs. This was for use in combination with capecitabine.[77] At the same time, it was also approved for mono-therapy use in patients with even more advanced disease.[78] The approval for combination therapy was based on improvements in progression free survival of 5.7

months for the ixabepilone arm compared to 4.1 months for the group receiving just capecitabine. The acceptance for use as a single agent centred around a twelve per cent response rate alone.

Overall, although these were modest benefits, it seemed like a useful drug for patients who were fast running out of options. A two month delay in disease progression wasn't exactly great but it wasn't bad either, when compared to nothing, which was essentially the alternative on offer.

However, in November 2008 the Europeans indicated they were going to reject the ixabepilone application, having reviewed essentially identical data to FDA. This was on the basis that the side effects seen, particularly a severe form of nerve damage, didn't justify what they saw as very small efficacy advantages. The risk-benefit analysis just didn't stack up in their eyes. BMS subsequently withdrew the ixabepilone application in Europe in early 2009.[79]

Despite the caution of the Europeans, the ixabepilone and capecitabine combination has become a widely used treatment regimen in the US for advanced breast cancer.[80] FDA had probably made the right call this time around.

XVII

The geographical ping pong of cancer drug determination graphically illustrates the difficulties everyone faces in making an appropriate assessment of the efficacy–safety equation. Regulatory authorities, such as FDA, often find themselves out on a limb, as the case of Avastin in breast cancer demonstrated so well. They frequently seem to be predominantly concerned with protecting the vulnerable few, to the detriment of the remaining majority.

One of the most fundamental of medical precepts is the Hippocratic proposition *primum non nocere*. This roughly translates as *first do no harm*. This is the philosophy which appears rooted at the very heart of regulatory review. By default, regulators aver on the side of caution, often giving undue prominence to side effects and toxicities. They want to avoid harm, at all cost. Seemingly, they would rather take the risk of rejecting an effective drug, than of approving a toxic one.

But in the context of cancer medicine, where the benefits and risk are often so fundamentally interwoven, this is the wrong balance. It is leading to the sacrifice of useful drugs, such as clofarabine in AML and Avastin in breast cancer. These are agents which have the potential to help some, through controlling their disease, although at the cost of causing unacceptable toxicity for others.

And this is where, as many of the Avastin proponents argued, the regulatory process potentially falls apart. It is impossible to make these kinds of risk-benefit judgements at the level of protecting *public* health, as regulators do, without fundamentally compromising the *private* individual physician–patient ability to make the same determination. With a growing future personalisation of drug therapy, it is a dilemma which can only ever deepen.

This insoluble paradox lay at the heart of the intractable Avastin puzzle.

XVIII

The loss of Avastin would make casualties of all those women who wanted the right to make their own determination, along with their oncologist, of how much risk they were prepared to trade, for the possibility of some sort of benefit. It was an exercise most went through many times, during the course of their disease.

The art of treating advanced malignancy often lies in the ability to tack back and forth, constantly navigating the least worst pathway between dangerous drugs and the loss of hope. The dead hand of the regulator has no place on the tiller. That could only result in a shipwreck on the nearest reef of rocks.

In the eyes of many, the Avastin saga also left FDA damaged and dented. The end of *War and Peace* documented the inglorious retreat of the *Grande Armeé* from the burning ruins of Moscow, to an ignominious return in tatters to Paris. Henceforth, Napoleon's reputation for credibility and capability was forever tarnished. Although on a less epic scale, FDA had suffered a similar rout and retreat.

It should have all been so different. FDA were to be applauded for originally approving Avastin, back at the beginning of 2008. By taking the courageous step of going against the advice of the father figures of ODAC, as well as a slice of public opinion, they'd reached a sensible decision and one they should have stuck to. But after that, they appeared to lose their nerve. Having put their head above the parapet, they suddenly seemed to decide they didn't have the appetite for a fight after all. From that point onwards, they appeared on the defensive and looking for a line of retreat.

They didn't seem to sufficiently grasp that having approved Avastin, however conditionally it might have been in their own eyes, it was going to be so much harder to reverse the decision, than to have never made it in the first place. In the intervening period, too many expectations had been engendered and the drug had become too entrenched. They had opened a Pandora's box back in 2008 but unlike in the myth, it didn't appear on this occasion that Hope had decided to hang around for too long.

FDA did however eventually emerge from the Avastin adventure as the nominal winners. But it had been a Pyrrhic victory, gained at a significant cost. They had drawn out proceedings for as long as they felt they decently could. Despite the fact that many others frequently found their actions indecently indecisive. This had inflicted untold stress and anxiety on terminally ill women, kept in agonising uncertainty over their future treatment options.

Although they had allowed themselves as long as they wanted for their own deliberations, along the way they didn't seem to have made the time to listen to the majority view of breast cancer experts. These were the experienced Avastin users, who were trying to tell them that this drug did work. You just had to know what you were doing and take the appropriate precautions. It was a message repeated by all those women who had testified to the fact that they were alive and relatively well, thanks to Avastin. They certainly wouldn't have been there without it.

Instead, FDA had chosen to drag their feet, in a display of inconsistency and incoherence. This prevarication and procrastination had been aided and abetted by their apparent abuse of the ODAC advisory system. By filling it with those members most closely aligned to their own position, they had undermined the credibility of the process of independent review. But maybe they had overplayed their hand this time, with the manipulation and machination becoming all too visible.

It was made worse still by FDA's inflections of the regulatory framework within which they worked. When Avastin was granted accelerated approval in 2008, the most reasonable obligation to have placed on Genentech would be that confirmatory trials should show an improvement in PFS, without any *impairment* of survival. That was broadly comparable to the requirements placed on similar drugs in the past. In those cases, a survival benefit hadn't been the essential pre-requisite it now seemed to have become. It was FDA, acting unilaterally, who subsequently transformed their position into a rigid requirement for evidence of a survival *improvement*.

It was also apparent, at the time of granting approval, that FDA were aware of at least the outline results of the AVADO trial. The Agency must have known that there was little possibility of these confirming the magnitude of effect on PFS seen in the E2100 study. It was pretty mature data by the time Genentech handed it over.

And yet only much later would they adopt the public mantra that *equivalence* of PFS between the various studies was now required for continuing approval. This made it extremely difficult for sponsor companies, such as Genentech, to play the game, when the other side appeared to be rewriting the rules as they went along.

However, the greatest damage inflicted on FDA came from their own detachment from reality. The Agency simply couldn't attune themselves to the weight of professional and public opinion, opposed to the removal of Avastin for use in breast cancer. They remained inflexibly and immutably wedded to the position that the regulations required FDA to withdraw the drug and along with it, any element of freedom or choice for the victim and carer. The argument that they had no alternative helpfully ignored their own malleable approach to interpreting the rules, when it was in their interests to do so.

Women and their physicians were simply asking for the possibility of making their own informed choices about the risks and benefits of the treatment options available to them. But the churlishly cloistered civil servants of FDA were unable to concede that anyone, other than themselves, had the right to such a determination. It exposed them as the detached and self-serving bureaucracy they really were. It seemed as though they would happily sacrifice the needs of patients and physicians, in the interests of preserving their own prehistoric policies and procedures.

Avastin wasn't a perfect drug. None ever are. It had profound toxicities attached to it. Furthermore, the "super-responders," whom it clearly helped, were probably less than ten per cent of the overall patient population treated with the drug. In the rest, the effects were more modest. But experienced physicians were confident they could use the drug safely, in the vast majority of patients. Furthermore, ten per cent of the commonest female cancer still added up to a sizeable patient population of responders.

In a situation like this, where the opposing arguments were so finely balanced and fiercely held, the only sensible course would have been to seek the compromise of the biomarker study Genentech had been proposing. It would have bought both sides more time and would actually have produced some new information which might finally have broken the deadlock, one way or the other. Most importantly, this route would have allowed the drug to remain available to those women wanting to take their chances with it.

But FDA couldn't find it in themselves to tread the middle ground. Ever since taking the original position of going against ODAC and granting an Avastin approval, FDA had seemed to be quietly seeking a way to reverse this decision. This had led them into an increasingly inflexible and intractable stance, characterised as much by prejudice and preconception as any other sentiment. It didn't exactly support the notion of a progressive partnership between sponsor companies and regulatory authorities.

Developing the most sophisticated and technically advanced drugs in the history of medicine, would henceforth carry the risk of being conducted in an atmosphere of mutual mistrust and misunderstanding. Suspicion was in danger of supplanting science, with decisions reached more on the basis of compulsive dogma than any underlying clinical data.

Battered and bruised, FDA were likely to become even more isolationist and idiosyncratic. Retreating to the comfort of precedent and policy, they would be less well equipped than ever before to deal with the technological revolution going on all around them. Attempting to regulate innovation was a pretty impossible task, that they had just become even more impossibly suited to.

There were no winners with Avastin in breast cancer. It wasn't a victory for protecting public health. With the loss of the drug, all patients lost the right of choice and individual determination. A significant minority were also deprived of access to a drug which might have been their last chance. FDA were left looking indecisive and disdainfully out of touch. And with Avastin off the market, Genentech were going to be about a billion dollars a year worse off.

The withdrawal would also have potential implications for the future sustainability of cancer drug development. Pharmaceutical companies had to be confident that drugs wouldn't be removed from the market, unless there was compelling evidence of a safety issue which clearly outweighed any potential benefits.

No one wanted an overtly dangerous drug remaining in circulation. You couldn't make money out of one like that anyway. Drug development was also an evolving process. It was forever a work in progress, as additional information emerged about a drug, once it was in the marketplace. New clinical trial results and anecdotal experiences gained through wider usage, conspired to constantly change the perceptions of the risks and benefits of a recently arrived agent.

There had to be some way regulators and pharmaceutical companies could react to that, as and when necessary. Each party had to recognise the often divergent needs of the other. When the interpretation of new information has the sort of subjectivity that nearly always characterises cancer drugs, then there has to be a greater capacity for common sense and compromise than had been the case with the Avastin conflict.

Pictures of cancer drugs are painted in shades of grey. It makes no sense to adopt positions of black or white with them. Or just black, in the case of FDA.

XIX

The Agency had prevaricated, equivocated and then rejected Avastin, despite is widespread use in breast cancer and well established place in the treatment of four other types of malignancy. They had also changed the rules along the way, to suit their own opaque purposes.

And that was with Genentech, the world's biggest and most successful biotechnology company. Just where, we wondered, did that leave the rest of us. What about small companies, with experimental drugs that didn't yet have the proven provenance of something like Avastin.

Lacking legions of lawyers, where did we now stand with FDA. Would they feel they could renege on previous understandings with anyone else they now felt like double crossing. Would they be chastened or emboldened by their experiences with Avastin. It was impossible to tell.

A few weeks after the Avastin dossier made its final journey to the desk of Commissioner Hamburg, it was the tenth anniversary of nine-eleven. Televisions were suddenly and constantly full of footage of the World Trade Centre in flames and collapsing.

After Avastin, the artificially enclosed world of drug development was coming to resemble the real world, post nine-eleven. Things had changed. No one seemed likely to play by the old rules anymore. But equally, no one was quite sure what the new rules were either.

The comfort of the familiar had been replaced by the confusion of the fathomless. The imagery of Ground Zero was an appropriate metaphor. Avastin had resulted in the collapse of the twin towers of common sense and compromise.

If FDA had been obstacles to progress before, they would be even more formidable opponents now. Along with our equally aghast biotechnology brothers, we had sat at Antisoma, watching Avastin unravelling to end up in the unedifying spectacle of lawyers sniping at each other, in a court which had reached a verdict, long before it was ever convened.

It wouldn't be that long before we were up before the judge. It would soon be our turn to argue the case for amonafide. If we lost, it now looked as though we could expect nothing short of the death penalty. The prospect was enough to stop us sleeping well at night. We would have slept even worse, if we'd known that FDA actually had us in their sights already.

In the midst of all the Avastin distractions, they'd still found time to come up with a little surprise for us.

We were now about to find out what it was.

NINE

19TH NERVOUS BREAKDOWN

The strains begin to show within Antisoma. The drug regulators threaten to derail everything the company is trying to pull off. A visit to the extraordinary world of the US Food and Drug Administration.

I

At the end of August, the very last patient, number 01305, had completed their participation in the amonafide ACCEDE study. This was a thirty four year old woman from Charleston, South Carolina.

She'd had a rocky course, nearly dying twice in the first month from pneumonia and other septic complications of the treatment itself. Despite being in intensive care for ten days and being hours away from hearing the Last Rites, she had somehow pulled through.

In large part this was due to the skill of her physician, Professor Rob Stuart. He somehow had the ability to bring people back from the brink of death when, by rights, they really should have tipped over the edge. Maybe God had also decided to give her a lucky break, embarrassed by how much misfortune he'd already heaped onto her.

Now though, one year on, she had received a bone marrow transplant and was in remission. She was back at home and back at work. Her prospects looked good.

We hoped this was an omen for the trial overall.

The safe passage of patient 01305 marked the end of the largest ever randomised controlled trial in secondary acute myeloid leukaemia. In all there were four hundred and thirty three patients, from over twenty countries, who'd been included in the study. It had started almost exactly three years earlier, in the summer of 2007 and had been an exhaustive undertaking, with thirty or so people working on it pretty much full time during that period.

We put out a press release to announce the event, including a quote from one of the main ACCEDE investigators. Richard Stone, from the Dana-Farber Cancer Institute at Harvard, was Director of the Adult Leukaemia Programme there.

"It will be fascinating to see if AS1413 can deliver on the promise suggested by earlier studies," he volunteered.[1] We were pretty interested to find out too. In fact, it was probably us who wrote those words for him.

But before we could reach that point, there remained an enormous amount of arduous work to be completed.

Running the ACCEDE trial had been hard enough but the bigger challenge now was to sort out the massive amount of data we had generated along the way and try to work out what it was telling us. It would take months to get to grips with it all.

II

For those four hundred and thirty three patients, we had documented more or less every aspect of their disease, for up to two years. From the moment they entered the trial, we recorded what drugs they had received for breast cancer five years earlier, all the way through to the severity of the headache they woke up with one morning twenty four months later.

Each tablet they'd swallowed during that period had been written down, each of thousands of individual blood tests recorded as a value of 4.89 or 5.73 or 2.91, or whatever it happened to be.

If someone had suffered from pneumonia, we would have documentation of what their temperature was at three pm on the fourth day of the illness and what dose of antibiotics they were given two hours later.

Outpatient visits, hospitalisations, progress and setbacks had all been captured in minute detail and with exhaustive documentation.

And as for the objective measure of their leukaemia disease, the bone marrow slides, whose results both the patients and the study literally lived or died by, these were examined by up to *three* different laboratories in different places. We wanted to be absolutely sure we were getting it right.

It was, in short, an awful lot of information to have to pull together, let alone work out just what it was telling you. It would all eventually end up in a central database and ultimately out of that would come hundreds, maybe even thousands, of pages of tables, summarising the *collective* experience of these four hundred and thirty three individuals.

We would, for example, know the *average* level of sodium in the blood of all the patients seventeen days after treatment, the *proportion* of patients with a rash on the back of the hand in the first three months of the study, what *fraction* of patients took a particular heart rhythm drug during the first seven days of treatment with amonafide or daunorubicin.

As well of course as the measures we really wanted to find out about, in terms of assessing whether amonafide was working or not. What proportion of patients had gone into remission. How many had gone on to receive a transplant. How many had died of early treatment related mortality. What remnant were still alive at six months or twelve months or two years.

Pretty much every bodily function was captured in a computation or calculation of some sort or another.

And if that weren't complex enough, we actually had to produce *three* differing permutations of all this data, for three different groups of patients.

III

Large clinical trials are conventionally broken down into three sets of patients, within the overall total population. The first group is called the *Per Protocol Population (PPP)*. This consists of those patients who followed all the requirements of the study and didn't deviate from it in any important way.

For example, the ACCEDE patients randomised to the cytarabine and daunorubicin arm were supposed to receive seven days of cytarabine treatment, along with three days of daunorubicin. That's what the protocol specified. But there may have been a patient who for some reason only received four days of cytarabine, rather than seven. They may have experienced a side effect, requiring treatment to be discontinued. Or maybe there had been technical problems with continuing to inject the drug. The patient's vein could have blocked off or the injector pump may have malfunctioned. Whatever the explanation, they hadn't received as much drug as they should.

There might be another patient whose bone marrow assessment hadn't been completed at the end of treatment. They could have refused the procedure in the first place. Or, the bone marrow slides may have been lost or damaged. Alternatively, the patient could have been really ill with a complication of some sort and the investigator might have overlooked the whole thing and not done it. Anything was possible in a clinical trial. However, irrespective of the reason, it was a substantial violation of the protocol. You would now be really struggling to work out whether the patient had responded or not.

These two patients *wouldn't* be included in the PPP, because they had each failed to comply with an important element of the protocol. Similarly, other patients who'd deviated in significant ways wouldn't be allowed past the portals of the per protocol population. The PPP is therefore really a reflection of what would happen in an ideal world, where everything went according to plan and nobody did something they weren't supposed to.

You are most likely to see an effect of your drug in this group, because it includes only those patients who've been on their best behaviour, as it were. Nothing has happened to them, which would complicate the interpretation of their results.

Of course things tend not to go according to plan in real life, either in clinical trials or clinical practice and so you usually end up losing about a third of your patients overall from the per protocol population. For one reason or another, they haven't been able to adhere strictly enough to the

445

requirements of the study. AML trials are notorious for this kind of problem.

The two patients above, excluded from the PPP, would however be included in the *Safety Population (SP)*. This comprises all patients who have received any treatment at all, for however short a period of time, even if it were only for one hour rather than seven days. The SP will include most but probably not all of the patients in the study. The reason it doesn't encompass everyone is that it's not unusual to have some patients included in a trial who get as far as being randomised to one treatment arm or the other but never actually receive any study medication.

In the ACCEDE trial, you could have a patient who agreed to enter the study on a Thursday afternoon and was randomised to the amonafide arm, with the doctor intending to start treatment on Friday morning. But if the patient died on Thursday night, or changed their mind that evening and withdrew from the trial, then they would obviously never actually receive any amonafide. That patient wouldn't be included in the safety population.

But they would still have been *randomised* and that is a kind of regulatory Rubicon which once crossed, has to be accounted for.

There is therefore a third group of patients called the *Intention To Treat Population (ITT)* which also has to be created. This is the most important of the triumvirate by a long way, because a regulatory authority will nearly always put most emphasis on and trust in, efficacy results from an ITT population. The ITT group includes all patients who were randomised in the trial, *irrespective* of whether they received any study treatment or not.

This means that within the ITT analysis you end up looking at the overall efficacy of a drug, even though it may be based partly on patients who never actually received any of it. Some of them might even turn out not to have the correct disease the study was intended for. Nevertheless, once entered into the trial, from an ITT perspective, there is no going back.

If that sounds a little counterintuitive, that's probably because it is. If you were conducting a survey to find out the response to a new television advertisement for example, you wouldn't include the opinions of everyone who just happened to have their TV turned on. You'd only be interested in the people who'd actually seen it. You wouldn't want those who'd popped out for a cup of tea whilst it was showing. And similarly, if you wanted to find out whether a drug worked, why would you look at patients who'd never even received it?

Regulatory authorities would argue that there is a rational basis for this apparent irrationality. In their view, an ITT analysis is the closest approximation to what happens in real life. They would point out that in reality, a surprisingly high proportion of patients don't keep up with the drugs prescribed for them, especially if they are taking them unsupervised, at home.

That applies to cancer medicines too, where there are now over fifty orally available drugs, which can be administered on an outpatient basis at home. You'd expect cancer patients to be wedded to taking their treatment, with an almost religious regularity. It is after all the only thing keeping them alive. However, up to *half* of patients prescribed hormonal therapy for breast cancer, for example, don't take the drug, the more so in younger than older women.[2] Similarly, up to twenty five per cent of leukaemia sufferers prescribed Gleevec don't keep up with their treatment.[3] The effort of staying alive appears to be too much for them.

So regulators would claim that you should lump in patients who never receive any treatment into clinical trial results, to give a better understanding of how an overall group of patients would do in the real world.

Additionally, they also like the ITT approach because it includes *all* the patients in the trial. You don't have to make any of the arbitrary assumptions which are necessary, when deciding to exclude some patients from the analysis. This is a particular limitation with the per protocol group, where there are no fixed rules about who can or can't be part of it. It is entirely at your discretion and varies from study to study. You have to make a judgement about who to reasonably allow in and who you can confidently keep out. You want to include as many people as possible but avoid letting in anyone who looks too different and doesn't fit with the rest. A bit like being a nightclub bouncer. Only it's usually less confrontational. Usually.

As an automatic response, regulators tend to distrust any approach which doesn't embrace everyone from a trial. As soon as you start excluding some patients, they become convinced it's because you are trying to hide something.

Maybe they have a point of some sort about the ITT approach. It does at least have the virtue of being all inclusive. It is the purest and least manipulated of data sets. However, the arguments in favour of it are partly negated by the excessive extremes to which they are sometimes taken.

Occasionally for example, a patient can be randomised to receive treatment *A* but by mistake be given treatment *B* instead. This could be due to a mix up at the pharmacy preparing the drugs or a mistake by the nursing staff giving them. It doesn't happen that often but it's not unheard of either.

If a patient had been given treatment B in error, you'd think the sensible thing to do would be to include their results along with all the other patients who'd also received treatment B. But in an ITT analysis, because they had been *randomised* to treatment A, you would have to include their results in the treatment A group, even though they had actually received treatment B.

Although this might appear irrational to most people, to regulators it made perfect sense. Everything was determined by what the patient had been randomised to. Once that had happened, there was no going back. It was a one way journey with no return. Legions of academic statisticians had built careers around devising ways to rationally justify such irrationality. It was an example of the mental hoop which regulatory inflexibility sometimes forced you to jump through.

IV

Being forced to jump through hoops was in fact the only reason we were undertaking all this work and creating all these different populations in the first place. It was purely because, for reasons often best known to themselves, regulatory authorities, in particular FDA, required it.[4] Not because we felt like it. There's nothing we'd rather have done less. It was bad enough trying to sort out one set of data, let alone three differing variants. We were doing it because they wanted it. And it was pointless trying to argue with them, so we had all long ago learned to just do this. It was the least slow way to be fast.

The important thing about all the frantic and frenetic activity we were currently engaged in with ACCEDE, was that we would be handing the whole lot over to someone else fairly soon. These were the people at FDA in the US and the multinational myriads at the EMA in Europe. Particularly at FDA, they would go through the data with a fine-tooth comb. The finest-tooth comb ever made in fact.

Every nuance of the clinical information would be interrogated and tested and treated as guilty until proven innocent. And even then they'd probably still consider it guilty. They would swarm all over it, calibrating and calculating and computing, to see if they could recreate the same results and reach the same conclusions as we had. It was like letting them into a house we'd built and having them knock it down back to the bricks, just to see if they could rebuild it the exact same way we had.

And it wasn't just the ACCEDE study we were talking about. They would require a similar level of detailed data for pretty much each and every clinical trial which had ever been conducted with amonafide. They would want each one of these studies presented individually. But they would also expect us to integrate all the patients, from all the studies, into one enormous overall database of *everything*.

They could use this, if they felt the need, to see how many patients had diarrhoea on day seventeen after treatment, averaged across every patient who had ever been given a shot of amonafide. If they wanted to know the total number of female Eskimos who had complained of a sore big toe two weeks after randomisation, this was the place to look. It was a compendium of all data on amonafide and could provide the answers to endless hours of regulatory *Trivial Pursuits* questioning.

The ability to conduct this sort of *collective* analysis was important but it came at the cost of introducing an extra dimension of difficulty to an already complicated situation. For regulators however, complexity frequently seemed a necessity. The more elaborate the demands they made, the more productive they felt they were being. Especially when it was someone else who would have to sort it all out and provide the answers.

However, if they wanted all this data, then we would have to go ahead and provide it for them. The balance of power had shifted. When a trial is ongoing, you tend to have control of the information and by virtue of that, the upper hand. If the regulators want to know something, they have to come and get it from you. There's nowhere else to go. If you are prepared to give it to them that is. But when you reach the point of wanting them to accept your data, in order to approve your drug, then the rules change.

They hold most of the cards from that moment on. They dangle a little bell in their hand and you have to come running whenever you hear it ringing. They never make your life exactly easy but they can also make it very difficult if they want to. So we would give them what they needed, whatever our views on the value or validity of it.

But you couldn't just hand over something of that complexity, for them to take it or leave it. It wasn't possible to put in the post and hope it fitted through the letterbox at the other end. We would have to meet with them and agree how to do things. How to provide them with what they wanted and in the format they needed it.

And *that's* when our problems started.

V

The ultimate objective of all those years of time, effort, investment and hope expended on developing a new drug, is to give the end result to a regulatory body, for them to then be able to make what they will of the data. And so it should really be a *partnership* along the way, with you and them working together. That way, you will hopefully produce something at the end of it all, which you can both live and work with.

But with regulatory authorities, it was never like that in reality. Rather than an active relationship where you communicated regularly, swapping information and checking out the other side's thinking, it was more like keeping in touch with a distant relative. Maybe there would be a card at Christmas, a round-robin e-mail in the summer, that was about it. This lack of contact made it much harder when you did eventually get back together again. It was like coming across someone from the past, who you'd known really well once and realising how much you'd now grown apart.

This was particularly so with FDA, although the Europeans weren't exactly *gregarious* either. There were a handful of fixed prescribed meetings which The Agency offered and indeed expected to have, during the course of a drug development programme. In fact, the right to have these was enshrined in a federal code, without which nothing could happen at FDA anyway.

But this essentially comprised one get together at the beginning, one somewhere in the middle and one at the end. You could request other meetings along the way, if specific things cropped up. But there was no guarantee of them being granted and it was more likely than not that they wouldn't be. It was all very offhand, almost disdainful. Not exactly what you could describe as *interactive*.

There appeared to be a number of possible reasons for this apparent reluctance of FDA to engage with the outside world. These were an eclectic mixture of practical problems and philosophical prejudices. One simple fact was that they were overworked. The remit of FDA was enormous, almost infinite in fact. They had a responsibility for regulating most things the average American might put into or on their bodies, with the exception of alcohol and tobacco. And yet their resources were finite to the point of woeful inadequacy.

Their constrained capabilities were diminished further by the inevitable inefficiencies inherent in an enterprise that large and that diversely disparate. The hierarchical structure of FDA was of a complexity which would have put the Holy Roman Empire to shame. You just had to look at all the different boxes on an organisational diagram, to realise that it could never work. And it didn't. They were constantly tripping over each other, unable to put a coordinated step forwards.

The resulting inertial inefficiency was recently bluntly captured by Dr Joshua Scharfstein, FDA's Principal Deputy Commissioner at the time.

"I keep two lists at FDA," he explained. "Those that are moving just fine and those that I wish would happen faster. And there's nothing on the first list."[5]

But that shouldn't have come as a surprise to anyone who'd seen FDA at work, at first hand. Just one example was how the people there collaborated internally. In any pharmaceutical company running a drug development programme, everyone would work together in a team so that the clinical people, the pharmacologists, the toxicologists, the drug manufacturing people, the regulatory people, and all the other specialities needed to keep the juggernaut moving, would interact in a continual and constant fashion.

At FDA they used to lump all the toxicologists together in one office, all the medical people in another office and so on. Which meant that they didn't work together, they didn't cross pollinate. Also, recent changes to work rules meant that drug reviewers could spend two days a week working from home. So they didn't collaborate well and found it difficult to sort out internal issues, because they seemed to rarely all meet in the same place, as fully functioning teams.

You quickly realised this, on those rare occasions when you did manage to get into FDA for a meeting. There would inevitably be ten or fifteen of them and often you could waste valuable minutes of the preciously allocated one hour, with the FDA people catching up with and updating one another. It probably wasn't uncommon for individuals working there to actually meet for the first time at these sponsor occasions.

So there weren't enough of them at FDA to begin with and those who were there worked most of the time with their hands tied behind their backs, due to the environment they were in.

They also seemed to suffer from the consequences of excessive Federal egalitarianism, when it came to employing people. There were some very smart individuals at FDA. You needed a big brain, as well as a good grip, to stay at the top of that greasiest of poles.

But there were also a number whom one suspected would have struggled to be picked up, outside of a Federal programme. A lot of the foot soldiers were like this. As in any bureaucracy, these were unfortunately the people you had to rely on to keep the wheels turning, however slowly.

It wasn't just that they didn't have the time to meet with sponsor companies, although it was undoubtedly part of the problem. It was much deeper than that. They didn't seem to *want* to meet. It was almost as though interacting with the outside world was a distraction and an annoyance. It diverted them from attending to the internal needs of the organisation which nurtured and sustained them. FDA definitely laboured under a defensive, almost siege, mentality. They *even* dressed like an army.

If you hadn't been to FDA before, it could be a bewildering experience to enter a meeting room, only to find a number of the Agency contingent wearing what appeared to be full military uniform. You wouldn't come across anything like that in Europe, where most regulators seemed to dress as though Poundland had just introduced a range of men's clothing.

Those working at the EMA might spend all day looking for a metaphorical smoking gun, in the drug applications on their desks. But they wouldn't have known one end of a real one from the other. The nearest they ever came to a weapon was the knife they sometimes used to stab you in the back. But in the US, it was a different matter altogether. These guys were tooled up for a fight before you'd even sat down.

They were actually members of the United States Public Health Service Commissioned Corps (PHSCC). It was one of the seven federal uniformed services, along with the Army, Navy, Air Force and Marines, amongst others.

Members of the PHSCC wore naval uniforms and carried the same ranks as officers in the Navy. The US Surgeon General was the ultimate head of the PHSCC, even enjoying the rank of vice admiral. The Corps consisted of doctors, dentists, nurses, pharmacists and environmental health personnel amongst others, forming a group of highly trained and mobile health professionals.

They were charged with the task of "protecting promoting and advancing the health and safety of the Nation"[6] and were used to being dispatched at short notice to disaster areas around the country or even abroad.

When they weren't running around the world's hot spots, creating lots of paperwork, their main task appeared to be taking up defensive positions at FDA, seemingly to repel the advance of companies actually engaged in trying to develop drugs.

Although deploying troops might have been going a bit far, you could understand the Agency's defensive self-protectionism, to a certain extent. They faced an almost impossible task as drug regulators. If they didn't approve drugs, they were attacked for holding back the pace of innovation. However, if they did allow something onto the market, which subsequently had to be withdrawn for safety or other reasons, they were pilloried and accused of having relaxed their stringent standards. In a way they just couldn't win.

And it was worse for them in the US, compared to their European colleagues. The EMA goes largely unnoticed and overlooked. Ninety nine point nine nine per cent of Europeans have never heard of it. The point zero one who have, all work in the pharmaceutical industry. What public opprobrium there is tends to be reserved for national authorities, which largely determine whether or not to fund a new drug's availability, such as the UK's National Institute for Clinical Excellence (NICE).

In the US, it was very different. There was a significant degree of American Congressional oversight of the Agency, more demanding freedom of information provisions FDA had to comply with and also more strident and vocal consumer advocacy groups, who often carried real political weight. Being caught in this constant crossfire made them cautious and conservative. They felt as though they weren't so much between a rock and a hard place but in the hard place already, with their face pressed right up against it.

For them, it was probably safest to *not* approve a drug rather than let one through. There was less risk involved, especially on a personal career level. By rejecting a drug, there wasn't anything to potentially unravel later on. No safety issues which might subsequently emerge, after a new agent had been on the market and used much more extensively. No controversy over new efficacy data, or the lack of it, as was more often the case.

And to make it easy for them, there was always a reason to turn a drug down if they really wanted to find one.

As if that weren't enough, there was also the example of Asteroid 6260.

Not many people working at FDA can expect to have an asteroid named after them and Asteroid *6260 Kelsey* is probably unique. It was originally discovered in 1949 by a German astronomer, Karl Wilhelm Reinmuth, working at the Landessternwarte Heidelberg–Königstuhl Observatory in Heidelberg. Which must enjoy the distinction of being the world's longest named institution.

Given its origins in far flung Germany, the obvious question is how and why did Asteroid 6260 end up being named in honour of an otherwise obscure FDA drug reviewer called Frances Kelsey, three thousand miles away in the US?

And furthermore, how did *she* end up at the White House, to receive the Congressional Medal for Distinguished Civilian Service, one of the highest possible civilian honours? Or become inducted into the US National Women's Hall of Fame?

The answers lay in the name on a drug dossier, which landed on her desk way back in September 1960, just one month after she had taken up a job as a medical reviewer at FDA. The case was considered a routine one, which is why it was given to the newcomer. She was aged forty six at the time and although originally from Canada, had most recently been working in hospital medicine in South Dakota.

The name of the drug was thalidomide.

This was already being widely used as a sedative, in over twenty other countries, by the time it was submitted for approval in the US, by the drug company Richardson Merrell, under the trade name *Kevadon*.

The subsequent story of the ten thousand or so tragic babies is of course well known. Towards the end of 1961, reports in Germany began to link thalidomide, taken during pregnancy, to an epidemic of severe birth defects which was then sweeping across Europe. These were characterised by highly unusual limb abnormalities and absent pelvic bones.

By the middle of 1962, the drug had been clearly implicated as the causative culprit and a tidal wave of recrimination broke loose, with conspiracy theories of suppressed evidence and corporate collusion flying around. But America escaped unscathed, with the exception of a handful of cases, largely the result of people having acquired the drug abroad. This deliverance was due solely to the fact that despite its widespread usage elsewhere, Frances Kelsey had refused to approve thalidomide for the US.

At the time, she didn't know about the unique thalidomide induced birth defects, otherwise known as *phocomelia*.[7] They hadn't surfaced yet. During the period she was reviewing the thalidomide submission, there was some discussion in medical journals about possible thalidomide side effects, including suggestions of nerve damage but nothing pointing to the looming disaster. Instead, what actually perturbed Dr Kelsey were a number of findings in the results of *animal* testing with thalidomide.[8]

Amongst others, there were changes suggesting the drug affected the working of the thyroid gland. In her view, that was a potential safety signal that required further explanation. She was also puzzled because thalidomide was being used as a sedative in patients but didn't appear to be having this effect on rodents.

She couldn't understand why the same thing wasn't seen in both species, which raised the question of how relevant the animal testing really was. If rodents weren't responding to the *known* effects of the drug, could they really be relied on to display any unexpected toxicity either?

Showing a degree of intransigence which was subsequently to become a hallmark of FDA, she insisted, over the next eighteen months or so, on further animal experiments before considering the drug for approval.[9] Before any of this could be completed however, the clinical catastrophe in Europe and elsewhere overtook events.[10]

All of a sudden, Dr Kelsey was a national heroine for having blocked thalidomide in the US.[11] Praise and plaudits rained down on her in a way it may be difficult to understand now, nearly half a century later, when we have much more sophisticated drug safety systems. Back then none of that existed. It was all down to her diligent detective work. And an extremely conservative approach to taking any risks.

Dr Kelsey went on to meet President Kennedy at the White House in 1962, to receive the highest possible governmental award, *The Congressional Medal*. Innumerable honorary doctorates and diplomas came her way. They even kept her at FDA until she was over ninety years old. She didn't retire until then. That's how highly she was regarded. And of course, there was the asteroid too. Her fame had finally become celestial.

VII

Half a century later, her celebrity status possibly seems something of an overreaction. Dr Kelsey certainly had the courage of her convictions and stood steadfast in the face of substantial opposition to her concerns at the time. And whilst her actions alone were responsible for saving countless thousands of American families from personal tragedy, the fact was that the thalidomide induced birth defects were actually *unconnected* with the animal testing objections raised by Dr Kelsey.

The animal findings and the human experience were independent phenomena. One had nothing to do with the other. But the lesson was never subsequently lost on those at FDA, that a *minor* concern had prevented a *major* catastrophe. There is always a reason for reservation with any drug. None are completely risk free. But after thalidomide, it became that much easier to act on drug doubts of even the most minimal magnitude and just say *no*.

As Kelsey herself said at the time of thalidomide, "there was something a little different about this one so it seemed better to be safe and sure."[12] *Safe and sure* is a mantra which subsequently seeped into the very core of the Rockville building which houses the Agency.

The lessons of thalidomide are often cited as a positive watershed, ushering in an era of tighter and better drug regulation.[13] Which is true, to an extent. Just one example of this was the realisation, post thalidomide, that the rat and dog species used up until then for safety testing, were actually incapable of detecting thalidomide like side effects during pregnancy. It turned out that you had to use the rabbit to pick these up. This resulted in rabbit testing for birth defects becoming an essential part of all drug safety screening. Which is partly why another such tragedy has been avoided over the past fifty years.

But in the US, thalidomide went on to exert a more subtle but also less beneficial influence on the regulatory milieu. Everyone at FDA wanted to be the next Frances Kelsey.

You didn't get invited to the White House for approving a drug, even if it turned out to be safe and effective. In fact you didn't get any thanks at all for that. It was just your job and was taken more or less for granted. But stopping the next potential thalidomide was a different proposition altogether. No one at FDA ever needed reminding of thalidomide but if they did, there were photographs of Frances Kelsey all over the place for many years afterwards.

It all helped contribute to a collective culture of conservatism. The Chairman of the FDA Alumni Association neatly captured the still prevailing environment at a 2012 award ceremony.[14]

"Dr Kelsey is an iconic figure in FDA history. There are hundreds, if not thousands, of FDA'ers who have followed Dr Kelsey's footsteps."

Tagging so doggedly behind her appeared in turn to have encouraged the *avoidance* of risk, sometimes seemingly almost at all cost, rather than the rational *assessment* of risk, which is what drug development should be all about.

And this negativity contributed to FDA's apparent reluctance to meet up on any kind of regular basis along the way, during the development of a drug. They seemed to prefer to act almost in isolation, or certainly at a very long arm's length. It kept companies at a disadvantage, as they tried to guess what the Agency's thinking might be on this or that issue. It also allowed them to change their minds and spring a new position out of the blue, catching companies unawares. As it turned out, they were shortly to do with us, over amonafide.

The more they could avoid a discussion, the less was the risk of having to concede or compromise on something. It allowed the Agency to keep more options open for later on, when they were actually reviewing a drug application. This was their favourite time for unleashing unpleasant and unanticipated surprises. They liked to preserve opportunities for prevarication and procrastination until the last possible and least expected moment. The more they avoided dialogue early on, the greater the chances for delay and dissimulation further down the line.

But maintaining this distance came at a cost. And it wasn't just in terms of helping to promote and perpetuate an anaemic and adynamic approach to drug approval. By cloistering themselves away, FDA were in turn becoming progressively more isolated and out of touch. And they knew it.

VIII

FDA's very own Science Board, chaired by Professor Barbara McNeil from Harvard Medical School, was responsible for advising the Agency on technical advances and emerging issues within the scientific community.

As far back as 2007, they had concluded:[15]

"FDA's inability to keep up with scientific advances means that American lives are at risk. Whilst the world of drug discovery and development has undergone revolutionary change...FDA's evaluation methods have remained largely unchanged for the last half century."

Despite this indictment from its *own* advisory group, nothing seemed to have changed at FDA three years later. An independent report emerged in the summer of 2010 from the Council for American Medical Innovation. This was a consortium of thought leaders from medicine, academia, government and the healthcare industry.

They found that:

"In the midst of the explosion of scientific knowledge and improvements, we have allowed our regulatory system to fall behind in its scientific skills and tools and instead become mired in processes that are unable to predictably balance the need for safety as well as patient benefits." [16]

Later that year, just before Christmas, Scott Gottlieb, himself a former Number Two at FDA, wrote in the *Wall Street Journal* that "Congress needs to modernise the way the FDA's review process is organised in order to increase efficiency and enable more cooperation." It also needed to force the Agency to "cultivate principles that are more permissive, when it comes to very bad diseases."[17]

Gottlieb provided a timely reminder that Congress had in fact passed the FDA Modernisation Act back in 1997, at the height of the AIDS crisis in the US. This had given the Agency wide discretion to reduce both the quantity and rigor of clinical trial data needed to approve drugs for seriously life threatening illnesses. But over the intervening thirteen years, FDA had "steadily disregarded the law's provisions."

As an indication of their commitment to change, out of a total FDA budget of well over three billion dollars, the Agency spent just eighteen million dollars in 2010 on the *Critical Path Initiative.*[18] This was their national strategy for modernising how new drugs were developed and evaluated. And that miniscule sum had to cover animal medicines and food too. By comparison, pharmaceutical companies spent sixty five billion dollars on research in the same year.

In an interview in 2010, Margaret Hamburg, the FDA Commissioner conceded that "the process of regulation does not allow you to respond in a timely way to emerging science or other important emerging concerns."[5]

But she subsequently appeared to have no realistic suggestion for a solution, offering instead an anodyne generalisation, remarkable only for the avoidance of any complicity on the part of the Agency.

"We are failing, as a scientific community and as a nation, to adequately deliver the promise of science to diagnose, treat, prevent or cure disease. We can bridge this gap, but success will require we work together on a new set of flexible standards of product review for the twenty first century through the emerging field of *regulatory science.*"[19]

She went on to elaborate, to her presumably confused audience, that "regulatory science is the science of the assessment and evaluation of the safety, efficacy, potency, quality and performance of a product."

She didn't unfortunately explain how you might go on to distinguish between *efficacy, potency, quality* or *performance*, all of which would seem to be variants on the same fundamental theme, of trying to determine whether a drug actually works. But then any bureaucrat would prefer the complexity of four terms, when one would do perfectly well on its own.

"We must invest in regulatory science to develop new methods, assays, standards and models which will help speed the development, review and approval of medical products that patients need and can rely on," she concluded, in a profusion of platitudes. There wasn't a single word about FDA changing its claustrophobic culture or antediluvian attitudes.

It was a masterly exercise in saying virtually nothing and committing to even less.

Diverting attention to regulatory science, whatever that really meant, wasn't so much confronting a problem as camouflaging one. After all, the process of approving a drug was only in part anything to do with *science* and there was more than enough of that around already. Ultimately, it was an exercise in arbitration between science, medicine, public policy, patient pressure, clinical consensus and often political posturing. And all of it undertaken in an environment of accelerated innovation and a rate of change of knowledge unprecedented in the history of medicine.

It would have been a huge challenge for any organisation, let alone a federally bureaucratised one. But nonetheless, that was the reality to which at some point FDA had to start acquiescing.

But there wasn't much sign of them doing so any time soon. They recognised the need for change but weren't ready to do anything about it yet.

You sensed it when you went there.

FDA were housed in a new building in Rockville, a satellite suburb of Washington. It was like arriving at a modern airport terminal, complete with armed security, an X-ray machine for hand luggage and a metal detector. But that's where the modernity seemed to cease.

Entering the building was like going through a time portal and back into an earlier era. It was as though your television had lost the signal and you were suddenly watching in black and white. Everything seemed blurred around the edges and motion was slower, as though obeying different laws of space and time from everywhere else.

You would come across people who didn't seem to have been exposed to the contemporary world for decades. This *wasn't* an organisation which could rapidly respond to the revolution raging around it. Science and medicine were moving at an ever faster pace, in the process putting an ever greater distance between themselves and the reactionary regulators of Rockville. Even the location *Rockville* sounded prehistoric. Like something out of the Flintstones.

So all in all, FDA were difficult to deal with. They were like some slumbering primordial beast, which you disturbed at your danger. And above all, they were unpredictable.

Which is why we shouldn't have been as amazed as we were, when their letter arrived.

IX

We had written to them a week or so earlier, asking for a meeting to discuss the transfer of the ACCEDE data from us to them. We needed to know what they wanted to see and how we should give it to them. And they had now replied.

However, they'd also taken the opportunity to casually drop into the letter a new clinical request. That might not have seemed unreasonable, except that it was something which potentially negated the whole point of the ACCEDE trial. It risked jeopardising the last three years we had devoted to this undertaking. It was less a letter and more a parcel bomb.

We had originally written to them requesting a *Type B Pre-NDA* meeting. NDA stood for New Drug Application.[20] It was the final point on the regulatory roadway. This was the moment when you handed over your drug submission to the Agency. It marks the end result of six or seven years of collective endeavour and contains the totality of information ever

458

generated on the drug. Which makes it a pretty significant milestone therefore. Like being born or dying, in a small biotech company it's the kind of life event you can only really rely on once.

FDA have three different types of meeting. *Type A* meetings are for really big emergencies – they've just decided they're going to force you to suspend your clinical trial, ban you for life, that sort of thing. *Type B* meetings refer to the limited number of meetings which you have a "right" to, during the development of a drug. These generally comprise one before you start any clinical trials, one at the end of Phase II and one at the end of Phase III, before you submit everything to FDA. *Type C* meetings, in the world of FDA logic, are defined as those which are neither Type A nor Type B.

FDA took the issue of meetings very seriously. They had even produced a fourteen page document on how to request a meeting, which aimed to "standardise procedures for requesting, preparing, scheduling, conducting, and documenting such formal meetings."[21]

That's why they were so cautious about having meetings. There was no sitting down and knocking things around, chewing the cud for a bit. All meetings had to be documented in detail and thus become formally entered into the record, so that there was no ambiguity later on down the line.

Our Type B meeting should have been pretty straightforward. That's certainly what we were expecting, when we requested it. All we needed to do was to clarify a few procedural points and confirm a series of technical issues which we'd already discussed with them in the past.

And that's what was covered by most of the *sixteen page* letter, which arrived back from them at the beginning of November. It was largely full of technical terminology, replete with turgid paragraphs such as:

In dataset ASOR instead of a single column PARAM, there should be separate columns for PR, CrC, Crd, Confirmed CR, Initial Documentation of CR+Cri, Maintained Cr+Cri and overall response. The corresponding censoring variables should be in 7 separate columns. The variables meant for sensitivity analysis should also be independently shown in separate columns. In dataset ASTTE instead of a single column ENDPT, there should be separate columns for OVS, OVS2, DOR, DFS1, DFS2, TNR and TPR.

These were the sorts of thing we needed to thrash out with them though. We had to define the precise structure of all that information from the ACCEDE trial. It was a kind of detailed inventory, so they could find out where everything was.

For the technically uninitiated it might as well have been in a foreign language. Even for the initiated, it was still a challenge. It was like having a conversation with someone in Klingon. This was the arcane language that Albert and the others in biometrics thought and spoke in. It meant everything to them but nothing to the rest of us.

But what did clearly mean something to *everyone* was a paragraph tucked half way down the letter, responding to a minor point of clarification about the primary endpoint for the ACCEDE study.

The *primary endpoint* is the single most important parameter, for deciding whether your drug has worked or not. You have to define it in advance and after that, any other efficacy measures become subservient and secondary to it.

From a statistical and a regulatory perspective, failure to meet your primary endpoint is effectively game over. No matter how well a drug does by other measures, falling short on the primary one means the study will be interpreted as a bust.

If you reach this unhappy point, you effectively have the choice of either giving up altogether with the drug, or starting all over again with a different study. It's not a good place to be in. Which is why agreement over the primary endpoint is paramount in designing any clinical trial intended for submission to a regulatory authority.

And we had already agreed this with FDA. It was quite clear from previous discussions with them, that the primary endpoint for the ACCEDE trial would be the complete response (CR) rate. This was the proportion of patients whose leukaemia had disappeared from the bone marrow and other parts of the body after treatment. We'd be measuring other things too but this would be the make or break marker of efficacy.

We were certain this was what we'd agreed, because we'd had to fight them tooth and nail over it.

X

Originally, FDA had wanted us to persuade clinicians to *delay* any subsequent treatment they might have wanted to give, for at least a month *after* a patient had achieved a response (with amonafide or daunorubicin). They wanted us to do more tests, four weeks later, to double check that the patient was still responding. They were insisting we confirm that the bone marrow was still free of disease, in the *absence* of any other therapy having been given in the meantime. And that's what they had wanted as the primary endpoint. The *confirmed* CR rate.

Effectively, this was two bone marrow examinations, at least thirty days apart, with each showing freedom from disease. And with no other treatment given in between them. The Agency seemed fixated with this for some reason. They wanted to reassure themselves that the remissions weren't just a fleeting phenomenon. It wasn't much good to anybody having a response which was here today and gone tomorrow.

They'd got it into their minds that four weeks was the minimum period to confirm a response was genuine and not just another case of Nature teasing everyone.

They kept referring to a set of guidelines, devised about a decade ago by a group of international leukaemia experts, recommending confirmed CR as a way of evaluating anti-leukaemia drugs. These were generally known as the *Cheson criteria*, named after the chairman of the working group which had originally produced them, Bruce Cheson from Georgetown University in Washington DC.[22]

In turn, we had gone back and reminded them that the same group of experts had more recently revised their guidelines and *dropped* this idea, because it was unworkable in modern clinical practice.[23] We even had some of our own ACCEDE leukaemia specialists explain to FDA that with recent medical advances, things had changed.

These days you *immediately* wanted to give the patient more treatment – a bone marrow transplant or more chemotherapy or whatever – as soon as they showed an initial complete response. As soon as possible. Maybe the same day, maybe the next day but you definitely didn't wait a whole month. AML wasn't exactly a disease characterised by the luxury of time to spare.

The shorter the interval between the patient achieving a complete response and then receiving further treatment, the better they did in the long term. Everyone knew that now, didn't they?

Well, in reply FDA, whilst acknowledging this divergence between clinical practice and *regulatory science*, still wanted us to go ahead and do what all our clinicians were telling us couldn't be done. Their insistence was matched only by our incomprehension.

Recognising a brick wall when we saw it and rather than start banging our heads against it, we had no choice but to give it a go. So we tried to get centres in the ACCEDE study to hold off on transplants and other treatment interventions, for at least thirty days after their patients had responded. We would try to collect the confirmed CR information FDA so fervently desired.

However, we then found ourselves spending the next few months in a series of placatory phone calls, trying unsuccessfully to explain to clinicians why we wanted them to do something that didn't make any sense, as far as they were concerned. And they pretty much all refused. And who, quite frankly, could blame them.

For patients and physicians alike, with the clock counting down, it didn't exactly seem the right time to take a month off to read the entire works of Shakespeare.

And so after a while we had to go back to FDA and show them that we had tried and failed. I'm not sure they completely believed us. Their attitude seemed to suggest that our failure was due not so much to the excessiveness of their demand but rather the effeteness with which we had approached it. In their view, it was nothing that a bit of moral fibre and a stronger backbone couldn't have sorted out. However, faced with our apparent lack of both these attributes, whilst they wouldn't drop *confirmed* CR altogether, they did at least agree that the primary endpoint could be changed to the *initial* CR rate.

That was the proportion of patients who achieved a remission in the first place, never mind how long it lasted for. It meant there was no need for the subsequent bone marrow and the consequent delay in further therapy.

It might not sound like a fundamental change of stance on their part, shifting from one definition of CR to another one. But getting a regulator to alter their mind on anything was a difficult uphill struggle and this had been no exception.

It was also a new one on us, for them to apparently see some reason and acknowledge the real world difficulties of what they were demanding. It wasn't in their nature to be that accommodating. Maybe in retrospect this should have been a warning to us. FDA didn't usually back down, especially when it made life easier for the sponsor.

XI

However, whilst they may have blinked in the past, they now appeared ready to poke us in the eye with a pointed stick. They suddenly seemed hell bent on making life as difficult for us as they could. Ticking away in their letter to us was that time bomb.

They had written back to say that instead of anything to do with response rates, confirmed or otherwise, they now wanted *overall survival* as the primary endpoint of the ACCEDE trial. It was completely out of the blue. Only a year ago we had discussed and documented with them, in writing, that the endpoint would be the initial complete response (CR) rate. We had that in black and white. There had never been any serious discussion of survival, as the main objective of the study.

No drug had shown a survival advantage in adult acute myeloid leukaemia for over twenty years and we didn't have any reason to expect we could be the first to do so now.[24] It just didn't seem possible in that disease. This was a potentially disastrous change of position by FDA. It was like visiting the doctor expecting him to just check your blood pressure and finding he was getting ready to give you a heart transplant instead.

The ACCEDE study had never been set up to *prove* any difference in survival between the amonafide and daunorubicin arms. We were obviously expecting it to be going in the right direction but not to be able to confirm it statistically. That would require two or three times the number of patients we already had in the trial. Which would be a non-starter. It was just too big to be possible. You would have to recruit pretty much every patient on Earth. Even that might not be enough. You'd probably have to extend the study to another, as yet undiscovered, universe where they also happened to suffer from leukaemia.

And even if you could undertake a study of this enormity, there was still the question of whether you could ever actually show an effect of one drug alone on survival, in a disease as complicated as acute myeloid leukaemia. There were just too many different interventions which happened to the patient along the way.

Recent drugs, like Mylotarg, had tried and failed and as a consequence were in danger of being relegated to nothing more than historical footnotes in the chronicles of cancer chemotherapy. Overall survival was definitely a death sentence as far as we were concerned. It would certainly be a fatal blow for us if FDA prevailed here, effectively rendering the ACCEDE study pointless. Antisoma would be dead and buried too.

But where, we wondered, had this change of mind by FDA come from and what were we going to do about it now?

XII

We eventually concluded that the Agency had probably been influenced by their experience of a year ago with Vion's laromustine. This was ultimately rejected by ODAC, for use in the treatment of acute myeloid leukaemia in the elderly. The drug had shown a very favourable effect on CR rate but appeared to actually *reduce* subsequent survival. This seemed to be because it caused a highly unusual pattern of deaths, due to a particular type of fatal lung damage.

Lots of drugs, amonafide included, resulted in fatal side effects, which could adversely affect survival. But they usually caused patients to die early on after treatment, *before* there had been enough time for a CR to develop. This meant the patient wouldn't have survived long enough to give the drug a chance to clear the leukaemic disease from the bone marrow. And so these deaths also dragged down the CR rate too.

With laromustine though, the fatal lung toxicity was *delayed* and so the patients were living long enough to have a chance of going into remission first. This resulted in a situation where the CR rate went *upwards* whilst the survival went *downwards*, whereas usually they followed each other in the same direction. With laromustine, there was an important disconnect between the two. Which meant that looking at CR remission rates *alone*, without also considering survival, would grossly overestimate the overall efficacy of the drug.

However, instead of seeing this for what it was, an issue peculiar to laromustine, FDA had apparently seized on it as an opportunity for defensive prevarication all round. They had applied their typical perversely syllogistic reasoning: *laromustine was a leukaemia drug and laromustine had a particular problem. Amonafide was a leukaemia drug and so amonafide must have the same problem.* Never mind that amonafide and laromustine were completely different molecules, with separate patterns of toxicity and fatality. In the rigidly iterative mindset of FDA, they were now one and the same, until proven otherwise.

But there was also a possible deeper dimension to this. It was at exactly the time we heard back from FDA, that they were also reaching the final stages of their deliberations over Avastin in metastatic breast cancer. They had to decide whether to revoke its usage, due to the absence of an effect on overall survival.

If they had already made up their minds to reject Avastin, then they possibly felt a need to put greater weight on survival with other drugs, amonafide included. It was a way of showing consistency and bolstering their position. With all their firepower concentrated on Genentech, the Agency didn't seem to mind how much collateral damage was incurred by other companies along the way.

Of course, we couldn't know for sure though what was going through their minds. We could only guess. However, what this new development did show was how the Agency behaved in a detached world, all of their own. They must have already been considering and debating the laromustine issue for ages. Given that it was FDA, it wasn't exactly going to have happened overnight. So did they really have to wait until now to let us know and in such an inadvertently indirect manner?

Well, the answer to that was clearly *yes*.

Arbitrary decisions such as this had the power to derail entire drug development programmes and even destroy companies. Obviously FDA had to react to new information they became aware of, whilst reviewing a new drug. This was particularly the case if it could have relevance to others being developed for the same indication, at the same time. But this had to be a process conducted rationally and not as a reflex reaction to cover themselves against any eventuality, however remote.

The chances of amonafide behaving like laromustine were so small that there was really no sensible scientific basis for having this concern. They were different types of molecules, which worked in different ways and produced differing patterns of efficacy and toxicity. They were also being developed for different types of AML patients. They couldn't really be more different.

The only thing they shared in common was that both were unfortunately in the hands of FDA. But none of that mattered to the Agency. The danger to them of taking a risk, however small and hypothetical, more than justified the cost of avoiding it, however great that might be for others. In situations like this, it wouldn't be FDA who would end up paying. Instead the tab would be picked up by companies which faced possible collapse and patients who were left bereft of potential new treatment options.

And although they were locked away in their command and control bunker, FDA couldn't exactly have been unaware of the consequences of flexing their muscles. The Agency knew they had the power to profoundly interfere in the lives of the people and companies in their sights.

They could even put people in *prison* if they really wanted to.

XIII

Which is exactly what happened to Scott Harkonen. The fifty eight year old former CEO of California biotechnology company InterMune had sanctioned his company issuing a press release in 2002, inaccurately claiming its drug *Actimmune* (interferon gamma) prolonged survival in patients with a rare form of lung fibrosis. This statement was based on a retrospective subgroup analysis, looking at just the least severely affected patients, whereas the results for the trial overall were negative. The implication from InterMune however had been that it worked for everyone.

It was a questionable thing to have done, although no patients came to harm as a consequence, However, for violating FDA rules and regulations on the promotion of drugs, he was convicted of wire fraud by a San Francisco court in 2009 with the prosecution seeking a *twenty year* prison sentence. Twenty years seemed excessive by most standards but showed how high the stakes could be if you did actually fall foul of FDA.

Fortunately an appeal court saw things more proportionately, with the judge finding that "the government had no evidence whatsoever that the press release had caused any loss or harm to anyone."[25]

Harkonen ended up in 2011 with a comparatively modest six month home detention and twenty thousand dollar fine. This seemed a much more reasonable punishment, especially when contrasted to the egregious case of Howard Richman. He at least had the good fortune to be pursued by the Securities and Exchange Commission (SEC) rather than by FDA.

Richman, aged fifty six from Houston Texas, was Vice President of a biotechnology company called Biopure. They had developed a synthetic blood substitute, called *Hemopure*. The company managed to gain approval in South Africa, where Hemopure did relatively well. However, it fared less favourably with FDA and was turned down by them in 2003.

Biopure played down the FDA rejection, characterising it as a minor technical issue rather than the major setback it really was. In particular, they failed to mention in SEC filings that substantial safety concerns had led FDA to put other clinical trials with Hemopure on hold. This omission helped them to raise a further thirty five million dollars in funding later that year. Eventually, an SEC investigation was instigated, after the implications of the regulatory decisions became more apparent to disgruntled investors.[26]

At this point, other Biopure executives came clean and received relatively light financial penalties in return. The former CEO got off with a one hundred and twenty thousand dollar fine for example. But for some unfathomable reason, Richman decided to contest a settlement. Even more inexplicably, he then proceeded to pretend he was suffering from cancer. He told the judge that he had been diagnosed with colon cancer and would be unable to attend court hearings.

He subsequently forged letters from his purported cancer specialist, saying he was undergoing surgery and chemotherapy. Caught in a web of his own lies, Richman was even forced to impersonate his supposed doctor, on a phone call to his own lawyer, so that she would confirm to the judge that his cancer had spread and become terminal. As a result of this intricate deception, US District Judge Patti Saris effectively dismissed the case against him in November 2007, having heard he now had just a fifteen per cent chance of survival.

It was only when all three of Richman's lawyers subsequently abruptly resigned that the truth came to light. At the end of 2009, Richman received a three year prison sentence for obstruction of justice. It was lenient in the circumstances, compared to the twenty years FDA wanted for Harkonen. Harkonen had done *one*, admittedly bad thing, by being less than honest in a press release. But Richman? Well, he was in a league all of his own.

Richman also received a one hundred and fifty thousand dollar civil fine, in respect of the SEC action. This however was *nothing* compared to some of the financial penalties FDA could bring to bear.

Their powers of remunerative retribution were amply demonstrated by the case of Michael Friedman who was President, Howard Urdell, Chief Consul and Paul Goldenheim, Medical Director, of the Connecticut drug company Purdue Pharma, which marketed a painkiller called OxyContin. This contained oxycodone, a semi-synthetic opioid drug used for mild to moderate pain. It was very widely prescribed but like all opioid type drugs, had a potential for abuse usage.

However, Purdue managed to grow OxyContin into a blockbuster drug, purporting it to be less open to abuse than other narcotics. But in 2007, charged by FDA with misrepresenting the addictive potential of oxycodone, Purdue paid a fine of seven hundred million dollars in civil and criminal restitution, with the three executives all pleading guilty to misdemeanour violations. They each received fines of five thousand dollars and four hundred hours of community service. However, the real whammy was that between the three of them, they were also forced to return *thirty four and a half million* dollars of previous compensation received from Purdue.

So FDA clearly had some serious clout. In fact they even had their own investigative detective agency, the *Office of Criminal Investigations* (OCI).

This department has the ability to conduct criminal investigations, in relation to potential violations of the Food Drug and Cosmetic Act. The OCI can also look into infractions of the Federal Anti-Tampering Act, along with suspected Mail Fraud, Wire Fraud, Trafficking, Conspiracy to Commit, Obstruction of Proceedings and many other areas of misdemeanour.

This wide ranging remit is fulfilled by about two hundred highly trained special agents, spread through field offices around the US. They work closely with other law enforcement agencies including the US Secret Service, the FBI, the US Postal Inspection Service, Immigration and Customs Enforcement and the Internal Revenue Service Criminal Investigations Unit.

As if that weren't enough, the OCI agents also have access to highly specialised backup, ranging from polygraph technicians to computing forensics. They even have a state of the art sixty five thousand square foot Forensic Chemistry Centre, located in a wooded eight acre site on the north eastern edge of Cincinnati. It's their very own CSI.

With their own police force and already accustomed to sitting as judge and jury on new drug applications, maybe it wasn't surprising that FDA sometimes acted with the sort of dismissiveness they now seemed to be displaying to us. Like many federal organisations, they had extensive powers of enforcement at their disposal. This was bound to engender an occasional imperiousness on their part. Admittedly, they weren't threatening to put us in prison. Not yet at least. But they had clearly already decided that amonafide was culpable.

XIV

They had helpfully concluded their letter: "*At this time it is uncertain if your submission would support approval,*" just in case we'd missed how big a spanner they'd thrown into the works. In other words, they appeared to have decided, in advance of actually seeing any data from the ACCEDE trial, that they might well not approve amonafide, come what may.

This was the very last thing we needed. A renegade regulator.

We *had* to get them to back track on the survival issue. We all knew that but no one was sure how to approach this. There was no point going back to them and complaining that this was unfair, they'd changed their minds and we were nothing like laromustine. That would be trying to use reason in a situation which was clearly driven by the irrational. We'd be well done for if we went down that road.

The simplest and boldest thing would have been to ignore them altogether and carry on regardless. Obviously you don't take a decision to disregard FDA lightly. Especially not with all the weapons in their war chest. But then we weren't exactly in a light position. On the contrary, ours was a distinctly heavy one.

It was too late to change direction now with ACCEDE and so maybe we had nothing to lose by ploughing on. We weren't planning to submit our completed application to FDA for another seven or eight months. Perhaps in that intervening period there would be a development with some other drug the Agency were looking at.

If that happened, maybe it would tip things back a little more in our favour. It wasn't impossible. Opinions in drug development could change with the rhythmicity of a pendulum.

It wasn't very probable though. Once they had dug themselves in, the Agency were unlikely to abandon such a well fortified position. Which meant we would end up having to slug it out with them later down the line, when we finally had some real data from the ACCEDE trial and we could all see what we were actually fighting about.

But that might not be too bad a fallback position to adopt.

The biggest danger of this approach however was that FDA would take our lack of response now as tacit acquiescence with their point of view. Which would leave us with an even bigger battle on our hands later on. There was also an understandable corporate concern that this was a potential liability, which we couldn't leave unresolved for another half a year.

Our investors wouldn't exactly be over pleased to learn we'd been sitting on something like this for months on end. The fate of the Biopure executives loomed before our eyes. It was unlikely any of us had the acting skills of Howard Richman either. So we had to do something right now to resolve the issue, that much was clear.

However, the debate, which was to go on and almost split the company, was not just *what* we did but *how* we did it too.

XV

As far as the process for a Type B meeting was concerned, the way it worked at FDA was for the sponsor company to write to them in the first instance, outlining the issues that needed the Agency's feedback. They would then meet internally to consider their views and a couple of weeks later would write back, giving their position, in principle, on the various points.

Depending on how much you liked or disliked what you saw, you could choose to leave it there and cut your losses. Alternatively, if you were brave or belligerent, you could go ahead and have the actual meeting with them, to discuss things in more detail. This was an opportunity to try to change their minds, if you were feeling lucky.

There was however always a real risk that you could inadvertently make things even worse for yourself by attempting this.

As well as being fraught with danger, the whole process was also a very cumbersome one, which largely ignored the communications revolution of the last decade. There were a lot of letters winging back and forth. Not brief e-mails, or phone calls. But *letters*. A messenger on horseback would probably have been more efficient.

Having now received a letter of response from FDA, containing the unexpected survival bombshell, what we couldn't agree on was whether it made sense to go ahead and actually get together with them. Should we grasp that rare opportunity to assemble in the same room and dance the carefully choreographed movements of an Agency meeting?

Or would we be better to keep a distance between us and them, instead *writing* back with our response, rather than meeting up. Should we keep them at arm's length, like a snake snared on a stick. That way you could stop it striking at you.

Proponents of meeting with the Agency argued that it would be best for both sides to sit down around the table. That way, we could get a much clearer sense of where this initiative had come from, whose idea it had been and how much support there appeared to be for it. It would give us a better opportunity to present our counter-argument. Always assuming we had one that is.

Others thought there was too much risk attached to meeting up with them. These sorts of events had the potential for immense unpredictability. It was like trying to anticipate the outcome of a DSMB meeting. At least those occasions had the advantage of dealing with people holding down normal jobs and living in the real world. People we could relate to, if not necessarily agree with.

Here, we didn't have that comfort. If we started challenging them on the survival issue, there was a real risk of someone from their side going off at a tangent and them ending up in an even more firmly entrenched position than appeared to be the case right now.

The wording of their letter had been that they *recommended* overall survival as the primary endpoint. When FDA recommend something, it is usually code for them forcing you to do it sooner or later, without stating it explicitly at the time. But for now at least, the letter *appeared* slightly more flexible than that.

If we started an open ended debate, we could easily lose control and end up with a much more unequivocal statement on this from them. And we definitely didn't want anything in black and white which was even more definitive that what we already had sitting uncomfortably on our desk.

Normally we would spend hours at Antisoma, rehearsing for those rare occasions when we did actually get to have meetings with FDA. Working out who'd speak and who wouldn't. Which person would say what and when they'd say it. But it always seemed a predominantly pointless exercise. It's sensible to invest in that degree of preparation, if you are going to be in control of events. But you never were with FDA. They might not like having meetings and may not grant them that often but when they did, then they definitely expected to be running things.

Ostensibly, these events were very formalised. There was an agreed list of things to be discussed, all of which had been circulated beforehand and you couldn't bring up something which wasn't on the list. They wouldn't discuss anything they hadn't been given advanced notice of.

But that didn't stop them bringing up something out of the blue, if they felt like it. That was always an ever present danger which you couldn't control for, however much you had rehearsed your side of things. They might throw something new into the mix. And then what would you do. No amount of dress rehearsals were going to help you out. And that was the danger of having a meeting now. We could end up being even worse off, due to something unforeseen suddenly coming into play.

XVI

Different parts of FDA were more prone than others to this kind of capricious unpredictability.

As far as drug review was concerned, the Agency divided themselves into the Center for Drug Evaluation and Research (*CDER*) and the Center for Biological Evaluation and Research (*CBER*). The former dealt with small molecule drugs, whilst the other one reviewed biologically derived products, such as antibodies and so on.

CDER was divided into a number of *Divisions* based around particular therapeutic areas. There were Divisions for Cardiovascular and Renal Products, Neurology Products, Psychiatry Products, Metabolism and Endocrinology Products, Pulmonary and Allergy Products, Analgesics, Anaesthetics and Rheumatology Products, Reproduction and Urologic Products, Gastroenterology Products, Dermatology and Dental Products, Anti-Infective and Ophthalmology Products, Anti-Viral Products and Special Pathogen and Transplant Products.

It was like all the different sections of a medical school library. And on top of all that, there was a separate Office of Oncology Drug Products, run by Richard Pazdur. At the time we were dealing with them over amonafide, this was divided into a Division of *Biologic* Oncology Products and a Division of *Drug* Oncology Products. (These Divisions would subsequently disappear at the end of 2011 when a new *Office of Hematology and Oncology Products* was created).

Each Division was headed by a Director, who ran it like a fiefdom. These Divisional Directors were a diversity of characters and personalities, which in turn influenced the nature of their departments. This meant there wasn't necessarily that much consistency across the Directors or the Divisions. It wasn't uncommon for each to form separate views on the same

470

issues, compounding even further the normal complexities of dealing with FDA.

The Division of Drug Oncology Products was headed by one of the deeper and more sophisticated individuals within the Agency. Dr Robert Justice had been Director since 2006 and had worked at FDA since 1985. He held a degree in Life Sciences from Massachusetts Institute of Technology, a degree in Biotechnology from Johns Hopkins University in Baltimore and a degree in medicine from the University of California. He was also a board certified haematologist and oncologist. So he really knew what he was talking about.

Interestingly though, he had twice left FDA, only to return again. In 1989 he had briefly resumed clinical practice in Honolulu. But having then come back to FDA, he left again in 2000 to spend two years working at the biotechnology behemoth Genentech, before returning to the federal fold. These vacillations set him apart from most of his peers at the Agency, who tended to have put down roots a long time ago. It was maybe indicative of a more inquiring mindset.

Dr Justice was quiet and thoughtful and didn't appear to be labouring too heavily under the burden of other competing agendas, which so often seemed to complicate dealing with senior Agency people.

If we could have met with him alone, then it probably would have been worth taking the chance. But you couldn't be that selective. You might get just him, or he might come with Richard Pazdur, the oncology supremo. That inevitably complicated things because with the two of them in the room, you were never quite sure where the balance of thinking, or the balance of power, was lying with any particular issue. They were both fairly reserved and didn't give much away. A lifetime of political manoeuvring had taught them to keep their cards close to their chests.

And then there was everyone else from the Agency, who would inevitably be involved in any meeting. It was all or none. And that was the drawback. You never quite knew who was going to turn up. They would send you a list of FDA attendees but you wouldn't always recognise the names, let alone have an insight into what they might say or do. Would this or that person be reserved and restrained, or did they have their own drum to beat.

Often they seemed to have an ulterior motive for some of the views they expressed, or the things they asked you to do. Maybe it was following up an idea put into their mind by some other drug they were reviewing. Maybe it was sounding out a general policy shift they were talking about internally, just testing the water as it were. Maybe it was a personal hobbyhorse they liked to ride.

Statisticians from FDA were particularly prone to having these. Usually it was some arcane new variant on a particular theme of statistical methodology, which had taken their recent fancy. Many of them seemed to believe that everything in life could be reduced to a mathematical algorithm. All they had to do was find the right one. They appeared to ignore the fact that clinical trials were conducted in the unpredictability of the real world and not as a computer simulation, where everything behaved perfectly.

And so they tended to come up with requests which just didn't make sense, or were unworkable, or frequently both. For them though, it was like playing with someone else's toys. If you put undue pressure or strain on them and they broke, it wasn't really your problem. Someone else would have to try mending them.

If these personal indulgences happened in a meeting however, you could easily waste ten or fifteen minutes of your allotted hour, slowly coming to the realisation that *yes*, they were serious about what they'd just said. You would then have to come up with a means of arguing your way out of it. If you could think on your feet that quickly. You only needed this to happen once or twice and then suddenly the clock was against you. You only had that hour. Meetings never ran over time at FDA.

There was also a liability more unpredictable than any of the FDA staff. You could walk into the meeting and find an actual *patient* sitting in there with the rest of the Agency. Which was the last thing you needed. That was enough to throw even the finest laid plans into disarray.

XVII

Back in 1996, President Bill Clinton had produced the ambitiously entitled *FDA Initiatives on Reinventing the Regulation of Cancer Drugs.*[27] It was aimed at trying to speed up cancer approval times and get more new drugs to more patients, more quickly.

Despite the bold title and vaunting ambition, it contained little of substance which was new. It did however introduce the *Patient Representative Program*. This placed a nominated patient volunteer, suffering from cancer, on to ODAC. The idea was to provide a patient perspective into the deliberations taking place, over whether to recommend approval of a new drug up for consideration before the Committee.

From about 2000, FDA got it in their heads to extend this to a parallel initiative called the *Patient Consultant Program*. The intention was to take a patient, suffering from whatever cancer a particular drug was intended for and get them involved in FDA decision making, during the actual drug development process. Exactly why they thought this was a good idea, remained a mystery to everyone else.

To help achieve this, they would attend meetings between FDA and the sponsor company and were expected to give a patient opinion on, amongst other things: "clinical trial design, endpoint determination, expanded access protocol development and clinical trial patient recruitment strategies."[28]

And to prepare them for their immersion into a world which most of us had spent years trying to become familiar with, all they received was a two day introductory workshop from FDA. Which would equate to just a *half* day workshop, if anyone else had been running it.

To most people outside FDA, it seemed an exercise too far in democratic devolution to allow lay people to take part in highly technical discussions about drug development. Never mind the fact that they were also in the grips of a terminal illness. This was a very different proposition from the idea of a patient representative on ODAC, where people from many different walks of life were already involved. The meetings were open to the public anyway and the discussions were less technical and more wide ranging.

In contrast, meetings with FDA, whether Type A, B, C or whatever, were a world of their own and largely impenetrable to the uninitiated. Despite that, the Patient Consultant Program had been running for nearly a decade now and FDA seemed to like it.

We'd experienced it first hand during a meeting with the Agency to talk about ASA404, our lung cancer drug. It was at a time when we were considering undertaking a Phase III trial with it by ourselves. We wanted to get together with them, to discuss the Phase II results and what sort of Phase III study we might need to conduct. Walking into the room at FDA, we were taken aback, to put it mildly, to see a stocky middle aged lady clasping the edge of the table, struggling for breath and not looking too well at all. There were plastic oxygen tubes under her nose.

"Jesus Christ," we thought, assuming she was from some other pharmaceutical company. "She's just had a bad meeting." They were having to *resuscitate* her.

It turned out she was there for us though. This was a lung cancer sufferer, who was also a Patient Consultant to FDA. There hadn't been any mention of her on the list of attendees but nevertheless she was introduced to us by FDA with all the flourish of a prestidigitator plucking a rabbit out of a hat. "Beat that," you could almost hear them thinking. "You may have a PowerPoint Presentation but we've got a *fucking* patient."

The Agency people all seemed quite comfortable with the presence of someone who might expire at any moment and so we decided to get on with it too. She chipped in quite regularly throughout the meeting though with well thought out intelligent points, although at least three quarters of what we were knocking back and forth must have gone over her head.

We were surprised by how much weight her words seemed to carry with the people on the other side of the table. They were paying her a much greater degree of deference than the frailty of her condition alone would have demanded.

Which was in fact good news, as her main thrust seemed to be *"stop pissing around and hurry up with these new drugs. We are dying out here."* Or words to that effect.

On that occasion, it had turned out to be a relatively neutral encounter. But there was no knowing what might unfold, if we went back now to talk about amonafide and found some AML patient in remission, propped up at the end of the conference table.

Would they be benignly altruistic, or malevolently resentful at the hand fate had dealt them. They could be a help or a hindrance but we'd have no way of knowing which. It was all part of the inherent unpredictability of what might happen if we decided to get together with the Agency, to air our differences over amonafide.

And even if we did meet, how would we approach things? Finding the right mixture of deference and defiance was important. If we were going to argue our corner we needed to mount a fairly robust defence. But it was a fine line. Come across as being too heavy handed and they could just dig their heels in even further. But to not land any punches at all would have meant a wasted journey and give them an even greater degree of confidence that they had you cornered.

And just what were we going to use as an argument against overall survival anyway? The fact that they'd changed their minds? That we didn't like it? Given the endless debate over just what was the best parameter, with which to measure the effects of an anti-cancer drug, it was probably as good a choice as any other. If you were to convene a panel of cancer experts to consider the issue, you'd almost certainly find more people in favour of using survival than against it. The fact that it was neigh on impossible for us to deliver on it didn't really come into the deliberation.

If we didn't have the answers to these issues though, there were plenty of others out there who thought they did.

XVIII

There are any number of regulatory "consultants" and Washington lawyers who make a good income out of giving advice on how to deal with FDA. We must have spent money on most of them over the next few weeks, mainly at the insistence of a small but highly vocal group in our US office.

Many of these consultants are ex-FDA employees who've lived off it ever since, claiming to still have the inside track on what's going on at the Agency. If you believed them, they talked to Richard Pazdur two or three times a day. He just couldn't make a big decision without phoning them for advice first. But you never heard anything of much value from these sorts of advisers. In reality, once you've climbed the wall and escaped FDA, you're on the outside from then onwards. The inner sanctum has closed its doors on you.

They didn't really have much more idea of what was going on over there in Rockville than we did. We might just as well have got out a pack of Tarot cards.

And so at the end of all this consulting, we didn't seem to be any the wiser about how to take on the Oncology Division, although many billable hours had been expended along the way.

So maybe, given this dearth of direction and depth about what to do if we did sit down with FDA, the best thing would be to *not* meet with them. Pass up the chance. Normally you would seize any opportunity to meet with the Agency, so few and far between were they. It increased your insight and understanding of them and if nothing else, it reminded you that however bad your world was, it could be worse. At least you didn't have to go to work at FDA every day. One hour in Gormenghast was definitely enough, let alone a lifetime. But on this occasion, maybe the risks outweighed the benefits.

Wouldn't it be better simply to *write* back to them, acknowledge their comment about the survival endpoint and suggest we met up in a couple of months' time, when we actually had some data? By the end of January we would have the CR rates for both arms of the study. The survival data wouldn't be ready until May or June but at least with the CR rates we'd have something concrete on the table to talk about. Which had to be better than the mere speculation we were all dealing in at the moment.

Substance was always better than supposition when dealing with the Agency. They were past masters at the art of summoning up hypothetical possibilities and permutations. It's what they spent all day doing. Trying to create new ways of looking at data, to put it in a less favourable light. They were black belts in the art of *what if* and without *real* results, would have us pinned to the floor in no time at all.

Being armed with *actual* data should increase our chances substantially. If the difference in CR rate between the two groups was looking unusually good for amonafide, then maybe the surprise of that would tip the argument back in our favour and we could hold on to it as the primary endpoint.

This approach would also give us our Type B pre-NDA meeting with the Agency that much nearer to the summer, when we were planning to start submitting the data package to them. We would therefore have an opportunity to create a favourable overall impression of the amonafide programme, at the exact time the submission started arriving on their desks.

If we met with them now though, any warm glow we hoped to create would have died away long before they started looking at the application. These nuances of psychology could sometimes be just as important for a drug's chances of survival as any of the actual clinical data. Like a lawyer with a guilty client, the verdict could be determined as much by courtroom tactics, as anything to do with the evidence itself.

It seemed like a good way forward. The only problem was that our regulatory people, and the legions of consultants in tow, were implacably opposed. Under *no* circumstances did they want to meet with FDA later on, when we actually had some data. It was now or never as far as they were concerned. We had to strike whilst the iron was hot. Never mind that it was the other side who had firm grasp of it.

The disagreement all stemmed from the actual mechanics of submitting completed clinical programmes to FDA. Like everything else to do with the Agency, it wasn't always straightforward.

XIX

The normal process for submitting the enormity of a clinical trials programme starts with a Type B pre-NDA meeting with The Agency. This is to discuss the logistics of it all and to get some sense that they are happy for you to press the GO button. Then, usually about six months or so later, you are in a position to send all your data in support of your application for approval.

This is the *New Drug Application* and includes *all* the clinical studies and all of the non-clinical work too. All reduced to a box set of CDs. *Amonafide's Greatest Hits*, in one collectors' edition. Nearly all NDAs are now submitted in an electronic format but in earlier times this would have comprised literally a large truck load of paper documentation. Veterans of the pre-electronic era would typically celebrate an NDA completion with a souvenir photograph of the inside of a U-Haul trailer, piled floor to ceiling with boxes bearing the fruits of their labours.

Once it has been delivered, FDA then has sixty days to look through it all. In the past that didn't include the extra time needed to unload it from the lorry. They don't start reviewing it in any detail at this stage. That is what will take them the next six to twelve months. Instead, they are just checking that it looks broadly OK and that all the right bits seem to be there. They want to make sure you haven't forgotten any major studies or anything of that sort.

It's a bit like flicking through a book in a store, deciding whether you are going to buy it. Quite a big book though, obviously.

If they are happy with this cursory examination, then they will accept it for review, which is when the formal in depth detailed analysis of every nut and bolt starts.

If however they think there is no hope of it ever being approved and it would be a waste of their time and effort to even review it, then they can at this stage reject the whole thing out of hand. They issue what is called a *Refusal To File Letter (an RTF)*. This happens in about five to ten per cent of NDAs submitted to the Agency. It's usually because even the most perfunctory examination of the data shows that the drug clearly doesn't have any credible efficacy, or because some important piece of information they were expecting to see, just isn't there.[29]

Whatever the reason for it, an RTF is a disaster for a company that becomes the hapless recipient of one. All that time and effort wasted, with success snatched away almost at the last moment. It's like spending your life savings to build the house of your dreams brick by brick, only to find at the end of it all that you never had any planning permission. And the council have just knocked it down.

Receiving an RTF also makes a company look somewhat inept, to put it mildly. It leaves people wondering what on earth you've been doing for the last five years, if you couldn't even put all the pieces in the box before posting it to FDA.

Our regulatory people had convinced themselves that delaying meeting with FDA, until we had some early results, would significantly increase the chances of a RTF decision at that point. We would effectively be sitting down with them and turning a bright spotlight on the CR rate. Putting it on stage, making it sing and dance. And if the amonafide results were anything less than stellar, the Agency might just tell us to f**k off at that point. They would probably put it slightly more diplomatically though.

The view of our people was that it would be *much* better to avoid directly discussing the initial results with them. Instead, just send the whole NDA in via the normal route and then sit back to wait for sixty days. That way, even if the amonafide data was marginal, then provided it weren't a complete bust, it would be much more likely to survive a superficial examination at this stage. Certainly its chances were better than waving it under FDA's nose, in a face to face meeting.

It may have seemed an esoteric distinction but tactically the two approaches were quite different. One was a head on cavalry charge, the other more of a Trojan horse.

The data would still have to get through the subsequent exhaustive review process but at least we would have overcome the danger of a refusal to file at that first step and bought ourselves some more time. Once the NDA had been formally adopted, it would be mired for months as it ground through the system, giving us a much better chance of fighting our corner. If we could make it through the front door, it would be that much harder to get us to leave, if we turned out to be an unwelcome house guest.

It probably didn't say too much about our optimism, over the eventual outcome of the ACCEDE study, that we were spending so much time in devising ways of sneaking it past the watchful gaze of FDA when the time came. However, trying to maximise the rules of policy and procedure, for your own advantage, were all vital parts of playing the game.

But right now, we just couldn't agree amongst ourselves on how to best approach the Agency. It all came down to psychology. Was it better to grab the bull by the horns now, or risk waving a red flag at it later on?

It may seem incredible to those unfamiliar with drug development that so much effort could be expended around something as simple as how to respond to a *letter*. Come to that, it was actually incredible to many of us who *were* very familiar with drug development.

It just showed how little we and they, as sponsor and regulator, understood each other. And how much suspicion swirled around, within the Machiavellian maelstrom of our mutual interactions.

The fact that we went through such convulsions and contortions was a consequence, as much as anything else, of the cultural clash between the fossil of Federal regulation and the general dynamism of entrepreneurial biotechnology.

FDA were essentially protectionist, placing weight on precedent and predictability and sought to define themselves through nebulous concepts such as *regulatory science*. Biotechnology on the other hand was innovative and revisionist, rewriting some of the rules of biology and drug development as it went along. It thrived on change and uncertainty.

It was never going to be easy for these two ends of a spectrum to find a way to coexist somewhere in the middle. This disparity was exacerbated further by a growing defensiveness of the regulators, the impatience of the industry with how long everything took and the ever accelerating pace of scientific innovation, which left everyone struggling to catch up.

In our case, we made things even worse for ourselves by expending a disruptively dangerous amount of effort and energy in debating how to respond. It should have been no more than another of the many strategic debates and disagreements we had all the time. But for some reason, it really kicked off in the two or three days following the arrival of the letter from FDA. Partly the stakes were high and the tensions even higher. If we blew this, then we blew everything. If amonafide fell apart now, then there was nothing left.

But there was more to it than that. Something more fundamental and less easy to define was at play. It was as though all the disappointment and disillusionment, ever since the ASA404 disaster in the spring, suddenly welled up and burst forth. Any individual antipathies and animosities within the company now seemed to all coalesce around this one issue.

The lack of cohesion ever since Ursula had left, taking the glue with her, now became apparent as things started to become unstuck. The FDA letter was becoming the boil of bitterness we needed to lance, before being able to feel comfortable again.

XX

Everyone developed a view on what the regulatory response should be. Pretty much all the people in the US and certainly the regulatory group, fuelled on by their army of advisors, believed we should march into FDA forthwith and give it to them with both barrels. We wouldn't be taking any prisoners. It was very *Wild West*.

Bizarrely, the strongest proponents over there seemed to be the people normally most removed from this area of the company's activities. The business people, in particular, became more stridently agitated and seemingly less objectively orientated, almost by the hour. Although quite outside their normal remit, they threw themselves wholeheartedly into the debate, attending every single meeting and teleconference and helping to fuel an atmosphere of combustible antagonism between the US office and the UK.

By contrast, nearly everyone on the other side of the Atlantic was aghast at the idea of such confrontational tactics, instead advocating the avoidance of immediate direct contact with FDA at all cost. Their view was that it would be much better to meet with the Agency in January, armed with some real data. Anything more than masterly inactivity would be suicidal at this stage.

Normally, that would have been the end of things. In a small company it was usual, essential even, for everyone to have a say on something of importance. But afterwards, you needed to make a decision and move on. But we were so riven by dissent that we couldn't reach an agreement. There was too much turmoil at the top, along with disturbing agitation amongst the rank and file as well. The normal structural relationships within the company, which would otherwise have contained something like this, seemed to have been breached.

If Ursula had still been here, she would never have let things get this far. But she was long gone now. And so ultimately, we found ourselves coming unstuck at the seams.

We arranged a video meeting for a Friday afternoon, having at least all agreed on one thing, which was that we had to reply to FDA by the following Monday, a good seven days after receiving their letter. We were however all unprepared for the firestorm of accusatory shouting and truculent table thumping which the discussion uncharacteristically but rapidly descended into.

No one could remember such a polarised meeting in the past. It was like a bear pit. We surprised ourselves with how worked up we were getting but by then we couldn't stop. It was like running down a hill. You had to keep moving faster and faster. You couldn't slow down, otherwise you'd fall over.

And so we all kept getting angrier and angrier, with a malicious momentum that seemed to urge us on to an even greater lack of restraint.

Rather than resolve it there and then, which the situation really demanded, we prevaricated. With all the dissimulation of an EU diplomat, in a delicate cucumber quota debate, we deferred the issue, insisting we needed more time to think about it over the weekend. That was probably the worst thing to do but also the only choice we had. The gap was too big to bridge. It meant however that many left the meeting still feeling antagonistic and *well*, unresolved. And then we all had a couple of days to let it fester, whilst we carried on plotting and scheming.

XXI

Eventually a decision emerged in the early hours of Monday morning, after a series of increasingly frantic phone calls between various members of the management team. To the amazement of most of us in the UK, we found that we'd decided in the end to go ahead and meet with FDA. The *agents provocateurs* in the US had predominated.

The decision left some individuals more than a little exposed. It was probably a bad idea to have held such an open debate the previous Friday. It allowed people to develop passionately unambiguous positions, from which there was now no possibility of retrenchment. A number had gone out on a limb and the final decision had just cut the legs out from underneath them.

Instead, we should have thrashed it out with a few of us behind closed doors, until we'd reached some semblance of a decision. That way, as the alcoholics did in their meetings, what was said there and seen there, could have stayed there. We would have been able to emerge with a united front, however much disagreement there may have been behind the scenes. We would have avoided appearing as the fractured and disjointed team we were now in danger of becoming.

Over the next few days though, something of a compromise emerged. It had to really, because otherwise the company might have broken in half, under the weight of the two opposing camps.

Normally, for a meeting like this with FDA, you would take along a dozen or so of your own people. That was partly to cover the wide range of technical issues they might spring on you but equally importantly, to make sure you weren't outnumbered. That was very important. You needed the same physical presence as them to balance things out. Like for like. Those were the rules. That's just how it was done.

But this time, we eventually decided to send only a small group of three or so people, essentially from regulatory affairs. We wouldn't include more than one person from the clinical group. This emasculated proposal somehow made the idea of a meeting more palatable to those vehemently opposed to the whole concept.

The convoluted idea behind it was that we could then approach the survival endpoint indirectly, almost as a procedural issue, rather than attacking it head on with a phalanx of physicians in tow. Bringing along a whole clinical contingent of our own would inevitably force the meeting to focus on the survival question from the outset. A group of drum majorettes parading up and down would have drawn less attention to it.

By travelling light, we hoped to give the impression that it wasn't something of real concern to us. We were just there to tidy up loose ends and this was one of them. Maybe we hoped our apparent insouciance would rub off on FDA and make them less likely to dig their heels in.

There was also the practical advantage that if their clinical people started to get difficult, it would be easier for us to back off, hopefully before any irreparable damage was done. We could plead that we didn't have the right people there to engage with them.

It would allow us to dip a toe in the water to see how hot it was first, rather than plunging headlong in and risking getting badly burnt.

In reality, it probably didn't make much strategic sense to dance around the issue like this, almost taunting it rather than tackling it directly. It had all the weakness of the compromise it clearly was and few apparent advantages.

But no one seemed to have a better alternative.

XXII

By now, with only days to go before the meeting, the extent of the psychological plotting, at certain levels within the company, had come to resemble the most egregious excesses of a Borgian papal conclave. Some of us in the UK had given up on any further involvement in the feverish pre-meeting preparations going on in Boston. We only engaged when an opportunity presented itself to provoke or antagonise our US colleagues. That's what it had come to.

The worst example of this involved one of the statisticians, based in London. The US regulatory people were adamant that they needed him to attend, as FDA were planning to bring along a couple of their own statisticians. Because they wanted him so badly, we in the clinical group were equally insistent that he shouldn't go. We fought for days, like parents in a particularly acrimonious custody case.

E-mails flew back and forth between London and Boston, eventually consisting of little more than: *He's coming. No he's not. Yes he fucking is. No he fucking isn't.* We didn't even have enough mutual respect left to invest any greater imagination into our insults.

It was symptomatic of the stress and strain some in the company were experiencing. The attack from FDA and our difficulties in mounting an effective defence made it clear, probably for the first time, that we were fighting a war we might well not be able to win. Even if we were successful in this skirmish, then how many more were just over the horizon?

We weren't sure how much fight we had left in us now.

XXIII

The emaciated meeting eventually went ahead but afterwards, it proved hard to work out what the outcome really meant. This wasn't helped by the fact that those of us, who hadn't actually been there, didn't necessarily any longer completely trust the version of events from those of our colleagues who had. That's how bad things had become.

The Agency did however agree to acknowledge the previous meetings we'd had with them, where they had confirmed that the primary endpoint would be the CR rate. So in that sense, they appeared to back away from now wanting overall survival at all cost. Simply *acknowledging* the existence of a previous meeting, which was already extensively documented, didn't seem at face value to be a seismic shift in their stance. But regulatory machinations were like the workings of a watch. A tiny movement in one cog here could result in a magnified rotation in another one elsewhere and ultimately this would all add up to a visible change in position of the hands on the watch face.

But then, they also indicated that all the endpoints, including survival, would now ultimately be a *review issue*.[30] This was code for them keeping all options open. Saying something was a review issue was a way of indicating that they weren't prepared to give an opinion at this stage. They wanted to see all the data first, before deciding which way they were going to turn. It would allow them to pretty much change their mind again at a later date, once they had looked through the results.

They also asked us to provide a lot more detail on the technical ways we were going to statistically analyse the survival data. This was a bad development, because it could easily turn into an open ended dialogue on survival. That would keep the issue firmly at the forefront of FDA's mind in the months ahead, whereas we would much prefer to have it buried for quite a while to come.

It was difficult to work out where we stood. FDA seemed to retreat on one front and advance on another, leaving us in a penumbral cloud of confusion as to their real intentions. That made it difficult for any of us to claim a victory. The meeting hadn't provoked them into digging their heels in. In fact on one level they appeared to have backed off a bit, by reverting to CR as the primary endpoint. But then again, the unresolved spectre of overall survival was still out there, ready to haunt us for months to come.

They had also given themselves plenty of leeway. The catch all designation of *review issue* was a permit to change their minds anytime they wanted to. Once they had actually reviewed the NDA, they could argue that it was too different from what they had originally envisaged. Their position would be that this changed the dimensions of the debate sufficiently to justify any *volte face* they now felt like pulling off. It wasn't an unreasonable point of view. Just as you wouldn't buy a house without a structural survey, they were insisting on seeing the foundations upon which the various endpoints rested, before deciding which ones were solid enough.

It was the ace up their sleeve, which effectively left them holding all the cards.

Additionally, we had now lost the opportunity to meet with them later on, nearer to the NDA submission, when it might have counted for more. We'd used up all our invitations to visit them at home and the front door was now firmly bolted shut.

XXIV

The overall uncertainty of our position with FDA was as absurd as the fact it had even arisen in the first place. It just showed how confusing and misleading it could be when two parties tried to muddle along, without any real understanding of each other. Things weren't helped by the fact that each seemed to be aiming for mutually exclusive objectives. A company wants its drug approved, at almost any cost. FDA's mission often seems to be to prevent this, come what may.

It's an unhappy state of affairs, with each side groping and fumbling for the pathway of least resistance between the two of them. Faced with such inefficiency and ineffectiveness, it was a good job we weren't attempting anything serious. We were only trying to find a cure for cancer after all.

In terms of our internal factions, it was probably a stalemate. This ambivalence seemed to make it harder to heal the division, as each side was able to interpret the outcome as more favourable to their own position.

And so the rift remained, although simmering at a lower heat, as it would right up until the unveiling of the ACCEDE results three months later.

This left us as a dispirited and divided force, under a seemingly fractured command. It wasn't exactly the best prepared state to be in for the rigours lying ahead of us. But nevertheless, we marched inexorably onwards towards our final showdown, which wasn't that far off now.

TEN

GIMME SHELTER

The end is drawing near for Antisoma. The few remaining lifelines disappear, one by one. Now they are left clutching a single straw.

I

With the Red Army closing in on Berlin in April 1945, for the German High Command the dying days of the war were increasingly played out underground.

The Führerbunker, located about nine metres below the gardens of the old Reich Chancellery at Wilhelmstrasse 77, covered a total area of about twenty thousand square feet. It was roughly the same size as our offices in Chiswick. Here the Führer issued orders to armies that now existed in name only and commanded generals who were already dead, or deserting him by the day. The Reich was paying the final price for having fought a war on too many fronts.

As the last few months of 2010 rolled around, we also found ourselves fighting in a number of different directions and were beginning to develop a bunker like mentality all of our own.

The last subterranean days in Berlin were characterised by exuberance, drinking, drugs and random spontaneous couplings. It was a final desperate desire to enjoy life, when death was so imminent. We weren't quite as bad as that yet but the more the pressures mounted, the more a sense of disproportionate cheerfulness and denial seemed to engulf the building and those within it.

Unlike the ragged remnants of the Wehrmacht High Command, we weren't really physically entombed deep underground, although frequently the office was so quiet that we could have been. The normal buzz and busyness were now often absent, replaced by a strange sepulchral silence. You could almost feel it, like being draped with a heavy blanket.

As with Hitler's imaginary armies, where finally the campaign on his bunker battle map came to bear little resemblance to the dwindling capacity on the battlefield, so with us there was now a marked disparity between perception and reality.

Our website still proclaimed that we had a "diverse portfolio of products in development" and that they "target tumors by several different mechanisms and are intended for the treatment of a range of cancers."[1]

But in reality we were now down to just *two* remaining clinical studies, one each with amonafide and AS1411 and both in leukaemia. Rather than diversity, we were dealing with a distinct dearth of products.

Furthermore, both studies were winding down towards their natural conclusions. Our denouement was not that distant. But as we marched towards it, we found that we had to deal with attacks from three differing directions, each of which would leave us in an ever more weakened state, as we approached our final destiny.

II

The first assault came from the Novartis ATTRACT II study with ASA404. This was the ongoing trial in lung cancer, using ASA404 as second line treatment, after patients had failed on initial chemotherapy. Novartis had kept it going, even after the failure of ATTRACT I in the first line context.

It had now reached the point where a data monitoring committee (DMC) were going to have an interim look at the data, to see if it was worth carrying on or not. No one held out much hope of it surviving and we had quietly been down playing it, ever since April and the demise of ATTRACT I.

The data review was due to take place in the middle of November and during the month or so beforehand, ATTRACT II slowly started coming to life again within our corporate conscience. It was like stumbling across an object you'd long ago discarded in the attic and wondering if it might actually be of some value now. Conversations would start up, prefaced by phrases such as *What if...Maybe...Luck might change...You never know.* We began drafting press releases to encompass both the more likely event of ATTRACT II failing but also the remote possibility of it surviving.

There was something about reading in black and white how unexpectedly exciting a positive result it was and what new doors it had opened, which seemed to elevate this potential outcome in people's minds. It started to occupy a greater prominence than the odds warranted. One or two people began to genuinely believe there was a real chance of things holding up and like some sort of *deus ex machina*, a positive ATTRACT II result was going to descend upon us and place a *Get Out Of Jail Free* card in our hand.

We seemed to spend increasing amounts of time at management meetings speculating on our personal probabilities of a positive outcome. Given the statistical design of the ATTRACT II study, there was something like a five per cent possibility of a positive result, just due to chance alone and so the odds had to be a bit better than that. But realistically not much more so. Somewhere between five and ten per cent was probably about right.

It was also hard to anticipate the effect on our battered corporate image, should ATTRACT II get through an interim look. It was after all just that,

485

an *interim* stage. The study would still have to go the distance to completion, sometime the following year. It would be the *final* results at that point which really counted. And there was obviously no guarantee of what those might look like. You wouldn't exactly bet your house on the outcome.

Nevertheless, it would still be an encouraging development, which should be reflected by an increase of some sort in our valuation. It might even be possible to raise some money on the back of. The biggest benefit though, would be the psychological boost for us. It would be confirmation that we still had some credit at the Cancer Casino. That maybe our luck was about to change.

It could even help the odd patient or two.

The ATTRACT II study aimed to recruit over nine hundred patients altogether and the interim look was scheduled to happen after two hundred and fifty patients had died. That was the number of deaths needed to see whether the drug had any life left. The study consisted of two groups, one receiving the established drug docetaxel, which was widely used for the second line treatment of lung cancer, and the other docetaxel plus ASA404. If there were *fewer* deaths in the ASA404 group, then the study could continue to completion. If not, then it would come to an end there and then.

The DMC comprised four oncologists, one cardiologist and a statistician. They would meet by telephone to review the results. The chairman would then phone Novartis, with the outcome of their deliberations and they would relay it on to us. It was a re-run of ATTRACT I back in April.

III

The days leading up to the DMC meeting were listless and long. Suddenly, no one wanted to talk about the possible outcome anymore. That would lend it a prominence the odds simply didn't justify. But no one could put it out of their minds either. This was drug development after all. You just never knew what was going to happen next. The unexpected and the improbable were more frequent occurrences than not.

What if...Maybe...Luck might change...You never know. The mantra replayed though our minds.

However, when the call did eventually come, late one evening in the middle of November, it only added to the chill winds already blowing around outside in the winter night. The study was completely negative, with the two groups almost superimposable. There was no difference between them. ASA404 was having no discernible effect.

It was the result we'd expected but not the one we'd secretly hoped for. At least it had the virtue of being unambiguous. Which is probably what Novartis wanted. There was a sigh of relief, palpable all the way from the Swiss Alps to Swiss Cottage, that the outcome had been so clear cut. They

486

could now extricate themselves from the whole ASA404 programme and move on to other things. It was time to get on with their lives.

A resoundingly negative result was infinitely preferable to an ambiguous one. It might *even* have been better than if things had turned out positive at the interim stage. That would have left them still tied to ASA404 but also with the continuing uncertainty of whether the final outcome would be success or failure.

At least this was a clean break. No more risk. The hundreds of millions of dollars they had expended on the drug so far would quickly be forgotten. It was just a bad night at the tables. They'd make it back. There would be another game, on some other day.

For us, it was more of a blow. Even though failure had always been by far and away the most likely outcome, that realisation did little to diminish the sense of disappointment, when actually confronted with it. There was even a momentary sense of injustice. Just what, we asked, had we done to deserve such a run of bad luck.

The prevailing sentiment was one of having been selected out for singular misfortune. Maybe we even felt a little bit sorry for ourselves. Self-pity was however a luxury we could ill afford. The fight to survive had just become that much harder still. We had to focus all our remaining energy on simply trying to stay alive.

Glyn's irrepressible optimism meant he had probably believed more than most that the outcome would be positive and provide an opportunity to regain our momentum. He kept up his normal cheery demeanour but you didn't have to look too hard to see that it was a show for the benefit of the rest of us. You had to admire his ability to soldier on, even managing a semblance of insouciance.

But it wouldn't take long before he was on an upward trajectory again. Glyn was like a game of *whack a mole*. However hard and repeatedly you knocked him down, up again he'd pop, almost instantaneously.

IV

In any event, none of us could afford to dwell on our misfortune for too long, as we had to deal with the practical problem of what to do next with ASA404. It was a game of pass the parcel now. Novartis didn't want it anymore and were going to give it back to us. But if we were left holding it, then we would rapidly become liable for all sorts of big bills.

There was about a million dollars payable in a couple of months to support patent protection for a start. It we didn't want to spend that kind of money, we had to pass it on to someone else.

And that would most likely be Cancer Research UK. They had owned ASA404 originally, before we'd acquired it off them, prior to starting the clinical development all those years ago. If we gave up on the drug now, CRUK might take it back and see if they could sell it on to someone else. Maybe someone with a keener eye or luckier hand, who could discern promise we had overlooked.

The dilemma we faced therefore was whether to hold on to what had until so recently been the jewel in our crown. Or abandon something which was now no more than a millstone around our neck. ASA404 had failed pretty comprehensively in two large Phase III trials. Obviously that wasn't a good start. But there were a number of drugs which had also shown little or no promise in lung cancer and yet had proven useful agents in other tumor types.

The tyrosine kinase inhibitors Sutent and Nexavar, which had revolutionised the treatment of kidney cancer, were both examples, as was the antibody Erbitux which had become a mainstay of treatment for cancer of the colon. Each generated sales of billions of dollars a year and didn't seem to have been too badly dented by their melt down in lung malignancy.[2]

And so perhaps all was not lost with ASA404. Maybe it had simply been the wrong drug in the wrong place at the wrong time, as far as lung cancer was concerned. Now it just needed to be steered in the right direction. In a different tumor type, maybe it would come up trumps.

On top of that, there was now a huge amount of safety data with the drug, given that it had been through two large Phase III trials. This would mean that if you started another development programme, in a different cancer, you could probably get away with a smaller number of patients.

It would be possible to use all the existing lung cancer data, at least for safety purposes. You could apply it to other tumor types. It was unlikely that the side effects would vary that much between malignancies. You'd basically just have to prove the efficacy, which would require far fewer patients, than if you were starting from scratch.

It was possible therefore that we could turn the failure of ATTRACT I and ATTRACT II to our advantage. If amonafide fell apart at the end of Phase III, we would be left with seventeen million pounds sitting in the bank and a development team with nothing to do all day long, except fill in job applications. If that happened, there was an argument for piggybacking off all the work Novartis had already done and spending the remaining money running a couple of Phase II trials with ASA404 in new tumor types.

It would only need one to turn out positive and we could go off and do another Novartis type deal. Although no one thought it would be with Novartis again. This might make more sense, as a survival strategy, than the alternative of abandoning ASA404 altogether and scrabbling around, trying to find a company in an even worse state than us to get into bed with.

The more you thought it through, the less implausible it began to sound. That is until you tried to work out where you would actually go next with ASA404. The problem was the lack of a logical next step. We couldn't see any obvious signpost.

In all the animal experiments, ASA404 had worked best by far and away when combined with *taxane* type drugs. And we'd already looked at three of the major tumour types where they were widely used, prostate, ovarian and lung cancer.

There was no *convincing* evidence from any of these that ASA404 was adding anything extra. In particular those two big Phase III trials in lung cancer hadn't suggested a shred of activity. And that was obviously worrying.

Other drugs which hadn't made it over the lung cancer finishing line, such as Sutent, Nexavar and Erbitux, had at least given a clinical signal that they were doing *something*, that they'd put up some sort of a fight before eventually being defeated. It may not have been enough but it was obvious they had given it their best shot. By contrast, ASA404 had gone down in the first round.

And whilst they might not have pulled it off in lung cancer, by the time this happened, these other agents had all proved they worked elsewhere. That made it a lot easier to write off the one failed indication. It was after all a bit much to expect any one drug to work in every cancer, when most seemed to work in none.

With ASA404, that extra comfort wasn't there. It required a lot more faith to accept that the lung failure was a one off. That next time round we'd be luckier. It was entirely possible that ASA404 just didn't work. Period. That was the alternative interpretation. In which case we would be wasting our time doing anything further.

That was the choice we faced. In a way it was like a fractured marriage. Did you focus on how good it had once been in the past and make one final attempt to get things working again. Or did you cut your losses and walk away, uncertain though whether you'd actually find anyone any better. There is no answer to that kind of dilemma. Whichever way you ended up going, there was always the question remaining, in the back of your mind, about how things might have turned out, if you'd only taken the other pathway.

If we had been given long enough to mull it over, we may have convinced ourselves to hold on to ASA404. We had a long history together and in turbulent times there was comfort in familiarity. But as it happened, our hand was tipped for us by some of our larger investors. They made it clear that enough was enough and we would struggle to get support for sinking more money into what was seen as a lost cause. Antagonising our few remaining backers was a stick we definitely didn't want to start beating ourselves with.

And so our relationship with vascular disrupting agents appeared to have reached the end of the road. Ultimately all they had succeeded in disrupting were our carefully laid out corporate plans and the balance sheets of many institutions, who had invested in us, on the back of this new technology. But that was the high risk game we all played. If you couldn't afford to lose the punt, you shouldn't place the bet.

Other companies however, such as OXiGENE, continued to plough this particular furrow and time still has to tell what sort of harvest they will end up reaping.[3]

But for us, it was now all scorched earth and abandoning ASA404 altogether marked a further stage in our retreat back towards our final redoubt.

Once we'd absorbed the failure of ATTRACT II and the decision to pass on ASA404, it was back to business as usual.

In any event, we didn't have that long to dwell on things, because a few weeks later Oxford BioMedica re-emerged to threaten on a new front. They sprang a big surprise on us, by seemingly striking gold.

V

It wasn't only Oxford BioMedica who were chasing after gold. It was a commodity widely sought by many others.

That including African Mining and Exploration plc (AME). This was a small start up company, which had recently been put together by a group of seasoned mining professionals. It was headquartered in London and had an operational base in Bamako, the capital of Mali.[4]

After South Africa and Ghana, Mali is Africa's third biggest gold producer, responsible for fifty four tons in 2009 alone. So the country was a hot prospect, offering potentially rich pickings, for those prepared to accept the risks involved.

AME had permits to explore two areas of the country. One was a two hundred and fifty km² region, centred on the village of Koran, about eighty km southwest of the capital. The other was a sixteen km² zone around the town of Kayes in the west of the country and only twenty km from the prolific Tabakoto and Loulo gold mines.

Both permits encompassed areas which had been mined by locals for centuries and were scarred by extensive networks of shallow workings. The continued endeavours of these local artisans were testament to the possibility of huge reserves, waiting to be accessed by modern mining techniques.

Which was precisely what AME intended to do. But first, they had to find the gold. That would involve an eighteen month programme of structural analysis by satellite and aerial photographic interpretation. Then there was mapping and sampling of the existing artisanal pits and detailed ground magnetic and electromagnetic surveys. Finally, there would be some exploratory drilling. After that, it might all come to nothing. But then again they might, literally, strike gold.

To do all of this, they needed money. To find it, they eventually turned to Singer Capital Markets, based in Hanover Square in London's West End.

With a focus on small and medium sized UK companies, over a variety of different industries, Singer offered specialised corporate finance and corporate broking services. With their help, AME were eventually able to list on the London AIM stock market in November 2009, raising five million dollars in the process. The rest was now down to the geology of Mali and the goodwill of the gods.

Mining for new gold deposits and developing a new drug had many similarities. Both were high risk undertakings, requiring enormous amounts of capital and technical expertise. Each had a relatively low likelihood of success but an enormous upside if you did happen to get lucky. They were also both activities which took place in stages, over a prolonged period of time.

Those early artisanal mines were the equivalent of Phase I trials. They were initial probings, to see whether anything worthwhile might possibly be there. The more detailed exploratory activities being planned by AME were like Phase II trials. They comprised the painstaking gathering of all the essential information needed, as a prelude to focussing subsequent activities in the area most likely to yield results. And then came the huge investment of Phase III. This was when you went for broke and threw everything you had into actually trying to tap where you thought the seam was and seeing how much gold you might get out.

Given these parallels, it wasn't surprising that Singer also had experience of financing high risk biopharmaceutical companies. Months before AME, they had raised twenty million pounds for the UK based skin care company, Sinclair Pharma. And whilst the promise of gene therapy may frequently have seemed as distant as the famed Mali city of Timbuktu, Singer even thought they could raise money for Oxford BioMedica.

The wheels were set in motion after they answered a phone call from the company, one wet morning in late October 2010.

VI

Corporate financing consists of complicated transactions, with many involved parties. It's also an arcane process, with much laborious paperwork and is often conducted with an inefficiency more closely resembling the London of fictional Dickens, than the one of financial deregulation. The whole thing usually takes months to sort out.

The wheels of the Oxford BioMedica train may have started turning but they weren't spinning particularly quickly. And so news that they were planning to raise a whole load of money didn't break until a couple of weeks before Christmas.

If they pulled it off, it was going to be a nice festive present for them though. It meant they would now have new money and deeper pockets. They were intending to spend about eight million pounds on moving forward the clinical program with ProSavin and about five and a half million to establish a gene therapy manufacturing plant. Unsurprisingly, they didn't seem to be lavishing any of it on TroVax. Instead the rest would go in the bank, to help with the day to day running of the business.[5]

They were hoping to get hold of all this cash by selling new shares in the company, through a mechanism called a *placing and open offer*.

The *placing* part involved Singer Capital traipsing around Oxford BioMedica's existing larger institutional investors. The idea was to persuade them to commit to buying a slug of the new shares, in advance of them actually being issued. That way, a substantial proportion of the shares would be placed with proud new owners before they'd even been printed. The *open offer* was an invitation to *all* current shareholders to take up new shares, with a ratio of two new shares for every nine shares already held.

Furthermore, Singer Capital were prepared to *underwrite* the whole thing. Essentially, this meant they were agreeing to buy up any shares left over, after all the existing shareholders had decided whether to buy in or not. Having a share issue underwritten made it more attractive for investors. They were more likely to jump on board at the outset, if they knew the whole thing wasn't going to fall apart later on, due to lack of interest.

Effectively, Singer were providing a safety net. It was however a liability which could leave them stuck with anything, in between nothing and *everything*. Singer could, theoretically at least, end up holding the entire issue, if no one else accepted the invitation. It was their problem but by a circuitous route, it actually ended up becoming ours too. It unintentionally created a threat which would eventually hang over our head for months to come.

It was all to do with how Singer viewed the hand they would be holding, if they were dealt all the Oxford BioMedica cards.

Back in August, when Sinclair Pharma had raised twenty million pounds, they had also used a placing and open offer. However, it hadn't been underwritten by Singer Capital. They had offered their new shares to everyone at a price of twenty eight pence, which was two pence *higher* than the twenty six pence the shares were actually trading at on the stock exchange. In other words, the new shares were at an eight per cent *premium* to the existing ones.

Sinclair and Singer were able to do this because the company's shares were popular at the time and so institutions were prepared to pay a premium, to get hold of a decent sized block of them. You would have struggled to get that number in the market place, because not many people who had them wanted to sell. That would have increased the price you'd otherwise end up paying to beyond twenty eight pence anyway. It was simple supply and demand.

The situation with Oxford BioMedica was different. People weren't exactly falling over each other to pick up the shares. Because of this, there needed to be an incentive for them to invest and thus avoid a lot of unallocated stock at the end of the exercise.

One good way of doing this was to offer the shares at five pence. This represented a substantial one third *discount* to the eight pence they were already trading at in the market place. Effectively though, what this also meant was that OBM had to issue one third *more* shares than they otherwise would, had there been no discount.

It wasn't at all uncommon for biotechnology companies to be forced into this kind of tactic to have any hope of raising money. The markets were mercilessly unforgiving at the time. Companies in both Europe and the US were discovering that. OBM were far from alone therefore. However, whilst an arrangement such as this might have secured the deal, it also came at a cost.

VII

No company liked to put out more shares than absolutely necessary, because the more shares in existence, for any given value of the company, the less each one would be worth.

A play school simplification of the complex dynamics of the financial market place would be to imagine a company is worth one hundred pounds and has one hundred shares. Each share is then obviously worth one pound. If it then raises an extra fifty pounds, it would now be worth one hundred and fifty pounds. But if it could only do this by selling the new shares at fifty pence then it would need to issue one hundred new shares to raise that fifty pounds. This would then make two hundred shares altogether and so each would now be worth only seventy five pence. Which was good news if you had paid fifty pence for the new shares but not so good if you had paid one pound originally. You tended to end up with a lot of disgruntled existing shareholders that way.

And that is what happened to Oxford BioMedica. Just before the fundraising was announced, the share price had been about eight and a half pence and afterwards, with all those new shares washing around, this drifted down to about five and a half pence.

It was largely due to all the extra shares they had been forced to issue at a discount. These had not so much diluted out but rather drowned any possibility of the share price increasing, in parallel with the extra money raised. It had turned out to be an expensive way of raising money. And it probably left a lot of irate Oxford BioMedica shareholders, who had seen the value of many of their shares fall overnight.

Perversely therefore, despite all the new money, this left Oxford BioMedica with a not insignificant problem. A battered share price and volatile market capitalisation were every CEO's nightmare. It must have awoken them in the early hours of the morning, even more often than TroVax did.

It might also leave them keener than ever to get their hands on us and our money. They had found out the hard way just how expensive it could be to raise funds by other means at their disposal. They might now see us as a much easier and cheaper touch. If they could acquire Antisoma and its remaining cash, without having to resort to ruinous discounts, then maybe they could start to claw back the share price and drag the market capitalisation up again.

At least that's how we rationalised it to ourselves. Their problem therefore became our problem too. Oxford BioMedica would now be shadowing and stalking us even more closely than before. They were on the lookout for any new signs of vulnerability or weakness. The slightest wobble and they would be there shaking the whole tree, to see if they could topple it over.

They were out there now, biding their time and waiting for the right moment to make a play for us. We couldn't see them but we could definitely feel their presence.

For the remaining months to come, Oxford BioMedica would become the automatic yardstick, by which other possible arbiters of our fate were judged. Were OBM likely to be a better or worse proposition. The answer however was nearly always worse.

Our predicament was beginning to look precarious. The situation wasn't exactly improved therefore, when one of our few remaining assets started to unravel, just before Christmas.

VIII

We didn't take too much notice of the first death in the AS1411 study. After all, these were sick patients with leukaemia. But after the fifth one, we had to sit up and take notice. Especially as they all occurred in rapid succession. And they were all in India.

By this time, the leukaemia trial was running at full steam and had recruited about half the ninety patients we were aiming for. It had been going since the beginning of the year, with five centres in the US, all at prestigious institutions such as UCLA in Los Angeles and Weill Cornell in New York.

There were also about half a dozen centres scattered around medical schools in Korea and Taiwan. And then we had six Indian centres too. These were in New Delhi, Mumbai, Bangalore, Calcutta, Hyderabad and Pune. It was therefore a fairly global undertaking.

Going to a country such as India, with a palpable lack of sophisticated health care infrastructure, had always been a risk for a leukaemia study requiring advanced medical care and support. But we had managed to convince ourselves that we could sort it out by working with clinicians of the quality of Hari Menon in Mumbai. This would somehow overcome the obvious drawback that these people were practicing advanced western medicine, in facilities that would challenge a boy scout on a first aid course.

Things certainly seemed to go well to start with. In retrospect however this was probably because not much really happened for months on end and so there was little that could actually go wrong.

It seemed to take forever to penetrate the impenetrable Indian bureaucracy needed to obtain permission from the local authorities to start the study. The correct piece of paper never appeared to have been signed or stamped by the right person, in order to allow the next person to sign the next piece of paper.

The Indian Health Ministry in Mumbai seemed to move at the pace of the traffic in the surrounding streets. Which was not at all. Somewhere in India, tucked away in some anonymous government building, there must be a department which has succeeded in defying the laws of thermodynamics and attained the bureaucratic equivalent of *absolute zero*, the theoretically unachievable temperature, at which all known motion must cease.

Given it was India, we joked that these sorts of problems could be sorted out with a large enough wedge of rupees, delivered to the right person. A little greasing here and there. That's how you'd get things moving. None of this jumping through hoops, which officials at FDA seemed to delight in having you do. But apparently integrity had moved on in recent years, with the Indian Health Ministry seemingly a pillar of professional probity. And so there appeared to be little we could do to influence the glacial pace of events.

Which in some ways was actually a relief. Obviously no one fancied having to bribe a government official. It wasn't so much the act of corruption and moral turpitude it implied but rather the prospect of having to handle a holdall full of Indian rupees. Accidental contact with one of these filthy notes, which had previously been in contact with God alone knows what, represented a far greater health risk to the casual traveller than eating unwashed fruit, drinking out of the gutter, rolling around in raw sewage, or almost anything else the country could throw at you. Provoking a poisonous snake was probably more hazardous, although only just.

But eventually, just in time for the Monsoon season, the last document had reached its final destination, all signed and sealed. Recruitment could at last start at the six Indian centres. But then, nothing seemed to happen for a couple more months. This was partly because of the weather, which made it very difficult to travel. But it was also because that's just how it seemed to work in India. Things had to start off by *not* actually happening, for no obvious reason. Then equally mysteriously, one day they would suddenly spring into life.

And that's what happened with AS1411. Nothing occurred for ages, with potential patients seemingly disappearing into thin air. Or more accurately, thick, acrid, asthma inducing, polluting, traffic infested air. And then suddenly they would start materialising. One minute a patient would be two hundred miles away, in the middle of nowhere and the next they would have somehow made it to Mumbai, or Chennai, or wherever. How this happened was absolutely perplexing to us. But we weren't complaining. We were finally seeing some progress and it seemed that our long wait was coming to an end.

During our autumn, once their rainy season was over and it became easier for patients to travel, the Indian centres managed to put in about twenty patients. They were rapidly catching up and even surpassing the individual contributions of the other countries. Which would have been fine, if only the patients could have stayed alive long enough to get through the study. Instead, we were beginning to see an alarmingly high number of deaths.

IX

Of course leukaemia, especially the type of advanced disease we were looking at, is a terminal condition and patients will die. There was a depressing inevitability about that. But the study was specifically designed to select patients who were in good condition and had a high probability of living for at least six months. These were supposed to be the very best patients. A kind of *grand cuveé*, as it were. That was why, up until now at least, we hadn't seen many early deaths, in patients who'd been recruited in other countries.

But now they were expiring thick and fast in India and all of the fatalities were following a similar grim pattern. Patients were dying within a couple of weeks of starting treatment and in every case it was due to overwhelming infection, or uncontrolled bleeding. It didn't seem to matter which group of the study they were in either. The prospects were equally bleak, whether they were receiving the standard drug cytarabine alone, or the combination of cytarabine and AS1411.

When we started looking into things further it quickly became apparent that these deaths were due to complications of the *cytarabine* treatment. AS1411 had nothing to do with it at all. It was completely innocent.

The cytarabine was destroying the patient's bone marrow, which was necessary to get rid of the leukaemic disease lurking in there. At the same time however, it was also taking out all the normal bone marrow cells, along with the diseased leukaemic ones.

That's what you'd expect to happen, in the first few weeks after treatment with cytarabine. There was nothing you could do about it though. It was just how the drug worked. But after that the normal cells would grow back, over the next two to three weeks, hopefully without the leukaemic ones in tow.

That was all part of the normal process of using these sorts of powerful non-discriminatory drugs, which wiped out everything in their path. It's what we were anticipating and it came as no surprise. However, what we weren't expecting and what most definitely did come as surprise, was that the Indian patients were dying from this.

When the bone marrow is erased, the body quickly runs out of the various elements of the blood which are usually made by it. This includes components which, amongst other things, exist to fight infections and stop bleeding. Once the bone marrow starts regenerating, the blood rapidly reconstitutes.

But in the intervening period, the patient is vulnerable to overwhelming infections, whether they're bacterial or viral, fungal or others. They are also at danger from sudden uncontrolled bleeding, which can be rapidly catastrophic and frequently fatal.

The first few weeks after induction chemotherapy aren't a happy time. It's more like a bungee jump into hell. Dying of pneumonia, or bleeding to death, doesn't exactly seem a fair outcome after everything you've just been through.

Leukaemia units nurse patients through this vulnerable period, by protecting them in various ways from these dangers. Firstly, the individual with suppressed bone marrow would be isolated, as far as possible, from contact with bacteria or other potential pathogens. When you have no circulating blood cells to defend yourself, even otherwise innocuous bugs, such as those normally found in fresh food, can represent substantial dangers. As could those bugs which all of us shed around us constantly, without ever noticing the fact. Let alone what might be lurking on the toilet seat.

To circumvent these threats the patient would be kept in their own room, all by themselves, with their own toilet that no one else was allowed to use. They would most likely be in a unit with a positive air pressure system, to keep potentially contaminated external air at bay. The few permitted visitors would be wearing protective gowns and hats and overshoes. Food would also be carefully prepared, probably even sterilised before reaching the patient. All simple precautions but all highly effective in helping prevent infection.

Physicians also have much more sophisticated tools at their disposal. The risk of bleeding can be dramatically reduced by giving transfusions of one of the blood elements, called platelets, which are important for effective clotting.

If the patient develops an infection then there are a range of powerful and specialised antibiotic, antifungal and antiviral agents to choose from.

Many leukaemia centres also routinely use biological agents, such as GCSF (*Granulocyte Colony Stimulating Factor*)[6] which can accelerate the rate at which the bone marrow recovers. This in turn shortens the danger period for the patient.

Then there are also diagnostic and imaging facilities, laboratory services and intensive care support, all immediately available with just a phone call. These types of interventions explain why treating leukaemia has become more feasible and less fatal. They have become the regular standard of care for this type of high risk patient.

Or at least they have, if you are lucky enough to live somewhere that can afford the cost. Which, so it would seem, clearly didn't include India. The hospitals just didn't have enough isolation rooms to cope with the number of patients who needed them. We'd already seen this for ourselves when visiting the Tata Hospital in Mumbai, earlier in the year.

But we'd somehow naively hoped they would find room for our patients. We had absolutely no idea now, of how we'd ever managed to convince ourselves of this though.

Some hospitals were even worse off than the Tata. Never mind a lack of isolation facilities, so short of beds and space were they that patients were sent home, straight after receiving their chemotherapy. And that was to an *Indian* home, with those levels of cleanliness and hygiene.

If home happened to be a bush by the side of the road, your chances were bleak. They hadn't been great to start off with but they just got a whole lot worse.

The patients only came back to hospital if, or more often when, they had developed a complication and were already in big trouble. At some of the hospitals, money was only available for the relatively cheap anti-leukaemia drugs. If there was a subsequent need for the much more expensive antibiotics or other supportive drugs then, unless the patient could pay themselves, they didn't get them.

If you lived in a patch of shrubbery, it was unlikely you would be able to stump up the necessary cash. That was just the grim reality of how it was. This went a long way to explaining why we were seeing an early death rate of over thirty per cent at the Indian centres.

Despite the iniquities of the Indian healthcare system, the majority of patients were somehow still surviving, even taking these handicaps into account.

However, the big problem was the sizeable minority who weren't. It was certainly terrible news that so many patients were dying. But the greatest difficulty this created for us wasn't so much that the patients were passing away but that it was happening *too* prematurely.

Because they were dying so quickly after treatment, the drugs weren't being given a chance to work. It was too soon for the bone marrow to have regenerated and to find out whether there was any leukaemia left or not. That would take four or five weeks and these patients were giving up the ghost way before then.

If individuals didn't live long enough to see whether they were going to become responders and go into remission, then they were effectively "wasted" as far as the trial was concerned. There was no value to the study in having included them in the first place.

The dead patients didn't exactly get a great deal out of it either.

X

The Indian situation caused us considerable consternation, back in London. We didn't like the idea of patients dying. We weren't too keen on the potential demise of our project either.

We went over everything that was happening to the patients and just couldn't see anything specific about the trial itself, other than the cytarabine, which could be accounting for these deaths.

In a situation like this, any unanticipated toxicity might be expected to pick off the weakest patients first. These would be the ones with the worst leukaemia disease, or those with pre-existing damage to the lungs or liver, or some other vital organ. But there wasn't anything in particular which stuck out about the patients who weren't making it. There was nothing to separate them from those who survived. Except for the fact that luck clearly wasn't on their side anymore.

In the absence of any other clues, everything pointed to the patients dying from bone marrow complications of the cytarabine treatment they were all receiving. When we managed to get a few of the Indian clinicians on the phone to talk about this, they eventually volunteered that they quite often ran into these sorts of problems, when using high dose cytarabine. Sometimes these deaths seemed to come and go in inexplicable clusters. Quite often they had even higher death rates than we were seeing.

They'd kept pretty quiet about that one up until now.

It was difficult to know what to do about it though. Many of the people who were offered an opportunity to volunteer for the trial would probably end up being given no therapy at all, if they didn't take part. The money the hospitals were receiving for being in the study was helping to fund these patients. If we stopped the trial, potential participants would go untreated and almost certainly be dead within six months anyway.

If we allowed the trial to carry on, someone going into it would have about a one in three chance of dying within a couple of weeks, from complications of the cytarabine treatment they would be given. But conversely, if they were one of the majority who survived, then they had a chance of responding to therapy and deriving some benefit from having taken part. One or two might even be able to entertain the possibility of long term remissions, if they were suitable for subsequent consolidation treatment.

Our dilemma was whether to give them an opportunity to gamble their lives for a response, which at best would probably only delay a still inevitable death for the vast majority. Or did we just leave them, to take their chances untreated.

Before reaching a decision, we needed to examine the existing efficacy data for *all* those patients where we actually had it, from both India and also all the other centres elsewhere. We had to just be sure that the cytarabine was definitely doing *something* useful, in at least some of those who were being given it. If the cytarabine didn't appear to be doing very much, then it would obviously be difficult to justify the continued exposure of patients to this sort of risk. There wouldn't be any upside for them.

The study was an open unblinded one and so it was relatively easy to set about gathering whatever data we could lay our hands on. Finally on Christmas Eve, which was a Friday at the end of a long week, Albert and I sat down to look at the results.

The study was still ongoing and so we didn't have access to a lot of the information, much of which was still sitting in hospital labs at the various study centres all over the world. But we did have data, of some sort, from about forty patients overall. They had been in the study long enough for us to have a reasonable idea of whether they had responded or not.

For the patients who were receiving just cytarabine, about a third were showing a response, with their leukaemia going into remission. That wasn't bad for a group like this, nearly all of whom would have received cytarabine at some earlier point in the course of their disease. By this stage, most would have started developing resistance to the drug. It was, if anything, a better response than we were expecting. It certainly wasn't a figure anyone would be surprised or disappointed by.

What did come as a surprise however, were the results when we looked at the two other treatment groups. These were receiving the same dose of cytarabine but with the addition of a lower or higher dose of AS1411. From what we could see, it appeared that AS1411 wasn't doing *anything* extra, above and beyond the cytarabine by itself. It wasn't a good sign.

If it had any light, AS1411 appeared to be hiding it firmly behind a bushel. It wasn't exactly a shining star we could follow. Albert and I looked at each other.

We three kings of Orient are/Bearing gifts we traverse afar. This was beginning to look bad. It wasn't exactly a gift from the Orient.

Myrrh is mine, its bitter perfume/Breathes of life, of gathering gloom/Sorrow, sighing, bleeding, dying/Sealed in the stone-cold tomb.

A stone cold tomb seemed like the right kind of metaphor here.

Albert and I had a think about it. Things as they stood clearly didn't look too good for AS1411, or for us come to that. But then again, this was only ongoing and *incomplete* data. When the study started, we'd projected we would need a total of ninety patients in the trial, to really work out what was going on. And so far we weren't even half way there.

So it was too early to draw any *firm* conclusions, with less than fifty per cent of the patients recruited. But on the other hand, AS1411 would now have to do dramatically well in the remaining patients to catch up, let alone outstrip, cytarabine.

On top of that, AS1411 did have previous form, as far as not delivering was concerned. Which didn't exactly help our growing scepticism. Once again, it looked as though we were on the non-stop service to No Hope City. We seemed to have a season ticket in fact.

Deep down Albert and I both suspected that we were in deep trouble. We'd had better Christmas presents in the past.

At least the cytarabine appeared to be working well, which helped to simplify our problem with India. It looked like patients would have a reasonable chance of deriving benefit from receiving the drug. This seemed to justify the attendant risks and so we decided to continue the study there for the time being. We could leave things as they were for now, provided the body count didn't become too unseemly.

O tidings of comfort and joy/Comfort and joy/O tidings of comfort and joy.

However, the next fatality from India happened early in the New Year and then another one the very next day. It was considerate of them to have at least held off over the festive season.

These two deaths followed the same pattern as the earlier ones, occurring within the first few week of treatment and both being due to overwhelming infection. That backed us into a corner and we felt a need to act now.

XI

Some undefined psychological tipping point had finally been reached and the time had come to suspend further recruitment from any of the Indian centres. Maybe we'd hoped the New Year would bring a new break in our luck but that clearly wasn't going to happen. It was time to bite the bullet.

It wasn't so much that the patients were dying that forced our hand. We'd come to accept that's just how it was in their country. We couldn't change the world. What really swung it was the number of *unevaluable* patients this was coming to represent, as far as potential responders were concerned.

From what Albert and I had seen before Christmas, we knew we were going to need as many surviving patients as possible, to help work out what was going on, if anything, with AS1411. Clearly though, things weren't improving the way we needed them to.

Also, a study stacked with deaths just never looked good, whatever the explanation. It made regulators nervous, if nothing else and you never quite knew what they might do next, in a situation like that. This was a liability we could do without right now. Looking at it dispassionately, every dead patient was now an extra nail in our own coffin.

Having suspended the study in India and worked our way through the prodigious amounts of paperwork involved in doing this, we now had to decide whether there were any circumstances in which we might be able to restart the trial at some point.

We didn't want the investigators to feel we'd just abandoned them, when things started unravelling.

Maybe we could pay for all the expensive antibiotics and other supportive care the patients clearly weren't getting. Perhaps we could make extra funding available, to help the hospitals avoid sending patients back home to live in a bush or a box. Money was the only solution we had though. And it wasn't really much of one at that.

It is very difficult to step in and try overnight to influence ways of doing things, which have evolved over prolonged periods of time. Hospitals are inertial institutions and they just don't respond that quickly. It would take a long time for them to find a way of accommodating this kind of proposition, even assuming they wanted to.

And we were talking about Indian hospitals at that, where nothing happened at any pace greater than that of an ambling ox. A very slowly ambling, lame ox. We just didn't have the amount of time this would take.

Even if we had been able to put these sorts of dramatically remedial measures into place with any degree of alacrity, there would still have been multiple local obstacles to overcome.

It tended to create all sorts of problems if one patient started getting access to a demonstrably higher standard of care than another in the next bed, just by virtue of being in a clinical trial. This could be a source of considerable difficulty for hospital staff and was a situation they were understandably reluctant to find themselves in.

So in reality, there wasn't that much we could do. Which meant that suspending India was effectively terminating it. Which inevitably raised questions about the future of the trial overall.

Maybe we should take this opportunity to cut our losses and halt the whole thing. Particularly as it was highly unlikely that AS1411 would be able to pull ahead in the remaining laps of the race. Stopping now would save us quite a bit of money, something which was going to be in very short supply, if amonafide fell apart at the end of the month.

However, it was now early January and with the amonafide results due in just a couple more weeks' time, nothing was going to happen before then. But if amonafide tripped and fell it might well now take AS1411 with it, leaving nothing standing. Our cupboard would be well and truly bare.

It was another psychological setback. AS1411 was a drug which had often disappointed and many would be happy to see it die, if that turned out to be its eventual fate. It would be one of the best attended and most joyous funerals ever.

However, this intimation of its likely demise, coming so near to our own endgame, managed to emphasise further just how parlous our position had become. Like the imminent death of an infirm relative after a long illness, it served to remind us of our own mortality and how little control we really had over it.

January had begun as a bleak month in London, with much of the country still struggling to recover from earlier snow falls of Arctic proportions. However, the start of the New Year had mercifully been marked by the beginnings of a thaw in the woeful weather. At least for others that is.

For us though, it was like being in Narnia. It was forever winter now, as we edged towards the arrival of the amonafide results at the end of the month. We were buffeted by intermittent icy blasts of despondency and despair.

It was obvious now that nothing could rescue us. There was no wardrobe, to escape back through, into a more comforting world. We had to continue by ourselves, trudging onwards, even though we weren't looking forward to arriving at our destination. We had no choice. There was now nowhere else left to go.

It was time for us to confront our fate.

ELEVEN

TUMBLING DICE

Time is up. The news is not good. Fatally wounded, Antisoma is surrounded by a dangerous predator. Can this really be the end of the road?

I

Thursday January 27th 2011. It was the day before the amonafide ACCEDE results would finally become available. The long wait was almost over. It was also the date of the UK BioIndustry Association annual dinner, which was always held at the Natural History Museum in London.

Here, in this enormous Romanesque style building, the UK biotechnology industry gathered to greet the coming year and celebrate having survived the one just gone. Antisoma traditionally had a table at this event, where you could commiserate and collude with your colleagues and contemporaries.

It's a black-tie occasion, usually with about five hundred people and a lot of speeches on inward investment, clusters of innovation and industry initiatives. Failed drugs and dead patients tend not to come up too often.

It's a chance to leave the problems of reality behind and briefly engage in a fantasy world, where they don't exist. This year though, it was harder to forget the outside world.

Standing next to a case filled with a stuffed *eastern hare wallaby*, extinct since 1892, or another containing the long vanished *desert rat kangaroo*, we felt that maybe we were shortly going to have more in common with the exhibits on display, than the people gathered around them.

Tomorrow was the big day.

II

Over the last few months, all the data from the trial had flowed into our computer systems, with its disparate origins ranging from Latin America to Australasia. Albert and his group had been working remorselessly unforgiving hours, for most of January, to write computer programmes to analyse all this information. To work out what it was really telling us.

At some point during the preceding week, Albert's team had become aware of the results. They would have needed to unblind the data, thus unlocking the code showing which treatment each individual patient had actually received. They had to do this, in order to finalise their computer systems and road test their worthiness. It was the only way to make sure all the pieces finally fitted together.

But this created a problem. Although it was unavoidable that the biometricians had access to the unblinded data, the survive or fail, live or die data, no one else could see it yet.

Until they had finished their arcane art, finalised their programmes, run their analyses and actually produced the results, the rest of us had to remain *blinded*. We couldn't know what the data was looking like, in case we were tempted to go back and change a few things here and there, to try to influence the final results in our favour.

In theory, it wouldn't have been that difficult a thing to do either. As it happened, in between Christmas and New Year we had already reviewed, whilst still *remaining* blinded, over seven hundred pages of data about the efficacy parameters for all the patients, in order to work out whether they were responders or non-responders.

This has to be done because inevitably there are bits of information missing here and there, or occasional results that aren't quite consistent with one another. Working out whether someone is a responder or not involves bringing together information about what is happening in their blood, the bone marrow as well as other parts of the body too. Sometimes, it doesn't all add up. All the components won't slot together.

When this occurs you have to make *assumptions* about how to deal with the discrepancies. If something doesn't fit, you have to decide whether to throw it away, or alter its shape instead. What you end up doing can influence whether the patient is eventually classified as a responder or a non-responder. Typically, in a large study like ACCEDE this sort of arbitration would affect about twenty per cent of the patient data. You have to undertake this *blinded*, not knowing which treatment a particular patient received, otherwise there would always be the temptation to make decisions more biased in favour of your drug.

By contrast, if you had been looking instead at the *unblinded* data, it would be perfectly possible to change the odd assumption here and there, to shift a few more responders into your drug group and take some out of the other group. And sometimes a few patients moving around was all you needed, to alter the outcome of statistical testing.

It was like a ballot in a marginal constituency. It would only take a handful of voters to change their mind at the last minute and the most unlikely candidate could emerge the winner. Even if it were only by one vote, it was still a victory.

However whilst on paper it might have been possible to entertain some sort of clinical gerrymandering, in practice it would be almost impossible to start meddling with the ACCEDE data, without being detected. There are electronic tracking systems that follow every move happening within a database. Any changes would be identified, recorded and reported.

It wasn't therefore quite as straightforward as a bit of vote rigging in Kabul or Kandahar. The stringencies of clinical data quality control were about as unforgiving as a Taliban taskmaster.

And so it was highly likely that everyone else involved would find out and tell on you.

III

Despite that, a company couldn't afford to take any chances. And more importantly, it couldn't afford to be *seen* to be taking any chances. Regulatory authorities place a huge importance on sponsor companies having watertight policies and procedures in place, to keep control of the flow of data and ensure its integrity, up to the point of it becoming unblinded.

This means that biometrics groups have to be ring-fenced, whilst they are dealing with the unblinding of data. They can't allow anyone else, with influence over the trial, to see any of the unblinded information and also they can't tell them anything about it either.

In a large organisation like Novartis for example, this is fairly straightforward to achieve. The biometrics division would be tucked away somewhere, in their own building, far from the preying eyes of their colleagues. But Antisoma was a different proposition. We all sat in an open plan office, next to Albert and his colleagues. The fact that they were theoretically now separated by a virtual Chinese wall didn't make any obvious difference. We could still wander over and chat to Albert, whilst playing with the gonks and penguin paraphernalia that adorned his work station.

We had of course managed this complex choreography in the past, with other clinical studies. However, those previous occasions had been different. Everyone was interested to find out whatever results they might have been but they could afford to be patient and bide their time. It wasn't as though the survival of the company depended on it. This time there *was* a bit more at stake. The temptation to peek over the wall was enormous.

Given the overwhelming corporate implications of the ACCEDE outcome, we had to be certain that whatever was going on inside of the Chinese wall stayed firmly put there. If any of the rest of us got even the vaguest hint of what the results were looking like, then effectively the whole company would be deemed to be in possession of price sensitive information.

We would then be forced into making a public statement of some sort, almost certainly at short notice. We didn't want to do that until we were good and ready. That way, we could hopefully retain more control of subsequent events. When dealing with news announcements, nothing weakened your hand more than starting off on the wrong foot. You wanted to avoid being rushed into anything.

And so the pressure on Albert and his group, to avoid inadvertently giving anything away, was enormous. For most of January, we were pretty good at leaving them in peace. But as the days went on, the whole group became the subject of greater and greater casual visual inspection, looking for any clues or signs of significance. But they all did a superb job of remaining implacable.

The day before the big day, Albert brought in some cakes he'd baked the night before. But he'd managed to burn them. This prompted endless speculation over what it indicated about his mental motivation. Was it celebration or commiseration? Were burnt cakes a lucky symbol in Chinese culture? Or were they an early portent of impending doom? Did burnt cakes now signify burnt fingers to come? What had led him to choose cakes rather than biscuits? Come to that, what was the significance of him baking at all?

We were slowly working ourselves up into a frenzy of anticipation.

Everyone of course was desperate for some inkling of what was going on, of how things were looking. We all expected Albert to crack under the pressure, at least giving us a clue or two. But he was made of sterner stuff than that and we didn't really feel able to put him on the spot either, tempting though it was. Which was just as well, as we only found out later on exactly how much he had been struggling with the stress of it all. No wonder he'd burnt his cakes.

Eventually though, late on Thursday night, as we were nibbling on stilton tartlet, under the baleful glare of serried ranks of stuffed mammals, back in Chiswick Park, the last algorithm was executed, the final digit decided and the ACCEDE Phase III clinical database was at last ready to come to life and reveal its secrets.

IV

The plan was that Albert and I would meet first thing in the morning and go through the results together. We needed to check that everything made sense and sort out our initial impressions. How had amonafide fared against the competition. Was it a win, lose or draw? Only a win counted though. A draw was as good as a loss.

After we had decided whether to greet him with a whoopee cushion or a wet blanket, we would meet with Glyn and let him in on the secret at long last. Later, there would be a presentation to the rest of the company at four thirty, after the UK financial markets had closed for the weekend. Pretty much everyone from the US had flown to London in the preceding few days. Nearly the entire company was gathered expectantly in Chiswick Park.

What Albert and I were supposed to do up until four thirty wasn't quite clear though, as we would obviously be under the spotlight for the rest of the day. Whether it was success or suicide, it would be impossible to hide it for that length of time. Once we'd opened the box, whatever was inside was highly likely to escape and elude any attempts at re-capture.

Arriving at Chiswick Park that morning, it was as though I was seeing it for the first time. It really was a beautifully designed set of buildings and an inspiring place to work. Maybe it stood out so much today because, depending on how things went later on, I might well not be making that journey too many more times.

We had hired a small office for the day, in another building on the Park. That way, we could look through the results without everyone else following us every step of the way. If it came to it, we really didn't want our work colleagues to see grown men crying.

Having arrived at work, Albert and I wandered the five or six hundred yards from our building, chatting about anything other than the ACCEDE trial. I wish I'd looked up a few pastry recipes to swop. I was studying him closely for any telltale signs of what was to come. But he was as inscrutable as ever. I made a mental note never to work with a Chinese statistician again.

When we got there, most of the meeting rooms had banal names like "Canal" or "Balcony." Ours though was named "Hanoi," for some inexplicable reason. It was unclear why anyone would want to name a room after one of the world's most notorious historical trouble spots. It didn't seem a good omen. Maybe everything would have turned out differently, if only we had been convening in "Trafalgar" or "Waterloo." Even "Dunkirk" would have done.

V

We sat down and Albert opened up his laptop, fumbling with it as though he'd never seen one before. "Here we go," I thought. "This is it. Bread on the table time."

However, instead of coming out with what we all wanted to know, Albert proceeded to launch into an interminable slide show summarising the history of the amonafide programme and the key milestones achieved in the ACCEDE study. So many CRF pages, this number of data queries, that number of programming man hours. On and on he went.

To my amazement, I realised he was practicing his presentation for later in the day to the rest of the company. He was honing the slow build.

"*Albert*, what were the results. Did it fucking work or not?" He didn't miss a beat, instantly changing mental tack. His face was expressionless and his body language non-existent. Trying to read him, I didn't have a clue what was coming next.

Up came a bar chart on his computer.

"This is the amonafide response rate from the Phase II trial," he said, as a vertical red column propelled its way up the graph, coming to a halt at the forty two per cent level.

"And this is the amonafide result from ACCEDE." A purple column shot up next to the red one, stopping at virtually the same point. Forty three per cent.

Jesus Christ...it's going to work. It's the same as in Phase II.

I was struggling to stay calm. Compared to Albert's icy indifference, I was rapidly becoming an inferno of incomprehension. Had we been wrong to be so pessimistic over amonafide's chances? Should we really have harboured such certain suspicions that it would let us down at the last moment?

One of the most frequent disappointments in drug development is that larger and later Phase III trials end up showing a reduced effect, compared to the smaller and earlier Phase II ones. For one reason or another, the bigger trial fails, whilst the smaller ones may have succeeded.

But that didn't seem to be the case here with amonafide. The Phase III result looked like it was holding up. I could feel the cloak of disappointment and despair, which had been our constant mantle for many months, slipping ever so slightly.

Albert paused, dramatically. He was enjoying his moment as master of ceremonies.

"And this is the daunorubicin ACCEDE response rate."

This was it. The dauno result *had* to be less than the amonafide one. We *had* to be on to a winner now. I struggled to stare at the blurred screen, my pupils dilated to cocaine dealer dimensions.

A bright green column crawled up the graph like a trail of snot. I waited for it to grind to a halt at twenty five per cent, but it didn't even hesitate, it just kept on going. Thirty per cent, thirty five per cent. *For fuck's sake.* Forty per cent. Forty one per cent. It came to rest at forty two per cent. *Forty two per cent.* It was exactly the same as amonafide.

I couldn't comprehend it. In fact it was *beyond* comprehension.

"Stop pissing about Albert, this isn't the time for it. What's the real result?"

But I could tell from the look that came over Albert's face that these *were* the real results. It was the first emotion he'd shown in weeks.

The feeling of disorientation was indescribable. One moment we'd been teetering on the brink of bewildered belief and the next falling into a chasm of final failure.

The study was a bust. No difference *whatsoever* between amonafide and daunorubicin. The gap between them was so small, you couldn't even fit our remaining career prospects in there. It was incredible.

We looked at one other, each unable to find the words to break the silence. It wasn't exactly the first time we'd been in the position of looking at surprising results together. But this took some beating. We couldn't think of anything to say. We didn't need to. The results spoke for themselves.

It was a draw. Which meant it was a loss. The worst imaginable loss at that.

We carried on and looked through a bit more of the data. It didn't matter anymore but we had to keep on doing something, otherwise we'd probably have frozen in suspended animation.

The safety overall didn't look *too* bad but the early thirty day mortality of twenty per cent was a *lot* higher for the amonafide arm, compared to the twelve per cent for the daunorubicin group. Those early deaths were almost certainly dragging down the amonafide response rate. Maybe not by that much but probably enough to erode away any difference between the two groups.

It was too early to have any mature longer term survival data yet but the preliminary graphs showed no difference between the two treatment arms either. You'd have needed a crowbar to prise them apart, so tightly superimposed were they.

There was no comfort anywhere. No straws to clutch at. We sat and contemplated each other in a silence of disbelief. However we looked at it, there was nothing there to see. At least nothing we wanted to.

VI

Had we missed something or somehow screwed things up? Albert and his group had checked and double checked everything. Also, the results looked credible. Unwanted but not untoward. The amonafide result was the same as in the earlier Phase II study and so appeared to be a robust one. There wasn't anything obviously aberrant about it. The daunorubicin response rate was higher than we had anticipated, with our own best guess being nearer to twenty five than forty per cent. But our assumptions were based on the results of existing clinical studies with daunorubicin, which were over a decade old now.

It was quite possible that efficacy had crept up over the last ten years to forty per cent, in parallel with general improvements in clinical care. More patients were now living long enough after treatment to be able to achieve a response, if they were ever going to, thus bumping up the general outcome with daunorubicin.

We were also seeing the conclusion of the largest ever randomised trial in secondary AML. The ACCEDE results were likely to be more valid than any other data out there.

We sat and looked at each other a bit more. There appeared to be nowhere else to go. Poking and prodding through the collective data for the study, all the various parts seemed to fit together into a harmonious whole. Everything felt *right*. Usually, when there is something wrong with the way a clinical trial has been conducted, or the manner in which data has been analysed, then something sticks out. It doesn't synchronise with everything else and the whole thing doesn't quite hang together. But the ACCEDE trial wasn't like that. All the multiple myriad components flowed together.

Looking at each other, Albert and I knew that the study was OK. Nothing had gone wrong with it. Except of course that the result hadn't gone right.

Admittedly, we didn't yet have all the efficacy data from the study. Some of the results, such as final survival, wouldn't be available for another three or four months. But there was no point carrying on collecting that information any more. Those extra findings weren't going to change things now. If amonafide wasn't getting more patients into remission in the first place, there was no chance of it revealing other benefits further down the line. The facts already staring us in the face were too conclusive.

Less than a year ago, we had talked within Antisoma of the nuclear nightmare of both ASA404 and amonafide failing. But it had been in a dismissive sense, considering the inconceivable simply for the sake of completeness, only to enjoy all the more the reality of knowing it could never happen. No one *ever* thought it would actually come to pass. Even if it did, we'd have put other things into place by then, to soften the blow.

But it had, and we hadn't.

"We'd better phone Glyn," I eventually said to Albert. Albert made a terse phone call, letting Glyn know the moment had finally arrived. He didn't give anything away though. His tone of voice was completely nondescript. He'd have put more emotion into phoning Directory Enquiries. But then this wasn't exactly the kind of news you wanted to intimate over the phone.

We waited for Glyn to make his way over. I was guessing it wouldn't take him too long. Not really sure what to do with myself, I went for a walk around the building. It consisted of rows of glass walled company offices. They were full of people gainfully employed, in a way that looked like coming to a savage end later in the day for the people at Antisoma.

VII

Glyn's lanky figure framed the doorway of the Hanoi Room, a few minutes later. Only a Super Hero could have traversed the distance that quickly. But he'd still found time to pause and take his cape off.

511

To be fair to him, he had been very patient all morning. Many CEOs, knowing there was information available which would determine the fate of them and their company, would have marched over hours ago demanding to be put in the picture. But Glyn had been gracious enough to wait and give us time to get our ducks in a row. He was like that. Always measured, forever unflappable.

It was impossible to work out what must have been racing through his mind, as we sat down around Albert's laptop of last hope. Glyn had been around long enough to know the chances of success weren't high. But his almost pathological optimism would have driven him to the point of conviction that this one was finally going to be the big break.

However, he wasn't giving anything away. His face was implacable. You had to admire him for that.

Albert drew up his graphs of gloom, his charts of catastrophe. It seemed all the more damning still, seeing it the second time around. Glyn took the news very calmly. You really had to admire him for his composure. His face reddened slightly, as though he'd been slapped across it, which of course metaphorically he had been. But he covered up well what must have been a huge blow. To look at him, you would think he'd just received a speeding ticket through the post, rather than being given a death sentence in the dock.

This was now the fourth Phase III failure in a row he had been forced to deal with, since being at the helm of Antisoma. To his credit, not many companies like Antisoma manage to pull off four clinical programmes of that size. Not many are lucky enough to be that unlucky.

But everyone needs to win now and then. And Glyn, along with the rest of us, had just lost again.

All three of us sat around the table, still taking it in. We rambled on about how difficult it was to get drugs that worked in leukaemia and what a setback this result was for patients. There would now be no new therapy for them. But at the same time, we were all thinking and analysing, *"never mind the patients, just how fucked am I now?"*

Glyn left soon after that. I don't know if he flew back.

He probably needed some time by himself, to think it through. He'd now decided to let the members of the senior management team know individually during the afternoon and to bring forward the presentation to the rest of the company to three thirty.

You could see why. It's that much harder to keep a setback a secret from everyone else for very long. A success you can savour by yourself for quite a while. A disappointment, like this one, has to be divulged much sooner. You have to get it off your own shoulders and on to those of others.

Albert didn't want to go back to the office. He couldn't face the idea of facing anyone. The inquisitive stares, the inquiring stance. Now that he'd shared the burden with us, he could no longer carry it himself.

We couldn't think of anything to do, or anywhere to go. We'd spent enough time in the Hanoi Room though. For some reason, we ended up driving out to Osterly Park. This was a large stately home, near to Heathrow Airport. We felt the compulsion to travel. It didn't matter where. It gave us a transient sense of immediate purpose, which we were now desperately lacking.

It might have been sleeting. It was definitely very cold. And deserted. We wandered through the grounds, along a river bank with a wind whipping at our heels and our mood as bleak as the featureless winter landscape. If leukaemia were an element, it would definitely be a bitter, biting gale, like the one gnawing away at us now.

Neither of us had much to say and we walked around in a heavy silence. Nothing was open. No one was around. There wasn't even a place to get a cup of tea. It somehow seemed fitting. Everything was shut down, just like we effectively had been.

Eventually, it was too cold to stay. We were now as numb physically, as our minds were mentally. Albert still didn't want to go back to Chiswick Park but we really had to now. We couldn't hide all afternoon. Three thirty would come soon enough.

When it did, it didn't last long.

Albert ran through his presentation. He'd kept his slow build up and tease. That was resilience for you. Despite all the trauma, he was still going to put on a show.

There was silence from the amassed audience, up to the point where he showed his bar charts. There were a few gasps of excited expectation at the amonafide result. Albert paused and let the anticipation linger in the air for a moment or two. Then there were the groans of bitter disappointment, as he unveiled the daunorubicin outcome.

Everyone sat staring. It wasn't a PowerPoint slide they were looking at. They were seeing three wasted years of effort and endeavour. A dead drug and a decimated company stared back at them.

Twenty five people sat around the room, mute and motionless. It was as though it were empty. There weren't any questions from the audience. After all, the only one which really mattered now was *what happens next?*

And no one had the answer to that right then.

VIII

Over the weekend, those who'd flown in from the US just a few days earlier, in an atmosphere of eager expectation, returned home to a dashed destiny. An e-mail was constructed for delivery on Sunday to all the investigators involved in the ACCEDE trial. It simply stated that we had failed to meet the primary endpoint and that the amonafide programme would be abandoned from here on in. Four lines to summarise four hundred patients, four years and forty million dollars of effort.

But it said it all.

We also sent out another e-mail that weekend, to all those involved in the AS1411 leukaemia trial. In the final few days before the ACCEDE results, perhaps arising from a prescient anticipation of the coming calamity, Glyn had finally bowed to the inevitable. He'd accepted that we needed to abandon the AS1411 study. It was just looking too dismal. We couldn't blame AS1411 *per se* but nevertheless, the trial wasn't going the way we needed it to. The dead patients had a better chance of resurrection than the study itself.

He didn't want to give up on the programme completely though, hoping to keep it alive for some happier day in a different future. But for now, leukaemia was being jettisoned and the study terminated part way through.

The rest of us hadn't seen this coming. In a way, Glyn's abandonment of his previously unyielding adherence to the aptamer project, showed just how precarious a point we had reached. If that didn't matter anymore, what else did? If he could see that particular writing on the wall, it must be written pretty damned big by now.

IX

A press release went out at seven am on Monday 31st January, announcing the failure of the ACCEDE trial and the termination of both the amonafide programme and the AS1411 leukaemia study.

"This is hugely disappointing for patients, investigators, investors and employees," it said, possibly pointing out the obvious.[1] But there wasn't really anything else we could add, to embellish or adorn the bleak bluntness of the message. The markets were definitely disappointed. By the end of the day, our share price had fallen to two and a half pence. That left us with a capitalisation of fourteen million pounds, despite having nearly twenty three million in cash left. It showed exactly what the rest of the world thought of our prospects.

Over the next few days, a third of our shares changed hands, in the ensuing scrabble to dump the stock. We lost track and no longer knew who actually owned us. Most of the analysts and press wrote us off. *We wouldn't be able to survive this setback* was pretty much the universal conclusion.

On a brighter note, a number of the investigators sent us touching little notes of condolence and commiseration. Which was nice. But not very reassuring. It wasn't, after all, going to be them who decided what happened to us next.

In fact, it was very unclear in whose hands our fate would now lie. Our hope was that another biopharmaceutical company would come to make a bid for us. Oxford BioMedica were the most obvious contender, although there were other possibilities too.

We believed we were still, despite everything, an attractive proposition. There was the cash. There were the people. There were still two pre-clinical programmes. There was AS1411, in suspended animation. OK, there was the cash.

So we just needed to hunker down and wait for the cavalry to arrive. That's how we rationalised it to ourselves. There was even some clinical work that still needed to be done, to keep us occupied. Both the amonafide and the AS1411 studies had to be closed down, in an orderly fashion at all the sites which had taken part. We also had an obligation to write up a report of each trial, so that the results would be available, should anyone be interested in them at some future date. All of that would take a good three or four weeks to sort out.

People threw themselves into these largely meaningless tasks with a disproportionate degree of enthusiasm. There was a comfort in the familiarity of work. Despite that though, there was a sense of finality hanging in the air. We all knew the chances were very low of anyone acquiring us and wanting to hold on to many, if any, of the people.

Things weren't helped by the fact that the entire company had been put on notice of redundancy on the Monday, after the Friday of the amonafide failure.

X

It didn't say a lot for the optimism with which we viewed our immediate future.

Employment legislation in the UK provided for a statutory period of consultation, which had to be allowed to unfold, before anyone could actually be made redundant. That created a deadline of March 9th, about thirty days hence. We had up until then to effect a rescue plan of some sort, otherwise the Board intended to fire everyone, both in the UK and the US.

Antisoma would cease to exist, except in name. It would become a cash shell, devoid of any people or purpose, existing purely to be put out of existence by someone coming along and taking it off the shareholders hands.

In that first week after the ACCEDE announcement though, there was frenetic interest from many quarters. We were quickly contacted by every crazy company that couldn't raise money by themselves. These were the ones no one else would touch with a bargepole. From San Francisco to Singapore, all the basket cases were on the phone, desperate to get their hands on our cash.

But they were all hopeless causes. They'd reached their current state of destitute despair by virtue of having little of value and nothing worthwhile to offer. They were all broken or had bits missing and were unlikely to be attractive investment propositions for our existing shareholders. A bit like us in fact.

But they still consumed a lot of time and wasted a lot of effort, although this did serve to create an impression of purposeful activity for us. It stopped us sitting around, brooding darkly over the misfortunes of fate.

There were also a handful of privately owned biotechnology companies which would probably have been a good strategic fit for us. Their management teams appeared keen on the idea of a merger. We'd already begun talks with a number of them in the past few months, in anticipation of just this eventuality.

But now, when faced by reality, in each case the current venture capital investors decided they didn't want their company transitioning from private to public ownership, which would have been the consequence of them coming together with us.

They feared it would be impossible to achieve the same company valuations, when confronted by the full glare of the market place, as they could currently command privately. Being associated with the name *Antisoma* would probably be an additional millstone around their neck.

And so these possibilities all gradually fell by the wayside over the next few weeks. Companies which we had talked about almost dismissively, were now discarding us in droves.

That left Oxford BioMedica. They hadn't exactly hung about in the past. And neither did we now. Glyn had already met with John Dawson, shortly after the announcement of the ACCEDE failure. Finally faced by bleak reality, Oxford BioMedica had suddenly assumed a much greater prominence in our thinking. We'd have been all over them like a rash now, given half the chance. There had never been such excessive and enthusiastic overnight converts to the gene therapy faith.

We had also been hearing stories that John Dawson was thinking of moving the company from Oxford to London. They were nothing more than that though. Just rumours. We might even have made them up ourselves, to have something to pin our hopes to. If they were true however, it could mean he was interested in more than just our cash. He might have his eye on our building and perhaps even our people too. Pretty much everything remaining in fact.

Optimism flared up. There was a flickering flame of hope, amongst all the other burned bridges.

Compared to all the corporate cripples and casualties queuing at our door, it didn't seem too bad a proposition, all of sudden. It was amazing how the exigencies of fate could alter such long standing prejudices and preconceptions. They had just become our new best friend in the playground.

Glyn and John met for breakfast, for some reason in Runneymede of all places. It was better known for the signing of the Magna Carta, back in the thirteenth century. But unlike on that historic occasion, Glyn didn't return with an agreement. All he had was an *understanding* that OBM were considering a bid but didn't know how long it would take them to put it together. We couldn't fathom that one out. They must have been considering just this event for months now and presumably had some sort of outline plan in place.

Maybe they were waiting to see how much lower we could sink. Or perhaps we just looked a lot less attractive, now that the full extent of our injuries was plain for all to see.

However, in situations like that, you can only move at the pace of the slowest player. If they wanted to dawdle, there was little we could do about it. We couldn't exactly pretend they were in danger of losing out to some more ardent suitor. Our dance card was barer than a three legged leper's. And everyone knew that too.

XI

Showing a growing detachment from reality, we even started considering whether Antisoma could still survive by itself, in the absence of being taken over by someone else. We had quite a lot of cash left. The debtors weren't banging at the door just yet. But it was nowhere near enough to fund both the acquisition of a new clinical pipeline and its subsequent development.

Besides, our bigger investors seemed to have suddenly lost their original appetite for the risk of earlier stage drug development. They just weren't interested anymore. At least not in our hands. At best, they might have been prepared to entertain a Phase III project, if we could've got our hands on one. But that was way beyond our means now.

Another possibility which enjoyed an airing for a while, was for Antisoma to revert to a research organisation. The idea was to build this around the two remaining pre-clinical programmes we had, along with what was left of AS1411. It would be like making a pie out of the scraps and remnants you forgot to throw away. The biggest problem with this recipe though, was that none of these ingredients appeared to have any value attached to them anymore.

One of the programmes, the DCAM autoimmune project, was based in the US and we had been trying unsuccessfully to sell it for the last year. No one was interested, because it was too early stage. It wasn't helped by the fact that they didn't seem to believe it worked. Furthermore, we simply hadn't advanced it to a point where there was even a particular molecule we could identify for development. It would take another two or three years to get something to the clinic. That was just too long.

Similarly the other programme, which was a collaboration with the CRUK research laboratories in Sutton, was at a very initial stage. This was aimed at a cancer target called PPM1D, which was a particular type of oncogenic promoter enzyme implicated in many malignancies.[2] It too was years from a Phase I trial.

And as for AS1411, with so many failed clinical trials to its name, the project had now reverted to a pre-clinical status again. Directionless and discredited, no one knew what you might do with it next. Like the undead, it yearned to be put out of its suffering. But no one could find a way to kill it.

Looking at it objectively, we only had a handful of questionable assets. That was before taking into consideration the small fact that we had already fired all our scientists and closed down our labs. It didn't seem an overly promising proposition, around which to build a new research orientated Antisoma.

There was also the not inconsiderable problem of trying to carry on as a public company, with over fifteen million pounds in the bank and no real assets. You would spend all your time fighting off people trying to separate you from your cash. Just like we were now.

A research based Antisoma also wouldn't need more than a couple of the people we currently had. We were a development team, who wouldn't have any role to play in a discovery based organisation. You would still need to make nearly all the workforce redundant.

It didn't therefore seem much of a basis for building a new business. It wouldn't exactly be a phoenix arising from the ashes. More like a pigeon or a parrot. But despite these fundamental limitations, an unlikely triumvirate of Nick, Daniel and Chris started to coalesce around just this proposition. The rest of us suddenly realised they were working on a plan for the three of them to survive and remain, as the new Antisoma Research, built on these unpromising foundations.

Even if there had been a stronger scientific footing, it would still have been a somewhat unusual proposition for a research company to be run by three people from business development, corporate communications and clinical operations. But the anomaly of the situation didn't dampen their enthusiasm, as they beavered away, putting their plans into place. You had to admire both their opportunism and optimism.

They would spend hours in frenzied consultation, working up their secret blueprint. The three of them seemed to be constantly holding animated whispered conversations in the corridors, before disappearing to lock themselves in a meeting room for ages on end. There was a sense of urgency to their endeavours, which was in marked contrast to the listless apathy afflicting most of the rest of us. They had an escape plan and we didn't. All we could do was to look on, with a mixture of mild jealousy and profound bewilderment.

For the rest of us, it could easily have turned into a divisive experience, as we observed three of our colleagues so energetically planning a future which didn't include any of us in it. But that danger was probably negated by the sideshow of watching these highly intelligent men engaged with such seriousness, on an endeavour of such improbability.

They did eventually get to pitch their idea to the Board a week or so later. But by then it suddenly didn't matter any longer. They had missed their chance, if they ever had one. Overnight, developments had just taken an ominous turn. We were rapidly to discover that we no longer had much control over events or our destiny.

XII

Out of the blue, an enemy had emerged. And it wasn't our old adversary Oxford BioMedica. To our amazement, OBM had actually indicated to Glyn a few days earlier that they *weren't* going to be making a bid for Antisoma. All that courting, all that unrequited passion, was to count for nothing in the end.

We had been jilted at the altar and we weren't sure why. It looked as though OBM's long suffering investors couldn't be persuaded over the whole load of new shares they would need to issue, in order to make the acquisition.

Maybe it was too soon after the fundraising escapade at the end of the previous year. Perhaps they'd had enough of seeing their existing holdings diluted and they wouldn't give the management the backing they might have wanted. It was certainly an unexpected turn of events, to put it mildly. But then shareholders could be capricious like that. They may have been supportive, in principle, up to a point but then dug their heels in when it came to tying the knot.

Or maybe they just didn't want us anymore. Even though we were in the fire sale window at a massive markdown, we were still more than a bit damaged at the edges. Burnt to a frazzle just about summed it up.

Whatever the explanation for OBM dropping out though, it rapidly became irrelevant. We hardly had time to comprehend the implications of the discovery that even *they* didn't want us anymore. We'd been dumped but we didn't have time to get over it.

Instead we suddenly found ourselves facing an advancing army who appeared to be much better equipped and a lot more battle hardened than we were. Most of us had never heard of them before either, which increased the sense of unease.

ORA were a company based in St Peter Port, Guernsey. They specialised in identifying undervalued public companies, with useful piles of cash sitting in their coffers. Companies like Antisoma. If they liked what they saw, they would buy up enough shares to acquire a controlling interest. After that, they would steer the company, or rather its cash, in a new direction, jettisoning everyone and everything along the way if necessary.

They already had a big holding in a Sierra Leone diamond mining organisation, as well as interests in semiconductors and materials technology. Now, it seemed like they fancied the look of pharmaceuticals, all of sudden.

Corporate raiders, some had called them.

And the problem now was that they had just bought a significant amount of Antisoma stock.

This had been the one possibility we feared more than any other. An aggressive bid for the company, by someone interested in nothing but squeezing as much cash out of it as they could.

Obviously all the other prospective bidders for Antisoma weren't doing it just out of the goodness of their hearts either. But we genuinely thought that some of them were also interested in other things, such as the remaining projects or a few of the people.

But even if they weren't, at least events were being conducted in a civilised way. Convivial conversations, over cups of tea in historic market towns, had been the order of the day up until now.

But these people didn't fuck about.

XIII

They went on steadily buying up our shares, probably constrained only by the number of people willing to sell to them right now. Many existing shareholders were still holding on, hoping for a bid by another biopharmaceutical company, which would be at a premium to the current rock bottom share price. But that reticence would change sooner or later. ORA could afford to bide their time.

Knowing that they were out there though, changed the atmosphere within Antisoma overnight. We realised the game was up now. We were slowly being encircled and the chances of anyone else coming to the rescue were dwindling by the day. The bunker like mentality became evermore prominent. There was now a dejected sense of resignation to our fate. We suddenly came to the insight that we now no longer had any real control over *anything*.

Our future was being played out by an adversary we didn't know. *ORA*. They even sounded like some counter-insurgency division of the Red Army. Closing in on us. Seeking out our last hiding place. "*Enjoy the war, because the peace will be that much worse.*" As they used to say in Berlin, in the final days.

520

We were beginning to see what the long suffering German civilians had been on about.

Glyn was forced to watch what was left of his company being wrestled from his hands. His normal indomitable sprightliness was gone. Like most of the rest of us, he had a faraway look and deader eyes. And that was even before he was summonsed to meet with Richard Griffiths, ORA's own chief executive.

Richard Griffiths was a rich and successful businessman. He probably hadn't achieved all that by being easy going and accommodating in situations such as this. He rarely lost and he wasn't about to start now.

Glyn met him at the City offices of Canacord, our corporate advisors. ORA wanted a seat on the Board and a big say in what happened to the company from now on. Glyn wouldn't reveal exactly what took place during that meeting. He never talked to us about it afterwards. Perhaps it was too scarring.

That conversation though, effectively sealed the fate of Antisoma and everyone else within it.

The rumour which rapidly engulfed the company was that ORA wanted to divert the Antisoma cash into a uranium mining venture in Africa.

So they wouldn't exactly be needing any of our people then.

The fact that such a proposition seemed so plausible showed just how far we'd strayed from the comfortable familiar world of just a few weeks ago. We were now in uncharted territory and we had no normal points of reference to guide us.

News that they were after a seat on the Antisoma Board sent a wave of panic around the building. It suddenly became impossible to find anywhere to have a private conversation. We were an open plan office, with a number of meeting rooms and a couple of rows of small closed off work cubicles, which looked like something from a sperm donating facility.

Previously, you could wander into one at will. Now however, they were constantly full of people making calls to, or for the luckier ones, receiving them from, head hunting agencies and other possible sources of future employment. People were wandering around with plastic wallets full of business cards, collected over the years from long forgotten acquaintances, all of whom were now potential sources of new job openings.

This atmosphere of abandonment and retreat wasn't calmed any by an address Glyn gave to the entire company, the morning after his meeting with ORA. It was along the lines that rescue now seemed impossible and people should expect the worst, making their escape plans as best they could.

At least we knew where we stood now.

With defeat having finally been acknowledged, a curtain of calm seemed to descend over us. The phones stopped ringing, the normal chatter of casual conversation was absent. People were suddenly and inexplicably not around for long periods of time. Even the junk e-mail seemed to dry up.

In preparation for eventually abandoning the building, piles of cardboard boxes sprung up, like battlements around desks and cupboards, with people having to weave their way in between them, as though dodging sniper fire.

XIV

But in between packing up the past and preparing for the future, there were still a few things which had to be sorted out. Like working out a plan for turning us into the cash shell, that was now our inevitable final fate. Whilst the rest of us grimly struggled on, Eric by contrast now bloomed and flourished. He was like a man reinvigorated and rejuvenated by the challenge of cutting costs to the point of non-existence.

It was Eric who told us that we would all be laid off on March 9th, with only himself and a few administrative assistants remaining. They would keep things ticking over until someone, presumably ORA, had assumed complete control. Although he was now by far away the busiest person in the company, Eric seemed happier than anyone could ever recall him, as slowly but surely, the reins of the company slipped into his hands.

To help clear the decks, one outstanding task was to try and get rid of the few remaining assets. We wanted to make sure things were left as neat and tidy for the incoming occupants as we could manage.

There were actually a few expressions of interest in amonafide. Although the ACCEDE trial had failed, it wasn't because amonafide didn't work. It just hadn't worked any *better* than the anthracycline drug, daunorubicin. But anthracyclines were very poisonous agents and there were a number of situations where a drug like amonafide might be preferred over them. Despite its own toxic liabilities.

Rob Stuart from the Medical University of South Carolina, one of our staunchest allies over the years and an amonafide investigator himself, contacted us asking if we could provide him with the drug. He wanted to undertake a clinical trial, on his own initiative, in elderly patients with leukaemia. This threw us into a bit of a panic, as we had just ordered the destruction of all the remaining clinical supplies of amonafide. There was no expectation that anyone would have a use for them. We were however able to intervene just in time and rescind this.

But we couldn't simply hand over the drug supplies to Rob. We would also need to transfer all the regulatory obligations to him, as we would no longer be around to fulfil them. Additionally, there was a requirement for some sort of indemnity, which would avoid the prospective uranium mine having any future liability, should any disgruntled patients start suing, or behaving in other equally unreasonable ways.

In principle, none of this was a problem but it was very unclear whether any of it could now be achieved, in the limited amount of time available to us. Despite our best endeavours, we eventually just couldn't get things sorted out. We had disbanded or discarded all our normal operating mechanisms and without them, we could now no longer find a way to function.

The same problem applied to another offer for amonafide we had received from a small US start up company, ironically formed by some of the founders of Xanthus. They weren't prepared to offer any money for the drug right now but were willing to share any value they might uncover in the future. That probably wouldn't work though, given that we now had no future. However, it did go to show that a drug never quite died. There was always someone prepared to give it a new home and an extra lease of life.

This was even true of AS1411, which eventually went back to its biological parents in Louisville.[3] Some of the original Aptamera contingent had put together a new company. They happily welcomed home AS1411. As it turned out, we had only ever been its foster parents. In retrospect, it clearly should never have left home in the first place. There are some offspring who are just destined to stay put.

There were also one or two other odds and ends, from the past which we thought we could perhaps find a home for.

Nigel Courtenay Luck, one of the original founders of Antisoma, had since started another small company and was interested in AS1409. This was an antibody for melanoma, which we had given up developing a few years earlier. It had shown some initial promise but we hadn't taken it any further forwards, due to resource constraints at the time. However, Nigel had no funding to do anything with it and unless he could raise some very quickly, then it would probably be too late. There wouldn't be anyone left here for him to deal with. With time running out, the chances weren't looking good for this particular orphan finding a new family.

Eventually however Nigel and his partner Ray Spencer, who'd actually been Eric's predecessor as Chief Financial Officer at Antisoma, managed to pull things together. They still didn't have any money but we were able to hand AS1409 over to them, in the absence of any other obvious place for it to go.

It didn't however look likely that we would find anyone to relieve us of the two pre-clinical programmes. Apart from the practical problems created by the time constraints, the DCAM project was further hampered by the fact that we couldn't convince anyone it actually worked. And we didn't even own PPM1D ourselves. Instead we had a licence from CRUK, which was going to expire in a few months anyway. We couldn't give it away, because it didn't belong to us in the first place.

Disposing of our few remaining chattels wasn't exactly a fulfilling exercise therefore. There wasn't much left after twenty years of activity as a company. This sense of futility didn't help the already oppressive atmosphere surrounding us, as we sat watching a once vibrant entity dying in front of our very eyes.

XV

Its death throes became all the more marked after Glyn ambled up, late on in the afternoon of the last Friday in February and casually announced that today was his last day.

"What the fuck did you just say?"

It was true. He was leaving today. He had a deal.

Like the Führer, he'd decided to leave before the advancing army arrived. But whereas the former had ended up with a bullet in the brain, Glyn had been luckier with a payment in the pocket. He'd reached an agreement with the Board, as his contract allowed him to.

There would be more Board changes announced on Monday, apparently.

And that was it. Ten years at Antisoma and he was leaving in ten minutes time. No final get together. No farewell. Well, that wasn't strictly true. Glyn did send out a two line e-mail, saying he was going and how much he'd enjoyed working here. And then he was gone. Just like that.

Some of us couldn't quite believe it.

Given his decade long involvement with the company and attachment to his team, perhaps he couldn't deal with departing in a way which was any more protracted.

The rest of us though were now left in the bunker to fend for ourselves. We didn't even know who was running the company anymore.

There was a sense of abandonment but also begrudging respect. Glyn was only displaying the powers of survival which had propelled him to the top in the first place and subsequently kept him there for so long. In that sense, it was a naked display of ruthlessness, probably to be admired. If anything, it was a shame we hadn't acted like that more frequently in the past. Maybe things would have been different now.

However, whilst his leadership had all but vaporised over the last few weeks, his departure still left us feeling directionless and drifting. He had been the CEO for a decade, after all. We left for the weekend wondering what lay in store for us the following week.

We didn't have to wait long.

On Monday morning it emerged that Eric had done a deal at the same time as Glyn. Except he had now come back, as a consultant to the company for the next few months. To tie up all the remaining loose ends.

With Glyn gone, his moment had finally arrived. It was time for some *serious* business discipline from here on in. Subtlety and sensitivity suddenly went out of the window. He was a winner and we were losers. It was as binary as that for Eric. And he had no time for losers.

It was a salutary lesson in how pointless we had all become.

There was to be a Board meeting that evening, at which Barry would resign as chairman, along with one or two other non-exec directors. The next morning, Tuesday, there was going to be a meeting of the reconstituted Board with a new chairman and also a new member appointed by ORA. This would be Michael Bretherton, their Finance Director.

So they were finally here, almost at our front door. Soon, we'd be able to see them and them us.

XVI

The Board duly met for a final fateful time on Monday evening, after which there was a farewell dinner for the Directors at the River Cafe in Fulham. It was probably a fairly sombre affair, with two decades of disappointment to dissect over the duck confit with flageolet beans.

They could probably console themselves with the sweet trolley though. That should have been enough to take away any bitter aftertaste. The *Chocolate Nemesis* on the menu seemed an appropriately named selection.

Whilst they were enjoying a Last Supper that night, we were getting ready to say the Last Rites, prior to the arrival of ORA the next morning.

Tomorrow would be their day.

Ours was over.

EPILOGUE

FOOL TO CRY

Five years and fuck all. That's how it felt. Nothing to show for it all, except a profound sense of loss.

Maybe the Devil had finally managed to lay our souls to waste after all.

But there *was* more to it than that. We still had some fight left in us. We *still* had no sympathy for him.

Antisoma had been an opportunity to work with some fabulous people in some wonderful teams and on some truly innovative drugs. In the end, none of them had worked but at least we had done a good job of discovering that.

As it turned out, we'd been dealt some bad cards, played our best hand but ended up losing our shirts.

Cancer medicine hadn't exactly been progressed by any of our efforts. But unfortunately, as far as that dark domain was concerned, our experiences were more exemplary than exceptional.

Overall though, it had been the best of times, even when it was the worst of times.

But what were we going to do now?

We all wanted another go in the casino, to throw the dice again. We wanted to go up against the Devil, just once more.

Maybe next time it would be different.

You had to keep the faith.

POSTSCRIPT

Antisoma formally completed a compulsory redundancy programme on March 9th 2011, with virtually all the remaining staff leaving. One or two stayed a short while longer, to tie up the final financial loose ends. The company however effectively ceased to exist as a biotechnology enterprise from that date onwards.

By a strange quirk of fate, it all ended where it had begun. With Lucky Lara.

As we were in the very act of closing the doors for the last time, the final manuscript detailing the demise of the ATTRACT I trial popped through our letterbox. It had been written by Lucky and was just appearing in the coveted Journal of Clinical Oncology.[1]

It served as a public proclamation of our sins. The *J Clin Oncol* article became our last penance. On our death bed, Lucky, the High Priest of Oncology, had arrived to dispense the final sacrament.

On 11th January 2012, Antisoma, along with its remaining fifteen million pounds, was reclassified on the London Stock Exchange as an Investing Company.

It was somehow even able to report a small profit of a third of a million pounds, in October of the same year. The money men had finally achieved what medicine could never quite manage.

Earth to earth, ashes to ashes, dust to dust; in sure and certain hope of the Resurrection to eternal life.

REFERENCES AND NOTES

FRONT PAGE

[1] David Fricke. Online Exclusive: Keith Richards Uncut. Rolling Stone. 24 September 2002. http://www.rollingstone.com/music/news/online-exclusive-keith-richards-uncut-20020924

CHAPTER TWO

[1] McKeage M. *et al*. Randomised phase II study of ASA404 combined with carboplatin and paclitaxel in previously untreated advanced non-small cell lung cancer. Br J Cancer, 2008; 99:2006-2012.

[2] Cell Therapeutics eventually sold **Trisenox** to the US based company Cephalon in June 2005, for seventy million dollars up front and a further one hundred million dollars if certain future milestones were met.

[3] **Frank Baldino** was an American pharmacologist and scientist who, at the age of thirty three, was one of the co-founders of the pharmaceutical firm Cephalon, a company that was formed in 1987 and has grown to annual sales of three billion dollars.

Its best known product has probably been Provigil, use in treating narcolepsy, shift work sleep disorder and excessive daytime sleepiness resulting from sleep apnea. It became a best seller though largely due to use by individuals seeking to maintain alertness and combat fatigue without the side effects of caffeine and amphetamines. This particular use accounts for over ninety per cent of the drug's billion dollar plus annual sales.

Over the years, Cephalon has acquired a significant number of anti-cancer compounds for both solid tumors and leukaemias. Frank Baldino had gone out and found them. One of the best examples of his approach is a drug called bendamustine (Treanda) for use in leukaemias and lymphomas. Bendamustine had been languishing for decades, after being invented in an old East German lab in the 1960s, right in the middle of the Cold War. Cephalon stumbled across it and brought it to the US, where it was approved for use in haematological cancers in 2008. Despite being nearly fifty years old, bendamustine has rapidly established itself as a useful drug in managing leukaemias and lymphomas, selling over five hundred million dollars a year. That's the kind of magic Baldino was so good at.

He unfortunately died in December, 2010, aged fifty seven, due to complications of leukemia. The company was unable to survive without Baldino and was acquired in May 2011 by the Israeli giant Teva Pharmaceutical Industries, in a deal valued at nearly seven billion dollars.

4   **Avastin** (bevacizumab) is an antibody that interacts with a chemical called Vascular Endothelial Growth Factor (VEGF). VEGF (pronounced VEG...F) is produced in large quantities by tumors and is one of the major mechanisms by which they form the new blood vessels that cancers constantly rely on. Avastin doesn't therefore attack the blood vessels *directly*, as vascular disrupting agents such as ASA404 do. Instead, it works by switching off the signalling responsible for their formation. By blocking VEGF, Avastin slows down the rate of formation of *new* blood vessels, whereas VDAs work best on the *existing* already established vascular supply.

In addition to anti-VEGF antibodies, such as Avastin, there are another group of molecules which inhibit the VEGF signalling pathway. These act by blocking an important enzyme called tyrosine kinase, which is normally stimulated by VEGF itself. Tyrosine kinase plays a significant role in promoting the cellular growth and proliferation that are essential components in the physical formation of new blood vessels. Tyrosine kinase *inhibitors* include drugs such as Sutent and Nexavar.

Collectively, VDAs and anti-VEGF agents are known as *anti-angiogenics* and these have become a significant new class of anti-cancer compounds over the last decade or so.

The anti-VEGF approach is way ahead of the VDA one, with Avastin being approved for use in kidney, breast, lung, brain and colon cancer. The tyrosine kinase inhibitors are also used for a number of tumor types, including kidney, liver, thyroid and soft tissue cancers.

The vascular disrupting agents are quite a long way behind, as none have yet been approved for use in any particular cancer type.

5   **Herceptin** is an antibody that targets a particular growth factor known as HER2, located on the surface of breast cancer cells. HER2 is present in about twenty per cent of breast cancer patients and confers a worse prognosis than disease without HER2. Herceptin is used in combination with conventional chemotherapy in patients who are *HER2 positive* and it significantly improves the outcome of treatment. It was originally approved for use in 1998 and is one of the few drugs to have convincingly shown an improvement in survival in breast cancer patients.

6   Richard Warry. Drug for deadly prostate cancer. BBC News. 22 July 2008. http://news.bbc.co.uk/1/hi/health/7502238.stm.

7   **Abiraterone** is a drug which held on to its phenomenal potential. It eventually became one of the few examples of a Phase III study which was stopped early at an interim look, because the experimental arm (abiraterone) was doing so much better than expected. Abiraterone went

on to receive full approval from the US regulatory authorities shortly afterwards and Cougar was subsequently snapped up by pharmaceutical giant J&J in 2010).

8   OXiGENE Press Release. OXiGENE Reports Final Data From Phase 2 FALCON Study of ZYBRESTAT in Non-Small Cell Lung Cancer. 03 November 2011.

Best tumor response in terms of partial shrinkage (partial response) was 56 per cent in the Zybrestat (fosbretabulin) arm and 36 per cent in the standard therapy arm. Median Progression Free Survival (a measure of how long before the cancer starts to spread and get worse) was 8.6 months in the Zybrestat arm versus 9.3 months in the standard therapy arm. Median Overall Survival was 13.6 months in the Zybrestat arm versus 16.2 months in the standard therapy arm.

Overall, patients who received Zybrestat appeared to have disease which progressed more rapidly and which resulted in them living for a shorter period of time, compared to the patients who didn't receive Zybrestat.

9   Antisoma Press Release. Antisoma reports survival advantage for AS1404 in lung cancer and regains product rights. 4 June 2006.

10   **Chronic myeloid leukaemia** (CML) is a disorder of a particular group of white blood cells normally produced in the bone marrow, known as *myeloid* cells. It can occur at any age, but it is more common in middle-aged to older people and is quite rare in children. There are about a thousand new cases in the UK each year.

Myeloid cells comprise white blood cells which play a key role in fighting certain types of bacterial and other infection. One of the commonest myeloid cells is called a granulocyte and CML used to be referred to as chronic granulocytic leukaemia.

In CML, the bone marrow loses the ability to produce myeloid cells in the carefully controlled manner that normally occurs. This results in an overproduction of immature and non-functioning granulocytes (and other myeloid cells) which are known as blast cells. These abnormal cells eventually crowd out all the normal ones in the bone marrow and then start spreading to other parts of the body, particularly the spleen and lymph nodes.

The term chronic refers to the fact that CML usually develops over a long period of time and in the early stages of the disease most people will not be aware of any symptoms, and are nearly always diagnosed by chance as a result of other routine blood tests.

In the chronic phase, CML progresses very slowly and the leukaemia is often stable for a prolonged period. Usually, there are less than ten per cent of the abnormal blast cells in the bone marrow. There may be no symptoms and most people lead a normal life. In a small number of people however, the leukaemia may gradually move into an *accelerated phase*. In this stage the number of abnormal blast cells in the blood and bone marrow increases to about twenty per cent and the leukaemia develops more quickly. After some time (usually months) in the accelerated phase, the leukaemia transforms into a *blast phase*, which is then very similar to an acute leukaemia. The number of blasts cells in the bone marrow starts to spiral out of control and can be anywhere between twenty and a hundred per cent.

Until fairly recently, CML was life threatening with a limited life expectancy. Before the discovery of modern therapies, patients would typically spend between three and five years in the chronic phase of the disease. Some would then enter the accelerated phase, from which most died within eighteen months. Others would progress to enter the blast phase and here most would die within six months. The only exception to this progression would be the small minority of patients who could receive a stem cell transplant. For all the others, conventional chemotherapy was the only available option, with very limited success.

With the introduction of newer, specifically targeted therapies, such as Gleevec, this situation has now changed, with most patients managing treatment for ten years or longer without any problems from their disease. These newer drugs have heralded a new dimension in the treatment of CML, with the potential to turn a terminal illness into a long-term survivable disease.

[11] Antisoma Press Release. Antisoma Announces Global Agreement with Novartis for Cancer Drug AS1404. 19 April 2007.

[12] **Chronic lymphocytic leukaemia (CLL)** is a slowly progressive form of cancer, characterized by an increased production in the bone marrow of a type of white cell known as a lymphocyte. It is the most prevalent form of leukaemia and occurs predominantly in patients over fifty five years. There are about two and half thousand new cases each year in the UK.

Lymphocytes are part of the *lymphoid series* of white cells and so are different from the *myeloid* white cells that become cancerous in chronic myeloid leukaemia. There are two main types of lymphocyte (known as B and T cells) and they are key elements of the immune system. B cells ultimately transform into the cells which produce antibodies in the blood.

Lymphocytes are normally produced in a controlled way but in CLL the process becomes deregulated and out of control. The lymphocytes multiply too quickly and live too long, so there are too many of them circulating in the blood. These leukaemic lymphocytes look normal, but are in fact not fully developed and do not work properly. Over a period of time the abnormal cells replace the normal white cells, red cells and platelets in the bone marrow.

Although CLL starts in the bone marrow, it can spread to the blood, lymph nodes, spleen, liver, central nervous system, and other organs.

As the condition usually develops very slowly, many people with CLL do not need treatment for months or years. However, some people may have a more aggressive form of the illness and will need to have treatment much earlier. This usually takes the form of chemotherapy, often combined with antibody drugs directed against the leukaemic lymphocyte cells.

CHAPTER THREE

[1] President Barack Obama. A Cure For Cancer In Our Time. Speech to Joint Session of Congress. 25 February 2009.

[2] R. M Nixon. State of the Union message to Congress. 22 January 1971. (See Chapter Five).

[3] http://www.ahrp.org/cms/content/view/861/56/

[4] http://www.trisenox.com/pdf/TRISENOX_pi.pdf

[5] http://www.syntapharma.com/AboutUsHistory.aspx

[6] O'Day S. *et al.* Phase II, Randomized, Controlled, Double-Blinded Trial of Weekly Elesclomol Plus Paclitaxel Versus Paclitaxel Alone for Stage IV Metastatic Melanoma. J Clin Oncol 2009, 27:5452-5458.

[7] Prior to 2011, during the period elesclomol was being developed, **advanced melanoma** had remained bereft of effective treatment options for decades. Existing chemotherapy strategies were largely ineffective at achieving anything other than transient responses. However in March 2011, the immunomodulatory agent **ipilimumab** (Yervoy) was approved in the US, after actually managing to show a survival advantage. It does however have a very significant toxicity profile. In August of the same year the targeted therapy **vemurafenib** (Zelboraf) was also approved by FDA. This works against a genetic defect known as the BRAF mutation, present in about two thirds of melanoma patients. Vemurafenib showed very high response rates, in terms of tumor shrinkage, although it now appears that the duration of many of these responses may be relatively short lived.

Despite emerging limitations, both agents represent a significant advance in the treatment of the disease.

[8] http://ww.fda.gov/ForIndustry/DevelopingProductsforRareDiseases Conditions/default.htm.

[9] http:// www.eurordis.org/en/content/orphan-drug-lists-europe-and-us.

[10] Synta Pharmaceuticals Corp Press Release. Synta Suspends Elesclomol SYMMETRY Trial in Metastatic Melanoma. 26 February 2009.

[11] Synta Pharmaceuticals Corp Press Release: Synta Pharmaceuticals Announces Presentation of Preliminary Results of Phase 3 SYMMETRY Trial of Elesclomol in Metastatic Melanoma at ASCO 2009. May 30 2009.

[12] Synta did however manage to eventually retrieve the situation with elesclomol in other cancer types and go on to initiate clinical trials in ovarian cancer and leukaemia, with encouraging results to date.

[13] Erba H. *et al.* Phase II study of single agent clofarabine in previously untreated older adult patients with acute myelogenous leukaemia (AML) unlikely to benefit from standard induction chemotherapy. J Clin Oncol, 2008; 26 (May 20 suppl: abstr7025).

[14] Erba H. *et al.* Phase II Study of Single Agent Clofarabine in Previously Untreated Older Adult Patients with Acute Myelogenous Leukemia (AML) Unlikely to Benefit from Standard Induction Chemotherapy. Blood (ASH Annual Meeting Abstracts), 2008; 112: Abstract 558.

[15] Genzyme Press Release. Genzyme Reports Clolar Data Further Supporting Potential Of Product To Treat Adult AML Patients. 08 December 2008.

[16] Faderl S. *et al.* Clofarabine plus cytarabine compared to cytarabine alone in older patients with relapsed or refractory acute myelogenous leukaemia (AML): Results from the phase III Classic I trial. J Clin Oncol, 2011; 29 (suppl: abstr 6503).

[17] Genzyme Press Release. Genzyme Announces Results of Phase 3 Trial Of Clolar In Adult AML. 20 October 2010.

[18] The final results of the CLASSIC I trial weren't published until 2012 but they confirmed the earlier presentation of Stefan Faderl at ASCO in 2011, that the median overall survival in the clofarabine plus cytarabine arm was 6.6 months, compared to 6.3 months for cytarabine alone. It wasn't quite enough to get clofarabine over the finishing line. (Faderl S. *et al.* Clofarabine Plus Cytarabine Compared With Cytarabine Alone in Older Patients With Relapsed or Refractory Acute Myelogenous Leukemia: Results From the CLASSIC I Trial J Clin Oncol, 2012; 30:2492-2499).

[19] The **European Medicines Agency** is a decentralised agency of the European Union, located in London. The Agency is responsible for the scientific evaluation of medicines developed by pharmaceutical companies for use in the European Union. (It's not responsible for all drug approvals in Europe however. Thousands of medicines do not fall within its remit and are marketed in the EU in individual Member States in accordance with their national authorisation procedures).
Most of the Agency's scientific evaluation work is carried out by its scientific committees, which are made up of members from EEA countries, as well as representatives of patient, consumer and healthcare professional organisations. These committees have various tasks related to the development, assessment and supervision of medicines in the EU. For more information, see: www.ema.europa.eu.

[20] O'Connor O. *et al.* Pralatrexate in patients with relapsed or refractory

peripheral T-cell lymphoma: results from the pivotal PROPEL study. J Clin Oncol, 2011; 29:1182-1189.

21 Code of Federal Regulations. 21CFR 314.510. Approval based on a surrogate endpoint, or on an effect on a clinical endpoint other than survival or irreversible morbidity.

22 Food and Drug Administration Amendments Act of 2007 (FDAAA).

23 **Epigenetic modifications** to the genetic structure of cancer cells involve changes which, unlike mutations, do not alter the actual nucleotide sequence of genes themselves. Instead, they involve changes in regions which are in close proximity to the genes. DNA has a complex structure, whereby it is generally wrapped around special proteins called histones to form an arrangement called a nucleosome. In malignant cells, this histone protein can become chemically altered (a process known as deacetylation) which in turn can lead to silencing of tumor suppressor genes and activation of oncogenes located on the DNA wrapped around it. Histone deacetylase inhibitors reverse this chemical modification, resulting in tumor suppressor genes being switched back on and tumor promoting oncogenes being switched off.

There are a number of other types of epigenetic modification, apart from deacetylation, which play a role in cancer initiation and progression. The most common is *hypermethylation,* whereby certain regions of DNA, situated next to important regulatory genes, have extra chemical groups (methyl groups) added to them. This in turn results in an undesirable change in the normal activity of the adjacent gene. Drugs called *hypomethylating agents* (such as decitabine and azacitidine) act to remove these extra methyl groups and are widely used in the treatment of a number of cancers.

24 Whittaker S. *et al.* Final Results From a Multicenter, International, Pivotal Study of Romidepsin in Refractory Cutaneous T-Cell Lymphoma. J Clin Oncol, 2010; 28: 4485-4491.

25 Piekarz R. *et al.* Phase II Multi-institutional trial of the histone deacetylase inhibitor romidepsin as monotherapy for patients with cutaneous T-cell lymphoma. J Clin Oncol, 2009; 27:5410–7.

26 Schiller G. *et al.* Single-agent laromustine, a novel alkylating agent, has significant activity in older patients with previously untreated poor-risk acute myeloid leukemia. J Clin Oncol, 2010; 28:815-821.

27 Giles F. *et al.* Cloretazine (VNP40101M), a novel sulfonylhydrazine alkylating agent, in patients age 60 years or older with previously untreated acute myeloid leukemia. J Clin Oncol, 2007; 25:25-31.

28 www.fda.gov. ODAC Transcript. 01 September 2009.

29 Giles F. *et al.* Phase 3 randomized, placebo-controlled, double-blind study of high-dose continuous infusion cytarabine alone or with

laromustine (VNP40101M) in patients with acute myeloid leukemia in first relapse. Blood, 2009; 114:4027-4033.

Following discussion with FDA, the trial was subsequently allowed to continue and complete after modifications to reduce the dose of laromustine and to include usage of GCSF support.

30 Deisseroth A. *et al.* Toxicity of laromustine plus high-dose cytarabine in patients with relapsed acute myeloid leukemia. Blood, 2010; 115:430.

31 Kantarjian H. *et al.* Phase II Study of Clofarabine Monotherapy in Previously Untreated Older Adults With Acute Myeloid Leukemia and Unfavourable Prognostic Factors. J Clin Oncol, 2010; 28:549-555.

32 **Clofarabine** had originally been developed jointly in Europe by both Genzyme and another, smaller, New York based company called Bioenvision. A European regulatory submission had been made to the EMA, by Bioenvision in 2006, based on a single trial BIOV121. This was a study of 66 elderly patients with AML, recruited between July 2004 and November 2005 in the UK and Italy. The final results showed a 44 per cent complete response (CR) rate. (Burnett A. *et al.* European Development of Clofarabine as Treatment for Older Patients With Acute Myeloid Leukemia Considered Unsuitable for Intensive Chemotherapy. J Clin Oncol, 2010; 28:2389-2395).

The next year, Genzyme acquired Bioenvision for three hundred and forty five million dollars, in May 2007. In March 2008, having reassessed the regulatory situation, Genzyme withdrew the clofarabine application from the EMA. Following the completion of CLASSIC II enrolment (in December 2007) and the availability of preliminary results in the middle of 2008, Genzyme subsequently submitted the entire clofarabine package, including the BIOV121 study, as well as CLASSIC II, to FDA in November 2008. This in turn eventually resulted in the ODAC meeting of September 2009 to consider the application.

33 Roboz G. Treatment of Elderly Patients with Acute Myeloid Leukemia: Lowering the Intensity. ASH Education Book. 2009.
http://www.asco.org/ASCOv2/Home/Education%20&%20Training/Educational%20Book/PDF%20Files/2009/09EdBk.Leukemia.05.pdf

34 FDA Press Release. Pfizer Voluntarily Withdraws Cancer Treatment Mylotarg from US Market. 21 June 2010.

CHAPTER FOUR

1 The main function of **dendritic cells** is to process antigen material and present it on the surface to other cells of the immune system, thus functioning as *antigen-presenting cells.*

Dendritic cells are present in small quantities in tissues that are in contact with the external environment, mainly the skin (where there is a specialized dendritic cell type called Langerhans cells) and the inner lining of the nose, lungs, stomach and intestines. They can also be found in an immature state in the blood. Once activated, they migrate to the lymphoid tissues where they interact with T cells and B cells to initiate an immune response.

2 **Staging** describes the severity of a person's cancer based on the extent of the original (primary) tumor and whether or not cancer has spread in the body. Some staging systems cover many types of cancer; others focus on a particular type. The common elements considered in most staging systems are (i) site of the primary tumor; (ii) tumor size and number of tumors; (iii) lymph node involvement (spread of cancer into lymph nodes); (iv) cell type and tumor grade (how closely the cancer cells resemble normal tissue cells); (v) the presence or absence of metastasis.

The *TNM system* is one of the most widely used staging systems. Most medical facilities use the TNM system as their main method for cancer reporting.

The TNM system is based on the extent of the tumor (**T**), the extent of spread to the lymph nodes (**N**), and the presence of distant metastasis (**M**). A number is added to each letter to indicate the size or extent of the primary tumor and the extent of cancer spread.

For example, breast cancer classified as T3 N2 M0 refers to a large tumor that has spread outside the breast to nearby lymph nodes but not to other parts of the body. Prostate cancer T2 N0 M0 means that the tumor is located only in the prostate and has not spread to the lymph nodes or any other part of the body.

For many cancers, TNM combinations correspond to one of five stages from Stage 0 (*carcinoma in situ*) to Stage IV (distant spread). However, exact criteria for stages differ for different types of cancer. For example, bladder cancer T3 N0 M0 is stage III, whereas colon cancer T3 N0 M0 is stage II.

3 Staging *migration* is probably a more technically accurate term than staging-creep.

4 Lung cancers have conventionally been broadly divided into two types. About eighty per cent are *non-small cell lung cancer (NSCLC)* and approximately fifteen per cent are *small cell*. The remaining five per cent are accounted for by rare variants. There are three main types of NSCLC. The commonest is *adenocarcinoma*, which usually originates in peripheral lung tissue. Most cases of these are associated with smoking. It is however also the commonest form of lung cancer in people who've never smoked (non-smokers accounting for ten to fifteen per cent of lung cancers overall). Adenocarcinomas can be present for a relatively long period, before producing symptoms such as shortness of breath or fatigue. *Squamous-cell carcinoma* is the second most common type of

NSCLC. These typically occur close to large airways. A hollow cavity and associated necrosis are commonly found at the centre of the tumor. Squamous carcinomas tend to produce symptoms, such as coughing or coughing up blood, fairly early on. The remaining fifteen to twenty per cent of cases are accounted for by *large-cell carcinoma*. These are so named because the cancer cells are large, with prominent nuclei.

Small cell lung cancer is also known as oat cell carcinoma. It is very strongly associated with smoking, with less than five per cent of cases being in non-smokers. It is more aggressive than non-small cell disease with a tendency to spread more rapidly and widely to other regions including lymph nodes, bone, brain, adrenal glands, and the liver.

5   Lucky eventually wrote up the results of the ATTRACT I trial and the manuscript appeared in the Journal of Clinical Oncology (Lara P. *et al.* Randomized Phase III placebo-controlled trial of carboplatin and paclitaxel with or without the vascular disrupting agent vadimezan (ASA404) in advanced non-small-cell lung cancer. J Clin Oncol, 2011; 29:2965-2971).

The paper speculated on why there was such a discrepancy between the Phase II and Phase III results. In Lucky's opinion, the main reason was that the much smaller number of patients in the Phase II trial simply overestimated the size of treatment effect. There were just too few patients to accurately capture the true survival of those receiving ASA404. He also identified four other possible reasons: (i) staging migration; (ii) the fact that twenty five per cent of the Phase III patient population were Asian, compared to almost none in the Phase II trial and that these patients typically have better outcomes than comparable western ones do; (iii) greater use of subsequent therapies after first line treatment (for example, the use of subsequent therapy was 56 per cent in both arms of ATTRACT I, which was higher than the comparable ECOG trial 4599, where subsequent therapy was reported in 46 per cent of patients in the bevacizumab + carboplatin + paclitaxel arm and in 43 per cent in the control carboplatin + paclitaxel arm); (iv) a slightly higher dose of paclitaxel was used in ATTRACT I (200 mg/m^2) as compared with the predecessor Phase II study dose of 175 mg/m^2.

6   The **taxanes** are a group of drugs which includes paclitaxel (Taxol) and docetaxel (Taxotere). They prevent the growth of cancer cells by affecting cell structures called microtubules, which play an important role in cell function. In normal cell growth, the structural rearrangement of microtubules, to form a supporting "scaffold," is an important part of cell division. Taxanes stop microtubules from breaking down and rearranging properly. This prevents cancer cells from growing and dividing in an efficient manner, eventually leading to cell death.

Taxanes are widely used in in a range of solid tumors, including breast, ovarian, lung and prostate cancer.

[7]   Antisoma Press Release. Antisoma announces departure of Chief Operating Officer, Dr Ursula Ney, and restructuring of business. 01 April 2010.

[8]   **Name changed** to fictional one.

[9]   **Name changed** to fictional one.

[10]   Keefe A. *et al*. Aptamers as Therapeutics. Nature Reviews Drug Discovery, 2010; 9: 537-550.

[11]   **Monoclonal antibodies** used as anti-cancer drugs vary in their chemical structure. The earliest examples were derived from mice (using *hybridoma technology*, which utilised mouse antibody producing cells) and had an almost exclusively murine composition. Murine antibodies end in the suffix –**omab**. However, they had the drawback of being quickly recognised as foreign substances, when injected into humans and so were rapidly inactivated in the body. This later led to the development of *chimeric* antibodies (suffix –**ximab**), where a substantial portion (about sixty five per cent) of the mouse antibody structure was modified to incorporate a human component. These antibodies tended to produce less of an immunological response and so resulted in more prolonged efficacy. Subsequently, *humanised antibodies* (suffix –**zumab**), which are about 95 per cent equivalent to a naturally occurring human antibody, have become widely available. This has arisen from technical advances using recombinant DNA to create gene segments capable of producing the desired antibody. These gene segments are isolated and cloned into mammalian cell cultures which can be grown in a tank. The antibody proteins produced from the DNA of the cloned genes can then be harvested *en masse*.

Most recently, *fully human* antibodies (suffix –**umab**) have emerged, using transgenic mice or phage display libraries as a source of production. The more foreign and less human an antibody is, the greater the probability of eliciting an immune reaction, particularly upon repeated administration, which can severely limit the efficacy and duration of effect of the antibody.

[12]   Kelland L. & Ireson C. Discovery and development of anticancer aptamers. Mol Cancer Ther, 2006; 5:2957-2962.

[13]   http://www.browncancercenter.org/about-bcc/message-from-the-director.

[14]   Laber D. *et al*. Extended phase I study of AS1411 in renal and non-small cell lung cancers. J Clin Oncol, ASCO Annual Meeting Proceedings, 2006; Part I. Vol 24, No.18S (June 20 Supplement): 13098.

[15]   **Tyrosine kinases** are a family of enzymes which act as important mediators of the cellular signalling cascade. They play key roles in diverse biological processes such as growth, differentiation, metabolism and apoptosis, in response to both external and internal stimuli. There

are over ninety tyrosine kinases which have been identified so far. About two thirds of these span the cell membrane, thus having an extracellular receptor, whilst the remainder are located within the cytoplasm of the cell and thus lack any kind of associated receptor. Examples of transmembrane receptor tyrosine kinases include EGFR, the closely related HER2 (ErbB-2/Neu), platelet-derived growth factor receptor (PDGFR), vascular endothelial growth factor (VEGF) receptor, and c-kit/stem cell factor receptor. An example of a non-receptor (cytoplasmic) tyrosine kinase is the Bcr-Abl fusion protein, involved in the development of chronic myelogenous leukaemia (CML).

Tyrosine kinases have been implicated in the pathophysiology of many types of malignancy, including: non-small-cell lung, head and neck, colorectal, renal, prostate, thyroid, breast and primary brain cancers and also chronic myeloid leukaemia.

Tyrosine kinase *inhibitors* (TKIs) are effective in the targeted treatment of various malignancies. There are broadly two types of tyrosine kinase inhibitory compound. One class includes antibodies, which can interact with the extra-cellular receptor portion of transmembrane tyrosine kinases. Examples include cetuximab (EGFR), panitumumab (EGFR), trastuzumab (HER2), pertuzumab (HER2 and HER3) and bevacizumab (VEGFR). The other category comprises small molecule inhibitors which act on the intracellular portion of transmembrane tyrosine kinases, or on cytoplasmic non-receptor tyrosine kinases. Imatinib was the first to these to be introduced and it was followed by drugs such axitinib, bosutinib, cediranib, dasatinib, erlotinib, gefitinib, imatinib, lapatinib, lestaurtinib, nilotinib, pazopanib, semaxanib, sorafenib, sunitinib, and vandetanib. Although they share the same mechanism of action, namely inhibition of tyrosine kinase, they differ from each other in the spectrum of targeted kinases they interact with.

The diversity of malignant diseases associated with abnormal tyrosine kinase activation and the relative success of many tyrosine kinase inhibitors, in cancers which are largely refractory to conventional chemotherapy, make TKIs one of the most important types of anti-cancer therapy to have emerged over the last decade or so.

[16] The **mammalian target of rapamycin (mTOR)** is an enzyme, like the tyrosine kinase family but of a different class, known as *serine/threonine protein kinases*. These play an important role in regulating cell growth, cell proliferation, cell motility, cell survival, protein synthesis, and gene regulation. Not surprisingly therefore, abnormal mTOR activity is thought to be involved in the initiation of many cancers.

There are a number of mTOR inhibitors in development, although the two most advanced are temsirolimus and everolimus. Temsirolimus is approved for use in advanced kidney cancer patients with poor prognostic features. Everolimus is approved for use in a range of tumor types including kidney cancer, a particular form of pancreatic cancer (pancreatic neuroendocrine tumor), HER2-negative breast cancer (when combined with hormonal therapy) and tumors arising as a complication of a rare genetic disorder known as tuberous sclerosis complex.

[17] Merseburger A. *et al.* Sorafenib reveals efficacy in sequential treatment of metastatic renal cell cancer. Expert Rev Anticancer Ther, 2009; 9: 1429–1434.

[18] **Erbitux (cetuximab)** was developed by the New Jersey biotech Imclone Systems, before the company was acquired by Lilly in 2008. It is a monoclonal antibody widely used in colorectal and head & neck cancer. It targets and blocks a receptor on the surface of cancer cells, called the Epidermal Growth Factor Receptor (EGFR). Mutations affecting EGFR expression, or activity, result in over stimulation of cell proliferation and contribute to the development of cancer. EGFR is a member of the *ErbB family of receptors*, which consists of four closely related receptor tyrosine kinases: **EGFR** (**HER1**, ErbB-1), **HER2** (ErbB-2), the target for Herceptin, **HER3** (ErbB-3) and **HER4** (ErbB-4).

EGFR on the *surface* of the cell is linked to a growth stimulating tyrosine kinase enzyme on the *inside* of the cell. A number of small molecule tyrosine kinase inhibitors, such as erlotinib (Tarceva) and gefitinib (Iressa) inhibit this particular tyrosine kinase and so have similar effects to cetuximab.

[19] Tol J. *et al.* Chemotherapy, Bevacizumab, and Cetuximab in Metastatic Colorectal Cancer. N Engl J Med, 2009; 360:563-572. Progression free survival was 10.7 months in the group receiving Avastin and chemotherapy, versus 9.4 months in those allocated to Erbitux, Avastin and chemotherapy. It appeared from this study that patients with a particular tumor genetic abnormality called the *KRAS* mutation did particularly badly, when cetuximab was added on top of Avastin and chemotherapy, compared to patients without the mutation.

[20] The **RECORD-1** trial eventually showed only a modest two month improvement when everolimus was compared to placebo (4 months v 1.9 months) in kidney cancer patients who'd progressed on sunitinib or sorafenib: Motzer R. *et al.* Efficacy of everolimus in advanced renal carcinoma: a double-blind, randomised, placebo-controlled phase III trial. Lancet, 2008; 372:449-456.

[21] Antisoma Press Release. Antisoma starts Phase II trial of AS1411 in acute myeloid leukaemia. 6 August 2007.

[22] Löwenberg B. *et al.* Cytarabine dose for Acute Myeloid Leukaemia. New Eng J Med, 2011; 364:1027-1036.

[23] Stuart R. *et al.* Randomized Phase II trial of the nucleolin targeting aptamer AS1411 combined with high-dose cytarabine in

relapsed/refractory acute myeloid leukemia (AML). J Clin Oncol, 2009; 27:15s (suppl; abstr 7019).

24   Antisoma Press Release. Antisoma starts Phase II trial of AS1411 in renal cancer. 04 September 2008.

25   Rosenberg J. *et al.* A Phase II, single-arm study of AS1411 in metastatic renal cell carcinoma (RCC). J Clin Oncol, 2010; 28:15s, (suppl; abstr 4590).

26   Antisoma Press Release. AS1411 shows activity in kidney cancer but AML remains priority. 16 December 2009.

CHAPTER FIVE

1   Gibson G. *et al.* Creation of a Bacterial Cell Controlled by a Chemically Synthesised Genome. Science, 2010; 329: 52-56.

2   How scientists made 'artificial life'. BBC News. 20 May 2010.
http://news.bbc.co.uk/1/hi/sci/tech/8695992.stm.

3   Clive Cookson. Let there be life. Financial Times. 21 May 2010.

4   Waxman S & Anderson K. History of the Development of Arsenic Derivatives in Cancer Therapy. The Oncologist, 2001; 6:3-10.

5   Ebers G. Papyrus Ebers: Die Maasse und das Kapitel über die Augenkrankheiten, Hirzel Verlag, Stuttgart, 1889.
http://www.archive.org/details/papyrusebersdie00ebergoog.

6   Zhang X. *et al.* Arsenic trioxide controls the fate of the PML-RAR alpha oncoprotein by directly binding PML. Science, 2010; 328:240-243.

7   Mirand E. Legacy and History of Roswell Park Cancer Institute 1898-1998. Virginia Beach, VA: The Donning Company Publishers. 2004.

8   Tyzzer E. Present Status of Research. The Caroline Brewer Croft Fund: Cancer Commission. The Medical School of Harvard University Boston. 10 November 1905.

9   Clowes G. Jr. George Alexander Clowes, PhD, DSc, LLD (1877-1958): A Man of Science for All Seasons. J Surg Oncol, 1981; 18:197-217.

10   Ewing J. Neoplastic Disease; A Treatise on Tumors. WB Saunders, London. 1922.

11   Patterson G. The Dread Disease. Cancer and Modern American Culture. Harvard University Press, 1989.

12   Blair Bell W. The Medical Treatment of Cancer. The Lancet, 1922; ii:1005.

13   Anon. Some Aspects of the Cancer Problem. Arch Intern Med (Chic), 1930; 46(5):898-899.

14   **The National Institutes of Health** (NIH), dating back to 1887, is part of the US Department of Health and Human Sciences. It is the US government's medical research agency, occupying a main campus in Bethesda, Maryland, where it employs over 6000 scientists. The campus is also home to the NIH Clinical Center, the largest hospital in the world totally dedicated to clinical research.

The NIH has an annual budget in excess of *thirty billion* dollars, of which over 80 per cent goes to more than 300,000 research personnel at over 2,500 universities and research institutions throughout the US and other parts of the world. The NIH is made up of 27 Institutes and Centers, each with a specific research agenda, often focusing on particular diseases or body systems. The National Cancer Institute is part of the NIH.

The mission of the **NIH** is to "seek fundamental knowledge about the nature and behaviour of living systems and the application of that knowledge to enhance health, lengthen life, and reduce the burdens of illness and disability": www.nih.gov.

[15] http://www.cancer.gov/aboutnci/overview/mission.

[16] Dr Murray Shear Dies: Father of Chemotherapy. The NIH Record. 11 October 1983.

[17] Latosińska J & Latosińska M. Anticancer Drug Discovery—From Serendipity to Rational Design, Drug Discovery, (Ed.) El-Shemy H. ISBN: 978-953-51-0906-8, InTech, 2013.

[18] Beatson G. On Treatment of Inoperable Cases of Carcinoma of the Mamma: Suggestions for a New Method of Treatment, with Illustrative Cases. Lancet, 1896; 148:162-165.

[19] Obituary: Nobel Prize winner Huggins: "Discovery is our business. The University of Chicago Chronicle. 23 January 1997.

[20] University of Chicago. Press Release. Charles B Huggins MD, 1901-1997. 13 January 1997.

[21] Huggins C. *et al*. The effect of castration on advanced carcinoma of the prostate gland. Arch Surg, 1941; 43:209-223.

[22] Orange V. Coningham: A Biography of Air Marshal Sir Arthur Coningham. Methuen, London. 1990.

[23] Bari Revisited: A thesis by Curt Maynard. 2007. http://www.mathaba.net/news/?x=553328.

[24] Winternitz M. Collected studies on the pathology of war gas poisoning from the Department of Pathology and Bacteriology, Medical Science Section, Chemical Warfare Service, under the direction of M.C. Winternitz. Yale University Press, 1920.

[25] Goodman L. *et al*. Nitrogen Mustard Therapy. Use of Methyl-Bis(Beta-Chloroethyl)amine Hydrochloride and Tris(Beta-Chloroethyl)amine Hydrochloride for Hodgkin's Disease, Lymphosarcoma, Leukemia and Certain Allied and Miscellaneous Disorders. Journal of the American Medical Association, 1946; 3:132.

[26] Wilkinson J. & Fletcher F. Effect of beta-Chlorethylamine in Leukaemia, Hodgkin's Disease and Polycythaemia Vera: report on eighteen cases. The Lancet, 1947; 250: 540-545.

[27] Adair F. & Bagg H. Experimental and Clinical Studies on the Treatment

Of Cancer By Dichloroethylsulphide (Mustard Gas). Annals of Surgery, 1931; 93(1):190-199.

28 Dameshek W. *et al*. Nitrogen Mustard Therapy in Hodgkin's Disease. Analysis of 50 consecutive cases. Blood, 1949; 338-379.

29 Woods D. The relation of p-aminobenzoic acid to the mechanism of the action of sulphanilamide. Br J Exp Pathol, 1940; 21: 74–90.

30 Lewisohn R. The importance of the proper dosage of sodium citrate in blood transfusions. Ann Surgery, 1916; 24:618-623.

31 Leuchtenberger R. *et al*. The influence of "folic acid" on spontaneous breast cancers in mice. Science, 1945; 101:46.

32 **The International Cancer Research Foundation** was formed in Philadelphia in 1932 by an American businessman and entrepreneur William Donner, after his son had died of cancer in 1929. In 1945, it was renamed the William H Donner Foundation. The Foundation, now based in New York, provides grants to invited applicants only, to support research in cancer medicine.

33 New York Herald-Tribune. 09 August 1948.

34 http://massmoments.org/moment.cfm?mid=169.

35 Farber S. A lipid metabolism disorder -disseminated "lipogranulomomatosis" – a syndrome with similarity to, and important difference from Niemann-Pick and Hand-Schüller-Christian disease. Am J Dis Child, 1952; 84: 499-500.

36 The first published description of a case of leukemia in the medical literature dates to 1827, when French physician Alfred-Armand Velpeau described a 63-year-old florist who developed an illness characterized by fever, weakness, urinary stones, and substantial enlargement of the liver and spleen. Velpeau noted the blood of this patient had a consistency "like gruel," and speculated the appearance of the blood was due to white corpuscles. In 1845, a series of patients who died with enlarged spleens and changes in the "colors and consistencies of their blood" was reported by the Edinburgh pathologist John Bennett who used the term "leucocythemia" to describe this pathological condition. (Bennett J. Two cases of hypertrophy of the spleen and liver, in which death took place from suppuration of blood. Edinburgh Med Surg J, 1845; 64: 413).

37 Farber S. *et al*. Action of pteroylglutamic acid conjugates on man. Science, 1947; 106:619-621.

38 **Folic acid supplementation** has been used in many countries to help prevent spinal and other birth defects. There is however still an ongoing debate about whether folic acid given in this way results in a higher subsequent incidence of some cancers, such as colorectal and prostate carcinoma. The debate was recently summarised in a meta-analysis review of published trials examining this: Vollset S. *et al*. Effects of folic

acid supplementation on overall and site-specific cancer incidence during the randomised trials: meta-analyses of 50 000 individuals. Lancet Online, 25 January 2013. http://www.thelancet.com/journals/lancet/article/PIIS0140-6736 (12)62001-7/abstract.

39 Farber S. *et al.* Temporary remissions in acute leukaemia in children produced by folic acid antagonist 4-aminopteroyl-glutamic acid. New Engl J Med, 1948; 23: 787-793.

40 Farber S. Some observations on the effect of folic acid antagonists on acute leukaemia and other forms of intractable cancer. Blood, 1949; 4:160-167.

41 http://www.dana-farber.org/About-Us/History-and-Milestones.aspx.

42 Dameshek W. *et al.* Folic acid antagonists in the treatment of acute and subacute leukemia. Blood, 1950; 5:898-915.

43 Known today as Variety, The Children's Charity.

44 The Dana Foundation, based in New York, is a private philanthropic organisation founded in 1950 and named after Charles A Dana, a businessman from New York State.

45 The Eastern Cooperative Oncology Group (ECOG) was established in 1955 as one of the first cooperative groups launched to perform multi-center cancer clinical trials. Funded primarily by the National Cancer Institute (NCI), ECOG has evolved from a five member consortium of institutions on the East Coast to one of the largest clinical cancer research organizations in the U.S. with almost 6000 physicians, nurses, pharmacists, statisticians, and clinical research associates (CRAs) from the US, Canada, and South Africa. Institutional members include universities, medical centers, Community Clinical Oncology Programs (CCOPs), and Cooperative Group Outreach Programs (CGOPs). These institutions work toward the common goal of controlling, effectively treating and ultimately curing cancer. Research results are provided to the world-wide medical community through scientific publications and professional meetings.
Currently, ECOG has more than 90 active clinical trials in all types of adult malignancies. Annual accrual is 6,000 patients, with more than 20,000 patients in follow-up.
http://ecog.dfci.harvard.edu/general/intro.html.

46 Shear M. Invasion of the Ivory Tower- the AACR faces its second half century: Presidential Address. Cancer Res, 1969; 29:1319-324.

47 C.P. Snow. The Two Cultures. New Statesman. 06 October 1956.

48 Horwitz S. *et al.* Promotion of microtubule assembly in vitro by taxol. Nature, 1979; 227:665-667.

49 Legha S. *et al.* Phase I study of taxol using a 5-day intermittent schedule. J Clin Oncol, 1986; 5: 762-766.

50 Rowinsky E. *et al*. Phase II study of taxol in advanced epithelial malignancies. Proc Assoc Clin Oncol, 1988; 7:136.

51 www.phytonbiotech.com

52 Li M. *et al*. Effects of methotrexate therapy upon choriocarcinoma and chorioadenoma. Proc Soc Exp Biol Med, 1956; 93: 361.

53 Li M. *et al*. Therapy of choriocarcinoma and related trophoblastic tumors with folic acid and purine antagonists. N Engl J Med, 1958; 259:66–74.

54 De Vita V. & Chu E. A History of Cancer Chemotherapy. Cancer Res, 2008; 68:8643-8653.

55 Li M. *et al*. Effects of combined drug therapy on metastatic cancer of the testis. JAMA, 1969; 174:1291.

56 Farber S. *et al*. The effect of ACTH in acute leukemia in childhood. In: Mote JR, editor. Proceedings of the First Clinical ACTH Conference. New York: McGraw-Hill-Blakiston; 1950. p. 328–30.

57 Frei E. *et al*. Studies of Sequential and Combination Antimetabolite Therapy in Acute Leukaemia: 6-Mercaptopurine and Methotrexate. Blood, 1961; 18:431-454.

58 Perrin J. *et al*. Intravenous methotrexate (amethopterin) therapy in the treatment of acute leukaemia. Pediatrics, 1963; 31:833-839.

59 Patlak M. Breakthroughs in Bioscience. Targeting Leukaemia. From Bench to Bedside. Federation of American Societies for Experimental Biology, 2001.

60 Furth M. & Kahn J. Transmission of leukaemia to mice with a single cell. Am J Cancer, 1937; 31:276-282.

61 Skipper H. Perspectives in cancer chemotherapy: therapeutic design. Cancer Res, 1964; 24:1295-1302.

62 Simpson-Herren L. & Wheeler G. Howard Earle Skipper. In memoriam (1915-2006). Cancer Research, 2006; 66:12035.

63 Law L. Origin of the resistance of leukemic cells to folic acid antagonists. Nature, 1952; 169:628–629.

64 Val Jones. Extraordinary Physicians Honored For Advances In Medicine. Better Health. 24 March 2009.

65 Gaydos L. *et al*. The quantitative relation between platelet count and hemorrhage in patients with acute leukemia. N Engl J Med, 1962; 266:905-909.

66 DeVita V. *et al*. *Pneumocystis carinii* pneumonia: successful diagnosis and treatment of two patients with associated malignant processes. N Engl J Med, 1969; 280:287-291.

67 Freireich E. *et al*. Quadruple combination therapy (VAMP) for acute lymphocytic leukemia of childhood. Proc Am Assoc Cancer Res, 1964; 5:20.

68 Holland J. Hopes for tomorrow versus realities of today: therapy and

prognosis in acute lymphocytic leukemia of childhood. Pediatrics, 1970; 45:191-193.

69   Skipper H. *et al.* Experimental evaluation of potential anticancer agents. XII. On the criteria and kinetics associated with "curability" of experimental leukemia. Cancer Chemother Rep, 1964; 35:1–111.

70   Dameshek W. Therapy of acute leukaemia. Blood, 1965; 26:220-225.

71   Pinkel D. *et al.* Drug dose and remission duration in childhood lymphocytic leukemia. Cancer, 1971; 27:247–56.

72   DeVita V. *et al.* Intensive combination chemotherapy and X-irradiation in the treatment of Hodgkin's disease. Proc Am Assoc Cancer Res, 1965; 6:15.

73   DeVita V. & Serpick A. Combination chemotherapy in the treatment of advanced Hodgkin's disease. Proc Am Assoc Cancer Res, 1967; 8:13.

74   DeVita V. *et al.* Combination chemotherapy in the treatment of advanced Hodgkin's disease. Ann Intern Med, 1970; 73:881–895.

75   DeVita V. *et al.* A decade of combination chemotherapy for advanced Hodgkin's disease. Cancer, 1972; 30:1495–1504.

76   Canellos G. *et al.* Cyclical combination chemotherapy in the treatment of advanced breast carcinoma. Proc Am Assoc Cancer Res, 1974; 15:148.

77   Salmon S. Kinetic rationale for adjuvant chemotherapy for cancer. In: Salmon SE, Jones SE, editors. Adjuvant therapy of cancer. Amsterdam: Elsevier/North Holland Biomedical Press; 1977.

78   Nearly thirty per cent of women with cancer confined to the breast and seventy five per cent of women with nearby lymph node involvement will ultimately relapse. This is due to the residual presence of micrometastases, which are clinically occult tumors remaining after surgery. These have the potential to metastasise, resulting in significant morbidity and mortality. **Adjuvant treatment** is the administration of additional therapy after primary surgery to kill or inhibit micrometastases. Primary surgery for breast cancer is accomplished by lumpectomy followed by whole-breast irradiation or by mastectomy. Subsequent adjuvant treatment may include local irradiation after mastectomy, systemic therapy with cytotoxic chemotherapy, or endocrine therapy.

79   Bonadonna G. *et al.* Combination chemotherapy of Hodgkin's disease with adriamycin, bleomycine, vinblastine and imidazole carboxamide versus MOPP. Cancer, 1975:36, 252–259.

80   Santoro A. *et al.* Alternating drug combinations in the treatment of advanced Hodgkin's disease. New Engl J Med, 1982; 306:770–775.

81   Fisher B. *et al.* Surgical adjuvant chemotherapy in cancer of the breast: results of a decade of cooperative investigation. Ann Surg, 1968; 168:337–56.

82   Fisher B. *et al.* L phenylalanine mustard (L-PAM) in the management of primary breast cancer. N Engl J Med, 1975; 292:110–22.

83   Bonadonna G. *et al*. Combination chemotherapy as an adjunct treatment in operable breast cancer. N Engl J Med, 1976; 294:405–10.

84   Fisher B. *et al*. Five-year results of a randomized clinical trial comparing total mastectomy and segmental mastectomy with or without radiation in the treatment of breast cancer. N Engl J Med, 1985; 312: 665-73.

85   John Crewdson. Fraud In Breast Cancer Study. Doctor Lied On Data For Decade. Chicago Tribune. 13 March 1994.

86   Antman K. & Gale R. Advanced Breast Cancer: High-Dose Chemotherapy and Bone Marrow Autotransplants. Ann Intern Med, 1988; 108:570-574.

87   Berry D. *et al*. High-dose chemotherapy with autologous stem-cell support as adjuvant therapy in breast cancer: Overview of 15 randomized trials. J Clin Oncol, 2011; 29:3214–3223.

88   Berry D. *et al*. High-dose chemotherapy with autologous hematopoietic stem-cell transplantation in metastatic breast cancer: Overview of six randomized trials. J Clin Oncol, 2011; 29:3224–3231.

89   A few years after it was originally withdrawn, **thalidomide** was reintroduced as treatment for a complication of leprosy called erythema nodosum leprosum (ENL). It soon became the treatment of choice for the management of ENL reactions in leprosy and regulatory authorities granted exemption from licensing requirements to enable doctors to obtain limited supplies of thalidomide under strictly controlled circumstances for use in named patients. However, thalidomide's effectiveness in controlling neuritis, the major cause of permanent disabilities in leprosy, turned out to be modest at best. This limitation, combined with the difficulties of avoiding pregnancy in many of the under-developed countries it was used in, meant that the drug was eventually superseded by steroids and then more specific therapies, such as clofazimine. Unfortunately however, even today, a number of thalidomide babies continue to be born each year reflecting regulatory insufficiency and widespread use under inadequate supervision.

90   Palumbo A. *et al*. Thalidomide for treatment of multiple myeloma: 10 years later. Blood, 2008; 111:3968-3977.

91   DeVita V. On special initiatives, critics and the National Cancer Program. Cancer Treat Rep, 1984; 68:1–4.

92   Scott A. *et al*. Monoclonal antibodies in cancer therapy. Cancer Immunity, 2012; 12:14-21.

93   Bates S. Antibody Conjugates: The Future Is Now. Clin Cancer Res, 2011; 17:6388.

94   Verma S. *et al*. Trastuzumab Emtansine for HER2-Positive Advanced Breast Cancer. N Engl J Med, 2012; 367:1783-91.

95   Hurvitz S. *et al*. Phase II Randomized Study of Trastuzumab Emtansine Versus Trastuzumab Plus Docetaxel in Patients With Human Epidermal

Growth Factor Receptor 2–Positive Metastatic Breast Cancer. J Clin Oncol, 2013; 31: online. 04 February 2013.

[96] Kontermann R. (Ed.). Bispecific Antibodies. Springer-Verlag, Berlin. 2011.

[97] An **oncogene** is a gene that, when mutated or expressed at high levels, helps turn a normal cell into a tumor cell. Most damaged cells in the body normally undergo a programmed form of death known as apoptosis (cell suicide). Activated oncogenes can cause those cells to survive and proliferate instead. This then initiates a cancer causing cascade, as the damaged cell starts to divide uncontrollably. However, most oncogenes seem to require an additional step, such as mutations in another gene, or environmental factors, such as viral infection, to cause cancer.

Since the 1970s, dozens of oncogenes have been identified in human cancer. Many cancer drugs targeting these DNA sequences and their products are now in development.

[98] Chapman P. *et al*. Improved Survival with Vemurafenib in Melanoma with BRAF V600E Mutation. New Engl J Med, 2011; 364: 2507-2516.

[99] **BRCA1 and BRCA2** are human genes that belong to a class known as *tumor suppressor genes*. These are genes that protect a cell from one step on the path to cancer formation. When one of these genes is mutated to cause a loss or reduction in its function, the cell can progress to cancer, usually in combination with other genetic changes. Tumor suppressor genes play a critical role in regulating when cells are allowed to divide and increase in number. When DNA damage is detected in a cell, some tumor suppressor genes can stop the cell from multiplying until the damage is repaired. Also, specific tumor suppressor genes can stimulate cells with damaged DNA to commit apoptosis ("cell suicide"). When tumor suppressor genes don't function correctly, the cells with DNA damage continue to divide and can accumulate further DNA damage that can eventually lead to the formation of a cancer cell.

In normal cells, BRCA1 and BRCA2 help ensure the stability of the cell's genetic material (DNA) and help prevent uncontrolled cell growth. Mutation of these genes has been linked to the development of hereditary breast and ovarian cancer.

The names BRCA1 and BRCA2 stand for **br**east **ca**ncer susceptibility gene 1 and **br**east **ca**ncer susceptibility gene 2, respectively.

A woman's lifetime risk of developing breast and/or ovarian cancer is greatly increased if she inherits a mutation in BRCA1 or BRCA2. Such women have an increased risk of developing breast and/or ovarian cancer at an early age (before menopause) and often have multiple, close family members who have been diagnosed with these diseases. BRCA1 mutations may also increase a woman's risk of developing cervical, uterine, pancreatic, and colon cancer. BRCA2 mutations may additionally increase the risk of pancreatic cancer, stomach cancer, gallbladder and bile duct cancer and melanoma.

Men with BRCA1 mutations also have an increased risk of breast cancer and, possibly, of pancreatic cancer, testicular cancer, and early-onset prostate cancer. However, male breast cancer, pancreatic cancer, and prostate cancer appear to be more strongly associated with BRCA2 gene mutations

[100] **PARP inhibitors** are best able to achieve selectivity in tumor cell killing when used in tumors that *already* harbour DNA repair defects. Simultaneous dysfunction of two DNA damage repair (DDR) pathways, termed *synthetic lethality*, decreases the ability of tumor cells to withstand the DNA damage produced during normal cellular replication. Tumors harbouring the BRCA1 or BRCA2 mutation are already defective in one particular DNA repair pathway, which normally mends *double stranded* DNA damage. This means the cell becomes completely reliant on the remaining DNA repair mechanism, which mends *single stranded* DNA injuries. PARP inhibitors block this latter pathway, effectively leaving the cell defenceless to DNA damage of any sort.

[101] Tutt A. *et al*. Oral poly (ADP-ribose) polymerase inhibitor olaparib in patients with BRCA1 or BRCA2 mutations and advanced breast cancer: a proof-of-concept trial. Lancet, 2010; 376: 235-244.

[102] Ledermann J. *et al*. Olaparib Maintenance Therapy in Platinum-Sensitive Relapsed Ovarian Cancer. New Engl J Med, 2012; 366: 1382-1392.

[103] Fei S. *et al*. RAS Mutations in Cutaneous Squamous-Cell Carcinomas in Patients Treated with BRAF Inhibitors. N Engl J Med, 2012; 366:207-215.

[104] Astra Zeneca Press Release. AstraZeneca updates on olaparib and TC-5214 development programmes. 20 December 2011.

[105] Vasella D & Slater R. Magic Cancer Bullet: How a Tiny Orange Pill Is Rewriting Medical History. Harper Collins, New York. 2003.

[106] Nowel P. & Hungerford D. A minute chromosome in human chronic granulocytic leukemia. Science, 1960; 132:1497–501.

[107] Druker B. *et al*. Activity of a specific inhibitor of the BCR-ABL tyrosine kinase in the blast crisis of chronic myeloid leukemia and acute lymphoblastic leukemia with the Philadelphia chromosome. N Engl J Med, 2001; 344:1038–42.

[108] Mauro M. Defining and managing imatinib resistance. ASH Education Book, 2006; 2006:1 219-225.

[109] Tsimberidou A. *et al*. Farnsyltransferase inhibitors: where are we now? Expert Opin Investig Drugs, 2010; 19:1569-80.

[110] Harousseau J. *et al*. A randomized Phase 3 study of tipifarnib compared with best supportive care, including hydroxyurea, in the treatment of

newly diagnosed acute myeloid leukemia in patients 70 years or older. Blood, 2009; 114:1166-1173.

[111] Fowler N. *et al*. Lenalidomide and rituximab for untreated indolent lymphoma: final results of a phase II study. Program and abstracts of the 54th American Society of Hematology Annual Meeting and Exposition; December 8-11, 2012; Atlanta, Georgia. Abstract 901.

[112] Bang Y. *et al*. Clinical activity of the oral ALK inhibitor PF-02341066 in ALK-positive patients with non-small cell lung cancer (NSCLC). J Clin Oncol, 2010; 28: (suppl: abstr 3).

[113] About eighty per cent of **lung cancers** are non-small cell and approximately fifteen per cent are small cell. The remaining five per cent are accounted for by rare variants (including carcinoid tumors, adenoid cystic carcinomas, hamartomas, lymphomas, and sarcomas). About forty per cent of lung cancers are of the *adenocarcinoma* type, which usually originates in peripheral lung tissue. Most cases of these are associated with smoking. It is however also the commonest form of lung cancer in people who've never smoked (non-smokers accounting for ten to fifteen per cent of lung cancers overall). Adenocarcinomas can be present for a relatively long period, before producing symptoms such as shortness of breath or fatigue. *Squamous-cell carcinoma* accounts for about twenty five to thirty per cent of lung tumors. These typically occur close to large airways. A hollow cavity and associated necrosis are commonly found at the centre of the tumor. Squamous carcinomas tend to produce symptoms, such as coughing or coughing up blood, fairly early on. Ten to fifteen per cent of cases are accounted for by *large-cell* carcinoma. These are so named because the cancer cells are large, with prominent nuclei.

Small cell lung cancer is also known as *oat cell* carcinoma. It is very strongly associated with smoking, with less than five per cent of cases being in non-smokers. It is more aggressive than non-small cell disease with a tendency to spread more rapidly and widely to other regions including lymph nodes, bone, brain, adrenal glands, and the liver.

[114] Giaccone G. *et al*. Gefitinib in combination with gemcitabine and cisplatin in advanced non-small-cell lung cancer: a phase III trial—INTACT 1. J Clin Oncol, 2004; 22:777–784.

[115] Herbst R. *et al*. Gefitinib in combination with paclitaxel and carboplatin in advanced non-small-cell lung cancer: a phase III trial—INTACT 2. J Clin Oncol, 2004; 22:785–794.

[116] **Epithelial Growth Factor Receptor (EGFR) is a member of the tyrosine kinases** family of enzymes, which act as important mediators of the cellular signalling cascade. They play key roles in diverse biological processes such as growth, differentiation, metabolism and apoptosis, in response to both external and internal stimuli.

EGFR is a receptor which is activated by specific agents (ligands) which bind to it, including epidermal growth factor and transforming growth factor alpha.

EGFR is one of the transmembrane receptor tyrosine kinases, which also includes the closely related HER2 (ErbB-2/Neu), platelet-derived growth factor receptor (PDGFR), vascular endothelial growth factor receptor (VEGFR) and c-kit/stem cell factor receptor.

In general, tyrosine kinases have been implicated in the pathophysiology of many types of malignancy, including: non-small-cell lung, head and neck, colorectal, renal, prostate, thyroid, breast and primary brain cancers and also chronic myeloid leukaemia.

Tyrosine kinase *inhibitors* (TKIs) are effective in the targeted treatment of various malignancies. There are broadly two types of tyrosine kinase inhibitory compound. One class includes antibodies, which can interact with the extra-cellular receptor portion of transmembrane tyrosine kinases. Examples include cetuximab (EGFR), panitumumab (EGFR), trastuzumab (HER2), pertuzumab (HER2 and HER3) and bevacizumab (VEGFR). The other category comprises small molecule inhibitors which act on the intracellular portion of transmembrane tyrosine kinases, or on cytoplasmic non-receptor tyrosine kinases. Gefitinib and erlotinib are examples of small molecules which act on the EGFR tyrosine kinase. EGFR appears to be particularly strongly implicated in the pathogenesis and propagation of head and neck and non-small cell lung cancer.

[117] Mok T. *et al.* Gefitinib or carboplatin-paclitaxel in pulmonary adenocarcinoma. New Engl J Med, 2009; 361:947–957.

The IPASS trial recruited only previously untreated patients in East Asia, who had advanced pulmonary adenocarcinoma and who were non-smokers or former light smokers.

The 12-month rates of progression-free survival were 24.9% with gefitinib and 6.7% with carboplatin-paclitaxel. In a subgroup of 261 patients who were *positive* for the epidermal growth factor receptor gene (EGFR) mutation, progression-free survival was significantly longer among those who received gefitinib than among those who received carboplatin-paclitaxel, whereas in a subgroup of 176 patients who were *negative* for the mutation, progression-free survival was significantly longer among those who received carboplatin-paclitaxel .

The objective response rate was seventy one per cent with gefitinib versus forty seven per cent with carboplatin–paclitaxel in the mutation *positive* subgroup and one per cent (one patient) versus twenty four per cent respectively, in the mutation *negative* subgroup.

Overall survival wasn't that different between those who did or didn't receive gefitinib.

[118] R. M Nixon. State of the Union Message to Congress. 22 January 1971.

CHAPTER SIX

[1] In **myelodysplastic syndrome** (MDS) cells in the bone marrow are damaged (dysplastic) and therefore have difficulty making new blood cells. Many of the blood cells that are formed by the damaged bone marrow cells are defective. The body rapidly destroys most of these abnormal blood cells, leaving the patient with low blood counts because there aren't enough normal blood cells.

In about one-third of patients, MDS can progress to acute myeloid leukemia and in the past, MDS was referred to as *pre-leukemia* or *smoldering leukemia*. Despite that, it was previously classified as a disease of low malignant potential, as the majority of patients do not go on to develop leukaemia. However, it is now recognised that MDS is a *clonal* disease, meaning that there is a large population of abnormal cells that all originate from a single, abnormal cell. These abnormal cells have the same genes and share common abnormal growth properties. Because of its clonal nature, MDS is now generally considered to be a malignant condition in its own right, independent of those patients who eventually progress to AML.

[2] **Anthracyclines** act by inhibiting an enzyme called *topoisomerase II*, which plays an important role in the division of cells. It acts by helping to unwind the normally tightly coiled DNA strands which make up a cell's chromosomes. By inactivating topoisomerase II, anthracyclines prevent normal chromosomal replication and as the cell can't then divide, it subsequently dies.

Anthracyclines such as idarubicin, doxorubicin, daunorubicin, epirubicin and mitoxantrone (an anthracycline analogue) are used in a very wide variety of haematological and solid tumor malignancies.

Alkylating agents are a different class of compound which act, as their name suggests, by chemically modifying DNA through the addition of a chemical *alkyl* group. This sufficiently damages the DNA such that the cell can't usually repair it and so the cell dies.

Examples of alkylating agents include cyclophosphamide, chlorambucil, melphalan, lomustine, ifosfamide and busulphan. Like anthracyclines, they are used in the treatment of a wide range of malignancies.

[3] Anderson J. *et al.* Outcome after induction chemotherapy for older patients with acute myeloid leukemia is not improved with mitoxantrone and etoposide compared to cytarabine and daunorubicin: a Southwest Oncology Group study. Blood, 2002; 100:3869-76.

[4] Godwin J. *et al.* A double-blind placebo-controlled trial of granulocyte colony-stimulating factor in elderly patients with previously untreated acute myeloid leukemia: a Southwest Oncology Group study (9031). Blood, 1998; 91:3607-15.

[5] Erba H. *et al.* Amonafide L-Malate (AS1413) in Combination with

Cytarabine Is Equally Effective in Older and Younger Patients with Secondary Acute Myeloid Leukemia (AML); Final Data From a Phase II Study. Blood, 2009; 114: Abstract No.1047.

[6] Code of Federal Regulations. 21CFR 312.32. IND Safety Reporting.

[7] A **clinical hold** is an order issued by FDA to the sponsor to delay a proposed clinical investigation, or to suspend an ongoing investigation. When a study is placed on clinical hold, no new subjects may be recruited to the study and placed on the investigational drug; patients already in the study should be taken off therapy involving the investigational drug unless specifically permitted by FDA in the interest of patient safety.

Clinical holds can be initiated by FDA, if they consider that any of the following criteria apply:

(i) Human subjects are or would be exposed to an unreasonable and significant risk of illness or injury; (ii) The clinical investigators named in the IND are not qualified by reason of their scientific training and experience to conduct the investigation described in the IND; (iii) The investigator brochure is misleading, erroneous, or materially incomplete; or (iv) The IND does not contain sufficient information to assess the risks to subjects of the proposed studies.

http://www.accessdata.fda.gov/scripts/cdrh/cfdocs/cfcfr/CFRSearch.cfm?fr=312.42.

[8] The **Council for International Organizations of Medical Sciences** (CIOMS) is an international, non-governmental, non-profit organization established jointly by WHO and UNESCO in 1949. Located in Geneva, its main aim is to facilitate and promote international activities in the field of biomedical sciences, especially when the participation of several international associations and national institutions is deemed necessary. www.cioms.ch.

[9] WHO-UMC Causality System.
http://www.who-umc.org/Graphics/24734.pdf.

[10] Löwenberg B. *et al*. High-Dose Daunorubicin in Older Patients with Acute Myeloid Leukaemia. New Engl J Med, 2009; 361:1235-1248.

[11] Fernandez H. *et al*. Anthracycline Dose Intensification in AML. New Engl J Med, 2009; 361:1249-1259.

[12] **MedDRA**: Medical Dictionary for Regulatory Activities. This is an internationally used set of terms relating to medical conditions, medicines and medical devices. It was created to assist regulators with sharing information. It is also used by industry, academics, health professionals and other organisations that communicate medical information. http://www.meddramsso.com/public_about_meddra.asp.

[13] Common Terminology Criteria for Adverse Events. (CTCAE) v.4.03. US Department of Health and Human Services. National Institutes of Health. National Cancer Institute. 14June 2010.

[14] Oken M. *et al*. Toxicity And Response Criteria Of The Eastern Cooperative Oncology Group. Am J Clin Oncol, 1982; 5:649-655.

CHAPTER SEVEN

[1] **Gene cloning** is the process in which a gene of interest is located and copied (cloned) out of DNA extracted from an organism. When DNA is extracted from an organism, all of its genes are extracted at one time and so the DNA contains thousands of different genes. The genetic engineer then needs find the one specific gene that encodes the specific protein of interest. This involves the generation of *gene libraries*, from which a specific gene can then be selected.

[2] **Genetic engineering**, also called genetic modification, is the direct manipulation of an organism's genome using biotechnology. New DNA may be inserted in the host genome by first isolating and copying the genetic material of interest using molecular cloning methods to generate a DNA sequence, or by synthesizing the DNA and then inserting this construct into the host organism.

[3] **Gene therapy** is an experimental technique that involves inserting genes into the cells of a patient. Normally a heavily modified virus is used to carry the gene to the cell and then insert it alongside the existing genes already present on the cell's chromosomes.

Three broad approaches which are commonly employed include: (i) replacing a mutated gene that causes disease with a healthy copy of the gene; (ii) inactivating or "knocking out" a mutated gene that is functioning improperly; (iii) adding a new gene into the body to help fight a disease.

Although gene therapy is a promising treatment option for a number of diseases (including inherited disorders, some types of cancer, and certain viral infections), the technique remains unproven and is largely being tested in diseases that currently have no cure.

[4] **Therapeutic cancer vaccines** are an emerging, experimental type of therapy designed to stimulate the immune system (the body's natural defence mechanism) to find and fight cancer cells. Cancer cells pose a special challenge to the immune system because unlike viruses and bacteria, they are frequently not recognized as intruders. They are the body's own cells that have mutated (changed). As mutant versions of normal, healthy cells, cancer cells can effectively hide themselves and often go undetected by the immune system. They are not *foreign* enough. Cancer cells generally express certain molecules (antigens) on their surface, which are not present on healthy cells. However, the immune system normally fails to recognize these antigens as something to which it should react. The theory behind therapeutic cancer vaccines is that they should stimulate the immune system to recognize these molecules

as foreign and generate a response to attack cells that express them. Once the immune system is able to identify cancer-specific antigens, it can specifically attack and destroy any cells containing these antigens, without damaging normal cells.

A cancer treatment vaccine uses cancer cells, parts of cells, or pure antigens to attempt to increase the immune response against cancer cells that are already in the body. Vaccines are often combined with other substances or cells called *adjuvants* that help boost the immune response even further.

To date however, clinical experience with therapeutic vaccines has shown modest effects at best. Because it can mutate and change its immune appearance so rapidly, it appears that cancer, for the moment at least, is managing to stay one step ahead.

[5] http://www.genecards.org/cgi-bin/listdiseasecards.pl?type=full

[6] French Anderson W. Steady Progress. Human Gene Therapy, 1991; 2:99-100.

[7] Ashanti de Silva remains alive. The gene therapy approach required her to undergo a repeat procedure every three to four months, due to the fact that the modified white cells die after this period of time and so new ones then need to have the gene inserted into them. She also continued to receive regular injections of *pegylated adenosine deaminase*, which was an external source of the missing enzyme, derived from bovine sources.

[8] Anderson was sentenced to fourteen years in prison by a California court on 2nd February 2007, having been found guilty of sexually molesting the teenage daughter of a colleague at the University of Southern California.
http://www.the-scientist.com/?articles.view/articleNo/24738/title/Colleagues-upset-by-Anderson-sentence.

[9] The NIH established the **Recombinant DNA Advisory Committee (RAC)** in 1974 in response to public concerns regarding the safety of manipulating genetic material through the use of recombinant DNA techniques. Although the RAC's membership and responsibilities have evolved over time with scientific understanding and developments in this technology, it continues to serve the NIH, as well as the scientific and lay publics, as a critically important forum for open, public deliberation on the panoply of scientific, ethical, and legal issues raised by recombinant DNA technology and its basic and clinical research applications. Over the course of the Committee's existence, transparency and access have been its defining characteristics, enabling public acceptance of a critically important technology and creating an environment in which science can advance in an informed, safe, and ethical manner: http://oba.od.nih.gov/rdna_rac/rac_about.html

[10] Batshaw M. *et al.* **Clinical Protocol:** Recombinant Adenovirus Gene

Transfer in Adults with Partial Ornithine Transcarbamylase Deficiency (OTCD). Human Gene Therapy, 1999; 10:2419-2437.

[11] **The Office for Human Research Protections (OHRP)** is a branch of the US Department of Health and Human Sciences, as is FDA. Its remit is the protection of the rights, welfare, and wellbeing of subjects involved in research conducted or supported by the U.S. Department of Health and Human Services (which includes FDA). OHRP helps ensure this by providing clarification and guidance, developing educational programs and materials, maintaining regulatory oversight, and providing advice on ethical and regulatory issues in biomedical and social-behavioural research. http://www.hhs.gov/ohrp/.

[12] Wilson J. Lessons learned from the gene therapy trial for ornithine transcarbamylase deficiency. Molecular Genetics and Metabolism, 2009; 96:151-157.

[13] http://www.accessdata.fda.gov/scripts/sda/sdDetailNavigation.cfm?sd= clincalinvestigatorsdisqualificationproceedings&id=CD5EDDB44D61 AA37E040A8C0754D57E1&rownum=12.

[14] Target Genetics Press Release. Targeted Genetics Completes Acquisition of Genovo and Initiates Collaboration With Biogen. 20 September 2000.

[15] FDA Talk Paper. FDA places temporary halt on gene therapy trials using retroviral vectors in blood stem cells. 14 January 2003. http://cmbi.bjmu.edu.cn/news/0301/59.htm

[16] Cavazzana-Calvo M. *et al*. Gene Therapy of Human Severe Combined Immunodeficiency (SCID)-X1 Disease. Science, 2000; 288:669-672.

[17] Kohn D. *et al*. Occurrence of leukaemia following gene therapy of X-linked SCID. Nature Rev Cancer, 2003; 3:477-488.
Eventually two more children would also manifest a leukaemia like condition, meaning that in total, four out of twenty treated patients developed this complication.
(See: http://www.unifr.ch/nfp37/adverse01.html)

[18] Target Genetics Press Release. Targeted Genetics Provides Update on Inflammatory Arthritis Phase I/II Trial. 26 July 2007.

[19] http://www.msnbc.msn.com/id/20820827/ns/health-health_care/t/giving-gene-therapy-wrong-reaction

[20] The **p53 gene** is a *tumor suppressor gene*, which means its activity stops the development of malignant transformations within cells. Mutations in p53 are found in most tumor types, and so contribute to the complex network of molecular events leading to tumor formation. P53 defects can also rarely occur as an inherited disorder which predisposes to cancer, usually resulting in several tumor types in early adulthood (Li-Fraumeni syndrome).
Normally, in the cell, p53 protein binds DNA, which in turn stimulates another gene to produce a protein called p21, which acts to prevent cells

passing through to the next stage of cell division. However, mutant p53 can no longer bind DNA in an effective way, and as a consequence, the p21 protein is not made available to act as the 'stop signal' for cell division. Thus cells divide uncontrollably and ultimately become cancerous.

[21] Peng Z. Current Status of Gendicine in China: Recombinant Human Ad-p53 Agent for Treatment of Cancers. Human Gene Therapy, 2005; 16:1016-1027.

[22] Gabrilovich D. INGN 201 (Advexin): adenoviral p53 gene therapy for cancer. Expert Opin Biol Ther, 2006; 6:823-32.

[23] Introgen Therapeutics Press Release. Advexin BLA Not Sufficiently Complete to File. 02 September 2008.

[24] **Oncolytic virotherapy** is based on the ability of viruses to effectively infect and kill tumor cells without destroying the normal tissues. The concept arose from observations over a hundred years ago that some tumors appeared to spontaneously regress, following a viral infection. While some viruses seem to have a natural preference for tumor cells, most require modifications to specifically enter and replicate in malignant cells. The viruses are genetically modified so that they can no longer suppress genes present in normal cells, which act to prevent viral replication. However, in malignant cells, which lack these suppressor genes, the virus is able to replicate unimpeded.

Oncolytic viruses exert their anti-tumor effect partly through lysis (the destruction of the cancer cell) and also through the associated release of tumor antigens, which in theory should provoke an immune response against the tumor. For this latter reason, many oncolytic viruses have a gene inserted into them which encodes for an immuno-stimulatory protein, such as GCSF (Granulocyte Macrophage Colony Stimulating Factor).

Clinical trials to date have employed a range of viruses, including adenovirus, reovirus, measles, herpes simplex, Newcastle disease virus and vaccinia. Experience has confirmed that oncolytic virotherapy appears to be well tolerated. Encouraging initial efficacy data have also been seen in a number of tumor types, for example Amgen's OncoVex in malignant melanoma. (Senzer N. *et al.* Phase II clinical trial with a second generation, GM-CSF encoding, oncolytic herpesvirus in unresectable metastatic melanoma. J Clin Oncol, 2009; 27:15s:suppl; abstr 9035).

[25] Yu W. & Fang H. Clinical trials with oncolytic adenovirus in China. Current Cancer Drug Targets, 2007; 7: 141-148.

[26] Kirn D. Clinical research results with dl1520 (Onyx-015), a replication-selective adenovirus for the treatment of cancer: what have we learned? Gene Therapy, 2001; 8: 89-98.

27 Gene Therapy Clinical Trials Worldwide.
    http://www.abedia.com/wiley/index.html

28 **The Human Genome Project (HGP)** was an international 13-year effort, which formally started in October 1990 and completed in 2003, to discover all the estimated 20,000-25,000 human genes and make them accessible for further biological study. The project was coordinated by the U.S. Department of Energy and the National Institutes of Health. Additional contributions came from Japan, France, Germany, China, and others.
    Additional project goals included the determination of the complete sequence of the 3 billion or so DNA subunits (bases) in the human genome. Parallel studies were also carried out in selected animal models, such as the bacterium E. coli and the mouse to help develop the technology to interpret human gene function.
    http://www.ornl.gov/sci/techresources/Human_Genome/home.shtml

29 See: http://www.genetherapynet.com/viral-vectors.html

30 Parkinson J. Essay On The Shaking Palsy. Sherwood, Neeley & Jones, London. 1817.

31 **Glybera** was eventually approved in Europe in the summer of 2012. This was however on the basis of "exceptional circumstances" which meant that heavy restrictions were placed on its use. This effectively left Glybera on parole, with the prospect of having its freedom revoked at any time in the future. It wasn't exactly a ringing endorsement of gene therapy but at least it was a big step in the right direction.

32 Hole N. & Stern P. Isolation and characterisation of 5T4, a tumour-associated antigen. Int J Cancer, 1990; 45:179-184.

33 **Heat shock proteins** are intra-cellular molecules, which occur normally but which become markedly increased, as the name implies, when the cell is exposed to exaggerated temperatures or other types of stress. They are frequently detected in high levels in tumor tissue and many malignant cells appear to depend on elevated concentrations of heat shock proteins for their survival. They enhance the growth of cancer cells and protect tumors from treatments such as drugs or surgery. In particular, *heat shock protein 90* functions to stabilize many of the oncogenes and growth promoting proteins in cancer cells. They are therefore potentially important molecules in the development of cancer and are seen as possible targets in cancer therapy. Heat shock proteins also induce an inflammatory response, when released in tumors and can carry tumor antigens to antigen presenting cells. They have therefore become important components of anti-cancer vaccines.

34 Wood C. & Mulders P. Vitespen: a preclinical and clinical review. Future Oncol, 2009; 6: 763-774.

35 Wood C. *et al.* An adjuvant autologous therapeutic vaccine (HSPPC-

96; vitespen) versus observation alone for patients at high risk of recurrence after nephrectomy for renal cell carcinoma: a multicentre, open-label, randomised phase III trial. Lancet, 2008; 373:145-154.

[36] Testori A. *et al.* Phase III Comparison of Vitespen, an Autologous Tumor-Derived Heat Shock Protein gp96 Peptide Complex Vaccine, With Physician's Choice of Treatment for Stage IV Melanoma: The C-100-21 Study Group. J Clin Oncol, 2008; 26: 955-962.

[37] Wood C. *et al.* Survival update from a multicenter, randomized, phase III trial of vitespen versus observation as adjuvant therapy for renal cell carcinoma in patients at high risk of recurrence. J Clin Oncol, 2009; 27:15s, (suppl; abstr 3009).

[38] Julia Donnelly. Antigenics seeks cancer vaccine approval in Europe. Boston Business Journal. 21 January 2010.

[39] **Cellular therapy**, as the name implies, is a technique of trying to cure diseases using tissue (cells) rather than drugs or other interventions. It actually dates as far back as the 1920s and one of the best known examples would be bone marrow (or stem cell) transplantations. Cellular therapy can involve the administration of foreign cells derived from other humans or animals, or the use of the patient's own cells. If the patient's own cells are being utilised, the technique normally involves them being removed from the patient and then manipulated in the laboratory to either alter them (*e.g.* by inserting a gene into them) or activating them in some other way. The cells are then reintroduced into the patient, where they will hopefully go on to initiate a beneficial biological process which they would otherwise have been incapable of performing.

[40] Kantoff P. *et al.* Sipuleucel-T immunotherapy for castrate-resistant prostate cancer. *N Engl J Med,* 2010; 363:411-422.

[41] Huber M. *et al.* Interdisciplinary Critique of Sipuleucel-T as Immunotherapy for Castration-Resistant Prostate Cancer. J Nat. Cancer Institute, 2012; 104:1-7.

[42] Oxford BioMedica Press Release. Oxford BioMedica Announces Data Safety Monitoring Board Recommendation For TroVax Phase III TRIST Study. 01 July 2008.

[43] Oxford BioMedica Press Release. Oxford BioMedica Announces Outcome of FDA Review And Updates On TroVax Phase III TRIST Study in Renal Cancer. 06 July 2009.

[44] Harrop R. *et al.* MVA–5T4-induced immune responses are an early marker of efficacy in renal cancer patients. Cancer Immunol Immunother, 2011; 60, 829-837.

[45] Oxford BioMedica Press Release. Oxford BioMedica Announces Update on TroVax Development Strategy. 10 October 2012.

[46] http://www.arktherapeutics.com/main/research_development.php?content=products_cerepro

[47] Van Putten E. *et al.* Sitimagene ceradenovec: a gene-based drug for the treatment of operable high-grade glioma. Future Oncology, 2010; 11:1691-1710.

[48] European Medicines Agency Press Release. Ark Therapeutics Ltd withdraws its marketing authorisation for Cerepro (sitimagene ceradenovec). 11 March 2010.

[49] **Erbitux (cetuximab)** was developed by the New Jersey biotech Imclone Systems, before the company was acquired by Lilly in 2008. It is a monoclonal antibody widely used in colorectal and head & neck cancer. It targets and blocks a receptor on the surface of cancer cells, called the Epidermal Growth Factor Receptor (EGFR). Mutations affecting EGFR expression, or activity, result in over stimulation of cell proliferation and contribute to the development of cancer. EGFR is a member of the *ErbB family of receptors*, which consists of four closely related receptor tyrosine kinases: **EGFR (HER1**, ErbB-1), **HER2** (ErbB-2), the target for Herceptin, **HER3** (ErbB-3) and **HER4** (ErbB-4).

EGFR on the *surface* of the cell is linked to a growth stimulating tyrosine kinase enzyme on the *inside* of the cell. A number of small molecule tyrosine kinase inhibitors, such as erlotinib (Tarceva) and gefitinib (Iressa) inhibit this particular tyrosine kinase and so have similar effects to cetuximab.

[50] Geoffrey Smith. Astra Hauls Ex-CEO Lars Bildman Into Court. Business Week Online. 04 February 1998.

[51] Nyce was released from prison at the end of 2010. Despite originally confessing to the murder and having been convicted by a jury, he went on to write a book protesting his innocence and describing "the true, fact-driven account of an innocent man's nightmare journey through the American criminal justice system." Nyce J. Under Colour Of Law. Cygnus-1 Publishing LLC, USA. 2012.

[52] Julius Caesar. Act 1; Scene 2, 190-195.

CHAPTER EIGHT

[1] **HER2** is a receptor found on the surface of certain cancer cells. It is made by a specific gene called the HER2/neu gene. HER2 is a receptor for a particular growth factor called *human epidermal growth factor*, which occurs naturally in the body. When human epidermal growth factor attaches itself to HER2 receptors on breast cancer cells, it can stimulate the cells to divide and grow. In about one of every five breast cancer patients, the cancer cells make an excess of HER2 due to a gene mutation. Patients with *HER2 positive* breast cancer tend to have a worse prognosis, with a reduced response to treatment and a shorter overall survival, than those who are *HER2 negative*.

This gene mutation and the elevated levels of HER2 that it causes can occur in many types of cancer, not only breast cancer. Another disease where elevated HER2 plays a role, for example, is carcinoma of the stomach. Herceptin is also approved for use in gastric cancer and has a useful role in the management of the condition.

2 Slamon D. *et al.* Use of chemotherapy plus a monoclonal antibody against HER2 for metastatic breast cancer that overexpresses HER2. N Engl J Med, 2001; 344:783-792.

The addition of trastuzumab to paclitaxel chemotherapy was associated with a longer time to disease progression (median, 7.4 vs. 4.6 months), a higher rate of objective response (50 per cent vs. 32 per cent), a lower rate of death at 1 year (22 per cent vs. 33 per cent) and a longer survival (median, 25.1 vs. 20.3 months).

3 The gemcitabine trial originally failed to demonstrate a survival advantage when an interim analysis was undertaken at the time of the original approval, at the request of FDA. In this study, both survival and time to progression were *co-primary* endpoints. (Co-primary endpoints are used in certain situations where a trial has *more* than one primary endpoint. Special statistical techniques are required to deal with this, when it occurs). (Albain K. *et al.* Global phase III study of gemcitabine plus paclitaxel (GT) vs. paclitaxel (T) as frontline therapy for metastatic breast cancer (MBC): First report of overall survival. Journal of Clinical Oncology, 2004 ASCO Annual Meeting Proceedings (Post-Meeting Edition). Vol 22, No 14S (July 15 Supplement), 2004: 510).

However, when the survival data eventually became fully mature, a couple of years later, it finally became possible to statistically confirm a survival improvement for gemcitabine (Albain K. *et al.* Gemcitabine Plus Paclitaxel Versus Paclitaxel Monotherapy in Patients With Metastatic Breast Cancer and Prior Anthracycline Treatment. J Clin Oncol, 2008; 26:3950-3957).

4 Miller K. *et al.* Paclitaxel plus Bevacizumab versus Paclitaxel Alone for Metastatic Breast Cancer. New Engl J Med, 2007; 357:2666-2676.

5 www.fda.gov. FDA Briefing Document. ODAC. BLA 125085/91.08 Avastin. 05 December 2007.

6 **Response Evaluation Criteria In Solid Tumors (RECIST)** basically classifies four categories of change in the status of a tumor after treatment: (i) *Complete Response* (CR): *all* evidence of cancer, both clinically and radiologically has completely disappeared; (ii) *Partial Response* (PR): the overall tumor burden has decreased by at least 30 per cent, when measured radiologically; (iii) *Progressive Disease* (PD): the overall tumor burden has increased by at least 20 per cent, when measured radiologically; (iv) *Stable Disease* (SD): the tumor burden has neither increased by 20 per cent (PD) nor decreased by 30 per cent (PR). Obviously this is a gross over simplification and in practice it is hugely

more complicated. However, the four point classification is the fundamental basis of RECIST: Eisenhauer E. *et al.* New Response Criteria in solid tumors. Revised RECIST guideline (version 1.1). Eur J Cancer, 2009; 45: 228-247.

[7] www.fda.gov. Is Time to Progression an acceptable primary endpoint in breast cancer, or is survival the only acceptable endpoint? ODAC Meeting. 07 June 1999.

[8] www.fda.gov. ODAC Transcript. 05 December 2007.

[9] Miller K. *et al.* E2100: A randomized phase III trial of paclitaxel plus bevacizumab as first-line therapy for locally recurrent or metastatic breast cancer. Proceedings of the 41st Annual Meeting of the American Society of Clinical Oncology. Orlando, Fla. 2005; Educational Session.

[10] Albain K. *et al.* Gemcitabine Plus Paclitaxel Versus Paclitaxel Monotherapy in Patients With Metastatic Breast Cancer and Prior Anthracycline Treatment. J Clin Oncol, 2008; 26:3950-3957.

[11] Roche Press Release. Avastin approved in Europe for first line treatment of women with metastatic breast cancer. 29 March 2007.

[12] Breast Cancer Action Applauds FDA Recommendation to Deny Avastin for Breast Cancer Treatment. 05 December 2007. http://bcaction.org/2007/12/05/breast-cancer-action-applauds-fda-recommendation-to-deny-avastin-for-breast-cancer-treatment/

[13] Andrew Pollack. FDA extends Avastin's Use to Breast Cancer. New York Times. 23 February 2008.

[14] Zosia Chustecka. Experts Welcome Accelerated Approval of Bevacizumab for Breast Cancer. Medscape. 25 February 2008.

[15] Paul Goldberg. As Avastin decision nears, patient groups split on PFS in First Line Breast Cancer. The Cancer Letter. 22 February 2008.

[16] Roche Press Release. Avado Study of Avastin Plus Docetaxel Chemotherapy Showed Improved Progression-Free Survival in Patients With Advanced Breast Cancer. Results of Second Phase III Trial Support Potential of Avastin in Breast Cancer. February 12 2008.

[17] www.fda.gov. Proposal to withdraw approval for the Breast Cancer Indication for bevacizumab (Avastin). 29 June 2011. Transcript.

[18] www.fda.gov. Oncology Drugs Advisory Committee. Briefing Book, U.S. BL 125085/191 and 192: AVASTIN (Bevacizumab)–Genentech Inc, Appendix A. 16 June 2010.

[19] Miles D. *et al.* Phase III Study of Bevacizumab Plus Docetaxel Compared With Placebo Plus Docetaxel for the First-Line Treatment of Human Epidermal Growth Factor Receptor 2–Negative Metastatic Breast Cancer. J Clin Oncol, 2010; 28:3239-3247.

[20] Robert N. *et al.* RIBBON-1: Randomized, Double-Blind, Placebo-Controlled, Phase III Trial of Chemotherapy With or Without Bevacizumab for First-Line Treatment of Human Epidermal Growth

Factor Receptor 2–Negative, Locally Recurrent or Metastatic Breast Cancer. J Clin Oncol, 2011; 29:1252-1260.

21 www.fda.gov. FDA Briefing Document Oncology Drug Advisory Committee Meeting BLA STN 25085/191 and 192 Avastin (bevacizumab). 20 July 2010.

22 **Taxane** drugs are a class of cancer treatments which includes both paclitaxel and docetaxel, both of which had been used previously in Avastin trials (E2100 and AVADO respectively).

Anthracyclines are a different class of cancer treatments, including drugs such as doxorubicin, daunorubicin and idarubicin which are used in many types of malignancy, including breast cancer.

Capecitabine is an oral drug, which is converted in the body into an active cytotoxic agent called 5-fluorouracil. It is widely used in breast cancer.

23 www.fda.gov. ODAC Transcript. 20 July 2010.

24 Genentech Press Release. Genentech Announces Appointment of Sandra J Horning, MD., to Senior Vice President, Global Head, Clinical Department Haematology/Oncology. 28 July 2009.

25 At the time of the July 2010 ODAC meeting, Avastin was approved for use in the following cancers: breast (first line, combined with carboplatin and paclitaxel), kidney (first line, combined with interferon alpha), colon (first *and* second line, combined with 5-FU based chemotherapy), lung (first line, combined with carboplatin and paclitaxel) and brain (second line, monotherapy).

26 http://center4research.org/about-us.

27 **Equipoise** is a philosophical concept that a physician can only legitimately enter a patient into a randomised clinical trial if genuine debate and disagreement exists within the clinical community about the most optimal treatment choice.

28 **Inflammatory breast cancer** is a rare and very aggressive disease in which cancer cells block lymph vessels in the skin of the breast. This type of breast cancer is called "inflammatory" because the breast often looks swollen and red, or "inflamed." It accounts for one to five per cent of all breast cancers.

The disease progresses rapidly, often in a matter of weeks or months. It is nearly always stage III or IV at diagnosis. The five year relative survival for women diagnosed with inflammatory breast cancer is about thirty per cent, compared to about eighty per cent for women diagnosed with other types of invasive breast cancer.

29 In 2005, the drug **Ethyol** (amifostine), marketed by MedImmune, lost one of its indications, reducing the cumulative renal toxicity from cisplatin therapy in non-small cell lung cancer. The indication was withdrawn because of emergence of better treatment options for the

disease. Ethyol is however still marketed for reducing the cumulative renal toxicity following on from repeated cisplatin administration in ovarian cancer.

It is also used to attenuate the symptoms of xerostomia (dry mouth) arising from damage to the salivary glands after radiotherapy for head and neck cancers.

30 Genentech Press Release. Genentech Provides Update From Avastin FDA Advisory Committee Meeting. 20 July 2010.

31 Zosia Chustecka. Will the FDA revoke Bevacizumab's approval for Breast Cancer? Medscape. 21 July 2010.

32 Rob Stein. FDA considers revoking the approval of Avastin for advanced breast cancer. The Washington Post. 16 August 2010.

33 http://arenaoncology.med.nyu.edu/about-us.

34 Delthia Ricks. Ller fights to use Avastin for advanced breast cancer. Newsday. 21 August 2010.

35 http://www.vitter.senate.gov/public/index.cfm?FuseAction=PressRoom. PressReleases&ContentRecord_id=902AC27B-F5A3-3781-E25F-A8D2E60CA40C.

36 The Avastin Mugging. Wall Street Journal. 18 August 2010.

37 http://www.thepetitionsite.com/3/stop-the-fda-from-disproving-avastin-to-treat-metastatic-breast-cancer/.

38 Geraldine Satossky. My Battle With Cancer and the FDA. By Friday regulators may withdraw the drug that's keeping me alive. Wall Street Journal. 16 September 2010.

39 Michael Cummings. A touching but not very helpful plea. Letter. Wall Street Journal. 21 September 2010.

40 http://boards.medscape.com/forums/?128@733.DAbFanUFk1I@.2a02 158b!comment=1

41 http://archive.bcaction.org/index.php?page=recent-victories

42 Susan G Komen For The Cure. Statement on Avastin. 17 August 2010.

43 Zosia Chustecka. FDA delays decision on breast cancer indication for Bevacizumab. Medscape. 18 September 2010.

44 www.fda.gov. FDA begins process to remove breast cancer indication from Avastin label. Press Release. 16 December 2010.

45 www.fda.gov/downloads/NewsEvents/Newsroom/MediaTranscripts/ UCM237450.pdf.

46 EMA Press Release. European Medicines Agency completes its review of Avastin in breast cancer. 16 December 2010.

47 Roche. Press Release. Roche provides update for Avastin in metastatic breast cancer following reviews in Europe and the United States. 16 December 2010.

48 Rob Stein. FDA moves to remove Avastin approval for breast cancer. Washington Post. 17 December 2010.

49 http://alexander.house.gov/uploads/110810%20Letter%20to%20FDA%20regarding%20Avastin.pdf.

50 Joseph Rago. Breast Cancer and the FDA. The Wall Street Journal. 17 December 2010.

51 **VEGF** is a protein produced by normal cells in situations where the concentration of oxygen in tissues is too low. By acting to promote the formation of new blood vessels, VEGF increases the supply of blood to the tissues, thus helping to elevate the oxygen levels back to normal. In contrast to this normal situation, most cancers produce enormous excesses of VEGF, which helps drive the network of blood vessels the tumor needs to constantly lay down to maintain itself.
VEGF interacts with a series of *transmembrane receptor tyrosine kinases*, known as vascular endothelial growth factor receptors (VEGFRs) to stimulate the formation of new blood vessel cells, via activation of a complex series of intra-cellular signalling pathways.
Many malignant diseases, including breast cancer are associated with clinically detectable elevated levels of VEGF, which is correlated to a worse prognosis.
Antibodies such as Avastin act to prevent VEGF interacting effectively with the VEGF-receptor, thus preventing initiation of the cell signalling cascade which would normally follow. Small molecule VEGF inhibitors, such as sunitinib, sorafenib, axitinib and pazopanib don't usually block the binding of VEGF to its receptor but instead predominantly act "downstream" to arrest the signalling mechanisms and bring them to a halt.

52 Miles D. *et al*. Plasma biomarker analyses in the AVADO Phase III randomized study of first-line bevacizumab + docetaxel in patients with human epidermal growth factor receptor (HER) 2-negative metastatic breast cancer [San Antonio Breast Cancer Conference, December 2010, abstract].
SABCShttp://www.abstracts2view.com/sabcs10/view.php?nu=SABCS10L_939&terms

53 www.fda.gov. Submission of Genentech Inc in response to the Food and Drug Administration's Notice of Opportunity for a Hearing and Proposal to Withdraw Approval of AVASTIN (Bevacizumab) in combination with weekly paclitaxel for the first line treatment of patients with metastatic breast cancer. Docket Number: FDA-2010-N-0621. 16 Jan 2011.

54 www.fda.gov. Proposal to withdraw approval for the Breast Cancer Indication for bevacizumab (Avastin). 29 June 2011. Transcript.

55 Martin M. *et al*. Motesanib or open-label bevacizumab in combination with paclitaxel, as first line treatment for HER2-negative locally recurrent or metastatic breast cancer. Lancet Oncology, 2011; 12:369-376.

56   **Median** is a term most often used when describing clinical data. It is similar to but not exactly the same as an average.

In statistical parlance an average is referred to as a *mean*. To calculate the mean, you just need to add up all the data, and then divide this total by the number of values in the data set. For example, if you had five patients with five different progression free survival times of 3, 9, 15, 17 and 44 months, then the mean would be derived by adding up all the numbers and dividing the total (88) by 5 to reach a mean figure of 17.6 months.

The *median* is the middle number in a series, such that there are an equal number of lower and higher numbers on either side of it. In the example above, if the progression free survival times were 3, 9, 15, 17 and 44 months, then the median would be 15 months, as there are two numbers below this and two above it. (If you have an equal number of values in a data set, then the median is calculated by taking the average of the middle two figures).

Means are best used to summarise data that is fairly symmetrically distributed (*e.g.* 1, 2, 3, 4, 5) although in this situation the mean and median will often be the same anyway. However, clinical trial data is usually much more uneven and skewed in its distribution (*e.g.* 4, 18, 25, 39, 56). In these cases, the median provides a better summary of the data when compared to a mean. That is why nearly all clinical trials present median data when describing the results of the study.

57   A **hazard ratio** compares the *probability* of an event happening between two treatments.

The *probability* of an event happening in a given time interval is the length of time multiplied by the hazard. A *hazard* is the rate at which an event (death, disease progression or whatever) occurs. For progression free survival this would be defined as the slope of the *progression free survival curve*. The progression free survival curve is basically a graph of the percentage of patients who haven't yet progressed (or died), against the time that has elapsed since you started measuring progression or death in the first place. The hazard is therefore a measure of how rapidly subjects are progressing.

Therefore, if the hazard ratio is 2.0, then the rate of progression (or death) in one treatment group is twice the rate in the other group. However, a hazard ratio of two does not mean that the median progression free survival is doubled (or halved). A hazard ratio of two simply means a patient in one treatment group who has not progressed (or died) at a certain time point has twice the *probability* of doing so by the next time point, compared to a patient in the other treatment group.

58   The **National Comprehensive Cancer Network** was formed in 1995, as an alliance of 21 of the leading US cancer centres. Over 160,000 patients are treated annually at NCCN member institutions. The mission

of the NCCN is to be an alliance of leading cancer centers "devoted to patient care, research, and education and to improve the quality, effectiveness, and efficiency of cancer care so that patients can live better lives." In particular, the NCCN produces and continually updates comprehensive guidelines for the management of all solid and haematological malignancies. These are widely respected and utilized, both in the US and wider afield. www.nccn.org.

[59] Roche Press Release. Roche's Avastin receives broader EU label for women with metastatic breast cancer. 30 June 2011.

[60] www.fda.gov. Post-Hearing Submission of Genentech, Inc. In Support of Maintaining the Accelerated Approval of AVASTIN® (Bevacizumab) in Combination with Paclitaxel for the First-Line Treatment of HER2-Negative Metastatic Breast Cancer. DOCKET NO. FDA-2010-N-0621.

[61] www.fda.gov. Proposal to withdraw approval for the Breast Cancer Indication for Avastin Docket Number: FDA-2010-N-0621. Decision of the Commissioner. 18 November 2011.

[62] Genentech Press Release. FDA Commissioner Announces Final Decision on Avastin for Metastatic Breast Cancer. 18 November 2011.

[63] EMA Press Release. European Medicines Agency completes its review of Avastin in breast cancer. 16 December 2010.

[64] EMA assessment report for Avastin. EMEA/H/C/582/A-20/038. 28 February 2011.

[65] Friedman H. et al. Bevacizumab alone and in combination with irinotecan in recurrent glioblastoma. J Clin Oncol. 2009; 27:4733–40.

[66] Kreisel T. et al. Phase II Trial of Single-Agent Bevacizumab Followed by Bevacizumab Plus Irinotecan at Tumor Progression in Recurrent Glioblastoma. J Clin Oncol, 2009; 27:740-745.

[67] EMA refusal assessment report for Avastin. EMEA/H/C/582/II/0028. 20 January 2010.

[68] Perrin T. et al. A Phase 3 Trial of Bevacizumab in Ovarian Cancer. New Engl J Med, 2011; 365:2484-2496.

[69] Burger R. et al. Incorporation of bevacizumab in the primary treatment of ovarian cancer. New Engl J Med, 2011; 365: 2473-2483.

[70] Clinical Cancer Advances. ASCO's Annual Report on Progress Against Cancer. American Society for Clinical Oncology. 2011.

[71] Roche Press Release. Roche Medicine Avastin receives EU approval for the treatment of women with newly diagnosed advanced ovarian cancer. 23 December 2011.

[72] CBS News. Avastin unlikely to get ovarian cancer approval after disappointing studies. 29 December 2011.
http://www.cbsnews.com/8301-504763_162-57349695-10391704/avastin-unlikely-to-get-ovarian-cancer-approval-after-disappointing-studies/

73 FDA: Is the US really slower than Europe at approving new drugs. http://www.fda.gov/downloads/AboutFDA/Transparency/Basics/UCM247470.pdf

74 Up until the advent of Mylotarg, success in AML had been defined as a *Complete Response (CR)*, which essentially required that the bone marrow be free of leukaemic disease and that the cells in the peripheral blood had recovered to more or less normal levels. What usually happens in AML is that the diseased bone marrow crowds out all of the normal functioning cells and so the production of peripheral blood constituents, such as red cells, white cells and platelets comes to a halt. One of the requirements of a CR therefore is that the white cells (neutrophils) in the peripheral blood need to have recovered above a certain threshold of 1000/μL and the platelet count has to be greater than 100,000/μL.

Clinical trials showed that whilst Mylotarg was able to clear the bone marrow of disease, for some reason it was unable in many patients to produce the requisite recovery in white cells and platelets in the peripheral blood. So what Wyeth basically did was to create a whole new category of response – the so called CRp (*Complete Response without platelet recovery*). This still required that the bone marrow was free of disease but removed the additional hurdle of the peripheral blood having to recover above the limits required for a fully fledged CR.

Although evidence now shows convincingly that patients with a CRp don't do as well and die sooner than those achieving a full CR, Wyeth were somehow able to convince FDA that they should accept both categories of response, CR and CRp, as being effectively equivalent for the purposes of approving Mylotarg. The drug was therefore able to slip in through the back door whilst FDA seemed to be looking the other way.

75 www.fda.gov. Briefing document for the Oncology Drugs Advisory Committee. NDA: 022-489. Onrigin (Laromustine). 01 September 2009.

76 The trial, S0106, conducted by the Southwest Oncology Group, compared the effect of the addition of Mylotarg to standard induction chemotherapy alone. At a planned interim analysis in August 2009, the complete response rates were identical at 66% on the Mylotarg plus chemotherapy arm and 69% on the chemotherapy alone arm. Also, the rate of fatal toxicity was significantly higher with the addition of Mylotarg 5.7% versus 1.4% for patients receiving chemotherapy alone. (Petersdorf S. *et al*. Preliminary Results of Southwest Oncology Group Study S0106: An International Intergroup Phase 3 Randomized Trial Comparing the Addition of Gemtuzumab Ozogamicin to Standard Induction Therapy Versus Standard Induction Therapy Followed by a Second Randomization to Post-Consolidation Gemtuzumab

Ozogamicin Versus No Additional Therapy for Previously Untreated Acute Myeloid Leukaemia. Blood, 2009; 114 (abstr 790).

Other recently published trials (British MRC AML-15 and the Hovon-43 trials) have also failed to confirm clinical benefit for Mylotarg as part of induction therapy or in maintenance therapy of AML and found no improvement in measures of survival.

[77] Thomas E. *et al*. Ixabepilone plus capecitabine for metastatic breast cancer progressing after anthracycline and taxane treatment. J Clin Oncol, 2007; 25:5210–5217.

[78] Perez E. *et al*. Efficacy and safety of ixabepilone (BMS-247550) in a phase II study of patients with advanced breast cancer resistant to an anthracycline, a taxane, and capecitabine. J Clin Oncol, 2007; 25:3407–3414.

[79] European Medicines Agency Press Release. Bristol-Myers Squibb Pharma withdraws its marketing authorisation application for Ixempra. 19 March 2009.

[80] Roche H. & Vahdat L. Treatment of metastatic breast cancer: second line and beyond. Annals Oncol, 2011; 22: 1000–1010.

CHAPTER NINE

[1] Antisoma Press Release. Antisoma's Phase III trial of AS1413 completes patient enrolment. 08 September 2010.

[2] Partridge A. *et al*. Nonadherence to adjuvant tamoxifen in women with primary breast cancer. J Clin Oncol, 2003: 21:602-606.

[3] Noens L. *et al*. Prevalence, determinants, and outcomes of nonadherence to imatinib therapy in patients with chronic myeloid leukemia: the ADAGIO study. Blood, 2009; 113:5401-5411.

[4] www.fda.gov. Guideline For The Format And Content Of The Clinical And Statistical Sections Of An Application.
http://www.fda.gov/downloads/Drugs/Guidances/UCM071665.pdf

[5] Okie S. Reviving the FDA. New Engl J Med, 2010; 363:1492-1494.

[6] http://www.usphs.gov/aboutus/mission.aspx.

[7] **Phocomelia** a developmental anomaly characterised by absence of the upper part of one or more of the limbs so that the feet or hands or both are attached to the trunk of the body by short, irregularly shaped stumps. The condition, caused by interference with the embryonic development of the long bones, is rare and is seen primarily as a side effect of thalidomide taken during early pregnancy.

[8] Kuhen B. Frances Kelsey Honored for FDA Legacy. Award Notes Her Work on Thalidomide, Clinical Trials. JAMA, 2010; 304, 2109-2110.

[9] Ellen Rice. Dr Frances Kelsey: Turning the Thalidomide Tragedy into Food and Drug Administration Reform.
http://www.section216.com/history/Kelsey.pdf.

[10] McBride W. Thalidomide embryopathy. Teratology, 1977; 16:9-82.

[11] Morton Mintz. Heroine of the FDA Keeps Bad Drug Off of Market. Washington Post. 15 July 1962.

[12] Linda Bren. Frances Oldham Kelsey: FDA Medical Reviewer Leaves her Mark on History. FDA Consumer, March April 2001. http://www.fda.gov/fdac/features/2001/201_kelsey.html.

[13] Francis Kelsey was subsequently instrumental in the passing in 1962 of the *Kefauver-Harris Amendment* (named after Senator Estes Kefauver and Representative Oren Harris) to the 1938 Food, Drug and Cosmetic Act. This represented a revolution in FDA regulatory authority. The legislation gave FDA weight to demand that drug makers prove their products were safe and effective before receiving approval to market them in the United States.

Prior to the legislation, drugs could be sold 60 days after companies filed with FDA, if the Agency did not object. In addition, drug makers routinely sent new medications to doctors asking them to "try them out" on their patients, in advance of any regulatory review.

After the law was passed: (i) manufacturers had to provide evidence that proposed drugs were both safe and effective, demonstrated by adequate and well-controlled clinical investigations conducted by qualified experts; (ii)FDA were given 180 days to evaluate a new drug application, and the application would no longer become automatically effective; (iii) new drugs required an affirmative decision by the agency before marketing; (iv) manufacturers had to maintain records of adverse events associated with drugs and report these promptly to FDA.

The Kefauver-Harris Amendment effectively laid the groundwork for modern FDA drug approval requirements.

[14] FDA Alumni Association Receives Prestigious Frances.O.Kelsey Award. 02 October 2012.
http://www.fdaaa.org/activities/2012/100912.php.

[15] www.fda.gov. FDA Science and Mission at Risk. Report of the Subcommittee on Science and Technology. November 2007.
http://www.fda.gov/ohrms/dockets/ac/07/briefing/2007-4329b_02_01_FDA%20Report%20on%20Science%20and%20Technology.pdf

[16] The Battelle Technology Partnership Practice. Gone tomorrow? A call to promote medical innovation, create jobs and find cures in America. 10 June 2010.

[17] Scott Gottlieb. The FDA is evading the law. Wall Street Journal. 23 December 2010.

[18] In FDA's own words, the **Critical Path Initiative** aimed at "leveraging the knowledge we've gained from emerging scientific fields to enhance the tools FDA uses to evaluate new drugs, biologics and medical devices." Which was, as they admitted "a monumental effort."

http://www.fda.gov/ScienceResearch/SpecialTopics/CriticalPathInitiativ
e/ucm076689.htm.

[19]   Hamburg M. Innovation, Regulation and the FDA. New Engl J Med,
2010; 363:2228-2232.

[20]   The US **regulatory process** begins with an IND (Investigational New
Drug Application) which is the point at which FDA review and authorise
whatever non-clinical data there is to support an initial Phase I study in
humans. The NDA (New Drug Application) marks the end of clinical
development, when Phase III is complete and the whole drug package
(non-clinical and clinical) can be submitted for FDA to review and
decide whether to approve the drug for marketing. The European (EMA)
equivalent of the NDA is the MAA (Marketing Authorisation
Application). There is no pan-European counterpart of the IND, as
each country has its own specific requirements for authorizing the start
of a Phase I clinical trial.

[21]   FDA. Guidance for Industry: Formal Meetings with Sponsors and
Applicants for PUDUFA Products. February 2000.
http://www.fda.gov/downloads/Drugs/Guidances/UCM079744.pdf

[22]   Cheson B. *et al.* Report of the NCI sponsored workshop on definitions
of diagnosis and response in acute myeloid leukemia. J Clin Oncol,
1990; 8:813-819.

[23]   Cheson B. *et al.* Revised Recommendations of the International Working
Group for Diagnosis, Standardization of Response Criteria, Treatment
Outcomes, and Reporting Standards for Therapeutic Trials in Acute
Myeloid Leukemia. J Clin Oncol, 2003; 21:4642-4649.

[24]   At the time amonafide was being developed, no drug had shown a
survival advantage in AML for twenty years, since the combination of
cytarabine and idarubicin had done so at the end of the 1980s. (Berman
E. *et al.* Results of a Randomized Trial Comparing Idarubicin and
Cytosine Arabinoside With Daunorubicin and Cytosine Arabinoside in
Adult Patients With Newly Diagnosed Acute Myelogenous Leukemia
Blood, 1991; 77:1666-1674).
In 2012 however, a study emerged from Poland using a drug called
cladribine, which acted in a similar way to clofarabine. (Holowiecki J. *et
al.* Cladribine, But Not Fludarabine, Added to Daunorubicin and
Cytarabine During Induction Prolongs Survival of Patients With Acute
Myeloid Leukemia: A Multicenter, Randomized Phase III Study. J Clin
Oncol, 2012; 30:2441-2448).
When combined with standard chemotherapy in younger patients, this
combination finally appeared to show a survival advantage in the *overall*
patient population (rather than just selected sub-groups). Although it
awaits the validation of further clinical confirmation, it is just possible
that a chink might have developed in the previously impregnable defences

of the disease. The Holy Grail of improving survival may be in sight, at least in some AML patient populations.

25 Karen Gullo. Intermune Ex-CEO Harkonen Sentenced To Home Containment In Fraud Case. Bloomberg News. 15 April 2011.

26 **Biopure** was ultimately unable to gain regulatory approval for Hemopure in either the US or Europe. On July 16, 2009 the company announced it had filed for Chapter 11 Bankruptcy and entered into an agreement with OPK Biotech LLC for the sale of all its assets.

27 http://www.fda.gov/ohrms/dockets/ac/05/briefing/2005-4191B1_01_03-Reinvent-Cancer-Drugs.pdf

28 FDA. Drug Development Patient Consultant Program. http://www.fda.gov/ForConsumers/ByAudience/ForPatientAdvocates/PatientInvolvement/ucm123859.htm.

29 A **Refusal to File** decision used to be based, in FDA's words, on "extreme deficiencies, *e.g.* the total omission of a needed section or the absence of any study that was *even* arguably an adequate and well-controlled study." However, since the early 1990s, "applications have been refused when less extreme deficiencies existed, but when it was clear that the deficiencies were severe enough to make the application not approvable without major modification." In practice, the Agency should be considered likely to issue an RTF letter in response to applications which "on their face are not reviewable and at least potentially approvable, as submitted." http://www.fda.gov/downloads/Drugs/GuidanceComplianceRegulatory Information/Guidances/UCM080561.pdf. July 12 1993.

30 Because it was FDA, there was inevitably a procedure for documenting **Review Issues**. In it, they were defined as "substantive deficiencies or concerns identified by the review team during the initial filing review for an NDA or efficacy supplement, that appear to have been inadequately addressed in the application and merit particular attention during the review process." In practice however, FDA had almost complete freedom to interpret what constituted "substantive deficiencies or concerns" and hence might become a review issue. http://www.fda.gov/downloads/AboutFDA/CentersOffices/CDER/Ma nualofPoliciesProcedures/ucm081990.pdf. 08 May 2003.

CHAPTER TEN

1 www.antisoma.com. 10 November 2010.

2 Recka M. & Crino L. Advances in anti-VEGF and anti-EGFR therapy for advanced non-small cell lung cancer. Lung Cancer, 2009; 63:1-9.

3 Since the demise of ASA404, a number of companies have continued with the development of **vascular disrupting agents**, including Sanofi, Nereus, EpiCept, Myrexis and Astra Zeneca. Results to date

have however generally been disappointing. Most recently, Sanofi dropped its VDA, ombrabulin after it failed in a Phase III trial in sarcoma. This has left only two companies with significant activity in the area, OXiGENE and the Australian company Bionomics. Bionomics is pursuing ongoing Phase II trials in renal and ovarian cancer with its agent, BNC105. OXiGENE is attempting to put together a Phase III trial of fosbretabulin combined with chemotherapy for use in thyroid cancer. However, with a market capitalization of less than ten million dollars, it is unclear whether they will be able to fund this.

Currently therefore, no large scale clinical trial has convincing shown an effect with a VDA and the jury is still very much out. See: EP Vantage: Twilight of the Vascular Disrupting Agents. 16 January 2013. http://www.epvantage.com/Universal/View.aspx?type=Story&id=37969 7&isEPVantage=yes

[4] http://www.ameplc.co.uk.

[5] Oxford BioMedica Press Release. Oxford BioMedica Announces Proposed Firm Placing and Placing and Open Offer of GBP20 million fully underwritten by Singer Capital Markets Limited. 13 December 2010.

[6] **Granulocyte Colony Stimulating Factor (GCSF)** is a special type of protein called a growth factor. It stimulates the bone marrow to make white blood cells (granulocytes). Although occurring naturally, it can also be manufactured with recombinant DNA technology and used in patients receiving chemotherapy which normally wipes out the bone marrow. GCSF can accelerate the rate at which the bone marrow recovers and starts producing white cells again, thus reducing the likelihood of serious infections developing.

CHAPTER ELEVEN

[1] Antisoma Press Release. Antisoma reports outcome of AS1413 Phase III trial. 31 January 2011.

[2] PPM1D is an enzyme known as a *protein phosphatse* which acts to inhibit the activity of the very important *p53 tumor suppressor gene* in the cell (see Chapter Seven, Note 20). By developing drugs to antagonise PPM1D, the corresponding blockage of the p53 tumor suppressor gene should be removed, thus allowing it to regain its normal function of attenuating and preventing tumor proliferation.

[3] Antisoma announced on 28 April 2011 that they had sold AS1411 to Louisville based Advanced Cancer Therapeutics for fifty thousand dollars up front. That was quite a bit less than we'd spent on it over the years.

POSTSCRIPT

[1] Lara P. *et al.* Randomized Phase III placebo-controlled trial of carboplatin and paclitaxel with or without the vascular disrupting agent vadimezan (ASA404) in advanced non-small-cell lung cancer. J Clin Oncol, 2011; 29:2965-2971.